Utah's
Weather and Climate

Edited by
Dan Pope
and
Clayton Brough

Utah's
Weather and Climate

Edited by
Dan Pope
and
Clayton Brough

With contributions from
William J. Alder, M.S.
Chief Meteorologist, N.W.S. Forecast Office, S.L.C.
Gaylen L. Ashcroft, Ph.D.
Climatologist, Utah Climate Center, Utah State University
R. Clayton Brough, M.S.
Climatologist, News 4 Utah, KTVX Television
Sean T. Buchanan, Esq.
President, WeatherGeographic, S.L.C.
James M. Duthie, B.S.
Meteorologist, News 4 Utah, KTVX Television
Rodney D. Griffin, M.S.
Science Department Chairman, Alta High School
David R. James, M.S.
Science Teacher, Eisenhower Junior High School
Donald T. Jensen, Ph.D.
Climatologist, Utah Climate Center, Utah State University
Daniel W. Pope, B.S.
Chief Meteorologist, News 4 Utah, KTVX Television
Dale J. Stevens, Ph.D.
Professor of Geography, Brigham Young University
Benjamin T. Tolman, Esq.
Computer Consultant and Typographer, S.L.C.
Peter J. Wilensky, B.S.
Meteorologist, N.W.S. Forecast Office, S.L.C.

Utah's
Weather and Climate

Edited by
Dan Pope
and
Clayton Brough

Printed by
Publishers Press
1900 West 2300 South
Salt Lake City, Utah 84119

Front cover photograph:
The picture of lightning was taken in August 1994, west of Salina, Utah, by Michael Branham of Aurora, Utah. Mr. Branham donated this picture to the editors for use in this publication

Back cover photographs:
The picture of Fall foliage in Utah was taken by a News 4 Utah television viewer and donated to Dan Pope, Chief Meteorologist of KTVX Television.

The picture of a skier enjoying Utah's "Greatest Snow on Earth" was taken by Lee Cohen and is the property of Snowbird Ski Resort. Snowbird Ski Resort donated this picture to the editors for use in this publication.

Table of Contents

Utah's Climate

Climate of Utah

by
R. Clayton Brough, Rodney D. Griffin,
Daniel W. Pope and Dale J. Stevens

Utah's climate and weather are both delightful and variable. During the summer, most populated areas experience daytime temperatures that are warm but not too hot, and nighttime temperatures that are cool but pleasant. Precipitation in the summer comes primarily from thunderstorms. Winter temperatures are most often invigorating but not extremely cold, while the snow seems to fall in exactly the right places. Normally, valley floors do not have extensive accumulations of snow for long periods of time, but mountain snows build to great depths and store large amounts of water for domestic, industrial, and agricultural needs. Utah's mountain snow also provides some of the best "powder" skiing in the world. Most spring and fall months experience mild temperatures and many sunny days.

Today's climates within Utah are as varied as those encountered in the southern states of the United States, northward to the interior of Canada. In the extreme southwestern area of Utah cotton can be grown, while in the higher valleys of northern Utah only grasses and some cereal grains are effectively cultivated. In some of the higher mountains permanent snowfields can be found.

Some weather phenomena that have been reported in the state since 1847 include numerous flash floods (caused by intense summer thunderstorms), snowmelt floods (which result from rapid warming or rain falling on heavy mountain snowpack), and hailstorms, tornadoes, blizzards and droughts. They have all made an impact on the landscape and residents of the state. About the only major weather phenomenon that has not been reported within the confines of Utah is a hurricane. However, remnants of hurricanes have brought heavy rains, hail and damaging winds to parts of the state.

Prehistoric Climate of Utah

Any attempt to reconstruct climatic conditions of the prehistoric past depends on information inferred from natural climatic indicators. These indicators include plant and animal fossils found in sedimentary rock, the type and thickness of the rock itself, glacial erosion and sediments, tree ring analysis and pollen studies. From these and other sophisticated indicators scientists have arrived at the following conclusions about Utah's prehistoric climate:

In the early period of the earth's existence, temperatures were much warmer than they are today. Such conditions did not allow for the widespread vegetation types that currently exist. Land masses were repeatedly overrun by large seas, and extreme temperature and precipitation conditions occurred.

About 200 to 250 million years ago there was a marked cooling trend over the northern hemisphere which was more favorable for the growth of luxurious vegetation. During that time, Utah's coal and oil fields were in the formative stages. These important modern natural resources resulted from major changes that occurred during Utah's prehistoric climate and geology.

About 150 million years ago a widespread drought occurred which resulted in extremely large sandstorms. The dust bowl days of the 1930's in the Great Plains area of the United States were a gentle picnic in comparison to this ancient "dry spell." Sand swirled for centuries until it was piled in dunes thousand of feet high. Later, the mountains were pushed up to heights well above Utah's present mountain peaks. Eventually, another sea covered the area and endured for as long as a hundred million years. When the sea eventually disappeared, the windblown sand was revealed as the multicolored hills and rock outcroppings seen today in Utah's famous National Parks of Arches, Bryce, Capitol Reef, Canyonlands and Zion.

During the early Cenozoic Era (about 65 million years ago) another drastic climatic change took place which had a marked influence on Utah and the Central Intermountain Region. Temperatures gradually increased, with a peak occurring about 50 million years ago. This peak was then followed by a significant drop in temperatures and an increase in precipitation.

As recently as 100,000 years ago glaciers became abundant in the high mountains and northern regions of North America. This epoch is often called the "ice age." During this time a large inland sea developed over much of western Utah. This inland sea has been given the name "Lake Bonneville." In Utah, the last major accumulation of ice melted away about 10,000 years ago as the temperatures began to warm. Some scientists believe that we are now living in a relatively warm interglacial period and that another cooler period will eventually overtake our area. However, in our short lifetimes we will not experience the large changes that have previously taken millions of years to complete.

It is interesting to note that there is a somewhat cyclical pattern in temperature and precipitation amounts through time. The prehistoric record shows significant increases and decreases over long periods of time. Likewise, Utah's historic record of the past 15 decades demonstrates this same type of pattern on a much smaller scale. Charts of accurately recorded yearly temperatures and precipitation amounts for various locations in Utah fluctuate up and down, over and over again.

Climate Classification of Utah

Climate differs from weather in that it is a generalization of all major weather conditions of an area over a long period of time, usually for thirty years or more. Several different climate classification systems have been developed over the years, but the one that is relatively easy to understand and apply is the Modified Koppen System, which delimits various climate types according to vegetation response to temperature and precipitation patterns.

On a large scale, the climates of Utah can be divided into four types within the Modified Koppen System. They are: Desert, Steppe (Semiarid), Humid Continental-Hot Summer, and Undifferentiated Highlands.

In the *Atlas of Utah*, the description of these four climates can be found, a summary of which follows:

About 33% of the state consists of true desert. Deserts occur in areas where the average annual precipitation is less than one-half of the annual potential evapotranspiration. In these areas total annual precipitation is usually about five to eight inches. Utah deserts occur in two major areas: in the Great Basin to the west and in the Canyonlands region of the southeast. The Great Basin desert is a region of hot summers and cold winters, with winter temperatures averaging below 32°F. Much of the Great Basin region is dominated by sagebrush (Artemisia), a plant indicative of fairly good soils and able to thrive in cold winter regions. The Great Salt Lake Desert, which is located in the northern portion of Utah's Great Basin, is dominated by extensive areas of salt flats, many of which are devoid of plant life. Areas of more humid climates are located within the higher mountain ranges of the Great Basin.

The Colorado Plateau desert is located in Utah's Canyonlands. Meteorologically, the temperature and precipitation conditions in the northern portion of this desert are similar to the Great Basin. However, these two desert regions appear to be quite different due to the great contrast in exposed geological formations, vegetation types and topography. The southern portion of the Colorado Plateau desert maintains average winter temperatures above 32°F. Three local mountain ranges and several uplands within the Canyonlands area have resulted in local regions of humid climates.

The southwestern region of the state is a desert region also having winters averaging above 32°F. It is in this area that the highest mean annual temperatures in Utah are recorded, with Zion National Park and St. George averaging 61° to 62°F. This is a marginal extension of the Mojave Desert, as suggested by the presence of joshua trees in the vicinity of St. George.

Steppelands occur between the desert margins and the higher mountain regions. The average annual precipitation of the steppelands is less than the potential evapotranspiration, yet more than half of these regions average between eight and 14 inches of precipitation annually, creating a semiarid climate sufficient for the growth of short and medium grasses, sagebrush and other woody plants. Much of this grassland region forms the basis for Utah's livestock ranching industry. Most of the state's steppeland area experiences winters averaging below 32°F., with only the southern margin enjoying less severe conditions. Approximately 40% of the state is steppeland—the most extensive climatic zone in Utah.

Located along the Wasatch Front from the Idaho border southward almost to Nephi is a narrow belt of humid climate where the total annual precipitation is in excess of the potential evapotranspiration. Within this more humid climate type the winters are fairly cold, again with temperatures averaging below 32°F. The summers, however, are quite hot, with mean July temperatures being about 77°F. This great range in average mean monthly temperature is due in part to the state's mid-latitude position in the interior of a large continent. The climate is therefore referred to as humid continental-hot summer. One of the major factors which influences precipitation amounts for this region is the Wasatch Mountain Range, which acts as a barrier to moisture-laden winds approaching from the west. As the approaching air rises to clear the mountain crest, temperatures drop, creating conditions that cause the air to give up its moisture. The extent and effect of this phenomenon is reflected in the concentration of population, industries and intensive agriculture within this humid area, though it occupies only 3% of the state's land area.

Approximately 24% of the state consists of mountainous regions having an undifferentiated highland climate. Mid-latitude highland climates are generally considered as humid regions with severely cold winters and cool to cold summers. The treeless summits of many of these mountain ranges have a tundra climate, where the temperatures are too cold to permit the growth of trees. Mean monthly summer temperatures in Utah's highland regions are usually below 72°F. Within the highland climate zone there can actually be a great variety of temperature and precipitation conditions ranging from the cool summers of the Wasatch Range's "back" valleys to the alpine tundra conditions of the higher Uinta peaks.

Controlling Factors in Utah's Weather

Utah's weather and climate can be explained by a variety of factors or controls. They include altitude above sea level and latitudinal position about midway between the North Pole and the Equator which is in the path of the prevailing Westerly Winds. Of equal importance are the Polar and Subtropical Jet Stream winds and air masses, the state's position on the edge of a semipermanent high pressure system, local and surrounding mountains, and the Sierra Nevada's to the west and the Rocky Mountains to the east.

If the average altitude above sea level were calculated for the state it would be approximately 6,100 feet. Although this is an average value, it does not mean that most of the population resides at that elevation. In fact, a majority of the people live at approximately the 4,500 foot level. As altitude increases, air temperature normally decreases, thus the relatively high altitude of Utah is partially responsible for the state's cool temperatures.

Utah's latitude also plays an important role in determining the type of weather the state receives. Utah is situated between 37° and 42° north latitude. This mid-latitude position means that the effectiveness of the sun is not nearly as great here as it would be closer to the equator, but much more energy is received than farther to the north. This position, associated with the earth's axis, also accounts for the state's distinct seasons. The latitude of Utah is also in the zone of the prevailing Westerly Winds, where there is constant interaction between polar and tropical air masses and associated frontal activity. When low level tropical moisture moves into Utah from locations off the southern California coasts to the Gulf of Mexico, summertime thunderstorms increase in intensity and winter and spring storms often produce heavy, wet snowfalls.

The existence of a Subtropical High Pressure Cell to the southwest of California also has significant impact on the state's weather and climate. This pressure cell which increases and decreases in intensity with time and also moves northward and southward with the seasons, often acts as a barrier to moist air that would otherwise invade the state.

All mountains have some influence on air flow movement, but the large ones have a significant impact. The main chain of the Rocky Mountains often protect Utah from the cold arctic weather of the northern Plains, while the Sierra Nevada and Cascade Mountains often prevent low level moisture associated with Pacific storms from reaching the state. Therefore, by the time Pacific storms reach Utah, they have usually lost some of their low level moisture. Because of this and the Great Basin's low topography, Utah is the second driest state in the nation. (Nevada is the driest.) The local mountains are also effective in causing increased rainfall and snow with increased altitude. When storms move into Utah from the west, they impact against the high Wasatch and south central mountains of Utah, causing "orographic lifting" (or the forced lifting of air) which "squeezes" out moisture that otherwise might pass over the state. They likewise act as barriers to air mass flow and are often responsible for areas being rather dry. The Uinta Basin is a good example of an area surrounded by mountains that hinders the movement of moist air into the region.

The Sierra Nevada and Cascade Mountains also play an important part in determining the type of snow that falls in the highlands of Utah. Because of the long distances that storms have to travel and the mountains they have to pass over to reach Utah, the snow that falls is often light and fluffy, and is known as "powder." This "powder" snow, when deep enough, gives skiers the feeling they are "floating on air" as they ski down a slope. This is one of the main reasons that many skiers call Utah's snow "the greatest snow on earth."

CLIMATIC ZONES

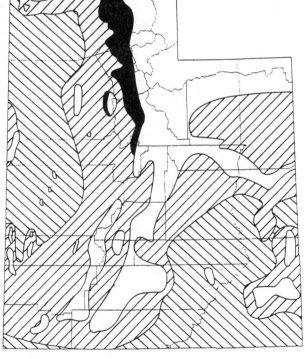

LEGEND

☐ Undifferentiated Highlands		▧ Steppe
■ Humid Continental-Hot Summer		◨ Desert

Modified Köppen Classification

Utah Weather Records
by
William J. Alder and Donald T. Jensen

Temperature

Highest	117°F	St. George	July 5, 1985
Lowest	-69°F	Peter Sink	February 1, 1985

Greatest Precipitation (Inches)

5 minutes	1.03"	Bryce Canyon	August 11, 1975
10 minutes	1.03"	Bryce Canyon	August 11, 1975
15 minutes	1.53"	West Valley City	September 3, 1983
25 minutes	2.10"	Ogden Canyon	August 8, 1941
1 hour	5.00"	Morgan	August 16, 1958
2 hours	5.00"	Morgan	August 16, 1958
3 hours	5.00"	Morgan	August 16, 1958
6 hours	5.50"	North Ogden	September 7, 1991
12 hours	6.00"	Bug Point	September 5, 1970
24 hours	8.40"	North Ogden	September 7-8, 1991
Month	25.45"	Alta	December 1983
Water Year	98.37"	Alta	October1983-September 1984

Greatest Snowfall (Inches)

24 hours	55.5"	Alta (Mountain)	January 5-6, 1994
	35.0"	Kanosh (Valley)	February 5, 1953
Greatest Storm	105.0"	Alta	January 24-30, 1965
Greatest Monthly	244.5"	Alta	December 1983
Greatest Season	743.5"	Alta	November 1983-April 1984
Greatest Year	808.5"	Alta	September 1983-June 1984

Barometric Pressure/Sea Level (Inches of Mercury)

Highest	31.13"	Milford	December 9, 1956
Lowest	29.01"	Salt Lake City	December 1, 1982

Highest Wind Speeds

Mountain (+8,000')	124 mph	Hidden Peak, Snowbird	November 8, 1986
Bench (5000'-8,000')	120 mph	Bountiful Bench	November 11, 1978
Valley (below 5,000')	104 mph	Hill Air Force Base	April 4, 1983

Utah Deaths from Natural Phenomena
by
William J. Alder

1 January 1950 - 31 December 1995

Lightning:	43
Avalanches:	42
Flash Floods:	21
Earthquakes:	0
Tornadoes:	0

Salt Lake City Weather Records
by
William J. Alder

Temperature

Highest	107°F	July 26, 1960
Lowest	-30°F	February 9, 1933

Greatest Precipitation (Inches)

5 minutes	.50"	July 13, 1962
10 minutes	.92"	July 13, 1962
15 minutes	1.26"	July 13, 1962
30 minutes	1.79"	July 13, 1962
1 hour	1.94"	July 13, 1962
2 hours	1.99"	July 13, 1962
3 hours	1.99"	July 13, 1962
24 hours	2.41"	April 22-23, 1957
Month	7.04"	September 1982
Water Year	25.15"	October 1981-September 1982
Calendar Year	24.26"	1983

Least Precipitation (Inches)

Month	0.00"	October 1952
Water Year	8.16"	October 1933-September 1934
Calendar Year	8.70"	1979

Greatest Snowfall (Inches)

24 hours	18.4"	October 17-18, 1984
Storm	23.3"	January 6-10, 1993
Month	50.3"	January 1993
Season	117.3"	1951-1952
Depth	26"	January 11, 1993

Least Snowfall (Inches)

Season	16.6"	1933-1934

Barometric Pressure/Sea Level (Inches of Mercury)

Highest	31.09"	December 8 and 9, 1956
Lowest	29.01"	December 1, 1982

Wind Speed

Highest	94 mph	June 3, 1963

Temperatures and Sunshine

Temperatures

by
William J. Alder and R. Clayton Brough

Utah's temperatures vary greatly with changing altitude and latitude. The mountains and elevated valleys have the cooler climates, while lower areas of the state have higher temperatures.

Generally, there is about a 5°F., decrease in temperature for each 1,000 feet increase in altitude, and approximately one degree decrease in average yearly temperature for each one degree of increase in latitude. Thus, equivalent areas in the southern counties of the state generally experience average annual temperatures two to four degrees F., warmer than those at similar altitude in the extreme northern part of the state. However, there are several exceptions to these generalities, because strong temperature inversions periodically affect many Utah valleys and humidities often differ significantly from one season to another.

Temperatures above 100°F., occur during most summer seasons in many of the lower valleys of the state. The low humidity makes these high temperatures and hot sunshine more bearable in Utah than in the more humid regions of the country. The low humidity also enables evaporative "swamp" coolers to operate very efficiently.

The highest official maximum temperature ever recorded in Utah was 117°F, observed on July 5, 1985, at St. George in southwestern Utah. The warmest thermometer reading ever for Salt Lake City was 107°F., on July 26, 1960.

Sub-zero temperatures occur during most winters in all but the warmest (or southernmost) areas of the state. However, prolonged periods of extremely cold weather are infrequent. Most climatic data show that January is generally the coldest month of the year.

The lowest official minimum temperature ever recorded in Utah was -69°F., recorded on February 1, 1985, in uninhabited Peter Sinks at the top of Logan Canyon. The lowest temperature ever recorded in an inhabited area of Utah was -50°F., observed on February 6, 1899, at Woodruff.

Temperature Inversions

by
William J. Alder and R. Clayton Brough

Many times each year, especially in late fall, winter, and early spring, many valleys of northern and western Utah experience temperature inversions.

Inversions occur when air near the ground radiates (or loses) heat to space during the nighttime hours. As a result, warmer, lighter air rises and rests on top of the cold, heavier air, creating stable and stagnant weather conditions in lower elevations. These inversions are caused by the existence of a cold surface high pressure system (called "The Great Basin High") and warm high pressure conditions aloft. When these inversions last beyond a few days they can reach 2,000 feet above the valley floor and produce pollution and extensive fog in the valleys. This effect is more pronounced when there is considerable snowcover in the valleys.

Fog

by
William J. Alder and R. Clayton Brough

Fog is a cloud that is close to the ground. It forms when air near the ground cools and water vapor in the air condenses into tiny but visible water droplets. Fog tends to form first in the lower areas and along and over bodies of water such as the Great Salt Lake and Utah Lake. In January 1931, Salt Lake City logged a record 21 days of dense fog which reduced visibility to one-quarter mile or less. In January of 1985 and again in 1992, 16 days of dense fog were recorded in Salt Lake City.

In Salt Lake City, November through February are considered the "fog months." Since 1948, there have been an average of 12 days of heavy fog in this four-month period. By month, the average number of heavy fog days are: one day in November, four days each in December and January, and three days in February.

Air Quality and Pollution

by
William J. Alder and R. Clayton Brough

The valleys of the Wasatch Front of northern Utah experience their greatest concentrations of nitrogen oxides, carbon monoxide and particulates from November through February. Ozone reaches its highest concentrations in June through August. Highest concentrations of nitrogen oxides and carbon monoxide occur during the morning and evening rush-hour periods of traffic. Ozone reaches its peak during early afternoon. During the spring and fall months, there are minimal short-lived episodes of pollution. During these transition seasons, sufficient circulation exists due to weather systems to preclude significant pollution episodes.

Surface visibility is reduced due to the pollution in the atmosphere. Back in the coal burning days, Salt Lake City recorded 29 days in January 1944 of haze and smoke that reduced the visibility to six miles or less. Additionally, 25 days of haze and smoke were noted in November 1937, and 26 days in November 1944. As in the case of heavy fog, November through February are the "pollution" months. An even 100 days of haze and smoke was noted in this period during the late fall and winter of 1943-1944.

Since 1948, there has been an average of 41 days of haze and smoke during November through February. December and January average 13 days, February eight days, and November seven days.

Wood Burning Advisories

by
William J. Alder

In the fall of 1992, a Wood and Coal Burning Control Program was instituted by the Department of Environmental Quality for the State of Utah, in cooperation with the public, to control woodsmoke emissions and carbon monoxide along the Wasatch Front. The woodburning program was started because chemical analysis of particulate filters showed that 16% of the particulate on the filters came from woodsmoke. The idea is to prevent an exceedance of the particulate, or PM10 (National Standard of 150 micrograms/cubic meter), and the carbon monoxide standard (9 parts per million) during winter inversions. The program starts on November 1 and ends on March 1.

The Wood and Coal Burning Control Program uses three colors (green, yellow and red) to let the public know when they can or cannot burn wood or coal in stoves or fireplaces. Green means wood/coal burning is allowed. Yellow means a voluntarily reduction of all wood/coal burning. Red means to stop all residential burning—unless the wood/coal stove or fireplace is the only source of heat for the home. Warnings and fines may be levied against anyone ignoring a no-burn period.

Ultraviolet Radiation

by
R. Clayton Brough and Daniel W. Pope

Problems Caused by Ultraviolet Radiation and Overexposure

Skin cancers and cataracts are increasing throughout the world. Many scientists believe that these and other serious health problems are now due to decreasing levels of ozone in the upper atmosphere and increasing levels of ultraviolet radiation reaching the Earth's surface, as well as the growth in outdoor work and recreation activities.

Skin cancer, which is mainly caused by overexposure to the sun, is at epidemic proportions in the United States—with one in six Americans now expected to develop this disease in their lifetime. Furthermore, cataracts, which are responsible for a large percentage of blindness in the world, have been attributed to chronic exposure to the sun's rays.

In the early 1990's, the American Academy of Dermatology announced that the incidence of malignant melanoma in the United States increased 321% between 1950 and 1989, and that since 1973, melanoma has been increasing about 4% per year. Based on this same data, the Academy predicted that over one million new cases of skin cancer would be diagnosed each year in the U.S. At the same time, the American Academy of Ophthalmology and other eye care groups predict that the incidence of cataracts in the U.S. will increase to 1.6 million cases annually by the year 2000.

Types of Ultraviolet Radiation:

While the sun's rays are essential for both plant and animal life, the very short ultraviolet (UV) wavelengths can actually damage living cells. They contain enough energy to destroy DNA molecules in human skin and eyes—which is why overexposure can lead to skin cancer and the development of cataracts.

Unlike many other types of solar radiation which are visible to the human eye, the shortest wavelengths—or ultraviolet rays—are invisible. These UV rays are divided by scientists into three groups according to their wavelength and relative hazard to human health:

UV-A rays = These are the longest of the three UV wavelengths. They contribute to premature aging, wrinkling of the skin, sunburns, and various forms of skin cancer.

UV-B rays = These are stronger than UV-A and pose a much greater risk of skin cancer than UV-A. UV-B rays are more intense in the summer, and at higher altitudes and when closer to the equator. They are the most common cause of sunburns, and often cause premature aging, skin cancer, cataracts, and immune system disorders.

UV-C rays = These are the shortest and most dangerous of the three UV wavelengths. However, nearly all UV-C races are absorbed by the Earth's atmosphere.

Dangers of Ultraviolet Radiation:

While a small amount of exposure to sunlight can be healthy and pleasurable, too much can be dangerous. Exposure to UV rays is linked to a number of harmful health effects.

Skin Cancer and Skin Damage: Since the middle of the century, the incidence of skin cancer cases has increased rapidly. In fact, sun bathing and tanning only began to be fashionable in the 1920's and 1930's. Prior to this time, people considered untanned skin as a status symbol, indicating they did not have to work outdoors. Today, medical researchers divide people into six skin types: Types I and II usually have blue, green or hazel eyes, and blond or red hair and freckles, and have a very high risk of getting skin cancer. Type I never tans and always burns, and Type II tans minimally. Those who have dark skin, including most blacks, are Type V or VI. Light skinned people are much more likely to develop skin cancer than dark skinned people—with the incidence rate of malignant melanoma in whites about twenty-fold that of blacks in the U.S.

Some effects of sunlight on the skin are visible within hours or days (e.g.: sunburn and tanning); other effects are delayed and cumulative and may be seen in months to years (e.g.: skin cancer and photo aging). Eighty percent of the UV exposure occurs before the age of 18 and the damage is cumulative over time.

Premature Aging: Sun exposure also causes premature aging of the skin. As much as 90% of the signs of aging, such as wrinkles and loss of elasticity, are actually caused by the sun. Photo aging of the skin is different than normal chronological aging. Regular sun bathers show photo aging changes early in life (before 30 years of age); while chronologically aged skin shows changes later (after 40 or more years of age). Freckling, fine wrinkling, and dilatation of capillaries are often seen early in the photo aging process; later on the photoaged skin develops irregular pigmentation, often called liver spots. Both photo aging and chronological aging causes wrinkling and loss of skin elasticity; however, they occur much earlier when the skin has been overexposed to the sun.

Cataracts and Eye Disorders: Cataracts are a leading cause of blindness worldwide. For example, in the United States cataracts affect about 1% of the population—or about 2.6 million people—and cause about 9% of all blindness. However, in India cataracts affect about 4% of the population—or about 35.8 million people—and cause about 55% of all blindness. UV exposure is one of the risk factors in the development of cataracts. Corneal sunburn, growths on the outer surface of the eye, and other eye diseases are also known or suspected to be related to long-term exposure to UV radiation. While dark-skinned people are less likely to develop skin cancer, dark-eyed people are more likely to develop cataracts. The suggested reason is because dark eyes have more of the dark pigment, melanin, which absorbs more solar radiation, leading over time to more damage to the lens of the eye.

Immune System Damage: While an understanding of how UV radiation causes the suppression of the immune system is only now emerging, it appears that specific cells in human skin play a role in human immune response. In some people—and especially those with weakened immune systems—UV-B appears to destroy or further weaken these protective immune cells, thus reducing the body's defenses against certain diseases. For these individuals, UV-B may also interfere with the effectiveness of immunizations administered through the skin.

The UV Index

In response to the increasing incidence of skin cancer, cataracts, and other health problems caused by exposure to the sun's harmful ultraviolet radiation, the National Weather Service (NWS), the U.S. Environmental Protection Agency (EPA), and the Center for Disease Control and Prevention (CDC) have developed an experimental "Ultraviolet (UV) Index" to help people prevent overexposure to the sun's harmful rays. This UV Index is derived from ozone data via satellite observations, atmospheric pressure, temperature forecasts, and expected cloudiness. It is issued by the National Weather Service every day for 58 U.S. cities (including Salt Lake City) for the one-hour period around noon the following day. The UV Index is as follows:

Index Value	Exposure Level
0-1	Minimal
3-4	Low
5-6	Moderate
7-9	High
10+	Very High

Based on the above UV Index, fair skinned (Type II) people can burn (around noon time) within the following amount of time:

Index Value	Burn Time (Fair Skin)
0-2	60 minutes
3-4	45 minutes or more
5-6	30 minutes
7-9	15-24 minutes
10+	10 minutes or less

Also, the NWS, EPA and CDC have issued the following description of skin phototypes:

Never Tans/Always Burns: Skin color in unexposed area: pale or milky white; alabaster. Tanning history: develops red sunburn; painful swelling; skin peels.

Sometimes Tans/Usually Burns: Skin color in unexposed area: very light brown; sometimes freckles. Tanning history: usually burns; pinkish or red coloring appears, can gradually develop light brown tan.

Usually Tans/Sometimes Burns: Skin color in unexposed area: light tan, brown, or olive; distinctly pigmented. Tanning history: infrequently burns; shows moderately rapid tanning response.

Always Tans/Rarely Burns: Skin color in unexposed area: brown, dark brown, or black. Tanning history: rarely burns, shows very rapid tanning response.

Common-Sense Approach to Sun Exposure

Although the thinning ozone layer and increased outdoor activity are reasons for health experts to be concerned, no one is advocating that Americans avoid the sun. Rather, medical associations, such as the American Academy of Dermatology and Skin Cancer Foundation, recommend that people adopt a common-sense approach to being outdoors, and offer the following suggestions:

1. Minimize sun exposure at midday when the sun's rays are the strongest.
2. Liberally apply a sunscreen that protects you across the broadest range of UV-A and UV-B sunlight. When the UV Index is Moderate, wear at least a SPF-15 or higher on all exposed parts of the body before going outdoors; or if the UV Index is High or Very High, wear at least a SPF-30.
3. Reapply the sunscreen often, even on cloudy days.
4. Wear protective clothing.
5. Wear a hat with a brim that shades the face.
6. Wear sunglasses that screen out (or block) UV radiation.
7. Never let children stay in the sun without adequate protection. (Because sunscreens should not be used on children under six months old, their sun exposure should be severely limited.)
8. Make sun protection a year-round activity, not just something practiced during the summer months.

Role of Reflective Surfaces

The role or reflective surfaces is also important in determining the amount of UV radiation people receive. Snow, sand and water all reflect UV rays and can intensify exposure. For example, fresh snow reflects 85% of UV radiation, white sand reflects about 18%, and water reflects about 5%. Obviously, lifestyle decisions can override other factors in determining a person's risk from exposure to the sun. People who work or play outdoors for long periods of time are at greater risk of the harmful effects from UV exposure. Activities such as skiing, sunbathing, or swimming can lead to extremely high exposures.

Suntans and Tanning Parlors

The Environmental Protection Agency (EPA) has stated that the "use of tanning parlors also increases risk, because UV radiation from any source contributes to long-term damage" of a person's skin and health. Also, Dr. David Reuben, MD has written:

"A suntan is not a sign of health. It is a crude defense mechanism: your body's desperate—and always unsuccessful—attempt to protect you from damage that can be irreparable. Your system throws a dark curtain of pigment called melanin over you to keep dangerous UV radiation from doing even more harm. But it is too late. Once a suntan appears, the damage has already taken place. ...Exposure to ultraviolet rays...destroys the elastic fibers that keep healthy skin taut and supple. The tens of millions of women who have pursued that 'fresh, young-looking' golden tan are discovering that years of sunbathing have left them with yellowed, sagging skin.

"A particular danger to the eyes exist in tanning parlors, whose lamps emit large doses of dangerous UV light. According to the American Medical Association, 'simply closing the eyes, using regular sunglasses or putting cotton balls over the eyes may not protect against eye damage.' "Many medical experts mince no words in their opinion of tanning parlors. Dr. Michael J. Franzblau, clinical associate professor of dermatology at the University of California at San Francisco School of Medicine, says, 'No sane person should ever go into one.'" (David Reuben, "Suntan's Can Kill You," *Readers Digest*, June 1990, pp.119-123.)

Sunshine
by
R. Clayton Brough and Dale J. Stevens

Utah receives plenty of sunshine. On an annual basis, Salt Lake City receives 67% of all possible sunshine, averaging 125 clear days, 101 partly cloudy days, and 139 cloudy days a year. In comparison, Milford receives 70% of all possible sunshine, averaging 151 clear days, 103 partly cloudy days, and 111 cloudy days. Salt Lake City's sunniest month is July (with 83% possible sunshine), while Milford's brightest month is June (with 83% possible sunshine).

The average daily accumulation of solar energy generally increases the farther south one travels from the Utah-Idaho border. Average daily accumulations range from 400 langleys in the northern part of Utah, to about 500 langleys in the extreme southwestern part of the state. (A langley is a unit of radiant energy equal to one gram calorie per square centimeter.) The greatest energy accumulations occur during the summer months. Logan/USU averages about 670 langleys per day during July, and Salt Lake City about 690. South of Utah, Las Vegas, Nevada averages about 748 langleys in June. By contrast, the accumulations during the month of December are 275 langleys at Las Vegas, while in the northern portion of the state, Salt Lake City accumulates an average of only 154 langleys and Logan/USU 148 langleys.

Sunrise and Sunset Table

SUNRISE AND SUNSET AT SALT LAKE CITY, UTAH
MOUNTAIN STANDARD TIME

DAY	JAN. Rise A.M.	JAN. Set P.M.	FEB. Rise A.M.	FEB. Set P.M.	MAR. Rise A.M.	MAR. Set P.M.	APR. Rise A.M.	APR. Set P.M.	MAY Rise A.M.	MAY Set P.M.	JUNE Rise A.M.	JUNE Set P.M.	JULY Rise A.M.	JULY Set P.M.	AUG. Rise A.M.	AUG. Set P.M.	SEPT. Rise A.M.	SEPT. Set P.M.	OCT. Rise A.M.	OCT. Set P.M.	NOV. Rise A.M.	NOV. Set P.M.	DEC. Rise A.M.	DEC. Set P.M.
1	7 52	5 11	7 38	5 45	7 02	6 19	6 12	6 52	5 27	7 24	4 59	7 53	5 00	8 03	5 24	7 44	5 54	7 01	6 24	6 10	6 58	5 24	7 32	5 01
2	7 52	5 12	7 37	5 46	7 01	6 20	6 10	6 53	5 25	7 25	4 58	7 53	5 00	8 03	5 25	7 43	5 55	6 59	6 25	6 09	6 59	5 23	7 34	5 01
3	7 52	5 13	7 36	5 48	6 59	6 21	6 09	6 54	5 24	7 26	4 58	7 54	5 01	8 03	5 26	7 41	5 56	6 57	6 26	6 07	7 00	5 22	7 35	5 01
4	7 52	5 14	7 35	5 49	6 58	6 22	6 07	6 56	5 23	7 27	4 58	7 55	5 02	8 03	5 27	7 40	5 57	6 56	6 27	6 05	7 02	5 21	7 36	5 00
5	7 52	5 15	7 34	5 50	6 56	6 23	6 05	6 57	5 22	7 28	4 57	7 56	5 02	8 02	5 28	7 39	5 58	6 54	6 28	6 04	7 03	5 20	7 36	5 00
6	7 52	5 15	7 33	5 51	6 55	6 24	6 04	6 58	5 21	7 29	4 57	7 56	5 03	8 02	5 29	7 38	5 59	6 52	6 29	6 02	7 04	5 19	7 37	5 00
7	7 52	5 16	7 32	5 53	6 53	6 26	6 02	6 59	5 19	7 30	4 57	7 57	5 03	8 02	5 30	7 37	6 00	6 51	6 30	6 01	7 05	5 18	7 38	5 00
8	7 52	5 17	7 31	5 54	6 51	6 27	6 01	7 00	5 18	7 31	4 56	7 57	5 04	8 01	5 31	7 35	6 01	6 49	6 31	5 59	7 06	5 17	7 39	5 00
9	7 52	5 18	7 30	5 55	6 50	6 28	5 59	7 01	5 17	7 32	4 56	7 58	5 05	8 01	5 32	7 34	6 02	6 47	6 32	5 57	7 07	5 16	7 40	5 00
10	7 52	5 19	7 29	5 56	6 48	6 29	5 57	7 02	5 16	7 33	4 56	7 58	5 05	8 01	5 33	7 33	6 03	6 46	6 33	5 56	7 09	5 15	7 41	5 00
11	7 52	5 21	7 27	5 58	6 47	6 30	5 56	7 03	5 15	7 34	4 56	7 59	5 06	8 00	5 34	7 32	6 04	6 44	6 34	5 54	7 10	5 14	7 42	5 00
12	7 51	5 22	7 26	5 59	6 45	6 31	5 54	7 04	5 14	7 35	4 56	7 59	5 07	8 00	5 35	7 30	6 05	6 42	6 36	5 53	7 11	5 13	7 43	5 00
13	7 51	5 23	7 25	6 00	6 43	6 32	5 53	7 05	5 13	7 36	4 56	8 00	5 07	7 59	5 36	7 29	6 06	6 41	6 37	5 51	7 12	5 12	7 43	5 01
14	7 51	5 24	7 24	6 01	6 42	6 33	5 51	7 06	5 12	7 37	4 56	8 00	5 08	7 59	5 37	7 28	6 07	6 39	6 38	5 49	7 13	5 11	7 44	5 01
15	7 50	5 25	7 22	6 02	6 40	6 34	5 49	7 07	5 11	7 38	4 56	8 01	5 09	7 58	5 38	7 26	6 08	6 37	6 39	5 48	7 15	5 10	7 45	5 01
16	7 50	5 26	7 21	6 04	6 38	6 35	5 48	7 08	5 10	7 39	4 56	8 01	5 10	7 57	5 39	7 25	6 09	6 36	6 40	5 46	7 16	5 09	7 46	5 01
17	7 49	5 27	7 20	6 05	6 37	6 37	5 46	7 09	5 09	7 40	4 56	8 02	5 11	7 57	5 40	7 23	6 10	6 34	6 41	5 45	7 17	5 08	7 46	5 02
18	7 49	5 28	7 18	6 06	6 35	6 38	5 45	7 10	5 08	7 41	4 56	8 02	5 11	7 56	5 41	7 22	6 11	6 32	6 42	5 43	7 18	5 08	7 47	5 02
19	7 48	5 29	7 17	6 07	6 33	6 39	5 43	7 11	5 07	7 42	4 56	8 02	5 12	7 55	5 42	7 21	6 12	6 31	6 43	5 42	7 19	5 07	7 47	5 03
20	7 48	5 31	7 16	6 08	6 32	6 40	5 42	7 12	5 06	7 43	4 56	8 02	5 13	7 55	5 43	7 19	6 13	6 29	6 44	5 41	7 20	5 06	7 48	5 03
21	7 47	5 32	7 14	6 10	6 30	6 41	5 41	7 13	5 06	7 44	4 56	8 03	5 14	7 54	5 44	7 18	6 14	6 27	6 45	5 39	7 22	5 06	7 49	5 03
22	7 46	5 33	7 13	6 11	6 28	6 42	5 39	7 14	5 05	7 45	4 57	8 03	5 15	7 53	5 45	7 16	6 15	6 25	6 47	5 38	7 23	5 05	7 49	5 04
23	7 46	5 34	7 11	6 12	6 27	6 43	5 38	7 15	5 04	7 45	4 57	8 03	5 16	7 52	5 46	7 15	6 16	6 24	6 48	5 36	7 24	5 04	7 50	5 04
24	7 45	5 35	7 10	6 13	6 25	6 44	5 36	7 16	5 03	7 46	4 57	8 03	5 17	7 51	5 47	7 13	6 17	6 22	6 49	5 35	7 25	5 04	7 50	5 05
25	7 44	5 37	7 08	6 14	6 23	6 45	5 35	7 18	5 03	7 47	4 57	8 03	5 17	7 51	5 48	7 12	6 18	6 20	6 50	5 33	7 26	5 03	7 50	5 06
26	7 44	5 38	7 07	6 15	6 22	6 46	5 33	7 19	5 02	7 48	4 58	8 03	5 18	7 50	5 49	7 10	6 19	6 19	6 51	5 32	7 27	5 03	7 51	5 06
27	7 43	5 39	7 05	6 17	6 20	6 47	5 32	7 20	5 01	7 49	4 58	8 03	5 19	7 49	5 50	7 09	6 20	6 17	6 52	5 31	7 28	5 02	7 51	5 07
28	7 42	5 40	7 04	6 18	6 18	6 48	5 31	7 21	5 01	7 50	4 59	8 03	5 20	7 48	5 50	7 07	6 21	6 15	6 53	5 29	7 29	5 02	7 51	5 08
29	7 41	5 42	7 03	6 19	6 17	6 49	5 29	7 22	5 00	7 50	4 59	8 03	5 21	7 47	5 51	7 05	6 22	6 14	6 55	5 28	7 30	5 02	7 52	5 08
30	7 40	5 43			6 15	6 50	5 28	7 23	5 00	7 51	4 59	8 03	5 22	7 46	5 52	7 04	6 23	6 12	6 56	5 27	7 31	5 01	7 52	5 09
31	7 39	5 44			6 14	6 51			4 59	7 52			5 23	7 45	5 53	7 02			6 57	5 26			7 52	5 10

Add one hour for Daylight Saving Time if and when in use.

Prepared by
NAUTICAL ALMANAC OFFICE
UNITED STATES NAVAL OBSERVATORY
WASHINGTON, D.C. 20390

Lightning and Precipitation

Lightning

by
William J. Alder, R. Clayton Brough
and Daniel W. Pope

General Information About Lightning

Each year, hundreds of Americans are hit by lightning, resulting in dozens of deaths and injuries. In fact, lightning causes more deaths per year in the United States than those from tornadoes or hurricanes.

Average U.S. Deaths Per Year
(Based on 30-Year Normals)

Floods	140
Lightning	90
Tornadoes	80
Hurricanes	30

In addition, lightning sparks thousands of fires and causes millions of dollars in damage to homes and businesses each year in the United States.

In Utah, lightning is the number one killer among natural phenomena:

Utah Deaths From Natural Phenomena
(1 January 1950 - 31 December 1995)

Lightning	43
Avalanches	42
Flash Floods	21
Tornadoes	0

Briefly described, lightning is a massive electrical discharge, caused by the flow of electrons between oppositely charged parts of a cumulonimbus (thunderstorm) cloud or between the cloud and the ground. It's formed when clouds become electrically polarized—with a net positive charge near the top of the cloud and net negative charge in the lower part of the cloud. Exactly how this polarization occurs is still a mystery. However, a number of researchers suggest that a channel of electrons—called a stepped leader—sometimes flows out a cloud and moves towards the ground. The approach of this leader increases the ground's positive charge and draws a similar stream of positively charged electrons—called a pilot streamer—upwards. When the leader and streamer meet, a closed circuit is created and electrical current begins to flow. Electrons are discharged onto the ground and an upward moving return stroke heats the air and makes lightning visible.

Lightning is very powerful. It can discharge millions of volts of electricity, propel return strokes at nearly the speed of light, and heat surrounding air up to thousands of degrees Fahrenheit. When this superheated air explodes away from the electrical current it creates a shock wave called "thunder."

Lightning is extremely dangerous, highly unpredictable and very fickle. It can strike and destroy one object without touching another one nearby; or it can hit an object and travel across the ground for dozens of feet electrocuting anything in its path.

Here are five interesting facts about the affect of lightning on people and objects:

1. In 1991, lightning killed 73 people in the United States with five times as many males as females killed by lightning. The 10-39 age group tended to be the most susceptible to the dangers of lightning with 62% of the fatalities falling into that range. Also, 21 people perished standing under a tree, 12 died out in the open, and 10 in a boat.
2. Lightning does strike the same place twice. The Empire State Building in New York City is struck on the average of about 23 times per year.
3. On September 1, 1939, lightning hit and killed 835 sheep on the top of Pine Canyon in the Raft River Mountains of Box Elder County, Utah.
4. On June 28, 1956, a lightning bolt struck the top of a home in Cedar City, Utah, leaving a 10-foot wide hole in the roof.
5. On May 30, 1987, a giant coal truck (having tires seven feet tall) was hit by lightning at a strip mine near Providence, Kentucky. The six-wheel, 177,000 pound truck "felt like it had been picked up and set down, and shook all over." One of the six $4,000 steel-belted tires was blown from the rim and landed 30 feet away, another was turned inside out and a third went flat, leaving only one of the four rear tires intact. (Contrary to popular belief, the "rubber tires" of a car or truck do NOT protect people from lightning. Instead, the metal covering of the vehicle usually protects the occupants by conducting the electrical discharge across the vehicle and down into the ground.)

Lightning Safety Rules

Lightning normally strikes the tallest object in an area, and is particularly attracted to metal and objects near or on water. In other words, lightning loves three things: height, metal and water. Also history has shown that lightning's most likely targets are tall, isolated structures that are close to water, such as hilltops, swimming pools and lakes. These safety rules will help save your life:

1. If inside a building or a metal-enclosed vehicle, remain inside.
2. Inside a home, avoid using telephones and electrical appliances.
3. If outside, seek cover in a large enclosed building or metal-enclosed vehicle.
4. If outside and there is not time to reach a large enclosed building or metal-enclosed vehicle, follow these rules:
    a. Do not stand underneath a natural lightning rod such as an isolated tree (move away from any

tree a distance that is twice the height of the tree).

b. Avoid projecting above the surrounding landscape as you would if you were standing on a hilltop, in an open field, on a beach, or fishing in a small, open boat.

c. Get out of and away from open water.

d. Get away from metallic equipment.

e. Get off of and away from motorcycles, scooters, golf carts, bicycles, and tractors without enclosed cabs.

f. Put down golf clubs.

g. Stay away from wire fences, clotheslines, metal pipes, metal rails, and other metallic conductors that can carry lightning to you from some distance away.

h. Avoid seeking shelter in small, isolated sheds or other structures in open areas.

i. If in a forest, seek shelter in a low area under a thick growth of small trees.

j. In open areas, go to a low place such as a ravine or gully, but be alert for flash floods.

k. If you are isolated in a level, open area and you feel your hair stand on end (indicating that lightning is about to strike), drop to your knees and bend forward putting your hands on your knees and your chin to you chest. Do NOT lie flat on the ground.

Utah's Lightning Statistics

1 January 1954 - 31 December 1995

Year	Deaths	Injuries
1954	1	0
1955	0	0
1956	1	1
1957	1	2
1958	0	0
1959	0	1
1960	2	1
1961	0	3
1962	0	1
1963	4	11
1964	0	1
1965	0	2
1966	1	3
1967	1	0
1968	0	2
1969	0	1
1970	0	0
1971	0	0
1972	1	3
1973	1	1
1974	0	0
1975	0	1
1976	1	3
1977	2	3
1978	1	0
1979	1	0
1980	1	0
1981	3	8
1982	0	2
1983	0	0
1984	2	6
1985	2	4
1986	2	2
1987	2	2
1988	0	6
1989	2	1
1990	1	2
1991	3	5
1992	2	7
1993	2	6
1994	1	2
1995	2	7
Total	43	100

Lightning Deaths and Injuries by Month

Month	Deaths	Injuries
April	3	0
May	1	12
June	6	20
July	10	24
August	15	31
September	6	9
October	2	4
Total	43	100

Lightning Deaths and Injuries by County

County	Deaths	Injuries
Cache	2	7
Carbon	2	4
Daggett	1	1
Davis	1	1
Duchesne	4	7
Emery	0	6
Garfield	3	4
Grand	2	3
Iron	1	0
Juab	2	0
Morgan	1	2
Piute	1	1
Rich	1	0
Salt Lake	3	27
San Juan	6	3
Sanpete	3	0
Sevier	0	1
Summit	2	6
Tooele	0	5
Uintah	2	3
Utah	2	10
Wasatch	1	3
Washington	0	2
Wayne	1	1
Weber	2	3
Total	43	100

Lightning Deaths and Injuries by Gender

Gender	Deaths	Injuries
Males	35	64
Females	8	27
Unknown	0	9
Total	43	100

Activities that led to Lightning Deaths

1954	riding a horse
1956	baling straw
1957	herding sheep
1960	working on a waterline
1963	herding sheep
1963	herding cattle
1966	near a lake
1967	mowing a lawn
1972	weeding sugar beets
1973	under a tree
1976	holding an umbrella
1977	fishing from a small boat
1977	on a camping trip
1978	riding a horse
1979	working on a farm
1980	UP&L lineman
1981	under a tree near a golf course
1981	riding a dirt bike
1981	fishing near a creek
1984	in a backyard
1984	under a tree
1985	jumping over a ditch
1985	under a tree on a golf course
1986	on a scenic overlook above a river
1986	deer hunting
1987	under a tree
1989	fishing at a lake
1989	setting up a tent
1990	at a picnic table near a reservoir
1991	under a tree
1991	near some trees on a ridge
1992	on a barren ridge
1993	under a tree
1993	hunting in a field
1994	under a tree
1995	rock climbing
1995	watering trees with a hose

For specific details on the circumstances that led to the above deaths and injuries, write to:

Meteorologist-in-charge
National Weather Service Forecast Office
2242 West North Temple Street
Salt Lake City, Utah, 84116

Precipitation

by
R. Clayton Brough and Dale J. Stevens

Precipitation in Utah varies greatly, from an average of a little less than five inches over the Great Salt Lake Desert to more than 60 inches at the top of the northern Wasatch Mountains. The average annual precipitation in the major agricultural areas of the state generally ranges between 10 to 16 inches. As a result, irrigation is vital to the profitable production of most crops. It is fortunate that the major agricultural areas of the state are adjacent to the mountains. There is usually adequate irrigation water except during periods of severe drought. The areas of the state below an elevation of 4,000 feet (all in the southern portion of the state) generally receive less than 10 inches of moisture annually.

Utah's wettest water-year on record since 1895 occurred in 1994-1995, when the state as a whole recorded 16.67 inches of precipitation. (A water-year goes from October through September.) Other very wet water-years include: 1940-1941, 16.57 inches; 1981-1982, 16.38 inches; 1982-1983, 16.22 inches; 1972-1973, 15.66 inches; and 1908-1909, 15.29 inches.

Utah's most severe winter since 1899 occurred during the 1948-1949 winter season. It was the coldest winter on record, and an accumulation of 78 inches of snow was reported at the Salt Lake City Airport during the season. This accumulation was 18 inches greater than the previous record of 1936-1937. Nearly a 25% loss in some livestock herds was reported, tourist trade reached an all-time low, and 10 people died from exposure, snowslides and other direct effects of the weather.

Utah's driest period since 1899 was recorded during 1976. In that year, the average precipitation over the state was 7.70 inches, compared to a previous record low accumulation of 8.79 inches in 1966. The drought extended into 1977, causing disastrous consequences throughout the state, including the serious depletion of soil water and the loss of many perennial plants. Water rationing and emergency transportation of water occurred in many communities, and ski resorts, farming and other investments that depend upon good snowcover were financially strapped.

Precipitation in the 90's

by
William J. Alder

After the unprecedented wet years in the mid-1980's, precipitation over Utah in the late 1980's and early 1990's was either normal or below normal levels. This decline in precipitation lasted for a six year period. The deficit of moisture was especially felt in the north. This caused reservoirs to drop to their lowest levels in many years. In November 1992, Bear Lake dropped to 5,905 feet above sea level—its lowest level since 1935. However, during the water-years of 1989-1990 through 1991-1992, state precipitation actually averaged between 100 and 110% of normal. But this was due to summer rainfall and above normal amounts of precipitation in the south.

1992-1993 was a great year for water statewide with abundant snowfall in the mountains and water-year percentages above to well-above normal levels. During this period, Bear Lake rose six feet and Lake Powell 56 feet. The state average for the water-year of 1992-1993 was 129%.

1993-1994 was another lean year for water with the majority of the state below to well-below normal on moisture with the state average a puny 89%.

The water-year of 1994-1995 was another abundant year with generous amounts of precipitation. Storminess frequented the state from fall through the spring months with one of the greatest mountain snowpacks on record recorded in the southern part of the state. The state average by the end of the water-year was 144% of average.

1995-1996 was wet in the north and very dry in the south. In fact, on May 14, 1996, Governor Mike Leavitt signed an agricultural drought disaster declaration for San Juan County and asked for federal drought disaster assistance.

Floods and Flash Floods

by

William J. Alder and R. Clayton Brough

Floods and Flash Floods

Floods are a natural and inevitable part of life along the rivers of our country. Some floods occur seasonally when winter or spring rains, coupled with melting snows or torrential rains associated with tropical storms, drain small tributaries and fill river basins with too much water, too quickly. Other floods are sudden, resulting from heavy localized rainfall. These flash floods are raging torrents which rip through river beds, urban streets, and mountain canyons after heavy rains, sweeping everything before them.

U.S. Floods and Flash Floods

The transformation of a tranquil river into a destructive flood occurs hundreds of times each year throughout the United States. In fact, floods and flash floods are the number one weather-related killer in the country. No area of the United States is completely free from the threat of floods. On the average, each year over 300,000 Americans are driven from their homes by floods and flash floods; 140 people are killed; and around $2 billion worth of property is damaged or destroyed.

In the Spring and Summer of 1993, extended, heavy rainfall caused record flooding in much of the Upper Mississippi River Basin. The Mississippi and Missouri Rivers were closed to shipping before and after the flooding, and millions of acres of productive farmland were flooded in the Midwestern United States. Property damage alone exceeded $10 billion.

Utah Floods and Flash Flood Deaths

In Utah, over 360 flash floods and more than 170 snowmelt floods have occurred since 1853. Also, since 1950, 21 people have been killed by floods or flash floods in Utah, making such floods the third greatest weather-related killer in the state (after lightning and avalanches):

Utah Flash Flood Deaths, 1950-1995

Date	#/Gender	Activity	County
8/26/52	1/male	water flooded tunnel	Emery
9/17/61	5/males	in narrow canyon	Washington
9/17/61	1/female	drowned in flood waters	Kane
6/10/65	7/m/f/ch	camping along a creek	Daggett
9/5/70	2/m/f	car went off bridge	San Juan
2/18/80	1/female	car crossed creek	Washington
6/24/83	1/male	crossing raging water	Millard
5/13/84	1/male	debris and mud flow	Carbon
5/14/84	1/male	mudslide hit bulldozer	Tooele
2/18/86	1/male	rain-swollen canal	Box Elder

Snowmelt Floods

Runoff from melting mountain snow causes "snowmelt floods." Such runoff usually reaches its peak in May or early June. Sometimes this runoff causes flooding along lower mountains and valley streams. In the Spring of 1983, rapid warming during the last week of May and the first part of June, caused rivers to rise dramatically throughout Utah. State Street, North Temple Street, and 13th South Street in Salt Lake City were tuned into rivers with sandbag boundaries. Interstate 15 in Juab, Utah and Millard Counties was inundated in places by water from swollen rivers and lakes. Rivers throughout the state carved deep crevices into canyon roads, leaving many summer recreation areas inaccessible for camping. The hardest-hit areas were in Juab, Utah, Beaver, and Uinta Counties. In addition, a massive mudslide blocked the Spanish Fork River in Utah County, trapping water behind the slide which eventually covered the town of Thistle with water.

The Danger of Flash Floods

Utah is occasionally subjected to locally heavy rainfall associated with summer thunderstorms. These heavy but short-lived storms can produce local flash floods in dry stream channels, as well as in perennial streams which create very dangerous situations for anyone caught in the path of the surging waters.

In Utah, flash floods typically occur when slow moving thunderstorms produce torrential rainfall.

These floods can roll boulders, uproot trees, wash away roads and automobiles, destroy buildings and bridges and scour out new channels. Rapidly rising water can reach heights of 30 feet or more. Furthermore, flash flood-producing rains can also trigger catastrophic mud slides. Often there is no warning that these sudden, deadly floods are coming.

Most flash floods in Utah have only caused limited damage, but a few have been very destructive and deadly. For example, on June 10, 1965, a flash flood killed seven people in the Sheep Creek area of Flaming Gorge in Daggett County. The National Weather Service account of this tragic event reads as follows:

One June 10, 1965, a husband and wife and their three children and two nephews drowned in a flash flood in Sheep Creek Canyon in the Uinta Mountains of Daggett County. They were camped in Palisades Campground along the snowmelt swollen waters of Sheep Creek. Heavy rains in the area turned the creek into a raging torrent.

Flash Flood Forecasts and Warnings

To protect yourself from flash floods, know when they may occur, what the warning signs are and what to do if you are caught in a flash flood. Be aware of the latest forecasts and warnings through NOAA Weather Radio and commercial television and radio broadcasts. To take full advantage of weather forecasts and warnings when there is a high potential for flash flooding, learn what the following terms mean:

- **A Flash Flood Warning** is issued when flash flooding has been reported or is imminent. If you are in the warned area, take immediate action to save yourself. You may only have seconds!
- **A Flash Flood Watch** means that the potential for flash flooding is high within the watch area. Be alert to signs of flash flooding and be ready to evacuate immediately, if necessary.
- **A Flash Flood Statement** is issued to provide follow-up information regarding a flash flood event.

Be Prepared for a Flash Flood

Know your area's potential for flash floods. For information, call the National Weather Service, Red Cross chapter, or local emergency management agency. In Utah, areas most prone to flash flooding include steep, narrow canyons and washes in southern and eastern Utah, any location near streams or rivers (especially those located downstream from a dam), and other low lying areas. Be aware of the latest weather conditions and listen for **Flash Flood Watches and Warnings**. NOAA weather radios, which may be purchased in stores, provide continuously updated weather forecasts and warnings for all of Utah. The average transmission range is 40 miles depending on topography, and there are five broadcast locations throughout Utah. It may be best to purchase a radio that has both a battery backup and a tone-alert feature which automatically alerts you when a watch or warning is issued. Watch and warning information is also available on the Emergency Broadcast System through local radio and television broadcasts.

Flash Flood Safety Rules

If you are caught in a flash flood situation, follow these safety rules:

- Head for higher ground and stay away from flood waters! Also stay out of areas that flood easily, such as dips, low spots, canyons, washes, etc.
- Listen for distant thunder. Runoff from a faraway thunderstorm may be headed your way.
- Monitor the water level of nearby streams for rapidly rising water.
- Never try to walk, swim, or drive through swiftly moving high water. Six inches of fast moving flood water has the power to knock you off your feet, and a depth of two feet can float your car! If you come upon flood waters, stop, turn around and go another way.
- Never camp along streams or in washes. Many flash flood deaths in Utah are due to people camping in these areas when a flash flood occurs.

Also, here are some automobile safety tips:

- Never drive through flooded roadways! Many flood fatalities are auto related! In your automobile, look out for flooding at highway dips, bridges and low areas. The depth of water can be deceptive as the road bed may not be intact under flood waters.
- If your vehicle stalls, leave it immediately and move to higher ground. Rapidly rising water may engulf your vehicle and its occupants and sweep you away. Remember, it's better to be wet than dead!
- Be especially cautious at night when it is harder to recognize flood dangers.
- Do not camp or park your vehicle along streams and washes, particularly during threatening weather conditions.

Finally, here is some advice on actions you should take after a flash flood has happened:

- Stay away from flood waters.
- If fresh food has come in contact with flood waters, throw it away.
- Boil drinking water before using. Wells should be pumped out and the water tested for purity before drinking. If in doubt, call your local public health authority.
- Use flashlights, not lanterns, torches or matches, to examine buildings. Flammables may be inside.
- Report broken utility lines to appropriate authorities.

Hailstorms
by
R. Clayton Brough

Hail falls from large cumulonimbus clouds made of water drops and ice particles.

"A hailstone starts out as an ice particle. Ice particles build up into ice crystals by condensation. The ice crystals are blown up and down inside the cloud by very strong air currents, and as they are thrown around, they absorb more and more cloud drops. The cloud drops freeze onto the ice crystals in layers, like the skins of an onion. When they freeze near the warmer, lower part of the cloud, they freeze fairly slowly, and spread out as a layer of clear ice. When they freeze near the higher, colder part of the cloud, they freeze instantly, making a layer of frosty ice. By counting the layers of ice in a hailstone, we can tell how many times it was blown up and down inside the cloud, just as we can tell how old a tree is by counting the rings in its trunk. The more violent the air currents are, the taller the cloud will grow, and the bigger the hailstones are likely to be. Most hailstones are less than two inches in diameter, but they grow much larger on occasions." (Francis Wilson and Harold Gibson, *Spotters Guide to the Weather*, Usborne Publishing Company, 1979.)

Hailstorms occasionally happen in Utah, but most events cover only a relatively small area of the state. The largest and most damaging hailstorms usually occur during the warmer months of May through September when towering thunderstorms pass over the state.

Three of the most severe hailstorms ever recorded in Utah occurred along the Wasatch Front:

On August 19, 1945, thunderstorms associated with the remnants of a Pacific hurricane produced hailstones up to two inches in diameter which bombarded the Salt Lake Valley, killing birds, damaging trees, homes and stores, and causing extensive damage to nearly 50 airplanes at the Salt Lake City Airport.

On July 21, 1987 one to two inch diameter hailstones, injured a dozen people and damaged numerous cars in Utah County. Baseball size hail fell in Coalville. Wind and hail severely damaged or destroyed much of the fruit crop in Utah County. Damage estimated totaled about $9,000,000.

On August 4, 1991, ½" diameter hail fell for about 15 minutes to a depth of three inches at Snowbird. Forty-three people were injured when the hail and rain cause a large canvas canopy to collapse on 1,400 people watching a performance of the Utah Symphony.

Effects of Hurricanes
by
R. Clayton Brough and Dale J. Stevens

Moisture from the remnants of tropical storms or hurricanes occasionally reaches Utah from the Gulf of Mexico or the eastern Pacific near Baja California. This very moist air occasionally produces heavy rain and hail over parts of Utah.

One of these events occurred in the Fall of 1982, when severe flooding caused damage in excess of $5,000,000 in the Salt Lake Valley. The rains were attributed to considerable tropical moisture that moved into the state from dying Hurricane Olivia and the energy supplied from an active cold front and its upper-level low pressure system.

The precipitation associated with this storm began in extreme northern Utah on September 24, 1982. The main cold front moved into the area about September 26th, producing torrential rains in Davis, Salt Lake, and Utah Counties. Accumulations of around two to three inches in a twelve-hour period were reported. By the time the storm had passed, some locations in the above mentioned counties had accumulated over 6.5 inches of moisture.

Winter Storms
by
William J. Alder, and Daniel W. Pope

Winter storms in the form of blizzards, heavy snows, freezing rain, or sleet can be serious hazards to people in Utah. The following information comes from various government and scientific publications:

Forecasts and Warnings

The first line of protection from winter storms is to keep posted on weather conditions and forecasts for your surrounding area through television and radio. A few hours of warning before a storm hits can be the key to avoiding being caught in it, or at least to be better prepared to cope with it. To take full advantage of weather forecasts and warnings, learn and understand these common terms:

A **Heavy Snow Warning** is issued for valley locations when 4 or more inches of snow is expected to fall within 12 hours, or when 6 or more inches of snow is expected in 24 hours. In mountain areas below 7,000 feet, a heavy snow warning is issued when 6 inches of snow is expected to fall in 12 hours, or 10 inches in 24 hours. For elevations above 7,000 feet, a heavy snow warning issued when 8 inches of snow is expected in 12 hours, or 12 inches in 24 hours.

During the first half of January 1993, heavy snow warnings were repeatedly issued for many areas of northern Utah. On January 11, the governor of Utah declared a State of Emergency in Salt Lake County and activated the Utah National Guard to assist in snow removal. During this month, the Salt Lake City International Airport recorded a record snowfall of 23.3" from a single storm (January 6-10), and a record monthly snowfall (for any month) of 50.3".

A **Winter Storm Warning** is issued when the combination of heavy snow and other severe winter weather elements are expected. Stay indoors because blowing and drifting snow, freezing rain and/or reduced visibility may cause roads to become slippery, blocked or impassable.

A **Winter Storm Watch** is issued when the severe winter conditions detailed above are possible within the next day or two.

A **Blizzard Warning** means snow and strong winds of 35 mph or more will combine to produce a blinding snow (with near zero visibility), deep drifts, and life-threatening temperatures below 20 degrees, causing a wind-chill lower than minus 35 degrees.

In Utah, blizzards have been responsible for the deaths of at least 21 people since 1950. In fact, in December 1990, a severe blizzard—with heavy snow, cold temperatures and 40 mph winds—contributed to a major traffic accident of a bus and two semi-trucks between Coalville and Evanston that killed seven people.

Winter Weather Advisories are issued for several hazards which can cause significant inconveniences, including: snow, blowing snow, wind-chill, freezing rain or freezing drizzle and sleet.

Freezing rain or freezing drizzle is forecast when rain is likely to freeze as soon as it strikes the ground, putting a coating of ice or glaze on the roads and everything else that is exposed. Even small accumulations of ice can cause a significant hazard.

Sleet is small particles of ice, usually mixed with rain. If enough sleet accumulates on the ground, it will make the roads slippery.

Precautions and Safety Rules

Here are some precautions you should take—and safety rules you should know—before severe winter weather develops or is forecast:

Isolation:

Be prepared for isolation at home. If you live in a rural area of Utah, make sure you could survive at home for a week or two in case a storm isolates you and makes it impossible for you to leave. Also:

- Keep an adequate supply of heating fuel on hand and use it sparingly. Your regular supplies may be curtailed by storm conditions. If necessary, conserve fuel by keeping the house cooler than usual, or by "closing off" some rooms temporarily. Also have available some kind of emergency heating equipment and fuel so you can keep at least one room of your house warm enough to be livable. This can be a camp stove with fuel, or a supply of wood or coal for burning in a fireplace. If your furnace is controlled by a thermostat and your electricity is cut off by a storm, the furnace probably would not operate and you will need some kind of emergency heat source.

- Stock an emergency supply of food and water, as well as emergency cooking equipment such as a camp stove. Some of this food should be of the type that does not require refrigeration or cooking.

- Make sure you have a battery-powered radio and extra batteries on hand, so that if your electric power is cut off you can still hear weather forecasts, information, and advice broadcast by local authorities. Also, flashlights or lanterns would be needed.

- Keep on hand the simple tools and equipment needed to fight a fire. Also, be certain that all family members know how to take precautions that would prevent a fire—particularly when the help of a fire department may not be readily available.

Caution: Know how to use your emergency heating and lighting equipment safely to prevent fire or dangerous fumes. Use only safety listed equipment. Never introduce a fuel into a unit not designed for that fuel. Proper ventilation is essential. Burning charcoal gives off deadly amounts of carbon monoxide!

Travel:

Travel only if necessary. Avoid all unnecessary trips. If you must travel, use public transportation if possible. However, if you are forced to use your automobile for a trip of any distance, take these precautions.

- Make sure your car is in good working condition, properly serviced and equipped with chains or snow tires. Regularly check your breaks, heater and windshield wipers.

- Take another person with you if possible.

- Maintain a full tank of gas.

- Have emergency "winter storm supplies" in the car, such as a container of sand, shovel, windshield scraper, tow chain or rope, flashlight, and blankets or sleeping bags. It is also good to have with you heavy gloves or mittens, overshoes, extra woolen socks, and winter headgear to cover your head and face.

- Travel by daylight and use major highways if you can. Keep the car radio turned on for weather information.

- Drive with all possible caution. Don't try and save time by traveling faster than road and weather conditions permit.

- Don't be daring or foolhardy. Stop, turn back, or seek help if conditions threaten that may test your ability or endurance, rather than risk being stalled, lost, or isolated. If you are caught in a blizzard, seek refuge immediately.

Keep calm if you get in trouble. If your car breaks down during a storm, or if you become stalled or lost, don't panic. Think the problem through, decide what's the safest and best thing to do, and then do it slowly and carefully. If you are on a well-traveled road, show a trouble signal. Set your directionally lights to flashing, raise the hood of your car, or hang a cloth from the radio aerial or a car window. Then stay in your car and wait for help to arrive. If you run the engine to keep warm, remember to partially open a window enough to provide ventilation that will protect you from carbon monoxide poisoning. Also, keep your car exhaust pipe and radiator clear of snow and ice, and move your arms and legs often to maintain good blood circulation.

Wherever you are, if there is no house or other source of help in sight, do not leave your car to search for assistance, as you may become confused and get lost.

Note: If you regularly commute long distances through metropolitan areas, you might want to consider purchasing a CB radio or cellular phone—so that if you're stalled or in trouble you can contact help via your CB radio or mobile phone.

Overexertion:

Avoid overexertion. Every winter many unnecessary deaths occur because people—especially older persons, but younger ones as well—engage in more strenuous physical activity than their bodies can stand. Cold weather itself, without any physical exertion, puts an extra strain on your heart. If you add to this physical exercise, especially exercise that you are not accustomed to—such as shoveling snow, pushing an automobile, or even walking fast or far— you are risking a heart attack, a stroke, or damage to your body. In winter weather, and especially in winter storms, be aware of this danger and avoid overexertion.

Lake Effect Weather
by
William J. Alder and R. Clayton Brough

The Great Salt Lake has some influence on the local weather climate of its surrounding communities. The high salt content in the water of the lake (which averages 15% on the south arm and 25% on the north arm of the lake, compared to 3½% for the world's oceans) prevents most of the lake's surface from freezing during the winter months. This open water naturally adds moisture to the air flowing over the lake, enhancing precipitation along the Wasatch Mountains and producing heavy "lake effect" snowstorms.

"Lake effect" snowstorms generally occur five to six times a year during the fall and spring months. Such snowstorms usually develop when a cold northwest storm moves over the warmer Great Salt Lake. The warm, moist lake air then rises into the cold air above, causing dense clouds to form. The clouds then drop heavy snow downwind from the lake. The strongest "lake effect" storms appear to happen when there is a 10-15 degree F., temperature difference between the waters of the Great Salt Lake and the air flowing over it. On October 18, 1984, a "lake effect" snowstorm dropped up to 18 to 24 inches of snow on the east benches of the Salt Lake Valley, causing over $1,000,000 worth of damage to utility lines, homes, businesses and cars.

In addition, the large surface area of the Great Salt Lake is responsible for an average daytime "sea breeze" of eight to 12 miles per hour over nearby valleys. This breeze often lowers afternoon temperatures in areas near the lake by as much as two to four degrees F., during late spring and early summer.

"Lake Stink"

Occasionally it is possible to smell foul odors that originate from the Great Salt Lake. These odors can be smelled in populated areas located several miles or farther from the shore of the lake.

Winds associated with a cold front (moving northwest to southeast over the lake) often churn up the water in the Great Salt Lake and encourage the release of bacterial odor from decomposing aquatic vegetation, brine shrimp and flies. The winds then carry this odor downwind to populated areas. These pronounced odors are usually detected during the fall months, although the odor also occurs during the summer season.

On October 24, 1983, Wasatch Front residents described the day as one of the worst "lake stink" days they had ever experienced in Salt Lake and Davis Counties. Brisk northerly winds in the wake of a cold front stirred up the rotting aquatic marsh vegetation in the lake, and the combination of a high lake level and low salinity resulted in an above normal amount of vegetation available for decay around the lake. Also, the decomposition of brine shrimp and flies added to the smell. The 'stink' was detected by people as far south as Juab County.

Greatest Snow on Earth
by
James M. Duthie

Winter storms that affect Utah generally originate in the North Pacific Ocean, where cold Arctic air encounters the relatively warmer Pacific waters. As these storms move inland some of their moisture falls over the Cascade and Sierra Nevada Mountains. However, upon encountering the abrupt rises of the Wasatch and central/southern Utah mountain ranges, the cold, wet airmasses rise "orographically"—or are forced upward by the rise in surface elevation. The airmass cools further as it rises, leading to enhanced condensation and precipitation. Higher altitudes and generally lower temperatures produce the colder, drier "powdery" snow for which Utah is known.

It is the structure of the snow crystals that makes Utah snow unique. Utah is the second driest state in the nation (after Nevada), and the cold, relatively dry conditions produce light, crystalline snowflakes called "dendrites." These snowflakes are thick and symmetrical, and float slowly through the cold atmosphere to the surface, accumulating as fluffy "powder" in the mountains. Often, storm fronts that move through northern Utah are followed by brisk northwest upper-level winds, which are aimed directly the mountain peaks. Additional moisture is drawn from the warmer waters of the Great Salt Lake, which never freeze, and snowfall in the mountains may continue for days, even after the main storm has passed. It is not unusual to see an additional 24-36 inches of snowfall in the day or two following a storm, all because of this northwesterly flow of cold air across the Great Salt Lake and over the Wasatch Mountains. After such a storm, skiers will likely find several feet of fluffy powder at the resorts.

During late winter and early spring, tropical moisture sometimes arrives from the central Pacific. Due to the warmer source of this moisture, subsequent snowfall in Utah is often heavier and denser, with a higher moisture content. These late season wet snows undergo a thaw-freeze cycle as the days grow warmer, producing icy "corn snow" conditions, which makes for faster skiing.

Average temperatures in winter range from the single digits to the low 30's, with sub-zero readings common on clear nights following a storm. Highs may reach the 40's or 50's just preceding a storm front. Elevation is the greatest factor, as temperatures generally change 5°F per 1,000 feet in elevation. When inversions form in the valleys, ski resorts are often warmer. Of more concern is the wind-chill, which indicates the "apparent" temperature or "what it feels like." Wind chill is based on air temperature and wind speed. The higher the wind speed, the colder "it feels" on exposed flesh. Frostbite can occur quickly when wind-chills fall into the sub-zero range.

At Utah's northern ski resorts, mid-elevation snowfalls vary from 200 to over 500 inches per year. Utah's southwestern ski resorts average mid-elevation accumulations of over 300 inches per year. Most of the ski resorts in northern Utah usually receive their greatest monthly snowfall during December or January. The ski resorts in southwest Utah usually get their largest monthly snowfalls during January or March. The greatest six-month snowfall total ever recorded in Utah skiing history occurred from November 1983 through April 1984, when two of the highest ski resorts in northern Utah recorded snowfall totals of between 650 and 700 inches near their base elevations.

Estimated Average Snowfall at Utah's Ski Resorts:
* November-April snowfall
** Annual Snowfall

Resort	Base	Inches	Mid-level	Inches	Summit	Inches
Alta*	8,550	421	9,600	516	10,650	621
Beaver Mountain**	7,200	222	8,016	298	8,832	374
Brian Head*	9,600	360	10,453	382	11,307	405
Brighton*	8,755	389	9,627	441	10,500	493
Deer Valley*	7,200	174	8,300	268	9,400	362
Elk Meadows/Mt. Holly**	9,100	284	9,750	316	10,400	348
Nordic Valley**	5,400	155	5,900	202	6,400	249
Park City*	6,900	162	8,450	248	10,000	334
Powder Mountain**	7,600	349	8,250	414	8,900	479
Snowbasin*	6,400	168	7,750	280	8,800	392
Snowbird*	7,760	326	9,380	465	11,000	634
Solitude*	7,988	365	9,012	458	10,035	551
Sundance**	6,100	124	7,175	209	8,250	294
Wolf Mountain**	6,800	120	7,900	214	9,000	308

Note: Base, Mid-level and Summit elevations are in "feet" above sea level. "Inches" means inches of snowfall.

Avalanche Deaths: 1950-1995
by
William J. Alder and R. Clayton Brough

During the winter months, avalanches can occur in the vicinity of some of Utah's higher, steeper ski slopes. Heavy or dense snowfall accumulating on an unstable snowbase often trigger avalanches. Because of this, many back-country areas or isolated ski slopes must be skied with caution and proper equipment. From 1950 through 1995, 42 people have died from Utah avalanches.

Season	Date	Deaths	Sex	Location
1950-51	—	—	—	—
1951-52	—	—	—	—
1952-53	—	—	—	—
1953-54	—	—	—	—
1954-55	—	—	—	—
1955-56	—	—	—	—
1956-57	—	—	—	—
1957-58	3/9/58	2	Males	Snowbasin
1958-59	—	—	—	—
1959-60	—	—	—	—
1960-61	—	—	—	—
1961-62	—	—	—	—
1962-63	—	—	—	—
1963-64	3/29/64	1	Male	Snowbasin
1964-65	—	—	—	—
1965-66	12/31/65	1	Male	Park City
1966-67	2/12/67	2	Males	Pharaoh's Glenn
1967-68	2/19/68	1	Male	Rock Canyon
1968-69	—	—	—	—
1969-70	1/29/70	1	Male	Alta
1970-71	—	—	—	—
1971-72	—	—	—	—
1972-73	1/29/73	1	Male	Park West
1973-74	—	—	—	—
1974-75	—	—	—	—
1975-76	1/6/76	1	Male	Alta
1976-77	3/3/77	1	Male	Snowbird
1977-78	—	—	—	—
1978-79	1/19/79	1	Male	Helper
1978-79	4/2/79	1	Male	Lake Desolation
1979-80	1/11/80	1	Male	Evergreen Ridge
1980-81	2/1/81	1	Male	Cardiff
1980-81	3/1/81	1	Male	Millcreek
1981-82	3/22/82	1	Male	Park West
1982-83	—	—	—	—
1983-84	1/2/84	1	Male	Superior
1984-85	2/22/85	1	Male	Powder Mountain

Season	Date	Deaths	Sex	Location
1984-85	3/19/85	1	Female	Park City
1985-86	11/13/85	2	Males	Sunset
1985-86	1/6/86	1	Male	Provo Canyon
1985-86	2/17/86	1	Male	Big Cottonwood Canyon
1985-86	2/19/86	1	Male	Alta
1986-87	11/20/86	1	Male	Sugarloaf, Alta
1986-87	2/15/87	1	Male	Twin Lakes Res.
1987-88	—	—	—	—
1988-89	—	—	—	—
1989-90	11/25/89	1	Male	Tony Grove Lake, Logan
1990-91	—	—	—	—
1991-92	2/12/92	4	3-M/1-F	Gold Basin, La Sal Mountains
1991-92	4/1/92	1	Male	Mineral Basin, Snowbird
1992-93	1/16/93	1	Male	Sundance (in closed area)
1992-93	2/25/93	1	Male	Pinecrest, Emigration Canyon
1992-93	4/3/93	1	Male	Wolverine Cirque
1993-94	2/18/94	1	Male	Peak 10,420, B.C.C.
1994-95	11/7/94	1	Male	Snowbird (area not open)
1994-95	1/14/95	2	Males	Ben Lomond, Ogden
1994-95	1/23/95	1	Male	Midway
1994-95	2/12/95	1	Male	Gobbler's Knob, B.C.C.
Total Deaths:		**42**	**40 Males**	
			2 Females	

For more information on avalanches and safety rules, see the video *Utah's Weather Wonders: A Survival Guide That Can Save Your Life* (1994, 30 minutes). This video has been made available free of charge to all public schools and libraries in Utah. It is also available for $10.00 from News 4 Utah, Weather Department, 1760 Fremont Drive, Salt Lake City, Utah, 84104.

Winds and Tornadoes

Winds

by

R. Clayton Brough and Benjamin T. Tolman

Utah Winds

Winds at any location are the result of unequal heating and cooling of the earth's surface, pressure differences and topography. In Utah there are six major types of winds. The first four are named for the direction they come from and the last two are named after the phenomena that produces them. These six winds are:

Southerly Winds

Many times each year the western valleys of Utah experience strong southerly winds. These winds have been called "desert winds," because they usually bring warm air up from the southwestern deserts ahead of an approaching storm or cold front. The highest "desert wind" ever reported by a reliable weather observer was a 93 miles-per-hour wind gust that occurred on April 5, 1967 at Dugway.

Northerly Winds

The highest northerly winds recorded in Utah usually occur during or just after the passage of a strong cold front or low pressure system. The highest northerly wind gust ever reported for a mountain location was 124 miles-per-hour on November 8, 1986 at Snowbird's Hidden Peak (at 11,000 feet above sea level). The highest northerly wind gust ever reported for a valley location was 94 miles-per-hour on June 3, 1963 at the Salt Lake City Airport.

Easterly Canyon Winds

One form of topographic wind that creates serious problems several times each year is the "easterly canyon wind." These easterly winds usually occur when strong high pressure develops over southern Wyoming and deep low pressure develops over southeastern Nevada. When surface pressure differences are strong enough between the two areas, winds in excess of 74 miles-per-hour (or hurricane force) gust out of the canyon mouths along the western slopes of the Wasatch Mountains and cause significant damage in Cache, Weber, Davis, Salt Lake and Utah counties. On April 4, 1983, easterly canyon winds gusted over 100 miles-per-hour (103 mph at Ogden and 104 mph at Hill Air Force Base) and caused millions of dollars of damage to power lines, homes and personal property in those counties.

Westerly Winds

The highest westerly winds recorded in Utah usually occur during the passage of a strong cold front. The highest westerly wind gust ever reported by a weather observer was one of 77 miles-per-hour on February 18, 1983 at Milford.

Thunderstorm Winds

The highest winds from thunderstorms are those usually associated with lines of thunderstorms called "squall lines." These squall lines or large thunderstorms occasionally produce strong downdraft winds called "microbursts." Because these microbursts flow out in all directions once they reach ground, many weather observers only record them as a directional wind (N,S,E,W) and not as a thunderstorm-related wind. Nevertheless, according to available records, the highest thunderstorm downdraft or mircoburst ever recorded by a weather observer was a 121 miles-per-hour wind gust on May 31, 1994 at the Kimball Tower on the campus of Brigham Young University in Provo, Utah.

Tornadic Winds

On a few occasions, high wind speeds associated with or coming from tornadic activity have been recorded by weather observers. The highest recorded wind speed associated with nearby tornadic activity was an 89 mile-per-hour wind gust that occurred on August 13, 1984 at Brigham Young University in Provo, Utah.

Visible Measure of Wind Speed

In the absence of an anemometer (or windspeed instrument), the Beaufort Scale of Wind is a good reference for estimating wind speeds. The scale was invented in the early 19th century by Admiral Beaufort of the British Navy. Over the years the scale has been modified and refined as follows:

Visible Specifics	MPH
Calm, smoke rises vertically:	0-1
Direction of wind shown by smoke drift:	1-3
Wind felt on face, leaves rustle:	4-7
Leaves and small twigs in constant motion, light flags extend:	8-12
Raises dust, leaves and loose paper; small branches move:	13-18
Small trees in leaf begin to sway, crested wavelets form on inland waters:	19-24
Large branches in motion, whistling heard in telephone wires:	25-31
Whole trees in motion, inconvenience felt in walking against wind:	32-38
Breaks twigs and small branches off trees, impedes progress:	39-46
Slight structural damage occurs, chimney pots and slate removed:	47-54

Trees broken or uprooted,
considerable damage occurs: 55-63
Widespread damage: 64-73
Hurricane force, widespread damage: 74

High Wind Intensities

Here are the highest wind gusts (of 50 mph or higher) that have been recorded/reported at Utah locations through December 1995:

Location	Speeds (in MPH)
Alta	100
American Fork	60
Blanding	58
Bountiful Bench	120
Brigham City	61
Bullfrog	68
Canyonlands Nat. Park.	68
Cedar City	75
Centerville	104
Dugway	93
Eagle Range	64
Farmington	90
Flaming Gorge	67
Francis Peak	115
Hill Air Force Base	104
Holladay	56
Kearns	80
Lakeside	86
Lewiston	66
Logan	94
Logan Canyon	100
Magna	66
Midway	65
Milford	77
Moab	80
Monticello	60
Mt. Ogden	108
Naples	72
Ogden	103
Orem	80
Park City	80
Park City Gondola	120
Provo BYU Kimball Tower	121
Richfield	60
St. George	86
Salt Lake City	86
S.L.C. Int. Airport	94
Sandy	80
Smithfield	84
Snowbird (11,000')	124
Springville	80
Sundance	120
Sunset	68
Tooele	75
Trenton	79
University of Utah	78
Vernal	62
Wahweap	70
Wellsville	79
Wendover	82
West Valley City	68

Wind-Chill Chart

The temperature of the air is not always a reliable indicator of how cold a person feels. Other weather elements such as wind speed, relative humidity and sunshine exert an influence. Also, a person's clothing and metabolism affect how cold he or she feels.

Wind has a chilling effect on the body by removing body heat from exposed flesh. For example, an air temperature of 20°F with a wind of 10 mph, would have the same cooling effect on exposed flesh as a 4°F temperature in calm weather.

For more information on wind-chill and a free copy of a detailed wind-chill chart, send a self-addressed, stamped envelope to:

The Ultimate Wind-Chill Chart
c/o Dan Pope, Chief Meteorologist
News 4 Utah Weather Department
1760 Fremont Drive
Salt Lake City, Utah, 84104.

Whirlwinds or Dust Devils
by
Rodney D. Griffin

Whirlwinds or dust devils are quite common throughout the arid and semiarid environments of Utah. All that is required to produce a dust devil is moderate heating at the surface of the earth and some horizontal component of wind. Usually a temperature in the 80's (Fahrenheit) and 10-15 knot (12-17mph) winds are enough to do the trick. Dust devils are therefore almost always associated with fair, sunny weather during the warm half of the year.

Because the above conditions can occur almost anywhere in Utah, one would expect dust devils to be reported almost all of the time in various parts of the state. But, in fact, 90% are reported in the western valleys (often called the "west desert") of the Beehive state. The reason for this is implied in the name often applied to these twisting winds. It is usually only in the drier west deserts that there is enough loose and dry earth materials at the surface to be lifted by the wind and therefore become visible at a distance. In urban areas along the Wasatch Front, the progress of a dust devil can often be traced by the pattern of flying papers and other debris.

Utah's dust devils have been called "crypto-vortices" or "sneaky winds." On occasion, they have surprised unsuspecting roofers and construction workers in precarious positions. However, there are no reports of severe injuries due to Utah dust devils, and only a few accounts of damage to property, as noted below:

On June 7, 1974, a 60 miles-per-hour whirlwind 75 yards wide struck a boat marina near the Great Salt Lake and damaged a sign, roof, and small boat.

On August 5, 1985, a huge dust devil tore part of the roof off a business in Murray.

On June 15, 1996, a large dust devil more than 30 feet wide and about 500 feet high moved across the southwestern part of Salt Lake County, and did minor damage to some out buildings.

On a few occasions, large whirlwinds have been reported in the area of huge thunderstorm clouds. These are probably associated with "mircoburst" or downdraft winds from convective clouds. Sometimes the dust raised by this brand of dust devil may extend several thousand feet to near the base of the cloud. This may account for a few of the "twisters" or tornadoes that sometimes become a part of the official weather reports in the public media.

Generally speaking, the dust devil or whirlwind is a phenomenon that can be considered a fair-weather or warm-weather happening in Utah that is not particularly dangerous, and can bring a rather welcome relief to the routine of an otherwise uneventful summer afternoon.

Tornadoes and Waterspouts
by
William J. Alder, R. Clayton Brough,
Sean T. Buchanan, David R. James
and Benjamin T. Tolman

Atmospheric conditions are rarely favorable for the development of tornadoes in Utah due to the dry climate and the mountainous terrain. Utah ranks as having one of the lowest incidences of tornadoes in the nation, with only seven states having fewer numbers. From 1950 to 1995, 78 tornadoes and 14 waterspouts have been reported in the state.

In the central U.S., tornadoes are commonly one-fourth of a mile wide and often cause considerable destruction and death. However, Utah tornadoes are usually smaller in size, often no more than 60 feet wide (at the base), with a path length usually less than a mile and a life span of only a few seconds to a few minutes. They normally follow a path from a southwesterly to a northeasterly direction and usually precede the passage of a cold front. No one has ever been killed by a Utah tornado, although at least five injuries have been attributed to them.

About 72% of all Utah tornadoes and waterspouts have occurred in May, June, July and August, when severe thunderstorms occasionally frequent Utah. Also, 80% of all Utah tornadoes have occurred between the hours of 11:00 AM, and 5:00

PM, while waterspouts normally develop in the morning hours.

There have probably been more tornadoes and waterspouts in Utah than the following statistics and accounts indicate. And in recent years, an increasing number of these storms have been reported. But this is probably due to the increase in Utah's population and greater public awareness about these twisters.

Tornado Statistics for Utah

January 1, 1950 - 31 December 1995:

Number of Tornadoes by Year:

Year		Year	
1950	0	1973	0
1951	0	1974	0
1952	0	1975	0
1953	2	1976	0
1954	1	1977	0
1955	3	1978	0
1956	0	1979	0
1957	1	1980	0
1958	0	1981	2
1959	0	1982	3
1960	0	1983	0
1961	1	1984	6
1962	1	1985	0
1963	1	1986	3
1964	1	1987	3
1965	5	1988	1
1966	2	1989	6
1967	2	1990	4
1968	4	1991	5
1969	3	1992	4
1970	5	1993	6
1971	1	1994	0
1972	0	1995	2
		Total	78

Number of Tornadoes by Month:

January	1	July	10
February	1	August	18
March	3	September	8
April	4	October	0
May	16	November	2
June	13	December	2
		Total	78

Number of Tornadoes by Hour (MST):

1:00 AM	1	1:00 PM	8
2:00 AM	0	2:00 PM	12
3:00 AM	0	3:00 PM	11
4:00 AM	0	4:00 PM	8
5:00 AM	0	5:00 PM	7
6:00 AM	0	6:00 PM	4
7:00 AM	0	7:00 PM	3
8:00 AM	1	8:00 PM	3
9:00 AM	2	9:00 PM	0
10:00 AM	1	10:00 PM	0

11:00 AM	10	11:00 PM	0
12:00 noon	7	12:00 Midnight	0
		Total	78

Number of Tornadoes by County:

Beaver	3	Piute	1
Box Elder	7	Rich	2
Cache	4	Salt Lake	9
Carbon	0	San Juan	0
Daggett	0	Sanpete	4
Davis	7	Sevier	2
Duchesne	3	Summit	0
Emery	5	Tooele	5
Garfield	0	Uintah	4
Grand	2	Utah	6
Iron	3	Wasatch	0
Juab	0	Washington	2
Kane	0	Wayne	6
Millard	2	Weber	3
Morgan	1		
		Total	81

Note: Three of the above numbered tornadoes were counted twice because they traveled across county borders: June 5, 1953; May 4, 1961; and May 30, 1986.

Characteristics of Utah Tornadoes

Size of Tornadoes:

Funnel diameter is usually 10 to 20 yards wide.

Largest reported funnel diameters: 440 yards wide on December 2, 1970; 200 yards wide on May 30, 1986 and August 30, 1992; and 100 yards wide on May 6, 1981 and July 25, 1991.

Duration of Tornadoes:

Contact with the ground is usually only a few seconds to a few minutes.

Greatest amount of time on the ground: 15 minutes on July 9, 1962, July 25, 1991 and August 30, 1992.

Color of Tornadoes:

Usual color: gray or brown.

Other colors: black on July 9, 1962; red on July 24, 1981; and white on December 2, 1970 and March 29, 1982.

Number of Injuries:

1 male on August 14, 1968

1 female on April 19, 1970

1 male on April 23, 1990

2 people on June 2, 1993

(possibly two others: see event of July 8, 1989)

Stated Monetary Damage:

$ 1,200	June 1, 1955
$ 5,000	June 16, 1955
$20,000	June 3, 1963

$ 2,000	August 28, 1964
$10,000	April 17, 1966
$15,000	November 2, 1967
$50,000	August 14, 1968
$ 5,000	May 29, 1987
$ 3,000	May 29, 1988
$25,000	September 17, 1989
$ 500	March 23, 1990
$ 1,500	September 23, 1992
$ 8,000	April 4, 1993
$50,000	May 3, 1993
$15,000	June 2, 1993
$ 211,200	Total

Waterspout Statistics

January 1, 1950 - 31 December 1995:

Waterspouts over the Great Salt Lake:	10
Waterspouts over Utah Lake:	4
Total:	14

Number of Waterspouts by Year:

1980	0	1988	0
1981	0	1989	2
1982	2	1990	0
1983	0	1991	0
1984	0	1992	2
1985	2	1993	0
1986	3	1994	0
1987	3	1995	0
		Total	14

Number of Waterspouts by Month:

January	0	July	2
February	0	August	4
March	0	September	3
April	0	October	1
May	2	November	1
June	1	December	0
		Total	14

Number of Waterspouts by Hours (MST):

5:00 AM	1	12:00 noon	1
6:00 AM	1	1:00 PM	1
7:00 AM	3	2:00 PM	1
8:00 AM	0	3:00 PM	0
9:00 AM	1	4:00 PM	1
10:00 AM	2	5:00 PM	2
11:00 AM	0	6:00 PM	0
		Total	14

Most Analyzed Waterspout: **June 26, 1985**

Tornadoes and Waterspouts Before 1950

Waterspout, American Fork River, Utah County
August 19, 1869, time unknown, 40°27'N, 111°43'W

Utah's first officially reported tornadic activity occurred on August 19, 1869. It was described as a "funnel-shaped waterspout" and apparently formed over the American Fork River in American Fork Canyon, Utah County. Seven bridges were washed out and damages to roads were estimated at $1,500.

Waterspout, Great Salt Lake, Salt Lake County
August 16, 1889, time unknown, 40°44'N, 112°12'W

A waterspout was observed over the south part of the Great Salt Lake near Garfield Beach, Salt Lake County. It lasted 30 minutes. The pavilion next to the railroad was covered by an inch of water and an excursion boat was almost swamped.

Tornado, near Lewiston, Cache County
March 4, 1907, time unknown, 41°58'N, 111°53'W

Utah's first reported tornado touched down near Lewiston, Cache County. No further information is available about this tornado.

Tornado, Millard County
August 4, 1916, time unknown, 39°20'N, 113°30'W

A tornado was reported in Millard County during August. No damage was reported. (The actual date of this tornado is estimate from cloudburst flood data: Woolley, 1946.)

Tornado, near Woods Cross, Davis County
May 27, 1941, 1145 MST, 40°50'N, 111°55'W

A funnel cloud initially formed over the Great Salt Lake in Davis County and appeared as an intensely black cloud from which the typical twisting funnel descended, flicking the ground in four places along a zigzag path a few rods wide and approximately ten miles long. The tornado destroyed a barn and a pigpen located two and one-fourth miles southwest of Woods Cross. The tornado then struck near the South Bountiful Ward meeting house of the Church of Jesus Christ of Latter-day Saints. It shattered windows and broke and uprooted trees and utility poles. The roof and walls of an old brick residence were torn away. The roof of the meeting house and nearby double garage were also demolished. The tornado also did slight damage to some residences and trees about a mile to the east of the meeting house. Total monetary damages were estimated at $4,000.

Tornadoes and Waterspouts from 1950 through 1995

Tornado, Farmington Canyon, Davis County and Morgan County
June 5, 1953, 0900 MST, 41°00'N, 11°53'W

A tornado moved by Farmington Canyon in Davis County. It reportedly traveled eight miles and crossed the county line into Morgan County. It caused no damage and did not touch down in a populated area.

Tornado, Kannarraville, Iron County
July 14, 1953, 1700 MST, 37°30'N, 113°15'W

A small twister hit the town of Kannarraville, Iron County. It broke limbs off trees and tore off the metal roof of a garage. It lasted ten minutes. (The day and hour of this tornado is estimated from cloudburst data and other severe weather activity in southwestern Utah.)

Tornado, Laketown, Rich County
May 25, 1954, 1200 MST, 41°49'N, 111°19'W

A possible tornado (although no funnel-shaped cloud was seen) occurred in Laketown, Rich County. Reports indicate that weather conditions became dark and that the wind began to blow violently from the southwest. There was dust, hay, straw, and tree twigs blowing in the air. There was a roar for two or three seconds and then the wind decreased. Damage was noted in an area four blocks long by two blocks wide. A chicken coop was moved eight feet and new barn was flattened. Also, a small outbuilding was tipped over and another barn was lifted high enough to clear an eight foot shed, turned half way around, and then allowed to fall to the ground where it was smashed. A few strips of metal roofing were blown off a structure.

Tornado, Maeser, Uintah County
June 1, 1955, 1225 MST, 40°28'N, 109°34'W

A tornado moved northwestward across Maeser in Uintah County. Damage was done to residences, farm buildings, and other various structures. Tree tops were sheared off and garden plants were destroyed. Roads were strewn with debris and communication lines were severed. About $1,200 in damage was reported as a result of the storm.

Tornado, Fayette, Sanpete County
June 16, 1955, 1300 MST, 39°14'N, 111°50'W

A tornado moved northeastward for over two and a half miles through the eastern section of Fayette, Sanpete County. Large trees were uprooted and large branches were twisted and torn from trees. Thirty-foot long poles that were a foot in diameter were blown 100 yards. Metal roofing was carried across the valley and wrapped around trees and posts. Monetary damage was estimated at $5,000.

Tornado, Fayette, Sanpete County
June 16, 1955, 1300 MST, 39°14'N, 111°50'W

A second tornado in as many minutes moved eastward just to the north of Fayette, Sanpete County in an undeveloped area. No damage was done.

Tornado, Salina, Sevier County
August 7, 1957, 1730 MST, 38°57'N, 111°52'W

A small tornado hit the western part of Salina, Sevier County. It tore the roofs from a turkey processing plant and a service station. It moved north to the town of Redmond and uprooted trees, downed power and telephone lines, and buckled television antennas.

Tornado, near Green River, Emery County and Grand County
May 4, 1961, 1400 MST, 38°59'N, 110°10'W

A tornado touched down near the town of Green River, Emery County and moved eastward across the Green River into Grand County before leaving the ground and ascending back into the clouds. The tornado traveled nearly nine and half miles.

Tornado, Grouse Creek Valley, Box Elder County
July 9, 1962, 1430 MST, 41°30'N, 113°57'W

A long, black tornado traveled across the Grouse Creek Valley, Box Elder County. It moved in a northerly direction and remained in contact with the ground for about 15 minutes. It extended up to about 2,000 feet above the ground. It tore up the ground under it but it did not cross an inhabited area.

Tornado, Bountiful, Davis County
June 3, 1963, 1505 MST, 40°53'N, 111°53'W

A damaging tornado hit Bountiful, Davis County and moved in an east-northeast direction. The roof of the Bountiful Elementary School was ripped off doing $20,000 damage. Debris was scattered over a half-mile area along the tornado path. The storm tore the roof from the west side of a house across the street from the school. This roof then landed on an automobile in a nearby yard. Half a block away, a roof was removed from a shed and dumped into a small orchard 200 yards away. A Boxelder tree was stripped of all its limbs. A cottonwood tree with a truck three feet across was broken off a few feet above the ground and carried over a house. Two blocks away, the tornado touched down again and destroyed a two-car cinder black garage. The tornado skipped a half-mile up hill and destroyed one home under construction and damaged several others. In the same vicinity, several sheets of three-fourths inch plywood were removed from a stack and blown 300 feet through the air. One piece of wood was driven six inches into a telephone pole.

Tornado, Gunnison, Sanpete County
August 28, 1964, 1800 MST, 39°09'N, 111°50'W

A small tornado moved across Gunnison, Sanpete County from the west. It moved in an east-southeast direction. The path of the tornado was 10 yards wide and three-fourths of a mile long. A chicken coop had its rear wall blown out. Three large plate glass windows in a service station were shattered, in the process damaging two automobiles. The roof of a garage was also torn off. Monetary damages were calculated to be over $2,000.

Tornado, Magna, Salt Lake County
February 9, 1965, 0110 MST, 40°43'N, 112°06'W

A tornado that developed ahead of a cold front in Magna, Salt Lake County, destroyed a three-car garage and 30 feet of a six-foot high steel reinforced cement block fence. The frame of the garage was lifted over vehicles that were parked inside, somewhat surprisingly leaving them undamaged. Debris were scattered along a west to east path 500 feet in length. A heavy piece of timber that was 16 feet long was carried 150 feet away and an old automobile battery was blown 50 feet.

Tornado, Woodruff, Rich County
June 23, 1965, 1544 MST, 41°30'N, 111°09'W

A small tornado occurred in Woodruff, Rich County. It was observed by the official National Weather Service climatological observer. The tornado's path was measured at one-third of a mile long and was 16 yards wide. It seriously damaged a 14 by 50 foot trailer at the home of the weather observer. Generally, the path of the tornado was over open fields.

Tornado, Tooele County
June 25, 1965, 1410 MST, 40°45'N, 112°30'W

An airplane pilot and some Utah state highway department employees observed a tornado about 35 miles west of Salt Lake City in Tooele County. It was on the ground about five to ten minutes but did not economic damage in that isolated location.

Tornado, Provo Canyon, Utah County
July 9, 1965, 1530 MST, 40°22'N, 111°34'W

Two small funnel clouds combined together and dropped from the clouds to form a tornado in the Vivian Park Resort area of Provo Canyon, Utah County. Two-foot diameter trees were toppled and a large tent was damaged. The tornado knocked over the wife of the manager of a trailer court but she was not injured. The tornado had a path one-third of a mile in length and was 20 yards wide.

Tornado, Tooele County
August 9, 1965, 2010 MST, 40°45'N, 113°45'W

A tornado touched down about 75 miles west of Salt Lake City in a remote, uninhabited part of Tooele County.

Tornado, Springville, Utah County
April 17, 1966, 1450 MST, 40°09'N, 111°35'W

One of two funnel clouds dipped from the clouds in Springville, Utah County, to become a tornado. As it moved northeastward it toppled a tree and lifted a roof from a house. Monetary damages were estimated at about $10,000.

Tornado, southwest of Ferron, Emery County
May 9, 1966, 1330 MST, 39°03'N, 111°11'W

A tornado touched down five to six miles southwest of Ferron, Emery County. No damage was reported.

Tornado, northwest of Bryce Canyon, Iron County
June 16, 1967, 1400 MST, 38°00'N, 112°30'W

An airplane pilot observed a tornado about 25 to 30 miles northwest of Bryce Canyon, Iron County. It occurred in open country and caused no reported damage.

Tornado, Emery, Emery County
November 2, 1967, 0830 MST, 38°55'N, 111°15'W

A cone-shaped tornado, 20 yards wide, completely destroyed the Last Chance Motel in Emery, Emery County. Furniture and bedding were strewn for hundreds of yards. There were no injuries but more than $15,000 in damage was tallied.

Tornado, northwest of Dugway Proving Grounds, Tooele County
May 22, 1968, 1115 MST, 40°27'N, 113°03'W

One of several funnel clouds touching the ground to become a tornado about 20 miles northwest of Dugway Proving Grounds, Tooele County. The funnel clouds were first sighted over Cedar Mountain. The tornado lasted for about nine minutes. There was no damage.

Tornado, West Weber, Weber County
August 14, 1968, 1045 MST, 41°15'N, 112°05'W

A tornado formed ahead of a storm front in West Weber, Weber County. It initially touched down in a wheat field and then moved in a northerly direction. It tore the roof from a milking parlor and lifted a man and boy off the ground and set them back down again. One of the man's legs was injured. The tornado ripped the roof from a barn and spread seven or eight tons of baled hay across the area. A storage shed was also destroyed. A new home that was occupied by a woman and four children was leveled but the occupants were not hurt. The roof of the home was deposited 120 feet away. Elsewhere, a truck and camper were lifted by the tornado and carried 30 to 40 feet and destroyed. A short distance away, the tornado damaged a barn, haystack and another home. Total damage was placed near $50,000. The tornado's path was 35 yards wide and had a length of one and one-half miles.

Tornado, Salt Lake City, Salt Lake County
August 14, 1968, 1155 MST, 40°46'N, 111°53'W

A tornado moved through downtown Salt Lake City, Salt Lake County. The circulation was initially observed over the Salt Palace. The tornado then moved east-northeast across ZCMI and the University Club. Windows in the upper floors of ZCMI were shattered. The tornado was observed by personnel at the Wasatch Bureau Regional Office.

Tornado, near Collingston, Box Elder County
August 14, 1968, 1335 MST, 41°50'N, 112°05'W

A tornado moved across an open field near Collingston, Box Elder County. The storm retreated back into the clouds, crossed some nearby mountains and then touched down again in the wheat field in Cache Valley. No appreciable damage was done. The tornado was seen by a workman returning home from Cutler Dam. The tornado traveled over four miles and the path was 15 yards wide.

3 Tornadoes, Southwest of Hanksville, Wayne County
May 31, 1969, 1152 MST, 38°20'N, 110°54'W

An airplane pilot spotted three tornadoes about 10 miles southwest of Hanksville, Wayne County. The three twisters stirred up dust and then dissipated. They touched down in an uninhabited area so no economic damage was done.

Tornado, Anabella, Sevier County
April 19, 1970, 1320 MST, 38°42'N, 112°04'W

A tornado touched down in Anabella, Sevier County and damaged two trailers. The tornado "cut a path 40 feet wide and more than a mile long. A house trailer, measuring about 12 by 52 feet was lifted from its wood foundation and turned around about 90 degrees. Windows were broken in another nearby trailer." (*Salt Lake Tribune*, April 20, 1970). The tornado also "picked up and carried" a woman "about 30 feet as she was walking between her trailer home and a neighbor's place. `I don't know how far off the ground I was—a foot, I guess—but I know I wasn't touching the ground.... It was quite an experience,' [said the woman]. She said she had a headache after striking the ground." (*Deseret News* April 20, 1970.) According to a local newspaper, "the gust of wind picked...up [the woman] and tossed her end over katilt for about twenty feet like a tumble weed. Her invective embellished comment was: 'Well I've heard

of the Flying Nun but I never thought I'd be one.'"
(*Richfield Reaper*, April 1970.)

Tornado, Box Elder County
June 5, 1970, 1520 MST, 41°19'N, 113°00'W

A remote area of Box Elder County was visited by a tornado. An airline pilot spotted it about 50 miles west of Hill Air Force Base. No damage was reported.

Tornado, Centerville, Davis County
June 10, 1970, 1305 MST, 41°03'N, 111°54'W

A trio of three small funnel clouds spawned a tornado near Centerville in Davis County. It touched the ground only briefly in an unpopulated area west of Francis Peak. It was seen by many people.

Tornado, Thompson, Grand County
June 10, 1970, 1430 MST, 38°57'N, 109°43'W

An eastbound tornado moved through Thompson, Grand County. It leveled two small frame structures and demolished a 12 by 50 foot mobile home. It also tore limbs from trees. The twister traveled about three-fourths of a mile.

Tornado, below Timpanogos Divide, Utah County
December 2, 1970, 1503 MST, 40°24'N, 111°35'W

A high-mountain white tornado (that picked up and carried snow) was spotted a little below Timpanogos Divide, Utah County. It traveled in a southwesterly direction about a mile. The tornado was about one-fourth of a mile wide. It carried snow to above 1,000 feet and toppled trees that were a foot in diameter. There was a loud roaring sound as the tornado dipped down across the divide. One man some distance from the core was knocked down but was not injured. The twister occurred at about the 8,000 foot elevation and was observed by Tom Walker, former superintendent of Timpanogos Cave National Monument.

Tornado, western shore of Utah Lake, Utah County
September 2, 1971, 1900 MST, 40°10'N, 111°58'W

A tornado touched down along the western shore of Utah Lake, Utah County. No damage occurred from this short-lived tornado.

Tornado, near Newton, Cache County
May 6, 1981, 1145 MST, 41°52'N, 112°00'W

A tornado touched down near Newton, Cache County, about 15 miles northwest of Logan. It moved northeast at about 30 miles per hour through an irrigation ditch and across a hayfield. It lifted water out of a ditch to a height of seven feet and also toppled some fence posts. The length of the tornado's path was about one-half mile by 100 yards wide.

Tornado, north of Hanksville Airport, Wayne County
July 24, 1981, 1412 MST, 38°28'N, 110°42'W

A well-photographed red tornado (carrying red soil and dirt) touched down about three miles north of the Hanksville Airport in Wayne County. It occurred over a desolate area and was seen and photographed by Barbara Ekker, the official Hanksville weather observer.

Tornado, northeast of Milford, Beaver County
March 29, 1982, 1214 MST, 38°30'N, 112°53'W

A white tornado was observed 16 miles northeast of Milford, Beaver County, by the official weather observer at Milford. It was on the ground about three minutes. It churned up the snow covered ground and did no damage in that remote area. It moved in a northeasterly direction.

Tornado, 20 miles north of Milford, Millard County
May 3, 1982, 1234 MST, 38°46'N, 113°02'W

For the second time in less than two months, a tornado was reported north of Milford. This one occurred about 20 miles north of the city in Millard County and caused no damage.

Waterspout, Utah Lake, Utah County
July 28, 1982, 0700 MST, 40°21'N, 111°53'W

A waterspout was spotted over the northwest part of Utah Lake. It did not last long and caused no damage.

Waterspout & Tornado, Utah Lake, Provo, Utah County
September 13, 1982, 1720 MST, 40°13'N, 111°43'W

A waterspout over Utah Lake went ashore at the Provo Airport and damaged a security gate and small plane. The plane was tied down but the wind snapped the back wheel tie-down and flipped the plane on its back. The path of the storm was about one-half mile long.

Tornado, south of Provo, Utah County
August 13, 1984, 1930 MST, 40°10'N, 111°40'W

A tornado briefly touched down about five miles south of Provo near the eastern shore of Utah Lake. A wind gust of 89 miles-per-hour was recorded shortly thereafter on the Brigham Young University campus in Provo. No damage was reported although dust and debris was stirred up.

Tornado, south of Manti, Sanpete County
August 15, 1984, 1400 MST, 39°11'N, 111°38'W

A bulldozer driver spotted a tornado about five miles south of Manti, Sanpete County. It stayed on the ground for five minutes. The tornado kicked up dust and rocks and broke off fence posts.

Tornado, between Tremonton and Snowville, Box Elder County
August 16, 1984, 1629 MST, 41°49'N, 112°28'W

No damage occurred from a tornado that touched down near the Utah-Idaho border, between Tremonton and Snowville in Box Elder County.

Tornado, Box Elder County
August 16, 1984, 1629 MST, 41°39'N, 112°28'W

The second tornado in four minutes occurred in Box Elder County about 10 miles south of the first one. No damage was reported.

Tornado, Parker Mountains, Piute County
August 19, 1984, 1500 MST, 38°25'N, 111°55'W

A tornado was spotted near Otter Creek in the Parker Mountains area of Piute County. It was on the ground for 30 seconds and caused no economic damage.

Tornado, south of Roosevelt, Duchesne County
September 11, 1984, 1445 MST, 40°09'N, 110°04'W

A tornado was reported about 10 miles south of Roosevelt, near Myton, Duchesne County. A car was carried 30 feet by the twister. Two outhouses were knocked over and a pig pen was destroyed. Irrigation pipes were also scattered around the area.

Waterspout, Great Salt Lake, Tooele County
June 26, 1985, 0530 MST, 40°42'N, 112°10'W

A waterspout formed over the south end of the Great Salt Lake in Tooele County and could be seen 20 miles to the east. It was seen by more than a dozen experienced weather observers and was well photographed and videotaped before it dissipated over water. This waterspout was analyzed in a 30-page article entitled "A Great Salt Lake Waterspout," *Monthly Weather Review*, Volume 119, Number 12, December 1991, American Meteorological Society, Boston, MA. According to this article, "A waterspout funnel and spray ring were observed under the cumulus [cloud] line over the Great Salt Lake for about 5 min[utes] shortly after sunrise on 26 June 1985. Videotaped features strongly suggested that the funnel rotation was anticyclonic. ... The funnel was about 40 m [131.2 feet] across. Cloud base was approximately 800 m [2,624.6 feet] about lake level and the cloud tower above the funnel topped at about 5.5-6.5 km [3.4-4.0 miles] above lake level."

Waterspout, Great Salt Lake, Box Elder County
October 22, 1985, 1615 MST, 41°33'N, 112°52'W

A pilot reported a waterspout over the Great Salt Lake in Box Elder County. It was estimated to be 700 feet high and drew water up from the lake. The waterspout formed following the passage of a cold front.

Waterspout, Utah Lake, Utah County
May 22, 1986, 0617 MST, 40°19'N, 111°50'W

A waterspout developed over Utah Lake, Utah County. A Utah County Deputy Sheriff saw it touch the lake briefly. It formed beneath a thunderstorm. No damage was noted.

Tornado, Beryl Junction, Iron County and Washington County
May 30, 1986, 1730 MST, 37°40'N, 113°39'W

A tornado was reported by an official weather observer near Beryl Junction, Iron County. It traveled 3.5 miles and was 200 yards wide. The associated thunderstorm winds split several trees that downed power lines which in turn caused a grass fire. The tornado crossed into the northern portion of Washington County.

Tornado, Canyonlands National Park, Wayne County
August 31, 1986, 1430 MST, 38°22'N, 110°05'W

A tornado was observed over the Island-in-the-Sky area of Canyonlands National Park, Wayne County. It was on the ground 10 minutes in an undeveloped area and was seen by tourists and personnel at the park.

Tornado, Kearns, Salt Lake County
September 9, 1986, 1114 MST, 40°42'N, 112°03'W

A tornado was spotted in a field in the Kearns area of the Salt Lake Valley. It lasted for a minute and did no damage.

Waterspout, Great Salt Lake, Tooele County
September 10, 1986, 1000 MST, 40°50'N, 112°19'W

A railroad brakeman observed a waterspout over the south end of the Great Salt Lake, Tooele County. It occurred between Antelope and Stansbury Islands and lasted 15 minutes. Water was carried about a third of the way up the funnel. No damage was reported.

Waterspout, Great Salt Lake, Weber County
September 30, 1986, 1220 MST, 41°10'N, 112°25'W

A short-lived waterspout touched the water of the Great Salt Lake in Weber County several times before dissipating. A Utah Highway Patrolman who was located on the Antelope Causeway spotted the waterspout about 10 to 15 miles northwest of the north end of Antelope Island.

Waterspout, Utah Lake, Utah County
May 2, 1987, 0905 MST, 40°10'N, 111°50'W

A well-developed waterspout formed over the south end of Utah Lake., It churned up the water for several minutes and was well-photographed by the public. It lasted for about 15-20 minutes.

Tornado, south of Lewiston, Cache County
May 29, 1987, 1145 MST, 41°58'N, 111°53'W

A tornado skipped along a 1,500 foot path about one and one-half miles south of Lewiston, Cache County. It left a path of moderate damage. The tornado was about 40 yards wide. The roof of a hay barn was removed and two calf pens were turned over. Two fruit trees and one pine tree were uprooted. Two other pine trees were twisted out of the ground and dropped on a fence. Monetary damage was estimated at $5,000. The tornado was well-photographed.

Waterspout, Great Salt Lake, Weber County
August 15, 1987, 0710 MST

A pilot observed a waterspout over the Great Salt Lake west of Ogden.

Waterspout, Great Salt Lake, Davis County
August 15, 1987, 0740 MST

Tower personnel at Hill Air Force Base observed a waterspout over the Great Salt Lake.

Tornado, Plymouth, Box Elder County
August 25, 1987, 1135 MST, 41°53'N, 112°09'W

A cold-air-funnel type tornado touched down briefly just west of Plymouth, then receded back into the clouds.

Tornado, east of Benson, Cache County
August 25, 1987, 1205 MST, 41°48'N, 111°52'W

A cold-air-funnel type tornado touched down briefly between Benson and the Logan Airport, then receded back into the clouds.

Tornado, Lapoint, Uintah County
May 29, 1988, 1745 MST, 40°24'N, 109°48'W

A tornado, with a 30 to 60 foot wide funnel, hit a home three-fourths of a mile south of the center of the town of Lapoint. It damaged the chimney and roof of the home, and also knocked down a utility pole. Total damage was estimated at $3,000.

Tornado, Sandy, Salt Lake County
January 10, 1989, 0910 MST, 40°35'N, 111°53'W

A tornado produced a fair amount of damage to a south Sandy neighborhood during the morning hours of January 10, 1989. The tornado path began at about 11683 South and 1400 East to near 11400 South and 1380 East. The tornado's path was ¼ mile long and about 25 yards wide. Significant damage occurred to three roofs with minor damage to three others. The tornado tore a gaping hole in one roof. A camper that was bolted down at all four corners was lifted and thrown upside down into the street. Several fences were sheared off and the fence material was strewn about the neighborhood. Asphalt shingles

were driven ½ inch deep into both sides of one piece of the fence. A witness observed the tornado skipping down the street with debris blowing in a circular motion. Another witness said the tornado sounded like a train and caused his whole house to vibrate.

Tornado, Magna, Salt Lake County
March 2, 1989, 1815 MST, 40°42'N, 112°06'W

A tornado touched down near 3699 South and 7500 West. The storm produced a moderate amount of damage to the neighborhood, including tearing a swamp cooler from a roof, blowing away a small shed, throwing a trampoline into a tree, and breaking several windows.

Tornado, Hill Air Force Base, Davis County
May 11, 1989, 1645 MST, 41°07'N, 111°58'W

A small tornado briefly touched down south of a runway at Hill Air Force Base.

Tornado, Delta, Millard County
June 7, 1989, 1555 MST, 39°11'N, 112°35'W

A tornado was observed 10 to 15 miles south of Delta. The funnel was on the ground for approximately two to four minutes then receded back up into the clouds. The tornado occurred over a field and caused no damage to property.

Tornado, Midvale, Salt Lake County
July 8, 1989, 1615 MST, 40°36'N, 111°54'W

Strong microburst winds and a tornado hit the Midvale area just west of 1-15 at about 7200 South. Two minor injuries were reported from the winds: one from a motorcyclist who was tossed from his cycle onto the roadway, and another person that was hit by flying glass. The roof of a fertilizer company was blown off and/or damaged, boards from a lumber company embedded themselves in adjacent buildings, a boat and trailer from a car were blown onto the median, several windows were blown out of cars, a couple of semi-truck trailers were toppled, and numerous power outages occurred. Winds gusted to 53 mph in Holladay.

Waterspout, Willard Bay, G.S.L., Box Elder County
August 24, 1989, 1030 MST

A Utah Highway Patrol Trooper spotted a waterspout over Willard Bay, on the east side of the Great Salt Lake. The waterspout lasted for approximately seven minutes, but never moved on shore or caused any damage.

Tornado, Cornish, Cache County
September 17, 1989, 1530 MST, 41°59'N, 111°57'W

A small tornado briefly touched down in the town of Cornish at the end of the Cache Valley. It destroyed a barn and caused an estimated $25,000 in damages.

Waterspout, Great Salt Lake, Davis County
November 26, 1989, 1300 MST

Several people saw a waterspout about 10 miles west of Bountiful over the Great Salt Lake. The direction of the waterspout's movement could not be determined.

Tornado, Naples, Uintah County
March 23, 1990, 1230 MST, 40°25'N, 109°30'W

Several residents of Naples watched a funnel cloud touch down briefly. The tornado "ripped the roof off a storage shed...and slammed it through the bedroom wall of a mobile home." The "twister ripped the tin roof off [a] neighbor's shed and put a 2-foot by 4-foot piece of metal through the bedroom wall" of the mobile home, causing about $500 damage. (*Deseret News*, March 24, 1990.)

Tornado, northwest of Ogden, Weber County
April 23, 1990, 1645 MST, 41°17'N, 112°03'W

Three eyewitnesses reported a tornado at Farr West in the western part of Weber County (about five miles northwest of Ogden). The tornado was five to 15 yards wide, traveled only about one-tenth of a mile, and lasted less than a minute. Damage included: 20-25 shingles blown off an elementary school, a street light was damaged, a man was blown off a bike, a trampoline went airborne as high as a house, a swamp cooler was noted rolling down the road, and a picnic table was displaced from one yard to the one next door.

Tornado, south of Roosevelt, Duchesne County
July 8, 1990, 1450 MST, 40°16'N, 110°00'W

A tornado was reported to have momentarily touched down on a golf course about two miles south of Roosevelt. There was no damage.

Tornado, north of Magna, Salt Lake County
August 16, 1990, 1410 MST, 40°44'N, 112°06'W

A tornado was sighted along Interstate 80 in Magna by a motorist. It briefly touched down then dissipated. There were no injuries of damage.

Tornado, Erda, Tooele County
July 25, 1991, 1800 MST, 40°35'N, 112°15'W

A line of thunderstorms spawned a tornado in the Erda area just north of Tooele. The tornado moved from the southeast to the northwest for a distance of about 10 miles. It lasted for about 15 minutes, and its greatest width was about 100 yards wide. It uprooted a 60 foot tall dead tree, and split a 200 foot Cottonwood tree on a farm lot. The Cottonwood tree fell, and narrowly missed a house on the farm. Freshly cut alfalfa was displaced in half of a nearby field while hay on the other half of the

field remained in neat, untouched rows. A field sprinkling system received minor damage. The tornado also tore a door off a mobile home that was on the farm lot, and damaged several trees.

Tornado, northwest of Green River, Emery County
July 26, 1991, 1610 MST, 39°01'N, 110°13'W

Strong thunderstorms produced a tornado that briefly touched down about three miles northwest of Green River. The tornado was observed by an Emery County Deputy Sheriff who said the time the tornado was on the ground was hard to determine because of considerable blowing dust in the area.

Tornado, west of Green River, Emery County
July 26, 1991, 1615 MST, 38°59'N, 110°18'W

Strong thunderstorms produced a tornado that briefly touched down about six miles west of Green River. The tornado was observed by an Emery County Deputy Sheriff who said the time the tornado was on the ground was hard to determine because of considerable blowing dust in the area.

Tornado, east of Beaver, Beaver County
September 7, 1991, 1530 MST, 38°17'N, 112°32'W

A 30-foot wide tornado was spotted by two people. The funnel cloud lasted five to ten minutes but only touched down briefly. Since this tornado occurred in open country, it caused no damage.

Tornado, Brigham City, Box Elder County
September 10, 1991, 1200 MST, 41°31'N, 112°01'W

A 30-foot wide tornado touched down in several spots in the southeast portion of Brigham City about 1200 MST. It was located in the vicinity of 100 East and 400 North. The tornado touched down in several spots in a four by four block area. It uprooted or damaged about 20 trees, destroyed a shed, and peeled siding off a house.

Tornado, west of Beaver, Beaver County
May 21, 1992, 1115 West, 38°17'N, 112°51'W

A 45-foot wide tornado was spotted about 10 miles west of Beaver by a person driving south on I-15. After the person spotted the tornado, it lifted back into the clouds within a minute. Therefore, the total amount of time the tornado was on the ground is unknown. The tornado occurred in open country, and caused no damage.

Waterspout, Great Salt Lake, Salt Lake County
July 11, 1992, 1715 MST

A waterspout formed in a rain shaft over the south end of the Great Salt Lake during the early evening of July 11th. It was observed by National Weather Service personnel, and lasted about 10 minutes. It dissipated before it moved over land.

Tornado, near Kennecott Mines, Salt Lake County
August 30, 1992, 1316 MST, 40°30'N, 112°06'W

On the afternoon of August 30, a tornado was spotted by a number of people in the southwestern part of the Salt Lake Valley. It developed about 2:16 PM, near the Kennecott Mines on the Oquirrh Mountains, and lasted about 15 minutes as it moved eastward into West Kearns. The path length was less than one mile and it was 200 yards wide. As it passed over some power lines they arched. No damage or injuries were reported.

Waterspout, Great Salt Lake, Salt Lake County
August 30, 1992, 1428 MST

A pilot observed a waterspout over the south end of the Great Salt Lake around 3:28 PM, exactly 15 miles west of Salt Lake City. This waterspout touched down only temporarily and then dissipated.

Tornado, near St. George, Washington County
August 31, 1992, 1310 MST, 37°00'N, 113°28'W

Thunderstorms that had developed over the southwest portion of Utah produced a tornado ten miles southeast of St. George. A pilot spotted this tornado, which was about 20 yards wide and only remained on the ground for a brief period of time.

Tornado, Syracuse, Davis County
September 23, 1992, 1730 MST, 41°05'N, 112°04'W

A tornado was sighted at 6:30 PM by several people in Syracuse. It was about 25 yards wide and lasted for 10 minutes—traveling nearly two miles over ground. It tore an 8' x 4' section from a roof, ripped the shingles off other roofs, uprooted two trees, and flying debris damaged some car windows. This tornado caused about $1,500 in damages.

Tornado, Caineville, Wayne County
April 4, 1993, 1530 MST

Thunderstorms in southeast Utah produced a tornado at Caineville. Caineville is 25 miles west of Hanksville in Wayne County. The tornado was seen by several people. The tornado touched down 100 yards west of a restaurant. As the tornado moved toward the restaurant it tore off tree limbs and scattered 48 to 60 pieces of plywood and 300 2x4's that had been lying around. After it passed by the restaurant, the tornado briefly lifted. When it came back down, the tornado lifted a six ton motor home one and a half to two feet off the ground and then slammed in down on its side. The tornado also picked up a boat and threw it into a fence. With a lot of debris and dirt still in circulation, the tornado went into an open field and lifted back into the sky. This tornado caused about $8,000 in damages.

Tornado, Erda, Tooele County
May 3, 1993, 1940 MST

A tornado was reported at 8:40 PM in Erda, which is about five miles north of Tooele. The tornado destroyed the movie screen at the Motor Vu Drive-In Theater and turned over a trailer. A witness to the tornado was a woman who saw the screen "twisted in a whirling motion" as it was destroyed. Other objects in the area were untouched, lending credence to the idea of a tornado. This tornado caused about $50,000 in damages.

Tornado, near Leota, Uintah County
May 5, 1993, 1840 MST

A cold core funnel cloud produced a tornado near the town of Leota. It was spotted at 7:40 PM by a pilot flying south of Vernal. Because the tornado only lasted a few minutes and was in a sparsely populated region of the state, it caused no damage.

Tornado, North Salt Lake, Davis County
June 2, 1993, 1620 MST

A tornado was spawned by a thunderstorm cell at about 5:20 PM at the Center Street Park in North Salt Lake. The tornado was first seen as a funnel cloud to the southwest of the park. Everyone took cover before the tornado struck the ball field which displayed a hit and miss pattern of debris damage to the northeast of the ball field. It was on the ground less than five minutes. Two people received puncture wounds from flying debris and many individuals were covered with mud and dirt. Large tree limbs were broken and a couple of two-foot diameter trees were uprooted. Shingles were blown off some roofs and the fence surrounding the tennis court was damaged. The tornado also shattered three windows and bent the passenger door of the mini-van parked on the south end of the park. This tornado caused about $15,000 in damages.

Tornado, Chepeta Lake, Duchesne County
August 11, 1993, 1750 MST

A high-elevation tornado touched down three times near Chepeta Lake (elevation 10,500 feet) about 25 miles north of Roosevelt in the Ashley National Forest of the Uinta Mountains, at about 6:50 PM on August 11, 1993.

During the evening of August 11th, a line of thunderstorms moved across the Uinta Mountains. Below the thunderstorms, a tornado touched down three times. It's path width was up to a half mile wide.

The first touchdown occurred 12 miles southwest of an area known as White Rock Drainage. Only minor unorganized damage to 20 acres of forest was reported at this location.

The second touchdown was the most significant. At the west fork of the White Rock Drainage the tornado began to knock down and uproot trees over a

600 acre area. The tornado moved northeast along the drainage, throwing trees on the south side of the drainage to the north. Similarly, trees on the north side of the drainage were tossed to the south. This organized multi-directional nature of the damage is a classic signature and confirms the presence of a tornado.

The tornado lifted once more before touching down for the third and final time near Chepeta Lake Drainage. Here the twister damaged over 400 acres of forest. A troop of 125 scouts were camped near the area of the third touchdown. No one was injured, but four vehicles were damaged by the tornado. One truck was destroyed when two large uprooted trees fell on the vehicle—totally collapsing the roof.

The highest elevation where damage was found was at 10,800 feet—which makes this tornado the highest mountain tornado ever reported in Utah. (High-elevation tornadoes are rare in Utah. On December 2, 1970, a tornado occurred at the 8,000 foot level below Timpanogos Divide.)

Tornado, Emigration Canyon, Salt Lake County
November 5, 1993, 1545 MST
A cold northwest flow over the Great Salt Lake produced snow squalls which spawned a weak tornado. The tornado was reported by several people, who described it as white at the top and brown at the bottom—indicating it was picking up dirt. The tornado lasted about three minutes.

Tornado, Centerville, Davis County
July 29, 1995, 2015 MST
Severe pre-frontal thunderstorms developed along the Wasatch Front a produced a "gustnado" in the Centerville area. Witnesses indicated they heard a sound like a freight train and saw both trees and dirt moving in circular motions. The overall damage path was about one-half mile long and less than 176 yards wide. (The NWS officially listed it as 0.2 miles long and 100 yards wide.) The gustnado moved from south to north, with it apparently skipping into the air, not causing damage along the entire path length. One witness was briefly lifted into the air as the gustnado passed over. One house incurred $10,000 in damage. They reported severe tree damage, had two skylights lifted from part of the roof, and had an electric junction box removed from the side of the house. Their next door neighbor reported that two inch diameter willow branches were removed from the tree, transported 100 feet and over a single story building, and were wrapped tightly around the base of another tree. At the third house, a flag pole that had previously withstood 90 mph winds was snapped. The gustnado bent a six foot chain fence to a 45 degree angle towards the east.

Tornado, Pleasant View, Weber County
December 5, 1995, 20:25 MST
On the evening of December 5, a tornado touched down in Pleasant View, causing damage within a housing area about one-half mile long and 50 to 100 feet wide.   The storm that produced the tornado moved west to east. Witnesses reported heavy rain, then small pea-size hail, and finally strong winds.

One home sustained damage to roof shingles, a large portion of wooden fencing, and two sheds. Roofing shingles littered lawns at 3925 North. Many of the shingles were blown 300 to 600 feet away from their structures. The heaviest damage was at a home located on the corner of 900 West and 3925 North. At this home, three large 60-foot pine trees clumped near each other in the front yard were found leaning around 5° toward the east-southeast. The owner, who had lived there for 31 years, was in the attached garage at the time of the storm. He said he was going to take the garbage out to the street but waited in the garage until the rain and pea-sized hail had ended. As he started down the driveway, he heard a tremendous roar like a train and looked down the street to the west where he saw debris coming towards him. He quickly went back into his garage and closed the door. The tornado also damaged two homes under construction about 1/8 of a mile further east from the initial touchdown.

Tornado Safety Rules
Prepare a Home Tornado Plan:
Pick a place where family members could gather if a tornado is headed your way. It could be your basement or, if there is no basement, a center hallway, bathroom, or closet on the lowest floor. Keep this place uncluttered.

If you are in a high-rise building, you may not have enough time to go to the lowest floor. Pick a place in a hallway in the center of the building.

Assemble a Disaster Supplies Kit containing:
• First aid kit and essential medications
• Battery-powered radio, flashlight, and extra batteries
• Canned food and can opener
• Bottled water
• Sturdy shoes and work gloves

Also include in the kit written instructions on how to turn off your home's utilities.

Conduct periodic tornado drills, so everyone remembers what to do when a tornado is approaching.

Stay Tuned for Storm Warnings
Listen to your local radio and television stations for updated storm information.

Tornado Watches and Warnings are issued by county.

Know what a Tornado Watch and Warning means:
• A Tornado Watch means a tornado is possible in your area
• A Tornado Warning means a tornado has been sighted and may be headed for your area. Go to safety immediately.

When a Tornado Watch is Issued...

Listen to local radio and television stations for further updates.

Be alert to changing weather conditions.

Blowing debris or the sound of an approaching tornado may alert you. Many people say a tornado sounds like a freight train.

When a Tornado Warning is Issued...

If you are inside, go to the safe place you picked to protect yourself from glass and other flying objects. (Remember: it could be your basement or, if there is no basement, a center hallway, bathroom, or closet on the lowest floor.) The tornado may be approaching your area.

If you are outside, hurry to the basement of a nearby sturdy building or lie flat in a ditch or low-lying area.

If you are in a car or mobile home, get out immediately and head for safety (as above).

After the Tornado Passes...

Watch out for fallen power lines and stay out of the damaged area.

Listen to the radio or television for information and instructions.

Use a flashlight to carefully inspect your home for damage.

NOAA Weather Radio
by
William J. Alder

NOAA Weather Radio, known as the "Voice of the National Weather Service," broadcasts continuos weather information 24 hours a day. Recorded weather messages are routinely updated and are tailored to the weather information needs of people within the receiving area. During severe weather, the National Weather Service interrupts the routine broadcasts to provide special warning messages. These special warning messages will automatically activate those receivers equipped with an alarm feature.

The National Weather Service Forecast Office in Salt Lake City issues NOAA Weather Radio broadcasts for seven locations across Utah. In addition, the National Weather Service Office in Grand Junction Colorado issues a NOAA Weather Radio Broadcast for Vernal, making a total of eight broadcasts for Utah. The location and radio frequency of these broadcasts are as follows:

Cache Valley:	
Logan	162.400 MHZ
Wasatch Front	
South Mountain (Tooele)	162.450 MHZ
Vernon Hills (Tooele)	162.525 MHZ
Salt Lake City	162.550 MHZ
Southwest Utah and Utah's Dixie	
Milford/Cedar City	162.400 MHZ
Utah Hill (St. George)	162.475 MHZ
Lake Powell	
Navajo Mountain	162.550 MHZ
Uintah Basin	
Vernal	162.400 MHZ

These frequencies are not found on the average home radio. However, a number of radio manufacturers offer special weather radios to operate on these frequencies, with or without a warning alarm feature. Also, there are now many radios on the market which offer standard AM/FM frequencies plus the so-called "weather band" as an added feature. NOAA Weather radio broadcasts can usually be heard as far as 40 miles from the antenna site, sometimes more. Terrain plays a big part in determining the strength of the received signal in Utah.

Forecasting Utah's Weather

Forecasting Utah's Weather

by

William J. Alder, R. Clayton Brough,
Daniel W. Pope and Peter J. Wilensky

The Importance of Accurate Forecasts

The United States experiences more severe storms and flooding than any other country in the world. In a typical year it experiences 10,000 violent storms, 5,000 floods, 1,000 tornadoes and several hurricanes. In an effort to save lives and property, American meteorologists use the most powerful computers and scientific instruments available to predict future weather conditions and phenomena.

However, even with extensive training and modern equipment, meteorologists sometimes make inaccurate predictions. Why? Because computer forecast models are highly dependent on the data that goes into them, and accurate real-time data on changing atmospheric conditions are not yet available for everywhere around the world. Nevertheless, today's weather forecasts are much more accurate than they were ten years ago.

Accuracy of Short-Range Forecasts

Within the past ten years, the accuracy of short-range weather forecasts—for one to five days in the future—have improved significantly. In fact, across the United States, "Today's 3-to-5 day forecasts are as good as 1-to-2 day forecasts of a decade ago." (*A Change in the Weather Service,* U.S. Department of Commerce, NOAA, November 1993.)

When it comes to predicting Utah's daily weather and atmospheric phenomena, short-range weather forecasts are remarkably accurate. In fact, William J. Alder, Meteorologist-in-charge of the National Weather Service Forecast Office in Salt Lake City, Utah, recently stated:

"The National Weather Service is given the responsibility by law to issue forecasts for the protection of life and property due to hazardous or severe weather. We rely on the media-through radio and television weathercasts-to disseminate our watches, warnings, forecasts and other weather information. The Salt Lake City National Weather Service Forecast Office employs twenty-two professional meteorologists and seven weather specialists. We work around-the-clock shifts to maintain a close watch on the weather, and issue up to the minute warnings and forecasts. On the average, we feel our general forecasts have the following rates of accuracy:

Time Periods	Accuracy Rate
12-hour forecasts:	95%
24-hour forecasts:	85%
36-hour forecasts:	75%
48-hour forecasts:	70%
3-5 day forecasts:	65%

"In addition, our daily temperature forecasts are much better than they were a few decades ago. For example, the number of days in a year when the forecasted high temperature for Salt Lake City for the next day was off by more than 10 degrees has dropped from a total of 61 error days in 1949 to less than 10 error days since 1987. Here are the facts:

Years	# of Error Days
1950	55
1960	41
1970	22
1980	17
1990	8

(For more information on this subject, see the article "Are Forecasters Better Today? Probably." *Deseret News*, April 3, 1994, p.B-2.)"

Likewise, Clayton Brough, Climatologist for News 4 Utah Weather, has stated: "...Spring weather patterns are perhaps the most difficult to forecast when trying to time the passage of cold fronts and the rapid weather changes associated with such fronts. Yet, during the spring months of March to May…[News 4 Utah] weathercasters predicted tomorrow's (24-hour) major weather events (such as rain, snow, wind, or cloud cover) and particularly those relating to dry or wet conditions with an average accuracy of 95%...." (*Utah's Comprehensive Weather Almanac*, p.82-83.)

Accuracy of Medium-Range Forecasts

Medium-range computer models produce forecasts out to 10 days, although after day six the level of accuracy declines significantly. However, News 4 Utah weathercasters sometimes show these forecasts in conjunction with known climatological probabilities.

Accuracy of Long-Range Outlooks

Weather predictions issued for periods beyond ten days are rather general in nature and are usually called "outlooks". These outlooks are based on overall expected conditions-such as warmer or colder than normal or wetter or drier than normal. These outlooks make no attempt to forecast day to day changes. According to the *Encyclopedia of Climatology* (as quoted in *Utah's Comprehensive Weather Almanac*, p.83), the National Weather Service's: "...Monthly (30-day) and seasonal (90-day) temperature forecasts in temperate latitudes would be right about 60% on the average, while precipitation forecasts would rate less than 55%. All of these scores are higher than could be obtained by predicting values of the previous period to persist unchanged."

Beyond seasonal outlooks, the best long-range guides to future weather and climate conditions that science can presently offer are:

1. Analyses and summaries of past weather conditions—such as the numerous climatic charts for Utah cities and other locations found in this book and in other publications such as *Utah Climate* and *Utah's Comprehensive Weather Almanac* (see the Bibliography at the end of this book).

2. Daily or weekly probability charts and summaries—such as those for Salt Lake City and St. George near the back of this book.

3. Statistical projections based on what the weather has done in the past and, therefore, what it could do in the future if it followed a similar pattern.

Current Forecast Models and Methods

There are currently six major computer models, and two short range detailed subsets of one of these models, that are used by Utah meteorologists to predict daily weather changes. These models and subsets are called:

1. The "NGM" model (or Nested Grid Model, also called RAFS-Regional Analysis Forecast System) goes out to 48 hours

2. The "ETA" model (named after a letter in the Greek alphabet and a vertical coordinate in the model) goes out to 48 hours.

3. The "MESO-ETA" model, a highly detailed subset of the ETA, forecasts out to 33 hours.

4. The "ULAM" model (or Utah Local Area Model) generated by the University of Utah Meteorology Department from the ETA with forecasts between 12 and 24 hours out.

5. The "AVN" model (or Aviation model) goes out to 72 hours.

6. The "MRF" model (or Medium Range Forecast model) goes out to 10 days.

7. The "ECMWF" model (or European Center for Medium Range Forecasting model) goes out to six days.

8. The "UKMET" model (or United Kingdom Meteorological model) that goes out to six days.

These computer models sometimes vary considerable in predicting future weather conditions. This is because they emphasize different atmospheric variables and use different mathematical equations to arrive at their predictions. Because of this, weather forecasters not only have to determine what computer model(s) best describes the present state of the atmosphere (which they do by using current weather observations and satellite data), but they also have to decide what model(s) they feel presents the most

reasonable prediction for the future. And this can be very difficult, time consuming, and sometimes open to individual interpretation, experience and judgment.

New Improvements in Weather Forecasting (Doppler Radar)

The latest tool that meteorologists use for short-range forecasting is the Doppler Weather Radar. A nationwide network of these radars is almost complete and has already provided for great strides in the prediction of severe storms and hourly weather trends. Two of these radars are in Utah. One is on Promontory Point and provides coverage for the Wasatch Front and northern portions of the state. The second was installed during the summer of 1996 in the mountains east of Cedar City and covers much of the southern Utah.

These radars are specifically designed to detect clouds and precipitation, but what makes them unique is their ability to detect air motions within and around those elements (thus the Doppler label). This ability gives forecasters a wealth of information on the severity of storms and has led to greater accuracy in warnings for storms.

Another new system that is beginning to make its appearance in National Weather Service Forecast offices is the AWIPS computer system. AWIPS (or Advanced Weather Interactive Processing System) will streamline the forecast process by combining a number of separate data sets and communication systems into one. Using the latest technology, this system will allow meteorologists to manipulate these data sets in a myriad of combinations for use in the analysis of the weather, resulting in more timely and accurate warnings and forecasts.

News 4 Utah and the National Weather Service

In an effort to protect lives and property, News 4 Utah weathercasters and NWS meteorologists regularly share weather information, forecasts and products. This professional sharing of weather information has resulted in excellent communication and the completion of a number of co-sponsored projects between News 4 Utah weathercasters and the NWS Forecast Office in Salt Lake City. An example of this professional cooperation can be seen in the most informative video ever produced on Utah's severe weather phenomena:

Utah's Weather Wonders: A Survival Guide That Can Save Your Life (1994, 30 minutes). This video has been made available free of charge to all public schools and libraries in Utah. It is also available for $10.00 from News 4 Utah, 1760 Fremont Drive, Salt Lake City, Utah, 84104.

Weather on the Web
by
Daniel W. Pope

The Wonderful World of Weather on the World Wide Web: the Internet

Accessing weather information from your home computer has become one of the fastest growing ways to get a weather forecast. With the advent of speedy processors like the Pentium, and faster modems in the 14.4 and 28.8 BPS speed range, it has become easier to quickly and simply get this weather information. Companies, universities and private persons have popped up left and right on the Internet—more specifically the World Wide Web—each providing a different avenue for acquiring weather information.

Some commercial computer on-line companies like America On-Line and Compuserve provide limited weather information and access to the World Wide Web. Still others, like WeatherBrief, provide cost effective weather information via dial-up bulletin boards. The bottom line is that if you want to find weather information on your home computer you can do it rather easily. With a little computer know-how, a modem, and time well invested, you can be on-line getting your fill of weather information.

Multi-Media Computers

Nearly all computers you buy today are multi-media. This means that you already have all the ingredients you need to start receiving a weather forecast at home through a modem and a phone line. We won't go into the details of each Internet service provider or how you can get the service started. Suffice it to say that you will likely receive with your computer new software for the on-line companies and new software that will connect you to the Internet. You will have to do the leg work to find the one that best fits your needs and budget. You will have to follow the instructions contained with each "offer" to sign up, test and decide which service you like best. If you are reading this information and you have an old computer without the full multi- media information packets and software, your best bet will be to drop into any computer store and ask for information about getting on the Internet. We are sure that someone will be able to direct you quickly to what you need. The best software packages available now are Netscape and Internet Explorer. In the future there will likely be many more Internet computer software packages, so be open minded and just ask a few questions at your local computer store.

At the time of this writing, the cheapest way to get extensive weather information is to find a local Internet vender and subscribe to it's service. Commercial companies like America On-line and Compuserve offer Internet service, but the cost per hour of on-line usage is quite expensive. You can access their weather areas for informative weather data (and this may be all some of you will need), but if you want to find weather information that is both comprehensive and endless, the Internet—World Wide Web—is the place to be. Also, for those of you who prefer to just dial up weather information without some of the hassles of using the Internet and commercial services, WeatherBrief is one of the best and most cost effective. (Contact WeatherBrief at 1-405-359-0773 for more information on this service). But, for the purpose of getting the most weather information, we feel that accessing the Internet is the best way to go.

The Internet is not an easy thing to understand. You will be able to find the weather information you need, but it will not happen immediately upon jumping onto the information super-highway (the Internet). The Internet, and more specifically the World Wide Web, has limitless information and zones where you can find weather information. You should plan to spend several hours looking at and studying the World Wide Web before you will find a location or locations that meet your needs.

Once you find what you need you will likely use "bookmarks" to save the address of the location or locations you like best. These bookmarks will be available to you each time you access the Internet. You should know that many companies will have addresses that are always changing and moving. You may have to update your bookmarks, and you may have to do some work fairly frequently to keep accurate addresses and bookmarks on your computer. Here are some of the addresses we like and that we think will be around for years to come:

World Wide Web Weather Sites

News 4 Utah Weather. Contains weather forecasts and information very specific to Utah—including 3-D weather graphics. Home page:
http://www.4utah.com/weather.html

National Weather Service. Contains official government weather forecasts and information for Utah. Salt Lake City, Utah, home page:
http://www.wrh.noaa.gov/Saltlake/slc.noaa.html

Utah Climate Center, Utah State University. Information on available climatic data for Utah. Home Page:
http://climate.usu.edu/

University of Michigan, Meteorology Department. Contains extensive weather information with hundreds of weather Web sites and links.
http://cirrus.Sprl.Umich.Edu/wxnet

University of Utah, Meteorology Department.
Home page:

http://www.met.utah.edu/homepage.html

Weathernet. Home page:

http://cirrus.sprl.umich.edu/wxnet

Intelicast Weather. Contains lots of satellite/radar images and international weather information. Home page:

http://www.intellicast.com/weather

USA Today. Weather page:

http://www.usatoday.com/weather

CNN. Weather page:

http://www.cnn.com/WEATHER/index.html

The Future of Weather on the Internet

Because computers continue to improve in processing speed and because modems of the future will be able to send more information faster, we feel the Internet will soon become a medium where you can not only receive text information, but will it also contain video presentations much like you see now on cable and regular television. In other words, the same things you now see on television will be delivered, on demand, digitally to your home computer. You will be able to pick a tailor-made forecast, down load it like you now do text and pictures, and see a forecast for exactly what you want, only it will be your own personal weather forecast on your own personal computer.

Now, this will probably not happen until fiber-optics and high speed ISDN phone lines become the mode of Internet delivery to the home, or when the Internet is somehow delivered through satellite transmission to a satellite dish in your home. But the technology is there for this area to develop quickly in the next decade.

How much will this futuristic weather cost you? It is too early to tell. But if it follows some of the trends of today's Internet, it will probably not be very expensive and may not cost you any more than your Internet subscription does today. Also, it may become very economical for you to receive your city's five-day forecast, or weather forecasts for your favorite ski resort, recreational spot, or local, national, and international vacation sites.

Telephone Numbers for Weather Information
by
Daniel W. Pope

News 4 Utah Weather Forecast for the Wasatch Front:
801-553-7701 (SLC)
National Weather Service Public Service Desk:
801-524-5133 (SLC), 8:00 AM - 4:30 PM, Monday-Friday
Utah Highway Patrol Road Conditions:
801-964-6000
Avalanche Conditions
Logan: 797-4146
Ogden: 621-2362
Salt Lake City:364-1851/1591
Park City: 649-2250
Provo: 374-9770
Moab: 259-7669
Utah Ski Report:
801-521-8102
Air Quality (and wood burning) Conditions:
801-533-7239

Weather Terms and Definitions
Compiled by R. Clayton Brough

Climate: The average and expected weather conditions of an area over a long period of time— usually for 30 years or more.

Climatologist: A person who studies the climate and its affect on the environment. Climatologists analyze long-term weather patterns and make long-range weather predictions. Today, a professional climatologist usually has a degree in climatology, geography, or meteorology.

Cold front: The boundary between an advancing cold air mass and a relatively warmer air mass. Generally characterized by steady precipitation followed by showers.

Disturbance/Impulse: An unsettled area of weather located in the middle or upper part of the atmosphere. Clouds and precipitation are often present.

Fair: Less than 4/10ths opaque cloud cover, no precipitation, and no extremes in temperature, visibility or wind.

Front: The transition zone between two distinct air masses. The basic types are cold, warm, and occluded fronts. Stormy weather is often found along a front.

High: The center of a high-pressure area, which is an air mass with barometric pressure exceeding atmospheric pressure. Usually brings dry, fair weather, and is accompanied by outward wind flow.

Hydrologist: A person who studies the properties and distribution of water. Hydrologists analyze the earth's water supply and predict surface runoff. Today, a professional hydrologist usually has a degree in hydrology, engineering, or meteorology.

Inversion: Warmer air above colder air, a reversal of the normal situation.

Jet stream: Strong narrow bands of winds in the atmosphere. These winds often steer fronts and low-pressure systems.

Low: The center of a low-pressure area, which is an air mass with barometric pressure less than atmospheric pressure. Usually accompanied by cyclonic and inward wind flow, and often produces cloudy, stormy weather..

Meteorologist: A person who studies the atmosphere and its weather. Meteorologist analyze atmospheric phenomena and make short and medium-range weather forecasts. Today, a professional meteorologist usually has a degree in meteorology or physics.

Microburst: A strong local downdraft from a thunderstorm with peak gusts lasting two to five minutes.

Orographic uplift: Air forced vertically by hills and mountains. It can create clouds and rain.

Precipitation: Any water, whether liquid or solid that falls from the atmosphere to the ground. It includes rain, snow, hail and sleet.

Precipitation Probability: The stated probability (or percent change) of precipitation is a specific forecast giving the chance for precipitation at any point in the forecast area. For example: if a 40% probability is forecast for a specific location, measurable precipitation (above a "trace") should be received at that location four times out of 10 such forecasts; or there are four chances out of 10 that it will rain at a particular point during the period of the forecast.

Words used to qualify such probability forecasts—known as "expression of uncertainty"—are as follows:

%	Expressions	Area Qualifying
0%	None	None
10-20%	Slight chance	Isolated or few
30-50%	Chance	Scattered
60-70%	Likely	Numerous
80-100%	Near certain	Near certain

Ridge: An elongated area of high pressure in the atmosphere.

Showers: Precipitation that starts and stops suddenly, or that occurs for only a short period of time.

Trace: A precipitation amount too small to measure. Less than one hundredth of an inch of precipitation.

Trough: An elongated area of low pressure.

Virga: Streaks or wisps of precipitation falling from a cloud but evaporating before reaching the ground.

Weather: The condition of the atmosphere at any given time and place with respect to temperature, pressure, winds, humidity, cloudiness, precipitation, etc.

Williams Wave: A "wave" that forms on a cold front because of developing low pressure in Nevada. The wave moves eastward along the front, causing the front to stall and intensify. The front then produces heavy precipitation as it moves through Utah. This meteorological phenomena is called a "Williams Wave" after meteorologist Phil Williams who discovered that this type of storm can bring very heavy snow to Salt Lake City. A Williams Wave can bring four to six inches of snow in less than twelve hours to the valleys of the Wasatch Front, and one to two feet of snow within 24 hours to the higher Wasatch Mountains. Depending on the position of the jet stream and storm front, central and southern Utah can also experience Williams Waves.

Weather Instruments
by
Daniel W. Pope

Weather instruments are used to measure and predict changes in the atmosphere. The seven most common instruments are: maximum and minimum thermometer, barometer (air pressure), hygrometer (humidity), anemometer (wind speed), wind vane (wind direction), rain gauge, snow gauge (usually measured with a ruler).

If you would like additional information about weather instruments and companies that sell weather instruments, send a self-addressed, stamped envelope to

Weather Instruments
ATTN: News 4 Utah Weather Department
1760 Fremont Drive
Salt Lake City, Utah 84104

Weather Information for Gardeners
by
Daniel W. Pope

Through the different stages of development, fruit can withstand different critical temperatures.
Kill rates differ to the percentage of buds that could die if temperatures drop below the critical level.
Fruit trees should normally be planted in April.

CRITICAL TEMPERATURE CHART
STAGE OF DEVELOPMENT

FRUIT	KILL RATE	1	2	3	4	5	6	7	8	9	GREEN FRUIT
APPLES	50%	9	14	19	24	26	27	27	27	27	30
APRICOTS	50%		10	16	19	22	25	26			30
PEACHES	50%	10	13	16	20	24	26	27			30
PEARS	50%	8	13	20	22	24	25	26	26		30
PRUNES	50%	7	10	14	20	24	25	26	26		30
SWEET CHERRIES	10%	17	22	25	26	27	27	28	28	28	30
TART CHERRIES	10%	5	19	26	27	27	28	28	28		30

Early Planting Schedule

Asparagus, Cabbage, Onions, Spinach and Turnips
March 15 - May 1

Peas
March 15 - May 15

Broccoli
March 15 - July 15

Radishes
March 15 - September 1

Lettuce, Parsnips, Potatoes, Cauliflower, Parsley, Swiss Chard
March 20 - July 1

Late Planting Schedule

Dry Beans
May 5 - June 11

Celery
May 5 - June 15

Sweet Corn
May 5 - July 1

Summer Squash, Cucumber, Spinach
May 5 - June 20

Peppers, Eggplant
May 20 - June 20

Lima Beans, Cantaloupe, Tomatoes, Snap Beans, Winter Squash, Watermelon, Soybeans
May 20 - June 10

PLANTING TIPS

1. Start semi-hardy vegetables indoors:
Peppers	8 weeks
Tomatoes	6 weeks
Squash and Melons	3-4 weeks

2. Plant seeds when soil is very dry.
3. Pick an area that gets full sun all day and has good soil.
4. Pick recommended varieties of vegetables.
5. Around 15-20 days after you have planted your lettuce, radishes, etc., replant for a staggered harvest.
6. Add organic matter such as sawdust, compost, leaves, or straw to your garden. This will enhance the capacity of the water retention in sandy soil, and allow oxygen to get to roots in clay soil.
7. Water adequately - usually 1.50" per week.
8. Fertilize at time of planting and once per month.
9. Enjoy your harvest!

Freeze Dates and Freeze-Free Season

In addition, the following page of Freeze Dates and Freeze-Free Season for various Utah cities and locations has been prepared by the Utah Climate Center of Utah State University:

Freeze Dates and Freeze-free Season

Station Name	Last spring freeze			First fall freeze			Freeze-free			Period	Years
	Early	Avg	Late	Early	Avg	Late	Short	Avg	Long		
ALTA	May 23	Jun 16	Jul 6	Aug 20	Sep 10	Oct 16	56	87	120	1941-1996	23
BEAVER	Apr 28	Jun 5	Jul 3	Jul 29	Sep 15	Oct 14	43	102	157	1889-1993	77
BLANDING	Mar 25	May 13	Jun 23	Sep 6	Oct 11	Nov 9	94	152	224	1904-1996	86
BLOWHARD MTN RADAR	May 21	Jun 19	Jul 18	Aug 18	Sep 9	Oct 4	54	83	117	1964-1996	28
BRIGHAM CITY	Mar 29	May 2	Jun 2	Sep 4	Oct 11	Nov 13	112	163	227	1899-1974	61
BRYCE CANYON NATL PK HD	May 22	Jun 18	Jul 6	Aug 2	Sep 4	Sep 26	33	78	116	1959-1996	37
BULLFROG BASIN	Feb 23	Apr 3	Apr 29	Oct 16	Nov 9	Nov 24	176	222	274	1967-1990	21
CAPITOL REEF NATL PARK	Mar 16	Apr 24	May 26	Sep 21	Oct 23	Nov 12	138	185	231	1938-1996	33
CEDAR CITY FAA AIRPORT	Apr 28	May 18	Jun 30	Sep 2	Oct 1	Oct 31	76	137	176	1948-1996	47
COALVILLE	May 18	Jun 15	Jul 19	Jul 21	Sep 2	Sep 27	36	79	118	1948-1996	36
DELTA	Apr 15	May 15	Jun 19	Sep 2	Sep 29	Oct 28	76	137	186	1938-1996	50
DUCHESNE	Apr 23	May 23	Jun 25	Aug 9	Sep 21	Oct 21	68	121	173	1906-1996	81
DUGWAY	Apr 8	May 9	Jun 15	Sep 12	Sep 30	Oct 29	113	145	190	1950-1996	40
ENTERPRISE BERYL JCT	May 3	Jun 8	Jul 19	Aug 13	Sep 13	Oct 12	57	98	152	1948-1996	35
ESCALANTE	Apr 2	May 17	Jun 30	Sep 6	Oct 3	Nov 1	81	141	192	1901-1996	72
FARMINGTON	Apr 2	May 3	Jun 16	Sep 8	Oct 9	Nov 8	97	160	204	1900-1995	57
FILLMORE	Apr 6	May 14	Jul 2	Sep 3	Oct 5	Nov 3	63	145	196	1898-1996	68
FLAMING GORGE	May 5	Jun 6	Jul 5	Aug 25	Sep 13	Oct 14	61	100	164	1957-1996	36
GREEN RIVER AVIATION	Mar 25	May 2	Jun 1	Sep 10	Oct 4	Oct 30	116	157	200	1893-1996	92
GROUSE CREEK	May 15	Jun 14	Jul 5	Jul 31	Sep 9	Oct 14	54	88	154	1890-1996	27
HANKSVILLE	Apr 2	May 4	Jun 14	Jul 31	Oct 2	Nov 5	83	152	198	1910-1996	76
HEBER	May 11	Jun 13	Jul 20	Jul 29	Sep 5	Oct 13	27	85	130	1892-1996	103
IBAPAH	May 24	Jun 19	Jul 19	Jul 22	Aug 29	Sep 26	28	71	116	1903-1996	80
KANAB	Mar 19	May 7	Jun 26	Aug 2	Oct 18	Nov 12	48	166	230	1899-1996	65
LAKETOWN	May 10	Jun 16	Jul 13	Jul 21	Sep 7	Oct 4	22	84	125	1910-1996	79
LOGAN RADIO KVNU	Apr 24	May 16	Jun 23	Sep 9	Sep 27	Oct 24	95	135	171	1956-1996	38
MANTI	Apr 7	May 21	Jun 30	Sep 8	Sep 27	Oct 20	80	130	178	1928-1996	68
MILFORD	Apr 16	May 23	Jun 21	Aug 9	Sep 22	Oct 24	73	122	182	1906-1996	83
MOAB	Mar 10	Apr 16	May 18	Sep 16	Oct 17	Nov 9	138	186	242	1889-1996	101
MONTICELLO	Apr 29	May 29	Jun 27	Sep 3	Sep 28	Oct 21	84	122	178	1948-1996	46
NEPHI	Apr 12	May 15	Jun 14	Sep 6	Sep 30	Oct 31	94	138	190	1889-1996	56
OGDEN PIONEER P H	Mar 22	May 3	Jun 16	Sep 10	Oct 12	Nov 14	93	164	224	1902-1996	89
OREM TREATMENT PLANT	Mar 20	Apr 23	May 11	Sep 29	Oct 19	Nov 12	155	181	211	1982-1996	10
PANGUITCH	May 22	Jun 21	Jul 19	Jul 25	Sep 1	Sep 28	26	73	116	1904-1996	74
PARK CITY RADIO	May 3	Jun 8	Jul 19	Jul 30	Sep 13	Oct 17	11	97	143	1889-1991	41
PRICE GAME FARM	Apr 8	May 11	Jul 3	Aug 17	Oct 1	Oct 24	80	144	193	1888-1968	40
PROVO BYU	Mar 20	Apr 25	May 13	Sep 21	Oct 15	Nov 12	132	176	231	1980-1996	15
RANDOLPH	Jun 16	Jul 2	Jul 19	Jul 22	Aug 17	Sep 11	3	46	88	1892-1993	13
RICHFIELD RADIO KSVC	Apr 18	May 25	Jul 20	Aug 23	Sep 20	Oct 24	49	118	172	1893-1996	97
ROOSEVELT RADIO	Apr 24	May 17	Jul 10	Aug 26	Sep 25	Oct 28	63	131	171	1939-1996	51
SALT LAKE CITY NWSFO	Mar 11	Apr 27	May 28	Sep 17	Oct 16	Nov 14	126	175	240	1928-1996	67
SNOWVILLE	May 5	Jun 6	Jun 30	Aug 5	Sep 13	Oct 4	42	100	136	1948-1991	36
SPANISH FORK PWR HOUSE	Mar 25	May 1	Jun 14	Sep 17	Oct 13	Nov 13	125	166	226	1928-1996	66
ST GEORGE	Feb 12	Apr 4	May 20	Sep 21	Oct 27	Nov 24	136	209	274	1862-1996	102
TOOELE	Mar 15	May 5	Jun 17	Aug 30	Oct 14	Nov 8	122	163	237	1897-1996	98
TREMONTON	Mar 20	Apr 27	May 19	Sep 19	Oct 9	Oct 27	131	168	212	1979-1996	16
TRENTON	May 2	May 28	Jun 21	Aug 24	Sep 12	Oct 2	75	108	137	1948-1996	18
VERNAL ARPT	Apr 25	May 27	Jul 4	Aug 27	Sep 21	Oct 18	62	118	157	1894-1996	81
WENDOVER WSO AIRPORT	Mar 13	Apr 17	Jun 9	Aug 18	Oct 20	Nov 11	112	188	240	1911-1996	73
ZION NATIONAL PARK	Mar 9	Apr 15	May 14	Oct 4	Nov 1	Nov 27	162	202	245	1928-1996	67

Major Utah Weather Events

1847-1995

Compiled by
Sean T. Buchanan
from original material by
William J. Alder, R. Clayton Brough,
Daniel W. Pope and Benjamin T. Tolman

JANUARY 1

1910 - A combination of heavy rainfall, warm temperatures, southwest winds, and snow cover triggered serious flooding in southern Utah. Every stream and drainage course was filled to full capacity near Milford. By the time the water had concentrated in the channel of the Beaver River at Milford the stream was about 1¼ miles wide. The New Year's Day storm also caused damage to the water systems in and around St. George.

1979 - Salt Lake City recorded an all-time high barometric pressure of 31.01 inches.

JANUARY 1-9

1979 - Bitterly cold arctic air dominated all of Utah. Due to a lack of snow cover, ground frost permeated the ground to a depth of six feet in many areas. Many homes and businesses in northern and eastern Utah suffered heavily from frozen water pipes, which flooded many Salt Lake area businesses. Total damages soared to near $200,000.

JANUARY 2

1972 - Winds in excess of 60 mph snapped telephone and power lines in northern Box Elder County. Nearly 100 travelers were stranded near Park Valley by 10-foot snow drifts. Several calves were frozen to death.

1991 - Patchy areas of dense fog in the Salt Lake Valley produced a tragic chain reaction multi-vehicle accident (totaling 52 cars/trucks/semis) on I-215 and the Redwood Road area of North Salt Lake. Four people were killed and many more were injured.

JANUARY 2-3

1993 - A "big dump" of snow occurred along the central Wasatch Front and adjacent mountains. Some snowfall amounts for the storm included: Solitude Ski Resort 35", West Kearns and Spanish Fork 21", Taylorsville and Holladay 17", Tooele and Hogle Zoo 16", and Magna 15".

JANUARY 3-4

1991 - Moab received 8" of snow—the most in a 24-hour period since 10" fell in December 1949.

1992 - A southern California storm moved inland and spread snow across the entire state. St. George received 3-5" of the white stuff and Zion National Park picked up 4" of snow.

JANUARY 3-7

1981 - Sub-zero temperatures froze overhead fire protection sprinkler pipes as well as water mains in Salt Lake City, Ogden, and Logan. In Kingston (Piute County), frigid temperatures froze and broke 1½ miles of the city's water line.

JANUARY 4-7

1987 - The second snowstorm of the year dropped 43" of snow at Alta, 40" at Park City, and 13" at Tooele.

JANUARY 5

1974 - A major winter storm moved across southern Utah, dropping more than 12 inches of snow at Kanab and St. George, and causing automobile accidents totaling nearly $40,000 in damage.

1986 - Freezing rain, ice pellets, and vivid lightning accompanied a squall line/cold front across northern and central Utah.

JANUARY 5-6

1994 - Alta set a new state 24-hour snowfall record with 55.5" of snow. The snow contained 3.20" of water. The previous 24-hour snowfall record was 45.0" at Alta on January 22-23 1992.

JANUARY 6

1984 - Black ice created by freezing drizzle resulted in a massive traffic accident on I-15 just north of Salt Lake City.

JANUARY 6-7

1988 - A weather disturbance moved into northern Nevada the evening of the 6th, and developed into a major winter storm by the time it moved across Utah. The excitement began with freezing rain reported in Davis, Weber, and portions of Salt Lake County. Not a lot of freezing rain fell, but enough did to make things slick resulting in several auto accidents. Heavy snow followed. Some snowfall amounts from around the state included: Huntington Canyon 14-18", Ibapah 14", Nephi 8-9", and Delta 5".

JANUARY 6-11

1993 - A "once-in-a-100 year event" struck the heart of the Wasatch Front with nearly continuous amounts of heavy snow for a six-day period. Governor Mike Leavitt declared a State of Emergency in Salt Lake County the morning of the 11th due to massive amounts of snow. This action activated the Utah National Guard who assisted in snow removal. Some of the six day snowfall totals were:

Alta	79"	Bountiful	39"
Brighton	65"	Sandy	37"
Duck Creek	59"	North Orem	36"
Deer Creek Dam	53"	Holladay	34"
Heber	44"	Salt Lake Airport	30"
Monticello	41"		

JANUARY 7

1952 - Eureka (Juab County) was isolated for several days by a locally heavy snowstorm which produced 13 inches of snow that paralyzed all traffic in and around the town.

JANUARY 8

1957 - A lightning bolt struck the dome of the Capitol Building in Salt Lake City and a large hailstorm hit the Provo area. Three inches of snow fell in Provo after the hailstorm, snarling traffic.

1983 - Strong gusty winds were reported throughout the western valleys of Utah. Gusts over 60 mph were recorded in both Salt Lake and Utah Counties, with a 70 mph wind speed recorded at the University of Utah and 120 mph on the top of Hidden Peak at Snowbird Ski Resort.

JANUARY 9

1984 - A combination of freezing drizzle and snow grains caused a 30 to 40 car pileup near American Fork.

1990 - A January heat wave hit Utah. Cedar City recorded the hottest January day ever with a 70 degree reading. The University of Utah also recorded the warmest ever for January with 65 degrees.

JANUARY 9-11

1952 - A heavy snowstorm with 60 mph winds persisted for two days in Cache and Rich Counties. Snowdrifts up to 14 feet high blocked highways and isolated the towns of Garden City, Laketown, and Woodruff. Motorists sought shelter with local residents.

JANUARY 10

1964 - Winds of 40 to 60 mph picked up sheets of crusted snow at Sugarhouse Park in Salt Lake City, creating snowrollers that looked like large doughnut-shaped snowballs.

JANUARY 11

1988 - A vigorous cold front swept across Utah with heavy snow and hurricane force winds. Some wind gusts from around the state included: Park City 100 mph, Trenton 77 mph, Springville and Pleasant Grove 63 mph, Smithfield and North Ogden 60 mph, and the Salt Lake Airport 59 mph. In addition, lightning and thunder was noted at both Smithfield and Salem.

1993 - A record snow depth of 26" was measured at the Salt Lake City International Airport.

JANUARY 12

1963 - The high temperature of 4°F at Salt Lake City was the coldest 24-hour maximum temperature ever recorded, until December 22, 1990 when the mercury only reached a high of 2°F.

JANUARY 13-14

1971- Logan Canyon was the target of 22 mudslides. Deep snowpack along with unusually warm weather triggered the slides. Several summer homes were completely demolished by the slides and avalanches.

JANUARY 14

1953 - A heavy snowstorm centered along the east side of the Salt Lake Valley deposited 2.40 inches of precipitation in less than 24 hours, including a record 14.7 inches of snow at Salt Lake City in 24 hours. Cottonwood Weir, situated at the mouth of Big Cottonwood Canyon, reported 27.5 inches of snow and 3.95 inches of precipitation. Tremendous damage was done to roofs, and power and communication facilities were interrupted from Kaysville to American Fork.

JANUARY 15

1960 - A major snowstorm created hazardous driving conditions across Utah, resulting in 118 accidents in one day.

1975 - A snowstorm hit the Heber Valley, dropping 24 inches of snow, with six inches reported in two hours.

JANUARY 15-16

1987 - Strong easterly canyon winds howled along the Wasatch Front. Wind gusts included: Centerville 98 mph, Bountiful 89 mph, Ogden 80 mph, and West Valley City 52 mph. The winds dropped wind-chill temperatures to -50°F in some canyons. In southern Utah the same major winter storm dumped 14" of snow at Kanosh, 11" at Hanksville, and 5" at Bullfrog.

JANUARY 15-17

1995 - A near record 99.7" of snow fell at the Alta UDOT location in about a 68-hour period. The water amount in the snow was 6.64". The same storm responsible for the snowfall at Alta also hit the rest of the state with a strong cold front, laced with thunderstorms. Other snowfall amounts from around the state were: Park City 29", Springville 21", Provo BYU 17", Alpine 16", Bountiful and Sandy 13", Fillmore 11", Ogden 10", Salt Lake City International Airport 9", and Cedar City, and Payson 4".

JANUARY 16

1984 - A dozen stations across Utah reported record low temperatures of -9°F or colder. The coldest spot was Woodruff in the Bear Lake Valley with a low of -27°F.

JANUARY 17-18

1983 - South central Utah was hit hard by a strong winter storm. Mt. Pleasant (Sanpete County) received 8 inches of snow while Ephraim picked up 7 inches. The town of Spring City got the brunt of the storm with 15 inches.

1988 - A massive winter storm "clobbered" southern and eastern Utah. This was one of the biggest storms in this portion of the state in nearly three years. Some of the amounts of snow were as follows: Duck Creek 26", Monticello and Bryce Canyon 24", Hiawatha 15", Milford and Escalante 13", Castledale 12", Blanding 12-14", and Ferron 11" of snow.

JANUARY 18

1984 - Bitter cold temperatures were recorded across Utah. The uninhabited reporting station of Middle Sinks in Logan Canyon recorded an incredible reading of -64°F. Rich County had frigid readings with -40°F at Randolph. In the Cache Valley low temperatures included: Wellsville -39°F, Trenton -32°F, Smithfield -30°F, and -27°F at River Heights. Other reports from around the state included: Solitude and Thiokol -30°F, Heber -29°F, Fairfield, and Jensen -28°F.

JANUARY 18-19

1990 - A band of heavy snow rotated into the 4-Corners area. An awesome 14" of snow fell at Monticello and 10" at Blanding.

JANUARY 19

1986 - Dense fog contributed to two fatal accidents near the Great Salt Lake Beach. Meanwhile, fog-free Provo BYU reported a record high temperature of 57°F.

JANUARY 19-20

1937 - Salt Lake City received 9.8 inches of snow in 24 hours.

JANUARY 21-22

1985 - Old Man Winter unloaded copious amounts of snow in Salt Lake Valley, Utah Valley and the Uinta Basin. Utah County received 12-15 inches of snow with Payson receiving the Lion's share at 18 inches. Vernal had 9 inches.

JANUARY 22

1964 - The greatest 24-hour mountain snowfall ever recorded in Utah occurred at Brighton Ski Resort: 35 inches.

JANUARY 23

1949 - The second deepest snow ever measured at the Salt Lake City Airport was recorded on this date: 23 inches.

1990 - A fast moving cold front blasted across northern Utah during the evening hours. A peak wind gust of 117 mph was recorded at the top of Hidden Peak at Snowbird Ski Resort.

JANUARY 24-30

1965 - Alta received 105 inches of snow, the greatest amount of snowfall from one storm ever recorded in Utah.

JANUARY 25

1952 - A snowslide roared down Snowslide Canyon in Provo Canyon and covered the road, river, and railroad tracks for nearly ½ mile. Snow depths ranged from 35 to 70 feet.

1984 - Freezing rain fell in areas of Ogden and Tooele. Numerous avalanches occurred in the Wasatch Mountains.

1989 - Brrrrr!!! Was it ever cold. Some of the frigid morning low temperatures were: Middle Sink -46°F, Trenton -34, Lewiston/Logan Airport -30°F, Wellsville -28°F, and Providence -18°F. In addition, a record low maximum temperature occurred at Richfield of only 15°F.

JANUARY 26

1982 - An extremely strong wind gust of 120 mph was observed at the Summit House in Park City. At Snowbird Ski Resort winds reached 95 mph. The high temperature of 62°F in Salt Lake City was the warmest January reading ever.

JANUARY 27

1956 - A Tooele couple missed death by minutes when a tree was blown onto their trailer, crushing the living room which they had just vacated. The Heber Valley area was hit hard by winds with thousands of dollars in damage to buildings.

JANUARY 27-28

1916 - A record low barometric pressure of 28.96 inches was observed at Salt Lake City. In southwestern Utah at Modena (Iron County), the pressure dropped to 28.91 inches. Winds associated with the strong pressure gradient reached hurricane velocity, resulting in unroofed structures across southwestern Utah.

JANUARY 28

1956 - Gale-force winds (39-54 mph) hit Heber City, destroying two wearhouses valued at $9,000.

JANUARY 29

1911 - A landslide in Provo Canyon covered about 500 feet of railroad track to a depth of nearly 50 feet in some places.

1969 - Extreme blizzard conditions at the Point of the Mountain (between Sandy and Lehi) dropped visibility to zero and stranded over 150 automobiles.

1986 - Strong southerly winds gusted to 94 mph on the top of Hidden Peak at Snowbird Ski Resort.

JANUARY 29-30

1915 - Very heavy rains deluged parts of Utah. Some amounts included: Leeds (Washington County) 3.55", Hayden (Duchesne County) 3.50", New Harmony (Washington County) 3.26", and Tropic (Garfield County) 2.52" of rainfall.

JANUARY 29-FEBRUARY 1

1993 - A low pressure area developed over the northern Great Basin and drifted into southern Nevada. The wind flow around this storm, combined with an injection of tropical moisture, created a monstrous snow event across southern and central Utah. The intensity and duration of snowfall in western Wayne County was a "once-in-a-100 year" storm. Some storm totals for the two-day period included: Teasdale 49", Brian Head Ski Resort 43", Torrey 41", Bryce Canyon 35", Capitol Reef 27", Escalante 20", Modena 14", Kanarraville and New Harmony 12".

JANUARY 29 - FEBRUARY 2

1963 - Early state precipitation records were established at Deer Creek Dam in north central Utah. In 24 hours 5.08" of precipitation fell, in 48 hours 8.88", in 72 hours 9.59", and in 96 hours 10.13". These records were broken in the 1970's.

JANUARY 30

1980 - A major snowstorm blanketed Utah with 12" of snow at valley locations and two to three feet in the mountains and higher valleys.

JANUARY 30-31

1911 - A warm, rainy spell produced numerous floods across the higher elevations of northern Utah. In the vicinity of Alta, a disastrous slide occurred during the night of the 31st, demolishing a bunkhouse and killing four miners.

JANUARY 31

1985 - Bitter cold Arctic air settled over the entire state. Peter Sinks, an uninhabited, desolate depression located at the 8,100 foot level up Logan Canyon, plunged to -65°F. Sage Creek Junction (Rich County) dropped to -51°F.

FEBRUARY 1

1963 - An intense series of thunderstorms over Northern Utah flooded the Provo City water line, destroying over 500,000 fish at the Midway Fish Hatchery and damaging property in Heber City (Wasatch County), Vivian Park (Utah County), and Wellsville (Cache County).

FEBRUARY 1-2

1989 - A very strong cold front slammed into Utah from the north bringing heavy snowfalls to Wasatch Front communities. Ahead of the front strong south winds blew, including: Milford 61 mph, Salt Lake City International Airport 54 mph, Cedar City 52 mph, and Holladay 48 mph. Snowfall amounts were impressive with 10-20" falling in favored valley locations along the Wasatch Front. Magna was the winner with 20" of snowfall. A record was set at the Salt Lake City International Airport for the greatest 24-hour snowfall in February with 11.9".

FEBRUARY 2

1910 - Severe winds ripped down telephone wires from Salt Lake City northward. Damages amounted to $75,000. Water whipped by the wind washed away portions of the embankment and railings along the Great Salt Lake.

1985 - St. George received over one-fourth of its average annual snowfall with one inch in 24 hours.

FEBRUARY 3

1978 - Help was needed in the central Utah town of Helper as heavy snow caused a flat-roofed building on Main Street to collapse under tons of snow. In another part of town a man barely escaped injury when his aluminum carport awning crashed to the ground under the weight of the heavy snow.

FEBRUARY 4

1982 - A combination of very high easterly canyon winds and cold morning low temperatures produced wind-chill readings of -80°F in portions of the Salt Lake Valley. Winds speeds of over 80 mph were reported at the Fire Weather Station near the University of Utah. The strong wind gusts closed portions of U.S. Highway 89 between Ogden and Hill Air Force Base.

FEBRUARY 5

1953 - The state's greatest 24-hour valley snowfall occurred at Kanosh (Millard County) with 35 inches.

1982 - One of the coldest mornings ever recorded in northeast Utah. The bitter cold readings in Rich County included: Randolph -44°F and Woodruff -42°F.

FEBRUARY 6

1986 - Easterly canyon winds became severe along the western slopes of the Wasatch Mountains. The winds toppled two semi-trucks, blew a small jet off the runway at Brigham City, and downed eight power lines at Kaysville. Wind speeds reached 87 mph at Farmington and 80 mph at Centerville.

1989 - An Alaskan clipper put all of Utah into a deep freeze with record low temperatures set at many locations. Some of the frigid readings included: Middle Sink (Logan Canyon) -54°F, Roosevelt -47°F, Randolph -42°F, Heber -35°F, Richfield -33°F, Delta -26°F, and Salt Lake City International Airport -14°F.

FEBRUARY 7

1949 - During one of the worst winters in Utah history, heavy snowfall of up to 10 inches and hurricane force winds (74+ mph) closed roads in Delta, Milford, Cedar City, and Bountiful. Two men froze to death and schools closed down in the Davis, Weber, and Granite School Districts.

FEBRUARY 8

1985 - Hurricane force winds reached 105 mph at the Angle Station at Park City. Winds in the western valleys stranded many cars and several buses in snowdrifts on the west side of the Salt Lake Valley.

FEBRUARY 8-9

1953 - Millard County recorded one of the heaviest snowstorms to ever hit southwest Utah. Kanosh reported 42 inches of snow and 4.43 inches of precipitation. Cove Fort reported 4.75 inches of precipitation.

FEBRUARY 8-14

1962 - In Wasatch County, two feet of snow accompanied by rain and above-normal temperatures caused heavy runoff, resulting in one of the worst floods in Heber City history. Charleston and Wallsburg were also flooded.

FEBRUARY 9

1933 - The mercury at Salt Lake City plummeted to the coldest reading ever recorded, an Arctic like -30°F.

1986 - A brief burst of snow glazed up I-15 in Salt Lake County resulting in a 50 car pileup and numerous injuries.

FEBRUARY 10

1975 - Strong winds of 65 mph caused the derailment of a chair lift at Park City Ski Resort. The winds also prompted the shutdown of the gondola. Because of the strong winds, reaching 80 mph at some locations, the wind-chill temperature dropped to -50°F or colder above the 9,000 foot level.

FEBRUARY 10-12

1915 - Heavy rains hit parts of Utah. Some rainfall amounts included: Elberta (Utah County) 3.65", New Harmony (Washington County) 3.13", Heber City (Wasatch County) 2.80", and Provo (Utah County) 2.54".

FEBRUARY 11

1982 - Kanab (Kane County) just a few miles north of the Arizona border, received ¼ of their annual snowfall when six inches of snow fell in 24 hours.

FEBRUARY 12-13

1986 - Nearly three feet of heavy dense snow fell in the Wasatch Mountains. Sundance Ski Resort, located up Provo Canyon, received 36 inches. An avalanche destroyed a house in the Sundance area leaving only the pillars standing.

1992 - A band of heavy showers rolled through southwest Utah. Storm water totals in the mountains of the southwest were phenomenal: Little Grassy 5.00", Tenneco Mines 4.72", Midway Valley 3.00", Kolob 2.70", and Long Valley 2.20". Other water amounts from the storm were: Duck Creek 2.72", Zion National Park 2.11", Kanab 1.95", St. George 1.53", and Monticello 1.08".

FEBRUARY 13

1885 - A massive avalanche at Alta's Emma Mine covered ¾ of the town and killed 16 people.

1987 - An active squall line of thunderstorms produced winds up to 70 mph at Logan and 51 mph at Centerville.

1995 - A major winter storm hit in most areas of the state. The cold front associated with the storm stalled over extreme northern Utah. The front was dotted with thunderstorms moving through the heart of the Wasatch Front during the morning commute. Sundance, in the mountains of northern Utah, reported a wind gust of 120 mph. Laketown reported 17" of snowfall. In the southwest, St. George had a peak wind gust of 63 mph.

FEBRUARY 13-19

1985 - Widespread dense fog was blamed for many massive multiple vehicle accidents and three deaths along the Wasatch Front. On the 13th, 30 cars and several semis were involved in a pileup on the Beck Street overpass near North Salt Lake. On the 14th, another car/semi truck accident occurred in Kaysville. On the 15th, there was a multiple car mishap around Magna. On the 18th, a teenager drove his truck into the Jordan River and drowned. Beck Street was the site of another chain-reaction traffic accident on the 19th. The unwelcomed heavy fog dispersed on the 20th.

FEBRUARY 14

1910 - There was no love lost between Utahns and Mother Nature on this Valentine's Day as residents put up with the second severe day of strong winds in as many weeks. Salt Lake City recorded a wind speed of 52 mph. Nearly 200 bathhouses at Saltair were demolished. Waters of the Great Salt Lake washed out 4 miles of track belonging to the Western Pacific Railroad, causing about $50,000 damage.

FEBRUARY 15

1982 - Twenty-eight avalanches occurred in American Fork Canyon in Utah County.

1986 - One of the highest wind gusts ever recorded in Utah occurred on the mountain slopes above Park City: 120 mph.

FEBRUARY 16

1986 - Heavy rains continued for the fifth consecutive day, causing widespread urban flooding throughout portions of Davis, Weber, and Morgan Counties of northern Utah. The small community of Porterville (Morgan County) received 4.50 inches of rain in four days.

FEBRUARY 16-17

1984 - The "Great Salt Lake Effect" dumped up to two feet of snow on Tooele. At Dugway, snow drifts up to three feet deep closed many roads. The rest of the state received up to a foot of snow in the valleys with over 2 feet in the mountains.

FEBRUARY 17

1926 - A deadly snowslide in Bingham Canyon (southwest Salt Lake County) demolished 14 miners cottages, a 3-story frame boarding house, and killed 36 people and injured 13 others out of the 65 people who were in its path.

1986 - Additional heavy rain and snow from the past week brought rare February flooding to many areas of northern Utah. Cache, Morgan, Wasatch, and Weber counties were declared disaster areas with property damage totaling almost $4,000,000. An avalanche rumbled down Bridal Veil Falls up Provo Canyon, destroying a tourist shop, tearing away portions of the roadway, and clogging the Provo River.

1993 - A strong tropical surge of moisture riding in a southwest flow over Utah brought strong southerly winds to most areas of the state. Some reported wind speeds: West Kearns 68 mph, Tooele 57 mph, Delta 52 mph, West Valley 51 mph, Centerville 50 mph, and Cedar City 49 mph.

FEBRUARY 18

1983 - Hurricane force winds of over 74 mph in southern Utah knocked out power and phone lines, smashed windows, downed trees, and toppled walls. Damage estimates toppled the $4,000,000 mark, which included the loss of a 300 foot radio tower near Cedar City, a dozen aircraft damaged at the St. George Airport, and eight boats sunk at Lake Powell.

1986 - As rain finally tapered off, phenomenal eight-day precipitation totals were reported across portions of northern Utah: Wellsville (Cache County) 10.56", Deer Creek (Wasatch County) 9.76", Pineview (Summit County) 5.29", Midway (Wasatch County) 5.76", and Morgan (Morgan County) 4.48". A balmy low of 51°F was recorded at the Salt Lake City International Airport, the warmest minimum temperature reading ever recorded for February.

FEBRUARY 19

1986 - Strong south winds ushered another round of heavy rains into northwest Utah enhancing local flooding. Wind speeds were clocked at 119 mph at the Angle Station in Park City, 58 mph at Farmington, 54 mph at the Salt Lake City International Airport, and 52 mph at Provo BYU.

FEBRUARY 20

1971 - Easterly canyon winds gusting to nearly 100 mph destroyed over a dozen mobile homes in Kaysville and toppled eight moving railroad cars in Farmington. The winds also snapped power lines, blew over trees onto cars, broke windows, removed roofs, and twisted highway signs.

FEBRUARY 22

1993 - Strong winds laced with snow played havoc over the higher elevations of extreme northern Utah. Blizzard conditions were reported at mountain locations with I-80 closed for seven hours from Echo Junction to the Wyoming border. Schools were closed for the day in Rich County due to the hazardous weather conditions. In addition, 94 mph winds were clocked at Mt. Ogden.

FEBRUARY 23

1956 - A sharp change in temperatures occurred at Salt Lake City as the thermometer reached a high of 57°F at 2:50 PM, followed by a frontal passage and a temperature drop to 31°F by 6:30 PM—a fall of 26°F in less than four hours.

FEBRUARY 23-25

1993 - Heavy snow fell over many locations across northern and central Utah. Lightning and thunder accompanied some of the snow squalls on the evening of the 23rd in the south part of the Salt Lake Valley and across portions of Utah County. Some snowfall amounts included: Park City 30", Woodland 19", Eureka 18", Heber and Bountiful 15", Alpine and Tooele 14", Layton, American Fork, Provo BYU, and Centerville 11", Sandy 9-14", Nephi 8", Salt Lake Airport and Kearns 5", Vernal 3", South Jordan and Wendover 2".

FEBRUARY 25

1987 - A snowstorm produced an astounding 41" of snow at Duck Creek in the mountains of southwest Utah. The same storm also dumped 18" of the white stuff at Monticello and 11" at Bryce Canyon.

FEBRUARY 28

1972 - A mild reading of 69 °F was recorded at Salt Lake City. This was the warmest temperature ever recorded for the month of February.

FEBRUARY 28 - MARCH 2

1991 - Heavy rains fell across many areas of southern Utah, especially west of St. George in the Bull Mountain/Beaver Dam mountain range and on the south slopes of the Pine Valleys (under a strong southwest flow). Rainfall totals from the storm were very impressive: Little Grassy 6.30" and the Tenneco Mines (Gold Strike Project) 6.28" of precipitation. The same storm spread across the entire state with the following rainfall amounts: Ben Lomand Peak (northern Utah Mountains) 4.60", Kolob (southern Utah mountains) 4.00", Midway Valley 3.10", Zion National Park 2.23", Kanab 2.08", Hurricane 1.93", Monticello 1.64", Brigham City 1.60", and St. George 1.21".

FEBRUARY 29

1960 - The coldest leap year morning in the Salt Lake Valley occurred when the temperature plummeted to -4°F.

1988 - After the driest February on record at many locations across Utah, a line of thunderstorms moved from southwest Utah into the northern part of the state. Lightning knocked-out the radar system on a United

Airlines jet as it was landing at the Salt Lake City International Airport.

1992 - Many stations in Utah "leaped" into the record books with the hottest leap day on record. Some of the records included: Provo BYU 70°F, and Delta and Fillmore 67°F.

MARCH 1

1976 - Frequent wind speeds of 60+ mph were observed throughout western Utah. A vigorous cold front dumped up to one foot of snow in many areas of the state. Storm related damage reached a total of $350,000.

MARCH 1-2

1974 - A major storm moved across most of western and northern Utah, accompanied by 75 mph winds in Bountiful and 90 mph winds in Hunter (Salt Lake County). Buildings and roofs were damaged, large truck-trailers and aircraft were overturned, and numerous traffic accidents occurred.

1989 - A very strong squall line developed out ahead of a main batch of cold air and moved into northern Utah. The line was characterized by thunderstorms, strong winds, frequent lightning, hail, and a tornado. The Salt Lake City International Airport recorded the lowest barometric pressure reading ever for the month of March with 29.07". In addition, hail piled up 1" deep at the airport and lightning hit a Delta jet on takeoff, forcing it to return. The storms deposited .40" of rain in just one hour.

MARCH 2

1984 - Several people were injured in a fog-related chain reaction accident involving 15 cars in American Fork.

MARCH 2-3

1938 - Very heavy rains fell across southern Utah. Flooding was reported throughout the area and reports of damage to crops and property were widespread. Some precipitation amounts included: Alton (Kane County) 3.97", Bryce Canyon 3.08", Zion National Park 3.02", Tropic (Garfield County) 2.83", and Leeds (Washington County) 2.45".

1985 - A very large winter storm over western and northern Utah left behind more than a foot of snow in the Cache Valley, and three to six inches of snow was common along the Wasatch Front. Strong northerly winds behind the cold front blew snow into five foot deep drifts in the Cache Valley and four foot deep drifts in portions of the Salt Lake Valley.

MARCH 3

1978 - A large snowslide near Bridal Veil Falls in Provo Canyon deposited snow at depths up to 75 feet that covered 2,000 feet of the main road. It took three days for crews to clear the road. I-80 in eastern Salt Lake City was closed as winds gusting over 70 mph reduced visibility to zero. At least 50 cars were abandoned on the highway.

MARCH 3-4

1983 - Provo reported a wind gust of 69 mph on the 3rd. Cedar City received 15 inches of snow during the two days.

1993 - A weak storm entered extreme northwest Utah and then exploded over Ibapah (in the far west desert) producing five inches of snow overnight.

MARCH 3-6

1982 - Heavy snowfall of three to five feet fell in the northern mountains during the four-day period.

MARCH 5

1995 - Heavy rains fell in Washington and Kane Counties, producing heavy runoff in the Santa Clara River that washed out a 60-foot section of the sewer main that served Ivins and Santa Clara, discharging its putrid contents into the river. Rainfall amounts of 1.30" to 1.80" fell in a short period of time.

MARCH 6

1985 - 100 mph winds were reported at the top of the tram at Park City.

MARCH 7

1967 - Strong winds blew over a 120-foot brick wall at Nephi's Thermoid Plant.

MARCH 8

1961 - High winds toppled 15 telephone poles like dominoes in Spanish Fork, affecting southern Utah telephone service for several hours.

MARCH 9

1977 - Winds gusting up to 80 mph swept across much of northern and central Utah, ripping up trees, knocking over signs, and causing power outages. The storm kicked up huge clouds of dust over the Great Salt Lake Desert that resembled the dust bowl days of the 1930's. Following the storm, snows were driven horizontally by the winds. The dust that preceded the storm settled on top of power poles. When the snow turned it wet, the electrical insulators became conductors, causing the power to leak off insulators and setting the poles on fire.

MARCH 10

1978 - Raging flood-swollen waters of a nearby creek turned a golf course at St. George into a giant water trap. Water was running eight inches above the top of the reservoir at the peak of the flood.

MARCH 11

1990 - A major winter storm produced 10" of snow in less than 12 hours at the Salt Lake City International Airport.

1994 - The Randolph area received more snow than they had seen in a long time. Randolph received 10" of snow which tied the all-time record snowfall for a 24-hour period for any month. The record was previously set on May 11, 1983. In addition, 1.23" of precipitation was recorded which set an all-time 24-hour maximum precipitation record. The old record was .75" set on July 16, 1987.

MARCH 11-12
1906 - High winds blew down fences and sheds in Heber.

MARCH 11-13
1990 - A major winter storm dumped 36" of snow at Elk Meadows in the southern Utah mountains. Brian Head ski resort picked up 35".

MARCH 12
1957 - The Cache Valley experienced locally strong winds that damaged trees, signs, television antennas, and windows. The strong winds also overturned a heavy trailer on U.S. Highway 91 in the Salt Lake Valley.

MARCH 13
1959 - Winds gusting up to 71 mph ripped off a section of roof from Springville's public swimming pool building.

MARCH 13-14
1944 - A huge storm dumped 21.6 inches of snow in 24 hours at Salt Lake City.

MARCH 14
1920 - Unusually high winds blew throughout the southeastern counties of Utah, damaging trees, roofs, and barns.

MARCH 15-16
1984 - A squall line of thunderstorms and its parent cold front produced winds and heavy hail along the Wasatch Front. Very powerful wind gusts pushed ice to a depth of 20 feet along the east side of Farmington Bay while power poles were sheared off by wind blown ice on the flooded south end of the Great Salt Lake. A strong gust of 69 mph was recorded at Eagle Range on the west side of the Great Salt Lake.

MARCH 16
1988 - A localized strong easterly canyon wind event struck the Centerville/Farmington area of northern Utah with 80 mph winds. South Ogden recorded a wind gust to 51 mph.

MARCH 17
1993 - A flash flood went across I-15 about 20 miles south of Cedar City during the evening hours. The remnants of a natural dam that was formed by a landslide three years previous collapsed. This dam was located in the Zion NP/Kolob Canyon area. The mud, water, and debris that roared down Taylor Canyon was about 12 feet high and 45 feet wide. By the time it crossed the interstate it was about three feet high and still nearly 45 feet wide. There were five reported accidents/incidents. Three cars slid and rolled and one semi tipped on its side.

MARCH 17-18
1874 - Heavy snowstorms brought the total snow cover in Salt Lake City to a depth of 22 inches.

MARCH 18
1961 - Strong easterly canyon winds gusting to at least 84 mph caused over $1,000,000 in damage from Salt Lake City to Ogden. In Salt Lake City two youths were blown from a truck and injured.

MARCH 19
1994 - Lightning struck a house in Logan damaging a VCR, television, stereo, and telephone. The lightning also singed the rain gutter and blew out a chunk of cement from the foundation.

MARCH 19-20
1983 - "Lake Effect" snows moved off the Great Salt Lake and deposited 13" of heavy snow at Bountiful and 17" of snow in 24 hours at Snowbird Ski Resort.

MARCH 21
1995 - A wind gust of 87 mph was recorded along I-80 near Saltair, blowing a truck off the roadway and into the Great Salt Lake. Coalville also received strong southerly winds with a peak gust of 60 mph. The winds were blowing in advance of an approaching cold front.

MARCH 21-22
1973 - Up to 15 inches of snow fell on major populated areas of Weber and Box Elder Counties. The heavy, wet snow knocked down nearly 20 miles of power and telephone lines, closed schools for two days, and caused more than $1,000,000 in damage to buildings and livestock.

MARCH 22
1994 - In advance of a cold front, strong south winds howled across much of Utah. Some of the wind gusts included: Milford and Delta 75 mph, Cedar City 71 mph, Provo BYU 69 mph, and St. George and Maeser 66 mph. As a result of the high winds, an auto and hardware store in Milford had its roof blown off into a lumber yard next door. Also, road signs along I-15 near Cedar City were toppled, a window was blown out of a house in Maeser, and a swamp cooler was blown off a roof and across the road at Hamilton Fort.

MARCH 23
1983 - A vigorous cold front dumped up to 31" of snow at Alta Ski Resort. Up to 12" of snow fell in the Cedar City/Parowan area.

MARCH 23-25

1995 - A strong spring storm dumped an incredible 49" of snow on Brian Head Ski Resort in southern Utah.

MARCH 24-25

1983 - A trough of low pressure, influenced by the Great Salt Lake and the Wasatch Mountains, dumped over 18" of snow along the bench areas of Salt Lake, Utah, and southern Davis Counties. Alta Ski Resort picked up 31" of snow within a 24-hour period. The heavy wet snow was responsible for numerous power outages and broken tree limbs.

MARCH 25-26

1975 - A major winter storm moved into Utah, bringing moderate winds and heavy snowfall. Damage caused by wind-driven ice on Bear Lake approached $10,000.

MARCH 26-27

1985 - Hurricane force winds of 74 mph hit the Cache Valley. A house under construction was knocked 10 feet off its foundation.

MARCH 27

1977 - A damaging windstorm hit the Wasatch Front with winds approaching 100 mph. Extensive damage was done to many homes.

MARCH 27-28

1985 - A record-breaking snowstorm unloaded copious amounts of snow over central and southern Utah. Milford received a record 20.6" of snow in 24 hours. Other phenomenal amounts included: Cove Fort (Millard County) 32", Minersville (Beaver County) 30", Marysvale (Piute County) 24", Beaver (Beaver County) 22", Richfield (Sevier County) 18", and Loa (Wayne County) 17" of snow.

MARCH 29-30

1984 - Persistent east winds whipped across northern Utah. A wind gust of 86 mph was clocked at the Logan Airport. A peak wind gust of 82 mph was measured on the Bountiful bench, 78 mph in Smithfield, and 72 mph in Farmington. In the meantime, a storm system dumped heavy snow in southwest and south central Utah. Fresh snow depths included: Bicknell (Wayne County) 17", Torrey (Wayne County) 15", and Circleville (Piute County) 14".

MARCH 29

1967 - Winds of over 50 mph shorted out power lines, causing a fire that burned Circleville Elementary School, in Piute County, to the ground.

1985 - Easterly canyon winds reached 88 mph at Farmington.

1988 - Very cold temperatures were recorded in central Utah. A few of the colder reports included, Milford with 9°F, (a record cold low), Santaquin 15°F, and Payson 16°F.

1992 - Heavy rains hit the Cedar City area during the afternoon hours. One weather observer reported an even 1.00" of rain in a short period of time. The UHP in Cedar City reported "water gushing over the gutters" and across roadways in some places of town. Parked cars were covered with hail.

MARCH 30

1980 - A hard freeze in Utah's Dixie destroyed blossoming peaches, plums, and apricots.

MARCH 31

1982 - March didn't "leave like a lamb" as gusty winds howled throughout much of northern Utah. Wellsville, located in the southwest corner of the Cache Valley, reported a wind gust of 63 mph.

APRIL 1

1982 - Wind gusts were registered up to 58 mph in Milford, 57 mph at Provo BYU, 51 mph at Salt Lake City, and 50 mph in Monticello. In addition, up to 8" of snow fell along portions of the Wasatch Front.

1984 - A winter-like storm dumped 19" of snow in South Jordan and 10" of snow at Provo.

1985 - The snow finally melted at Utah State University in Logan, after establishing a new record of 128 consecutive days of an inch or more of snow on the ground.

APRIL 1-2

1986 - Two to three inches of rain fell in the valleys, and over two feet of snow in the mountains of northern Utah. Tooele received 3.12" of rain from the storm while Snowbird Ski Resort picked up 16" of snow. In addition, strong easterly canyon winds produced waves up to five feet high on the Great Salt Lake along the Southern Pacific causeway and on I-80 along the lake's south shore. Wendover, in the west desert, reported winds approaching 60 mph.

APRIL 1-10

Since 1888, all but two Annual General Conferences of the Church of Jesus Christ of Latter-day Saints has been held sometime between April 1-10. During the past several decades, many conference visitors and Utah residents have often remarked how predictably unsettled the weather is during L.D.S. General Conference. It is a fact that 67% of all April conferences have received measurable precipitation. During the April 1983 conference, 7.5" of snow fell.

APRIL 2

1936 - The coldest April morning in Salt Lake City history occurred when the mercury plummeted to a record cold 14°F.

APRIL 3

1983 - Heavy snowfall turned Easter Sunday into a winter wonderland. Some northern and central Utah valleys received up to 7" of snow in just two hours. Storm totals between 6-12" were common. Alta received 32" of snow in 24-hours.

1994 - Microburst winds caused some damage in the Riverton area of northern Utah. The winds overturned a trampoline, displaced the wall of a carport into the field next door, and blew a kayak into a tree.

APRIL 4

1985 - A strong northwest flow produced extremely high winds in some areas of Utah. The highest gust reported was 110 mph at the Park City Angle Station. Other powerful wind gusts included: Hidden Peak/Snowbird 100 mph, Snowbasin 70 mph, and Sundance 60 mph. In central Utah, a roof was blown off a service station in Huntington and two trailers were destroyed at a trailer park in Ferron.

APRIL 4-6

1983 - A "once-in-30-years" severe "easterly canyon wind" event set up along the Wasatch Front. Sustained wind speeds of 50 mph were common with gusts over 70 mph. A peak gust of 104 mph was recorded at Hill Air Force Base. Damage figures skyrocketed toward the $8,000,000 mark! Among the greatest damage: 54 Utah Power and Light Company transmission towers were either damaged or destroyed, and 15 to 20 semi's were blown over or damaged along I-15 in the Farmington/Centerville area. At the Hyrum cemetery, in the Cache Valley, dozens of tall fur trees were uprooted and toppled. In southeastern Utah, Monticello received up to a foot of snow.

APRIL 5

1958 - The greatest snow depth ever recorded in the state was measured at Alta: 179", almost 15 feet!

1967 - Vicious winds roared throughout Utah. At River Heights (Cache County) hurricane velocity south winds ripped the roof off of a house sending debris flying through the air for two blocks. In southwest Utah, a telephone booth was smashed at Cedar City and sand up to several inches thick was blown into homes. In central Utah, two planes were tipped over in Provo and several hundred feet of theater wall was blown down in Orem. The strongest wind gust measured was 93 mph at Dugway.

APRIL 6

1969 - Wind speeds above 60 mph in southeastern Utah damaged aircraft and hangar doors at Canyonlands Airport and tore the roof off of an automobile reconditioning building. Winds in Moab blew over a power pole that was carrying 69,000 volts of electricity, leaving the community without power.

APRIL 7

1902 - A strong south wind overturned several outbuildings at Deseret in central Utah.

1956 - Winds gusting to at least 75 mph in the Provo/Orem/Springville area tore the roofs off of houses, broke numerous windows, and ripped up a 70-foot evergreen tree in Provo and carried it across the street into a parking lot. The Salt Lake City Airport reported wind gusts in excess of 80 mph.

1988 - A very windy cold front passed through Utah producing strong winds across the northwest part of the state. Wendover recorded a wind gust of 63 mph, while Pleasant Grove reported 61 mph, and Trenton 60 mph. In the Wendover area, five semis were blown over and four vehicles (which included three police cars) had windows blown out.

APRIL 8

1995 - A cold front moving across the state produced wind gusts to 80 mph at Duchesne, resulting in broken tree branches and downed power lines. The same cold front brought thunderstorms to much of Utah, which produced ½" to ¾" diameter hail near the Salt Lake City International Airport and ¼" diameter hail at Cedar City.

APRIL 9-10

1974 - A major snowstorm, preceded by 45 mph winds, dropped 17.4" of snow at Salt Lake City, and caused $300,000 in damage to roofs, trees, and shrubs. Power lines were downed and a number of automobile accidents were reported.

APRIL 12

1983 - Vernal averages about ½" of snow in April, but a late winter storm dumped 6" of the white stuff in 24-hours.

APRIL 12-13

1986 - Hurricane force winds and a vigorous cold front plagued the state. Knolls (Tooele County) and Pleasant Grove (Utah County) both measured wind speeds of 75 mph. In southern Utah, winds over 60 mph were reported. At Lake Powell, the winds overturned a houseboat, destroyed a trailer, and blew camper shells off several trucks. Precipitation amounts of 1.00" or more were common across many parts of Utah.

APRIL 13

1983 - Along the Wasatch Front the second "canyon wind event," in two weeks, produced a peak gust of 90 mph at Farmington (Davis County).

APRIL 13-17

1984 - Warm weather brought on a rash of weather related problems. Slides were reported in City Creek, Emigration, Provo, and Ogden Canyons. Minor flooding occurred in southwest Salt Lake County, and along Hobble Creek and Spanish Fork Canyon in Utah County. A snowslide closed Little Cottonwood Canyon east of Salt Lake. Strong thunderstorms rumbled up and down the Wasatch Front with a peak wind gust of 77 mph reported at Wendover.

APRIL 14

1970 - Western Utah was hit by strong winds. Gusts up to 75 mph whipped up dust, limited visibility and contributed to two multi-car collisions near Knolls (Tooele County). Seven cars were involved in the accidents and two women were seriously injured. Winds also caused considerable damage to a Tooele chapel when a large aluminum/glass wall gave way.

APRIL 15

1935 - It was like the dust bowl days of the Great Depression across parts of western Utah. Strong, gusty, southerly winds persisted from sunrise to sunset producing an unusually dense and widespread dust storm over the entire western half of the state. Visibilities were reduced to near zero during the afternoon. Automobile engines were stalled by dust at Black Rock in the west central part of the state. Residents in Grantsville reported physical distress to themselves and animals due to the dust. Early afternoon showers in northern Utah precipitated unusually muddy rain drops. By dusk, the wind changed direction to the northwest, clearing the air.

1967 - Strong winds over the western part of Utah County blew over a 65-foot Ferris wheel, causing $10,000 in damage.

APRIL 16

1899 - Violent sandstorms at Ft. Duchesne (Uinta County) and Grover (Wayne County) increased in intensity throughout the day. They became very ominous by late afternoon, but were followed by clear skies and calm conditions after dusk. Salt Lake City recorded a maximum wind speed of 51 mph.

APRIL 18-19

1987 - A strong spring storm produced high winds across northern Utah. Some of the higher gusts included: Park City 99 mph, Logan 79 mph, Wendover 71 mph, and Kearns 42 mph. Four people drowned in Utah Lake when high winds capsized their fishing boat. The storm brought in a taste of winter with 22" of snow falling at Alta and 9" at both North Salt Lake and Holladay.

APRIL 19

1989 - Hanksville recorded the warmest April day ever with a record maximum temperature of 98°F. The previous all-time high temperature for April was 93°F set back on April 30, 1928.

APRIL 19-20

1966 - Sub-zero temperatures destroyed nearly 70 percent of Utah County's fruit crop.

APRIL 19-21

1982 - Record cold temperatures across northern Utah. Smithfield (Cache County) plunged to 13°F. Many fruit orchards reported lows in the teens that caused severe damage to fruit, in particular apricots, peaches, and cherries. Salt Lake City experienced the coldest temperature ever recorded so late in the spring as the mercury dropped to 22°F.

APRIL 21

1984 - A wind gust of 71 mph was reported in Farmington.

APRIL 22

1957 - "April showers" was an understatement in Tooele as over 3.00" of rain was reported. Two children in the community of Erda (Tooele County) awoke in their basement about 2:00 AM, to find their mattresses floating on 5-foot deep floodwater.

1965 - Gusty, dusty winds of over 63 mph in western Utah caused near zero visibility between Wendover and Grantsville.

APRIL 22-23

1931 - A very potent windstorm blew from an easterly direction for more than a day along the western slopes of the Wasatch Front. About 1,000 trees were uprooted in several northern Utah counties. About 350 power poles were blown over, 11 railroad freight cars were blown off their tracks at Farmington, and boxcars were unroofed on a moving train at Bountiful. In addition, many roofs were damaged, dozens of chimneys and hundreds of windows were broken, scores of advertising signs were damaged, and a few automobiles were overturned.

APRIL 23

1905 - In Ogden an "unusually severe" mountain wind did considerable damage to fruit trees, blew roofs off several large warehouses, and leveled many smaller buildings.

1958 - A localized storm dumped up to 18" of snow in the Salt Lake City area. Approximately 50 traffic accidents were reported due to poor visibility and slick streets.

APRIL 24

1899 - A dust storm passed over the northern half of the state. The wind had been southerly , but changed to northwest by mid-afternoon. This change brought a cloud of dust which enveloped everything.

1984 - Provo BYU reported a wind gust of 84 mph. The winds howled throughout the day as a cold front pushed into Utah. Other wind gusts reported: University of Utah 78 mph, West Valley City 68 mph, Orem 61 mph, and St. George 50 mph.

APRIL 25

1976 - A strong cold front intensified rapidly as it crossed over the Great Salt Lake. Peak wind gusts of nearly 90 mph were reported near the lake. Other wind gusts included: Salt Lake City 78 mph, Dugway 69 mph, and University of Utah 68 mph. As the winds blew, waves on the Great Salt Lake reached heights of 15 feet. Many boats were damaged during a sailing meet, and storm damage reached $450,000.

APRIL 25-29

1952 - A record snowpack followed by five days of temperatures more than 10°F above normal, sent water cascading down Utah's north central streams, causing widespread flooding. Floods from the Jordan River covered about 50 blocks of Salt Lake City's west side under six feet of water forcing nearly 400 families to evacuate their homes. In Ogden, two lives were lost due to flooding. Large areas of farm and pasture land west of Provo were inundated, with most residents from Provo Canyon forced to leave because of high water. Damage figures soared to $10,000,000.

APRIL 25-26

1975 - A late winter-like storm moved through Utah. South winds preceding the storm contributed to the death of four people who drowned when the high winds capsized their boat at Lake Powell. Heavy snow stranded many large trucks and campers between Salt Lake City and Wendover. Salt Lake City received 8.5" of snow from the storm.

1991 - A strong, wet weather system pounded northern Utah with a lot of snow. Thirty-seven inches of snow fell at Snowbird Ski Resort and 12" at Olympus Cove.

APRIL 26

1966 - Gale force winds ripped through Lehi (Utah County) toppling trees and demolishing buildings.

1986 - Very cold air behind a major spring storm combined forces with the Great Salt Lake and produced the "Dreaded Lake Effect." Snowfall totals included: Olympus Cove 12", Sugarhouse/ Holladay 9", and Bountiful 7". The storm also brought six inches of snow to several valley locations and a storm total of 44" at Snowbird and 42" at Alta.

APRIL 27

1966 - Winds gusting to 60 mph damaged shingles, awnings, and trees in Roosevelt (Duchesne County).

1970 - A major snowstorm preceded by strong winds swept across southern Utah. High winds pushed a car into a steel and concrete abutment north of St. George, killing the driver and seriously injuring the passenger. The snowstorm, one of the worst ever to occur so late in the spring, left

motorists stranded and caused many minor accidents.

1991 - Snow fell at the rate of two inches per hour across some valley locations of northern Utah. Bountiful received 12" of snow, Holladay and Kearns 7", Salt Lake Airport 6", and Tooele 5". Snowbird Ski resort was plastered with 24" of the white stuff.

APRIL 28

1973 - A pilot flying from Salt Lake City to Rock Springs reported areas of hailstones the size of golf balls between Salt Lake City and Wolf Creek Pass.

APRIL 29

1987 - A record high temperature of 83°F was recorded at Provo BYU.

APRIL 30

1946 - Very high winds removed a shop from its foundation in Trenton in the Cache Valley.

1983 - In Box Elder County, the community of Collinston received 2.00 inches of precipitation in 24-hours.

APRIL 30 - MAY 1

1988 - A major storm produced winter weather conditions across much of Utah. Cold air pouring in behind the storm kicked in the "Dreaded Lake Effect" at Tooele with 13" of snow and 2.13" water reported for the storm. In the southwest part of Utah, Meadow received 11" of snow while Fillmore picked up 6". Ahead of the storm, winds gusted to 68 mph at Cedar City.

MAY 1

1946 - Utah experienced its worst freeze in 30 years with valley temperatures dropping to -20°F.

1964 - A heavy, wet snow caused power failures throughout northern Utah. More than 14" of snow fell on Salt Lake City's east bench. Two Boy Scout troops stranded on an overnight camp near Mueller Park were rescued by jeep posses.

1995 - Severe thunderstorms moved through parts of Tooele and Utah Counties in northern Utah. Hailstones ¾" in diameter were reported at Rush Valley, Pleasant Grove, and Orem. In addition, a wind gust to 81 mph was recorded at Orem and 60 mph at Pleasant Grove.

MAY 1-9

1986 - Heavy snow continued to fall as Alta Ski Resort recorded a phenomenal 69.7" of snow during the period.

MAY 2

1985 - A peak wind gust of 72 mph was reported at Ogden. Winds in the Riverdale area west of Ogden destroyed a barn and blew a roof off the Southern Pacific Depot.

MAY 2-3

1991 - A cold front made its way across the state producing heavy precipitation falling in northern Utah and howling winds across southern Utah. Some of the precipitation amounts included: Washington Terrace

2.00", Ogden and Centerville 1.77", Collinston 1.22", and North Salt Lake 1.21". Wind gusts in the south reached 58 mph at Blanding.

MAY 3

1993 - Strong microburst winds occurred as a squall line and cold front moved through the state. Some of the higher wind gusts were: Stansbury Park 69 mph, Eagle Range 64 mph, Hill AFB and Kearns 62 mph, and Randolph 52 mph.

MAY 3-7

1993 - A very wet five-day period across all of Utah. Alta Ski Resort picked up a whopping 54" of snow and 6.48" of total precipitation. Other amounts of water from around the state included: Liberty 5.05", Olympus Cove 4.42", Bountiful 4.26", Sandy 4.02", West Valley 3.76", Payson 3.35", Peoa 2.88", Midway 2.86", Salt Lake City International Airport 2.77", Ogden 2.58", Provo BYU 2.52", Coalville 2.16", Logan KVNU 1.99", Monticello 1.06", and Milford 1.00".

MAY 4

1993 - Strong winds lashed Delta with a peak wind gust of 74 mph.

MAY 4-5

1984 - Corn Creek Dam gave way in Kanosh, flooding 9 homes.

MAY 4-9

1986 - Two powerful cold fronts lashed out across the state raising flooding fears. Precipitation totals reached 4.00" in the valleys. The heaviest hit areas with precipitation were from Weber County south into Utah County. Even areas of southern Utah picked up over 1.00" of precipitation.

MAY 5

1992 - The monsoon season started early with thundershowers in southern Utah. Lightning caused a rather extensive power outage in St. George for about two hours. Some of the rainfall amounts were: two miles east of Virgin had .60" in 10 minutes and Toquerville .40" in 15 minutes.

MAY 7

1925 - Heavy hail cut a path one mile wide and about 7 miles long, damaging alfalfa and sugar beets, and killing young chickens at Newton (Cache County).

MAY 8

1990 - A wind gust of 80 mph was clocked at Moab in southeast Utah.

1992 - Thunderstorms across central Utah produced pea-size hail to a depth of 3-4" in the Scofield area (where they even had to call out snowplows). Moroni logged .82" of precipitation.

MAY 9

1968 - Winds up to 82 mph at Wendover caused losses in excess of $127,000. The winds destroyed six trailer houses, damaged the Wendover Air Force Base, took the roof off the Western Hotel, and destroyed state highway sheds.

1985 - The marina at the Saltair resort along the southern shores of the Great Salt Lake took a blow as high winds damaged the facility and nearby boats.

1990 - A "disastrous" morning for fruit growing areas across northern Utah. Some of the colder temperatures were: Logan, Coalville and Midway 18°F, River Heights and South Jordan 24°F, Santaquin 26°F, and Murray 28°F.

MAY 10

1984 - A landslide at Salina (Sevier County) destroyed $750,000 worth of Utah Power and Light transmitters.

1985 - Heavy rain caused considerable flooding in the downtown area of Provo. Damage to businesses climbed to several thousand dollars.

1986 - Cache County reported strong winds, with Trenton receiving a gust of 67 mph.

MAY 10-11

1957 - Hail and thunderstorms killed 6,000 turkeys and badly damaged alfalfa and fruit crops in Juab County. The violent weather was also blamed for two traffic fatalities in Duchesne County.

MAY 11

1983 - A vigorous spring storm dumped heavy, wet snow on many areas of Utah. Over 6" of snow fell in many areas in the Salt Lake Valley. Salt Lake City International Airport received 1.44" of precipitation from the storm.

MAY 12

1902 - A hailstorm pounded Grover (Wayne County), stripping leaves off trees and in some cases cutting down alfalfa close to the ground that was eight inches high. Many of the hailstones were 7/8" in diameter.

1995 - Cold air behind a late season snow storm produced 4-5" of snow at Tooele and 1-3" from Davis County south to Utah County.

MAY 12-13

1984 - Flooding: a mudslide almost 400 yards wide was created by an overflowing Spring Creek at Nordic Valley Ski area. High water and a mudslide in Chicken Creek closed I-15 between Levan and Nephi. Mudslides occurred at the top of several Wasatch Front canyons including Settlement Canyon, Farmington's Rudd Canyon, Provo Canyon, and Fairview Canyon. One man was killed and another injured from debris flow at Clear Creek in Carbon County. In Salt Lake City, Liberty Park was sandbagged for flood control.

MAY 13

1992 - Thunderstorms erupted across northern Utah with the Uinta Basin getting hit the hardest. Lapoint, west of Vernal (Uintah County), measured .80" of precipitation in 20 minutes, and in Dagget County, Manila reported ¼" diameter hail.

MAY 13-14

1955 - Winds up to 80 mph blew over northwest Utah, causing widespread dust clouds. In some areas, highway traffic was reduced or suspended because of low visibility and blowing dust. In a few places, high winds blew down power lines and damaged buildings. A girl was injured by flying debris from a barn that was blown over at Eureka (Juab County), and a man was hurt when an airplane door was blown shut on his head.

MAY 14

1961 - A lightning-caused fire extensively damaged 19 motel rooms, two apartment units, and a garage on the summit of Parley's Canyon.

1976 - Winds up to 81 mph in central Utah lifted the roof off a Spanish Fork apartment house. In Cedar Valley, two cars were damaged when winds blew sprinkler pipes against them.

1978 - Winds gusting over 80 mph toppled 16 cars of the Western Pacific Railroad near Wendover. Damage figures reached $200,000.

1984 - A mudslide sent tons of mud down Middle Fork Canyon in Tooele County killing a man and burying his bulldozer. Six homes in Layton were engulfed by raging waters out of Kays Creek. Several blocks of Provo's 3rd South was turned into a canal. The Ogden River flooded its banks and washed into 10 summer homes. Bridges were washed out in three areas around the state, and slides occurred in Springville Canyon, Huntington Canyon, Bridge Canyon, and Emery County.

MAY 15

1993 - Thunderstorm activity became widespread across much of Utah. Three inches of hail were deposited at Monticello and Eastland in southeast Utah (San Juan County) and .80" of water fell in 30 minutes at Fremont Indian State Park.

1995 - Lightning struck a Cottonwood tree at Goshen (Utah County) setting fire to and destroying a 75 year old cabin in a remote canyon.

MAY 16

1952 - Strong canyon winds along the western slopes of the Wasatch Mountains caused $1,000,000 damage to property between Brigham City and Salt Lake City.

1993 - A weather observer five miles northwest of Kanab in extreme southwest Utah reported .75" of precipitation in just five minutes with a lot of hail. In fact the observer visited the area the next day and there was still ¼" diameter hailstones two feet deep in some places.

MAY 17

1949 - Heavy, intense rainfall fell in the vicinity of Ben Lomond Peak in the Wasatch Mountains resulting in a flash flood. The high rate of rainfall on a very precipitous bedrock drainage caused immediate runoff, sending water and debris across U.S. Highway 91 between Willard and Liberty in Box Elder County. Floodwaters cut 10-20 foot deep gullies in fields and orchards.

1993 - Heavy rain and hail hit portions of Carbon County in east-central Utah. Wellington picked up 1.88" of precipitation and hailstones. Hailstones ¼"-½" in diameter were common in Carbon City. Zion National Park also received .70" of precipitation in 30 minutes.

MAY 17-18

1987 - Heavy thunderstorms produced 2.10" of rain at Centerville in 3½ hours. Rainfall amounts ranging between one and two inches were common across northern Utah.

MAY 18

1991 - Strong winds kicked up across eastern and southern Utah. Some of the wind gusts reported were: Vernal 67 mph, and Monticello and Delta 60 mph. In addition, a roof was blown off a mobile home in Monticello.

MAY 18-19

1983 - Heavy rains of over an inch caused some urban and small stream flooding in areas of Cache County.

MAY 19

1957 - Strong winds in Weber County flattened a barn, blew the roof off a house, toppled trees, and blew down utility poles.

MAY 20

1951 - The central Utah town of Delta became a "delta of debris" as heavy rain washed out trees, sent boulders roaring down the streets, and poured a wall of mud and water six feet high over a highway for several hours.

1975 - A record-breaking snowstorm hit many areas of Utah, bringing 22" to Manila (Daggett County), 21" to Fillmore (Millard County), and 20" to Delta (Millard County). In Sevier County thousands of turkeys were frozen in the unusual storm. In Utah County, 25 power poles were downed in Payson with major power outages reported in the area.

MAY 21

1986 - Strong northwest winds reached hurricane force behind a vigorous cold front. Some reports of high winds included: Lakeside (Box Elder County) 86 mph, Orem 80 mph, West Kearns 71 mph, and South Salt Lake 70 mph. Winds blowing across the Great Salt Lake inundated I-80 with several inches of water.

MAY 22

1995 - Severe thunderstorms pelted portions of Box Elder County in northwest Utah. Penrose, northwest of Brigham City, received 1.30" of rain in just 30 minutes. Hailstones up to one inch in diameter were observed at both Penrose and Thiokol. One report indicated that hail piled-up to six inches deep on one of the roadways in the Thiokol test area.

MAY 23

1947 - A severe hailstorm hit Blanding, producing large hailstones measuring 1½" to 2" in diameter. Considerable damage was done to roofs during this brief but intense hailstorm. Many farmers reported that as much as 50% of their fruit crop was destroyed.

1957 - Hail covered the ground four to five inches deep in Ogden. The heavy rain and hail in Weber and Davis Counties caused some flooding to canyon homes.

1970 - Severe thunderstorms with estimated winds of 100 mph swept through Salt Lake, Davis, and Weber counties, dropping ¾" diameter hailstones in Woods Cross and southern Bountiful. Thirty-five people were injured. three single-engine airplanes were overturned, several 44,000-volt power lines were downed, six towers were destroyed, and 125 houses were heavily damaged. Losses totaled almost $1,500,000.

1983 - The "Floods of '83" began in earnest. Flooding closed a highway from Nibley to Millville in Cache County. In Sanpete County, a landslide in Twelve-Mile Canyon closed the canyon road south of Manti and caused flash flooding in the Pinchot Campground.

MAY 25

1961 - A strong whirlwind in Salt Lake City lifted a woman and carried her 30 feet. She had no significant injury.

1975 - Minimum temperatures ranged from 26°F to 32°F along the Wasatch Front. The apricot crop was virtually wiped out, but only minimal damage to other fruits was reported.

1992 - Memorial Day saw hail and heavy rains hit parts of southern Utah. Particularly hard hit were San Juan, Wayne, and Washington Counties. Hail up to one inch in diameter struck the Enterprise, Bicknell and Teasdale area during intense thunderstorms. Heavy rains included Torrey and Bicknell with 1.25", and Teasdale with 1.10". Hail up to 4" deep was noted in the Tropic Reservoir area just west of Bryce Canyon.

MAY 26

1924 - An unusually strong hailstorm lasted about 45 minutes at La Sal (San Juan County) and uprooted large trees, broke windows, and beat down alfalfa and garden crops.

1977 - Winds clocked to 65 mph caused major damage at the Flaming Gorge marina, and tossed boats out of the water at the Cedar Springs marina. Several 30-foot boats were washed ashore, and one sank.

1983 - 13th South Street in Salt Lake City officially went from a street to a river to contain spring runoff.

1992 - It was a severe weather day over most of Utah with widespread hail, strong winds, and heavy rains. Golf ball size hailstones fell in southwest Utah between Richfield and Glenwood. Minor flooding was noted in the Salt Lake Valley, Price, portions of Sevier County, and at Jensen east of Vernal. Funnel clouds were spotted in Sandy and Roosevelt. Some rainfall intensities were: two miles west of Price .79" in 18 minutes, Midvale .70"in 20 minutes, and Manti .50" in 15 minutes.

1994 - Thunderstorms produced strong microburst winds to 73 mph at Provo BYU.

1995 - Strong thunderstorms produced ½" diameter hail at Kanab and .50" of rain in 10 minutes at Delta.

MAY 27

1975 - A cloudburst swept through St. George, dropping 1.00" of rain in 15 minutes. This is more than St. George normally gets in all of May and June combined.

1986 - Easterly canyon winds reached 69 mph at Farmington.

1987 - Thunderstorms hit northern Utah, producing 1.83" of rain at Tremonton.

1993 - Localized heavy rains fell in eastern Utah with 1.05" of precipitation recorded at Castle Valley. The Castle Valley storm dropped .50" in 10 minutes and another .50" in 7 minutes.

1994 - Widespread severe weather hit northern Utah. Some of the higher wind reports were: I-80 Tooele exit 75 mph, Bountiful 72 mph, Randolph and Tooele 65 mph, Provo BYU 64 mph, and Springville 60 mph. A Cessna 140 airplane was flipped over at Salt Lake Airport II. At Herriman, a wheelbarrow containing 30-40 pounds of "stuff" was tossed 30 feet. In addition, hail up to ½" in diameter fell at South Jordan.

MAY 27-28

1956 - Thundershowers caused some local flooding in cities along the Wasatch Front. The heavy rain overtaxed sewers, damaged some orchards, tomato fields, alfalfa and grains, produced hail in Davis and Weber Counties, and caused interruptions of power transmission and communication services. A funnel cloud approached the ground in the Ogden area, but moved eastward and dissipated over the mountains.

MAY 28

1918 - The worst hailstorm in many years occurred at Brigham City. In addition to leaving hail on the ground, the storm left a ground cover of fallen cherries, apricots, peaches, and strawberries. Damage was near $15,000.

1977 - A funnel cloud was seen passing west of Brigham City. The storm caused hail and high winds but no damage.

1979 - A strong thunderstorm associated with a cold front cut a destructive path of hail and strong winds across Weber County in northern Utah. At Plain City, Pleasant View, and north Ogden, fruit, alfalfa, and wheat damage approached $250,000.

1983 - Flooding: Water from City Creek Canyon just north of Salt Lake City rushed into downtown Salt Lake. A mudslide above Salt Lake City in Emigration Canyon forced evacuation of several homes near Pinecrest. Centerville homes were damaged as Barnard and Ricks creeks flooded. In Bountiful, Barton Creek overflowed and washed out Lakeview Drive, snapping a sewer line and flooding nearby homes and businesses. In Tooele County, a two year-old boy fell into Middle Canyon Creek and later died. In Duchesne County, Lake Canyon Bridge washed out.

1989 - Strong southerly winds ahead of a cold front gusted to a record 69 mph at Salt Lake City, the highest ever recorded during the month of May.

MAY 29

1918 - Hail piled up to a depth of 3" during a severe thunderstorm at Morgan in northern Utah.

1983 - Flooding: Water spilled over East Canyon Dam spillway in Morgan County causing widespread flooding. High water washed out a road from Logan to Mendon as well as roads east of Richmond in Cache County. A slide caused closure of U.S. Highway 89 from Willard Bay to Perry in Box Elder County. All Tooele County canyons were closed.

MAY 29-30

1896 - Excessive rains flooded Salt Lake. Low areas in the west side of the Salt Lake Valley resembled large lakes, and rafts were needed to cross in some places.

MAY 30

1939 - A cloudburst up Spanish Fork Canyon caused considerable damage to homes in Thistle. In some areas east of Thistle, mudslides left mud and debris five feet deep on the highway.

1983 - Flooding: A mudslide moved into Farmington, destroying six homes and damaging 25 other homes, leaving some 200 people homeless. Moving earth over the weekend broke water lines at Fairview in central Utah, followed by a slide in Fairview Canyon, forcing residents to evacuate. Sandbaggers transformed North Temple Street and Walker and Cottonwood Lanes into sandbag-lined rivers, Salt Lake was cut east to west by a five-foot deep river down 13th South Street, and north to south by a State Street stream stretching from City Creek to 5th South. Nearly 40 families became stranded at Covered Bridge in Utah County when the bridge to town was declared unsafe. Highways were closed in Grand County. Runoff contaminated Vernal drinking water.

1989 - During the afternoon, lightning struck a house in Salt Lake City, going around the aluminum siding, knocking the telephone and microwave oven out, and hit the owner on the "butt."

MAY 30-31

1991 - Tremendous rainfall fell across Millard County in southwest Utah. In about a 24-30 hour period Garrison received a fantastic 4.00" of water. Other reports included: Eskdale with 3.64" and The Border Inn on U.S. Highway 50/6 with 2.28" of precipitation.

MAY 31

1984 - Heavy thunderstorms with pea-sized hail hit the Wasatch Front. Flash flooding occurred along the Logan River as already swollen waters received brief but heavy rains. The Cottonwood creeks were already full to capacity prior to the thunderstorms, which caused flooding at Cottonwood Trailer Park.

1994 - Severe weather blasted many areas of northwest and west central Utah. Thunderstorms embedded with damaging microburst winds, marble size hail, and heavy rains raised havoc. The Provo area was particularly hard hit with a recorded wind gusts of over 100 mph on the BYU Campus. Provo City activated the Emergency Operating Center for Utah County due to the severity of the storm. Damage throughout Provo was incredible with hundreds of large trees uprooted and many buildings reported significant damage. Total damage from the storm was around 8 million dollars. Other wind gusts reported from the thunderstorms included: Delta and Great Salt Lake State Park 81 mph, Little Cottonwood Canyon 73 mph, Magna 66 mph, Salt Lake City International Airport 62 mph, and South Jordan 60 mph. In addition, Dugway, picked up 1.24" of rain in a short time.

JUNE 1

1943 - Severe thunderstorms dropped 2.09" of rain on the town of Ephraim (Sanpete County), causing ditches to overflow into residential areas. The Sanpitch River was the highest it had been in many years.

1983 - Flooding: A 30-foot wall of water rushed out of Bountiful's Stone Creek, destroying three homes and damaging seven others, injuring seven people and forcing scores of families to flee. Nearly 60 families around Farmington's Steed Creek were evacuated and over two dozen families in Fruit Heights (Davis County) were evacuated. Also, water from Chalk Creek ran through a sandbag channel down Main Street in Coalville, forcing several families to evacuate.

1990 - Winter in June across much of Utah. A cold storm brought blizzard conditions, even to many valley floors, and caused the closing of State Route 191 north of Vernal for a time. Snowfall totals included: Meadow 8", Fillmore and Kanosh 4", Payson 3-5", Garrison 3", Vernal 2", and Milford, Beaver, Woodruff, and Holden 1" of snow.

JUNE 2

1983 - Heavy thunderstorms produced nearly 1.00" of rain in one hour at Bountiful, causing urban flooding.

1984 - Violent winds swept through Provo, picking up debris that damaged cars. A peak gust of 71 mph was recorded.

1993 - A wild cold front laced with severe thunderstorms took a direct hit on Davis County in northwest Utah. The hail ranged from ¼" to 1" in diameter. Along I-15 and in some locations of Bountiful the hail was 3-4" deep, and in one area of Woods Cross it was up to 6" deep. A tornado touched down in North Salt Lake, causing $15,000 in damage and injuring several boys who were playing baseball. High intensity rainfall reports included Castle Rock .62" in 10 minutes and Magna .40" in 10 minutes. High wind gusts included Dugway 84 mph and West Bountiful 74 mph.

JUNE 3

1963 - Salt Lake City Airport recorded a peak wind gust of 94 mph, the strongest gust ever recorded in Salt Lake City. The winds forced evacuation of the control tower at the Salt Lake City Airport and caused $45,000 in damage to hangars and airplanes.

1995 - Centerville received .79" of rain in 10 minutes .

JUNE 4

1872 - A heavy cloudburst filled a few St. George cellars with "water in place of wine." At the time, St. George had been striving to grow grapes.

1945 - A heavy rainstorm in Tooele dumped a record .95" of rain in only a few minutes time, causing torrents of water to sweep down streets and flood lower levels of buildings.

JUNE 5

1967 - The "worst flood in 20 years" hit Moab. Within 20 minutes the storm had produced such heavy rain that downtown streets became "raging muddy rivers." After the storm, curb-high sand deposits were left, residential streets were filled with rocks and debris, one apartment building was flooded, and sections of city yards were piled with sand.

1995 - A vicious, damaging wind storm moved through northern and western Utah during the late afternoon and evening hours. A strong cold front intensified as it moved into Utah, producing hurricane force winds behind the front. Some of the higher reported wind gusts were: Tremonton 95 mph, Highland and American Fork 90 mph, Pleasant Grove 88 mph, North Orem 86 mph, West Kearns 84 mph, Magna and Deweyville 75 mph, Provo BYU 72 mph, West Valley City 70 mph, Dugway 69 mph, South Jordan 66 mph, and Grantsville 63 mph. According to data received from the Western Insurance Information Service, damage estimates totaled 15 million dollars!

JUNE 6

1958 - A violent thunderstorm with marble-sized hail and 50 mph winds caused $75,000 in damage to fruit trees, berries, and crops in Pleasant Grove (Utah County). The frenzied storm lasted only about 15 minutes.

1986 - The Great Salt Lake peaked at 4211.85 feet above sea-level, the highest measured lake level in the past 139 years. Since 1963, the Great Salt Lake had risen 20 feet (12 feet in less than 4 years), more than doubled in aerial extent, and increased its volume nearly three-fold.

1995 - Snow fell as low as the 4,800 foot level along the Wasatch Front during the morning hours. Snowfall amounts ranged from a skiff to 1" along the bench areas of Salt Lake, in Tooele, and the Cache Valley.

JUNE 7

1960 - Hail killed 320 turkeys in Nephi. The storm also damaged crops and deposited 0.75" of rain/hail in 45 minutes.

1974 - A 60 mph whirlwind several blocks long and 75 yards wide struck a boat marina in the Salt Lake Valley and damaged a sign, roof, and small boat.

1985 - The thermometer hit 100°F—the earliest date for such a hot temperature recorded in Salt Lake City.

JUNE 8

1944 - Strong winds blew down trees and knocked out window lights at Richmond in Cache County.

1974 - Winds gusting to 92 mph occurred near Ivins (Washington County). The winds toppled outhouses, campers, and travel-trailers. One mobile home was torn apart and spread across five acres.

JUNE 9

1939 - At Brigham City, a peculiar hailstorm from the east left "a plainly visible white swath of hail one mile wide and four to five inches deep on the mountainside." Slight crop damage occurred in the valley from the second hailstorm in four days.

1958 - In what was claimed by older residents as the "most violent and damaging storm ever experienced in Pleasant Grove," almost 2/3 of an inch of water fell in 15 minutes, flooding basements, kitchens, and living rooms where windows or doors had been left open.

JUNE 10

1969 - Elmo and Cleveland (Emery County) were hit by a cloudburst that damaged three bridges and several miles of road.

JUNE 11

1965 - Rain on a heavy snowpack resulted in serious flooding in Daggett Counties' Uinta Mountains. Shortly after midnight, a flash flood in Sheep Creek Canyon near Flaming Gorge drowned a father, mother, three children, and two nephews who were staying at Palisade Campground. The flood completely destroyed five miles of newly paved highway, three recreation areas, and seven bridges. Damages were estimated at over $1,000,000.

1992 - Thunderstorms over southeast Utah produced a 68 mph microburst at the Canyonlands Airport west of Moab.

JUNE 12

1967 - Heavy rain and hail in northwest Salt Lake City flooded several areas. Boys floated down the flooded streets in boats.

1986 - West Point and Clinton (Box Elder County) received very strong thunderstorm downdrafts. The winds downed utility lines and tossed a roof end over end. In Davis County, 15 homes were damaged by wind.

JUNE 13

1854 - A destructive hailstorm rumbled through the Salt Lake City area with "hailstones as large as turkey eggs." The ensuing raging waters from the thunderstorm drowned a little boy.

JUNE 14

1973 - A 14 year-old Springville boy was sitting on a chicken coop when it was picked up by a dust-devil, turned around, and set askew on its foundation. The wind also knocked over 50 feet of brick wall, ripped off several awnings, and knocked a large tree onto a new automobile.

JUNE 14-15

1992 - Snow was reported down to about the 7,000 foot level with 9" of the white stuff falling on Mt. Timpanogos, 7" at Alta, 5" on top of the Mirror Lake Highway, and 3-4" on the Alpine Loop.

JUNE 15

1943 - The second hailstorm in two weeks in Box Elder, Davis, and Weber Counties did considerable monetary damage: fruit $250,000, hay $100,000, and turkeys $25,000.

1967 - Marble-sized hail fell for five minutes, ruining gardens and shelling fruit trees and shrubbery in Morgan.

1989 - Evening microburst winds struck West Kearns (Salt Lake County) with a gust to 78 mph.

JUNE 16

1929 - High winds between Salt Lake City and Ogden broke or uprooted many trees, overturned a great many barns and outbuildings, demolished 30 buildings at the arsenal near Ogden, and damaged property totaling more than $1,000,000.

1988 - Microburst winds produced a peak gust of 67 mph at Delta.

1993 - Strong winds accompanying an area of low pressure gusted to 81 mph at Wendover with a wall of dust observed in the west desert during the afternoon. In addition, a complex of thunderstorms became active in the Book Cliffs of northeast Utah and drifted over Vernal. Randlett received .66" of rain in about seven minutes and Vernal received .85" in 15 minutes.

JUNE 17

1969 - Unseasonably wet weather caused flooding throughout the Salt Lake Valley. Downtown Salt Lake City was hit the hardest by the rain. Streets were turned into rivers, with water covering automobile tires at the intersections. During a two-hour period, 1.50" of rain fell.

1995 - Heavy rainfall struck portions of southeast Utah late on 16th until about 8 AM on the 17th. A weather observer in Monticello reported 2.17" of rainfall. Rainfall was also heavy in the Arches area with 1.11" falling. In fact, .64" of rain fell in 10 minutes at Arches and .70" of rain fell in just seven minutes at Bridgeland. Also, Alta received 2" of snow.

JUNE 18

1972 - A large dust-devil in Bountiful tore part of the roof off a house under construction, and broke several glass windows in the immediate area.

JUNE 19

1918 - A heavy cloudburst in Mt. Pleasant (Sanpete County) produced a river of mud and water several feet deep, carrying large rocks, trees, dead cattle, and furniture across streets, lawns, and farms. Some houses were filled to the window sills with mud. One man lost his life in attempting to cross the flood.

The total loss in crops, buildings, city waterworks, and electric light plant and dam approached $100,000.

1984 - Central Salt Lake Valley experienced strong gusty winds. Cottonwood and Murray reported wind gusts to 65 mph, while Sandy reported a gust to 60 mph.

JUNE 20

1977 - A lightning bolt struck a home in Cornish (Cache County), downing a wire that started the attic on fire. The house was badly damaged.

1982 - Localized flash flooding occurred in southwest Sevier County. Basements were flooded in the town of Joseph as 1.00" of rain fell in 1 hour. Hail ½" in diameter stacked up 4" deep against buildings.

1993 - Lightning struck a motor home on I-15 about 10 miles south of Beaver. The lightning made a direct hit on the motor home's CB antenna, melting it and damaging the roof. The driver's side front tire was set on fire and destroyed and all tires were flattened. Luckily, no injuries occurred. In addition, winds gusted to 77 mph at Virgin in southwest Utah.

JUNE 21

1948 - Salt Lake City recorded its heaviest 24-hour rainfall ever for the month of June, with 1.75" of rain.

1989 - A frosty first day of summer across northern Utah. The coldest morning spots were: Randolph 25°F, Logan (Historic Farm) and Wellsville 27°F, and Providence and Garden City 28°F.

JUNE 22

1973 - A squall line with gusty winds tipped over two aircraft and stripped the roof off several hangars at the Wendover Airport.

1988 - Hanksville tied for the hottest June day on record with a scorching 110°F.

JUNE 22-23

1918 - Moab (Grand County) and Vernon (Tooele County) were the targets of some violent thunderstorms. In Moab, a flooded creek washed away several small dams and damaged the electric light plant. In Vernon, windows were broken and about 2,000 acres of crops were beaten down.

JUNE 23

1983 - Billions of gallons of water broke through the DMAD Dam northeast of Delta and spread across low laying lands and roads and flooded the towns of Deseret and Oasis with several feet of water. The spillway of the earthen DMAD Dam was destroyed by heavy rains and rapid spring runoff.

1985 - South winds gusted to 52 mph at Provo, blowing off roofing material and damaging cars in the Provo area.

JUNE 24

1952 - A brief but severe hailstorm, lasting about 10 minutes, occurred near Kanosh (Millard County), causing heavy damage to gardens, fruits, and some fields.

1988 - A sizzling 98°F at Logan USU tied for the hottest June day ever.

1989 - Snow fell in the Uinta Mountains, with 2-4" falling near the 10,000 foot level.

JUNE 25

1988 - Loa reported an incredible .92" of rain in 10 minutes along with ¼" diameter hail.

JUNE 25-26

1985- Unseasonably cold weather and thunderstorms moved into Utah. Golf ball-sized hail was reported across areas of northern Utah. One of several funnel clouds came within 100 feet of touching the ground on the east shore of the Great Salt Lake. A peak wind gust of 76 mph occurred in Springville (Utah County). Heavy rainfall amounts were common, with many reporting stations receiving well over 1.00" of rain. Cool morning temperatures were observed on the morning of the 26th. Bryce Canyon reported a low temperature of 23°F.

JUNE 26

1948 - A severe thunderstorm struck near Salem (Utah County), leaving behind hailstones that covered the ground one inch deep. Damage to fruits and other crops totaled $250,000.

1965 - Lightning falsely triggered fire alarms at two Provo public schools when it came close to the sensitive attic detecting devices, without actually hitting the buildings.

JUNE 27

1927 - "Families were driven to mountainside(s) to escape flood(s)" in the central Utah areas of Castle Gate and Kenilwoth (Carbon County). More than 100 feet of highway was swept away. At Price, 2.65" of rain fell in 24-hours, flooding basements, destroying crops, and flooding farmhouses with several feet of mud and water.

1970 - Winds of 80 mph began near Milford and moved into northwest Utah, damaging much of the area. Roofs were ripped off several houses, with one landing on top of a moving car in Provo, injuring the driver. Flying bricks and tree limbs broke windows in many areas. Blowing dust near Mills Junction caused a five car pile-up, injuring 12 people.

1995 - Showers and thunderstorms produced 1.00" of rain in 20 minutes at the Wendover Port-of-Entry, and .49" fell in 13 minutes west of Price along with ½" diameter hail.

JUNE 28

1892 - St. George recorded a sizzling temperature of 116°F. Until 1985, this temperature was the hottest ever reported in the state.

1962 - Flash flooding was the order of the day for the southwest town of Orderville (Kane County). A flood from the north and one from the south sent substantial amounts of water into stores, swimming pools, and basements.

1988 - Heavy thundershowers produced .52" of rain in 10 minutes at Cedar City in southwest Utah. Also, 50" in 10 minutes at Fayette, and .68" in 10 minutes at Henrieville.

JUNE 29

1910 - The worst rain and hailstorm in 32 years hit the central Utah town of Orangeville (Emery County). In some places hailstones accumulated four-feet deep. Bridges and roads were destroyed, livestock were killed, and cellars flooded.

1987 - A thunderstorm produced 1.50" of rain in 15 minutes at Ogden, flooding basements. In addition, 177 cloud-to-ground lightning strikes were detected in a one-hour period in Tooele County.

1995 - Severe thunderstorms deposited 1" diameter hail at Enterprise, cracking windshields.

JUNE 30

1968 - Winds at Roosevelt in eastern Utah exceeded 57 mph and caused damage to houses and power lines. The gusts also collapsed a hangar wall at the Roosevelt Municipal Airport and carried a steel granary over ¼ of a mile.

1984 - Hail fell at many sections across Utah. Hail ¾" in diameter put dents in cars and trucks in Duchesne. American Fork (Utah County) received marble-sized hail, and hail 4" deep piled up in the Cove Fort area (Millard County).

JULY 1

1968 - A cold morning for mid-summer across the state. In fact, Salt Lake City experienced its coldest July morning ever with a low of 40°F.

1990 - Thunderstorms produced strong microburst winds to 71 mph at Provo BYU and 61 mph at West Kearns.

JULY 2

1977 - A sudden windstorm generated high waves on Utah Lake, disabling three boats and necessitating the rescue of two people who had drifted three miles from where their boats capsized.

1986 - Microburst winds blasted across northern Utah. At Woods Cross, the winds blew a roof off a building.

JULY 2-3

1934 - A cloudburst dumped 2.44" of rain at Milford, causing flooding in the downtown area.

JULY 3

1900 - During a lightning storm, an electrical discharge passed down a chimney in a home in Salt Lake City, knocked the stopper out of the flue, filled the room with soot and gas, and slightly shocked three people in the room.

1924 - Two boys narrowly escaped death when they were caught in a 10-foot deep flash flood in the Vernal area.

1995 - Heavy rain fell across portions of northern Utah. Mountain Green logged .78" of rain in 10 minutes. Elsewhere, both Woodland Hills and American Fork received 1.65" of rain.

JULY 4

1925 - A flash flood in Vernal's Five Mile Creek struck a car containing nine occupants, and swept an eight-year-old boy from the automobile, drowning him instantly.

1986 - A severe thunderstorm pounded areas of Cache County. Wind speeds reached 74 mph in Logan and 70 mph at Hyrum. In addition to the strong winds at Hyrum, 1.00" of rain fell in less than 30 minutes just after the 4th of July parade. In other areas of the Cache Valley, trees were uprooted, car windows were broken, and two roofs were blown off. Hail in some portions of the northern Wasatch Front was intense enough to cause $1,000,000 in damage to the sour cherry crop. Lightning was responsible for setting off some fireworks prematurely at the Cougar Stadium in Provo.

JULY 5

1977 - In Carbon County, 3.00" of rain caused the worst flash flood in 25 years. The flood left a trail of muddy destruction from Helper to Carbon. The Carbon Country Club golf course's fifth tee was under three feet of water.

1985 - The thermometer at St. George reached 117°F—the hottest temperature ever recorded in Utah.

1994 - A vigorous squall line with associated severe weather (damaging winds) roared through the state, fanning wildfires. The emergency 911 phone lines in Salt Lake County were inundated with people thinking their house or a neighbor's house was on fire due to the density of the smoke blown into the Salt Lake Valley from the west desert. Visibilities were reduced to as low as ¾ mile in some areas. Major wind damage was sustained to the Woods Cross area just north of Salt Lake City. Some of the wind gusts reported were: West Bountiful 82 mph, Lewiston 66 mph, Randolph 65 mph, Salt Lake Airport and Kearns 63 mph, and Grantsville and South Jordan 61 mph.

JULY 6

1985 - A lightning bolt in the early evening hours struck a Utah Power and Light generating station in the Magna area, producing a fire ball that could be seen across the Salt Lake Valley. The domino effect put most of Utah's population into total darkness for nearly 5 hours, with some areas not receiving power until the next day.

1989 - Monticello recorded an all-time record high temperature for July of 96°F.

1994 - Utah's governor Mike Leavitt declared a state of emergency for Tooele County due to the severity of the wildfire situation.

JULY 7

1949 - Big Rock Candy Mountain, located northwest of Marysvale in central Utah, was the site of a massive flood of debris. Mud, rocks, and timber covered 400 feet of highway to a depth of three feet. Some boulders on the highway weighed nearly a ton.

1989 - A sizzling day in Moab with an all-time record high temperature recorded of 114°F.

1993 - Microburst winds gusted to 69 mph at Joseph.

JULY 8

1984 - Heavy rain fell across northern Utah. Sandy received 1.10" of rain in 20 minutes with many road washouts, minor mudslides, and downed power lines reported.

1989 - Hanksville recorded their all-time hottest temperature of 114°F.

1991 - Widespread thundershower activity occurred across the state, with .50" of rain falling in just 12 minutes at Heber.

JULY 9

1981 - Hailstones ½" in diameter piled up to a depth of 4" on Frisco Peak northwest of Milford in southwest Utah.

JULY 10

1975 - Lightning hit the KRGO radio station in Salt Lake City, knocking the station off the air and setting its studios on fire. A cloudburst caused flash flooding throughout much of Ogden, with 1" diameter hailstones falling in north Ogden.

1988 - Large thunderstorms produced hurricane force winds to 81 mph at the Bullfrog Marina on Lake Powell during the evening hours. One houseboat was sunk at Halls Crossing and a boat was blown off its trailer.

1991 - An active thundershower day across portions of Utah. Tabiona received 1.75" of rainfall, and Meadow received .50" of rain in 10 minutes.

JULY 11

1899 - A nasty thunderstorm rumbled across Heber. Lightning struck in six different places, burning several sheds and a barn and killing two horses. Nearly 1.00" of rain fell one hour. Also on this date, a localized cloudburst in the mountains east of Manti swept down Manti Canyon, striking the community of Manti. Buildings and other property were damaged.

1948 - Hail pounded areas north of Bothwell (Box Elder County) in extreme northern Utah, resulting in extensive damage to grain, with losses up to 90% in some fields.

1956 - Strong gusty winds blew down trees and damaged power transmission lines throughout the Salt Lake Valley. At Ephraim (Sanpete County), a violent thunderstorm flattened grain fields and killed several hundred turkeys.

JULY 12

1932 - Hail 5" deep fell at Escalante (Garfield County). The hail was ½" in diameter and fell in a one mile wide path, killing chickens and birds, breaking windows, damaging property, and destroying crops. The town was drenched with 3.24" of precipitation in 24 hours.

1984 - An area near Navajo Lake, in the mountains southeast of Cedar City, received a phenomenal 2.00" of rain in one hour.

1985 - Flash flooding near Bothwell (Box Elder County), flooded 14 homes, drowned eight cattle, and washed away cemetery head stones. Evening thunderstorm winds up to 71 mph raced through Utah County, toppling trees, billboards, and power lines.

1989 - Lightning detection equipment recorded 3,352 cloud-to-ground lightning strikes across the northwest corner of Utah between 3:15 PM and 10:45 PM. This was only a fraction of the total amount of lightning on this day as much of it was cloud-to-cloud.

1992 - A new state one-hour rainfall record was established at Sugarhouse in Salt Lake County. During this period, 2.45" of water was measured.

JULY 12-13

1962 - Heavy rainfall at Salt Lake City set intensity records with .50" of rain falling in 5 minutes, .92" in 10 minutes, 1.26" in 15 minutes, 1.79" in 30 minutes, and 1.94" in 1 hour.

1932 - A devastating hailstorm struck Box Elder County and northern Cache County. The cities of Park Valley, Tremonton, Clarkston, and Richmond were hardest hit by hailstones commonly 1½" in diameter.

JULY 13

1975 - Cloudburst rains over Thompson Creek sent huge rocks along with mud, silt, and other debris into the community of Annabella. Nearly 15,000 turkeys were killed as floodwaters roared from Cove Mountain into the brooding crops in Annabella.

JULY 14

1896 - Torrential rain lasting one hour flooded Eureka (Juab County), drowning two people and causing one to die of heart failure. Rails and railroad bridges were also torn up.

1953 - Very heavy rains near Cedar City resulted in massive flooding in nearby canyon areas. Huge boulders and rocks were brought down by the floods, carrying red clay onto the farms in Cedar Valley.

1964 - "Every street in Panguitch (Garfield County) was a running river from curb to curb" as the southern Utah city was hit by a cloudburst that deposited 1.85" of rain in 90 minutes.

JULY 15

1943 - A severe wind and rain storm near American Fork (Utah County) killed 10,000 turkeys valued at about $3.00 each. Also, trees were uprooted and homes and other buildings were damaged.

JULY 16

1975 - An electrical storm struck the Coalville area in northern Utah, and lightning split a tall tree to the base, killing a ram that was near the tree.

1986 - Lightning struck a house in the Holladay area in the Salt Lake Valley, causing a fire that resulted in $1,000,000 in damage to the house and its valuable contents.

JULY 17

1863 - A flood in Iron County's Pine Creek raised the creek's water level about 20 feet. The waters swept away a house and drowned four children.

1937 - Payson (Utah County) encountered heavy hail that covered a strip 1½ miles wide and four miles long. Some hailstones were 1" in diameter. Soldier Summit, located between Provo and Price, also reported 1" diameter hail.

1976 - A storm with strong winds knocked down a 70-foot elm tree onto a house in Pleasant Grove.

1985 - Hail of ½" to 1" in diameter fell in Sevier County, breaking windows, destroying crops, and damaging trees.

JULY 18

1918 - At about 10:00 PM, two large bolts of lightning struck and killed 654 head of sheep on Mill Canyon Peak in American Fork Canyon. According to one historical account: "Forked lightning had struck twice and split down two sides of the peak....There was about a seventy-five foot swath in between the dead sheep and where not a one was injured....The dead sheep all had to be moved to the opposite side of the canyon so as to be off the 'water shed.' [Men] counted them as

they were moved, six-hundred and fifty-four sheep had been killed."

1955 - At Eureka (Juab County) in west central Utah, a heavy rainstorm sent water racing through the town.

1960 - A large dust devil in Minersville damaged a filling station and broke windows in nearby houses.

1965 - Heavy thunderstorms flood Utah County's Timpanogos National Monument. In one hour, 2.40" of rain fell, resulting in two landslides. Floods also washed out paved highway, foot bridges, and trails. Damage was estimated at over $100,000.

1987 - Snow fell above 9,000 feet in the Uintah Mountains, startling campers. Light accumulations were noted above 11,500 feet.

1994 - Monsoon rains inundate portions of Washington County in southwest Utah. New Harmony received the lion's share of rain with 2.00" falling in just 50 minutes.

1995 - Thunderstorms produced microburst winds to 74 mph at Provo BYU. At Duchesne, .50" of rain fell in 10 minutes.

JULY 18-20

1985 - At Orderville (Kane County), three days of relentless thunderstorms dumped 3.00" of rain that flooded basements and businesses. Thunderstorms caused flooding in other sections of the state.

JULY 19

1951 - Tooele, Salt Lake, and Millard Counties reported considerable crop damage due to hail.

1955 - Cedar Breaks National Monument in southwest Utah received 3" of hail during a heavy downpour in the afternoon.

1972 - A 100 yard-wide whirlwind took the top off from several sheds and uprooted trees in Nephi.

1987 - A thunderstorm produced a microburst wind of 71 mph at Kearns in the Salt Lake Valley.

1990 - Heavy thunderstorms dumped .87" of rain in 30 minutes at Fruitland.

JULY 20

1968 - Heavy rain, thunder and lightning struck Provo and Orem, flooding several streets and basements.

1995 - At Park Valley in Box Elder County .60" of rain fell in 10 minutes.

JULY 21

1943 - Nephi was flooded when nearly 2.00" of rain fell in a short period of time. Water rushing out of Salt Creek Canyon was two feet deep in places.

1957 - During the evening hours, lightning struck a powder company plant near Spanish Fork. Hail ¼" to ½" fell at Richfield and Central, with crop losses ranging from 50-100%.

1987 - Moisture from the remnants of Tropical Storm Dora collided with a cold front over northern Utah, producing heavy rain, localized flooding, and large hail. The most severe weather occurred over Salt

Lake and Utah Counties. Rainfall amounts included: Kearns 1.85", Holladay 1.50", and Provo/BYU 1.08" of rain. Hailstones 2" in diameter hit Provo and Springville, injuring a dozen people and damaging numerous cars. Hail in Kearns was piled up 2-4" deep, with wind and water piling the hail up to two feet deep in some areas of west Kearns. Baseball size hailstones fell at Coalville. Damage estimates from the storm soared over the $9,000,000 mark.

1995 - A wild day across northern Utah with golf-ball size hailstones falling at Tooele, 1" diameter hailstones at Yost in Box Elder County, and 1.42" of rain in 30 minutes along with marble size hail at Hyrum.

JULY 22

1904 - The largest flood in 36 years swept down Cedar City's main canyon, flooding parts of the town and tearing out dams and ditches.

1943 - A cloudburst at American Fork (Utah County) killed over 5,000 turkeys.

1968 - Tintic in central Utah reported flood damage after 2.50" of rain fell in about two hours. Also, a valuable horse was killed by lightning.

1984 - Strong winds overturned a houseboat at Lake Powell. Near Dry Fork Canyon, .90" of rain fell in 10 minutes.

1995 - Coalville recorded a microburst wind gust of 66 mph.

JULY 23

1957 - Lightning struck, set afire, and destroyed a church house at Montwell (Duchesne County). Lightning bolts hit two other places in the same vicinity, and in one case knocked a boy over a fence and into unconsciousness.

1985 - Tremonton, in extreme northern Utah, set a new 2-hour precipitation record with 2.39".

1993 - A cold storm brought 6" of snow to the Mirror Lake area in the Uinta Mountains, and 3" of the white stuff to Hidden Peak at Snowbird Ski Resort.

JULY 23-26

1993 - A very cool and wet period across much of Utah with substantial amounts of rain and record low temperatures. Rainfall amounts generally ranged from 1.25" to 2.75".

JULY 24

1847 - The Mormon pioneers arrived in the Salt Lake Valley. On this date, Wilford Woodruff recorded in his diary, "There was a thundershower and it rained over nearly the whole valley; it also rained a little in the forepart of the night. We felt thankful for this, as it was the generally conceived opinion that it did not rain in the valley during the summer season."

1946 - Heavy rains sent mud and boulders out of Pleasant Creek Canyon, engulfing Mt. Pleasant in the community's worst flood. Main Street was covered under three to four feet of water; boulders, trees, and thick mud were deposited the length of the street. One huge boulder was dumped in an optometrists reception area, automobiles were carried five blocks away, pigs were killed, and considerable damage was done to the city cemetery.

1948 - Hailstones measuring 2" in diameter fell at Price in central Utah. The severe hailstorm damaged roofs and gardens, and numerous neon signs and windows.

1958 - In Nephi, high winds preceding a storm front lifted two empty steel grain bins 15 feet off the ground and carried them nearly 450 feet, depositing them intact.

1976 - Several residents from Orangeville were roasting hot dogs in Joe's Valley during a break in a rainstorm when lightning struck them. The metal hot dog rods served as conductors, carrying the electricity through them into the ground. Several people had curious red marks on their skin where the electricity had apparently passed through their bodies.

1990 - Early morning thunderstorms produced 1" diameter hail at Payson and .78" of rain in 45 minutes. In addition, hail 6-8" deep had to be plowed off of State Route 24 in Wayne County near Lyman. About 6,000 cloud-to-ground lightning strikes were detected in Utah between 12:30 PM and 8:00 PM. At about 6:00 PM lightning struck a runway at the Salt Lake City International Airport, leaving a few holes in the surface of the runway.

JULY 25

1983 - At Churchwells, near the Utah/Arizona border, 3.60" of rain fell in a three-hour period.

1991 - A line of thunderstorms produced heavy rain that reduced the visibility to one mile at the Salt Lake City International Airport. Also, a peak wind gust of 59 mph was recorded.

JULY 26

1960 - An all-time record hot 107°F was recorded in Salt Lake City.

1982 - A six-foot wall of water tumbled down Gate Canyon, about 20 miles south of Myton (Duchesne County.)

1986 - A considerable amount of hail was reported in the west portion of the Salt Lake Valley. Kearns received 1¼" diameter hailstones and West Valley City received Ping-Pong ball size hail.

JULY 27

1904 - A heavy cloudburst hit New Harmony, driving people from their homes and washing away foundations and several miles of roadway. The path of the flood covered several miles in length and was ½ mile in width.

1951 - A severe lightning and rain storm described as "the worst lightning storm in (the) history of (the) valley" caused $500,000 damage in Salt Lake, Bountiful, and Bingham. Salt Lake City streets were filled with water from curb to curb, sections of highway between Bingham and Copperton were completely destroyed. Two cars were virtually buried in mud from flash floods.

1983 - Severe weather hit Sevier County in southwest Utah as 3" of hail piled up at Redmond.

JULY 28

1896 - One of the worst flash floods to ever hit Eureka killed four people and turned the main street into a raging torrent.

1917 - Thunderstorms meandering over Huntsville (Carbon County) and Sunnyside (Carbon County), deposited more than 2.00" of rain in 24 hours. A more potent thunderstorm at Morgan (Morgan County) lasted two hours and brought a flood of boulders and gravel.

1952 - Hailstones measuring over 1" in diameter struck fields northwest of Parowan in southwest Utah, destroying $7,000 worth of grain and corn.

1982 - Severe thunderstorms lashed out over Utah. Downpours occurred at many areas with Salt Lake City picking up 1.11" of rain in 15 minutes. A waterspout was spotted over Utah Lake, and a funnel cloud above Provo Canyon. Hailstones ½" in diameter hit Orderville in south central Utah.

JULY 29

1883 - A massive Virgin River flood tore out all dams between Washington Field and Mesquite, Nevada. A massive eight hour flood, "the heaviest known in this part of the country," flooded Kanab Creek at Kanab. "Masses of earth as large as a common house floated down the stream with willows still standing." Floodwaters cut a channel 50 feet deep and 225 feet wide, killing several cattle, destroying crops, and opened a number of new springs.

1969 - A series of heavy thunderstorms struck sections of Utah. A cloudburst at Bountiful inundated 5th South with a foot of water. The Salt Lake City International Airport recorded 1.16" of rain in three hours. The heavy rain caused a United Airlines 727 to slide off the runway. At Moab, lightning struck a house and caused a $30,000 fire. In the Tooele area, old-timers said, "it was the worst storm in many years, the biggest in over 27 years" as rains deposited debris throughout the area.

1975 - At St. George, a highway patrol officer reported that an 18-foot wall of water swept down the Virgin River, after giant thunderstorms dumped 2.76" of rain at Zion Park headquarters.

1995 - A "gustnado" was observed in the Centerville area of northern Utah during the evening. (A gustnado is a microburst that once it touches the ground has some circular rotation but is not coupled with circulation aloft.) Substantial damage occurred at several locations. One person was briefly lifted into the air then dropped to the ground. A flag pole was snapped, which had previously withstood 90 mph canyon winds. At a construction site, a large outhouse (with no one in it) was pushed over.

JULY 30

1921 - Heavy rains at Hatch, in southern Utah, caused "the worst floods known" in Proctor Canyon. This was the second time damaging floods had hit the area within one month.

1939 - Moroni received a cloudburst of 1.64" of rainfall in just two hours.

1953 - Two consecutive cloudbursts 30 minutes apart sent floodwaters down Granite Flats in American Fork Canyon, causing 45 campers to seek cover as the water uprooted their camp. Some 100 canyon residents were stranded as the floodwaters smashed small bridges and washed out roads.

1958 - An intense rainstorm dumped nearly 2.00" of rain in 40 minutes over Fielding (Box Elder County), killing 1,300 turkeys in four foot deep floodwater. Farm equipment, poultry flocks, and calves were swept away by floods due to the heavy rainfall.

1961 - Nearly 1.50" of rain fell in less than 30 minutes near Richfield in southwest Utah.

1962 - Marble size hailstones flattened gardens and ripped leaves from trees at Lehi. On some farms nearly 60% of all crops were destroyed.

1965 - A series of heavy thunderstorms moved across Salt Lake, dumping up to 3.00" of rain in narrow Neff's Canyon. Resulting mud and water rushed into Salt Lake City, causing $200,000 damage to homes and highways.

1966 - Escalante in south central Utah, received 2.00" of rain in two hours, causing flooding to homes.

JULY 31

1912 - Heavy rains and floodwaters "washed out every street in Eureka. Water and debris entered the back doors of business houses and came out the front, washing out merchandise. Barrels of beer and empty beer kegs floated out front doors and down the canyon."

1936 - Autos were tipped over, seven homes were partially buried, and the main road along Willard in Box Elder County was buried under mud for nearly two blocks after cloudburst rains occurred in Willard Canyon.

1983 - Nearly 1.00" of rainfall in 10 minutes in the Grandview area of Provo caused a large mudslide at the Geneva Recreation Association Park. The same thunderstorm flooded the BYU Marriott Center. At

Kanab, heavy, slow-moving thunderstorms caused flooding which uprooted sagebrush and deposited rock across the highway.

1988 - Flash flooding occurred across portions of southwest Utah after heavy thunderstorms dumped 1.60" of rain in 40 minutes at Greenville near Beaver, and 1.10" of rain in 35 minutes at Modena.

1989 - A major flash flood event occurred in Cedar City and Cedar Canyon. Heavy late afternoon rains sent a flash flood cascading out of Fiddlers Canyon and into three subdivisions in the northeast portion of Cedar City. A number of cars were displaced, overturned, or relocated by the flood waters. At the Cedar City Airport .60" of rain fell in 12 minutes, reducing the visibility to 1/8 of a mile. Winds also gusted to 59 mph.

AUGUST 1

1916 - "Sleds, buggies, and other farming utensils" were swept away due to a flash flood at Fairview (Sanpete County). Water depths ranged from two to six feet within the city.

1955 - The largest flood in many years came down Parowan Canyon in southern Utah. Though the Parowan station recorded a moderate 0.85" of rain in one hour, it was probably heavier in the mountains.

1968 - A series of the most intense cloudbursts ever experienced in Utah occurred over the Monticello/Blanding area of southeast Utah. An estimated 6.50" of precipitation fell at Blanding in 24 hours. Over 2.00" of rain was measured in 40 minutes, with the rains breaking a number of state intensity records. Bluff, located 20 miles south of Blanding, was inundated by water, mud, and debris three feet deep.

1972 - Lightning caused problems in north central Utah. At Provo, a bolt struck a tree and knocked a limb through a bedroom window showering two children with broken glass. In Payson, lightning struck and killed five cattle, and in southern Salt Lake County a storage building at an outdoor movie theater was struck and set ablaze.

AUGUST 2

1919 - Heavy rains over the mountains near Moab caused a nighttime flood that did $25,000 damage to power plants, irrigation and water supply systems, and homes and farms.

1922 - Wasatch County was hit by a storm reported to be the "worst ever experienced." At Heber, Midway, and Charleston, streets were flooded and hundreds of chickens and several pigs were drowned. A Salt Lake County resident drowned when a cloudburst flood demolished his home in Magna.

1956 - A two hour torrential rain inundated Monticello (San Juan County). In some places water was two feet deep. A motor lodge received nearly $50,000 worth of damage.

AUGUST 3

1888 - Hailstones 1" in diameter hit Orangeville (Emery County). Gardens were destroyed.

1907 - The northern half of the state was visited by severe lightning and windstorms. Wind speeds up to 64 mph were observed in Salt Lake City. Also, considerable damage was done to small buildings and telephone lines.

1951 - The worst flooding in five decades hit Lehi and Alpine (Utah County).

1961 - Heavy rain near Levan (Juab County), produced a channel of floodwaters eight feet deep and 14 feet wide. New gullies were cut and numerous fish were killed.

AUGUST 4

1913 - A rain storm deluged the town of Moroni (Sanpete County) . In one hour and twenty minutes 1.54" of rain fell, and an observer in the center of the storm felt "convinced that 4.50" fell in three hours and 15 minutes." The storm was accompanied by high winds and hail measuring ½" in diameter.

1929 - Heavy rain flooded Milford's Main Street (Beaver County) under 13" of water, damaging stores and merchandise.

1951 - An intense 30 minute cloudburst over downtown Salt Lake City flooded hotels, theaters, and stores. Hundreds of basements were flooded, and traffic became snarled as boulders tumbled down 400 South and 500 South Streets. The City and County Building grounds became inundated with water. At Ogden, 3.03" of rain fell during the 24-hour period.

1954 - Heavy rain in Salt Lake dumped 1.55" in 3 hours. Runoff flooded streets and basements.

1991 - Thunderstorms produced a swath of hail in the south end of the Salt Lake Valley and up Little Cottonwood Canyon. Hailstones ½" in diameter hail fell for about 15 minutes to a depth of three inches at Snowbird. Forty-three people were injured when the hail and rain cause a large canvas canopy to collapse on 1,400 people watching a performance of the Utah Symphony. The same storm produced large hail across many portions of northern Utah. Hail reports were: Riverton and Point of the Mountain 1¾" in diameter, South Jordan 1¼" in diameter, Sandy 1" in diameter, Alta ¾" in diameter, and Logan ½" in diameter.

1993 - Koosharem, in southwest Utah, was drenched with .70" of rain in just 10 minutes, along with ¼" diameter hail, and Greenwich received .50" of rain in 12 minutes.

AUGUST 5

1943 - Cloudbursts lasting over 30 minutes in Helper (Carbon County) and Monroe (Sevier County) produced flash floods that damaged or destroyed highways, railroads, canals, power lines and mines, with homes, fields and crops either washed away or buried under mud flows. Damage totaled $250,000.

1948 - A flash flood near Sunnyside (Carbon County) in east central Utah killed a man.

1985 - A huge dust devil tore part of the roof off a business in Murray.

AUGUST 6

1901 - Floods north of Fairview (Sanpete County) washed out bridges and culverts, and carried away pigs and chickens. At nearby Milburn, a cloudburst sent an "avalanche of water freighted with trees and boulders" down into the valley. Part of the town was covered under three feet of water, mud, and boulders.

1945 - The worst storm and cloudburst in 15 years hit the central Utah community of Manderfield, causing considerable damage to crops and fields, drowning cattle, and closing U.S. Highway 91. Lightning struck a large transformer at the municipal power plant, interrupting electrical service for several hours.

1955 - Severe thunderstorms crossed northern Utah. Floods undermined several streets in Salt Lake City, while flash floods rumbled down Rose Canyon in the Oquirrh Mountains.

1957 - Nearly 2.00" of rain fell in 30 minutes, washing huge boulders and mud across U.S. Highway 50-6 in the Helper and Castle Gate area of Carbon County in central Utah.

1967 - Southern Utah was hit hard by cloudbursts. Heavy rain 30 miles northwest of Milford caused the derailment of 29 Union Pacific freight train cars. At Richfield, one-fourth of a mile of a county road was washed out. Near Kingston, heavy rains produced a wall of water four feet high.

1991 - Helper, in east central Utah, received 1.02" of rain in 12 minutes.

AUGUST 7

1915 - A severe electrical storm followed by cloudbursts caused considerable damage at Tintic (Juab County) in central Utah. Mine workers were forced to climb 2,000 feet out of the shafts when transmission lines were destroyed.

1941 - The heaviest floods in over 30 years hit the small town of Alton (Kane County) in southern Utah. Floods ripped a bridge out and carried it one-half mile down stream.

1993 - Cloudburst rains struck Carbonville with .95" of rain, with .54" of that falling in seven minutes.

AUGUST 7-8

1987 - Panguitch, in southwest Utah, recorded 2.50" of rain in 12 hours.

AUGUST 8

1941 - A severe cloudburst at Ogden dumped 1.40" of rain in one hour. Water flowed in torrents through the business district, destroying merchandise, and carrying automobiles. The Forest Service in Ogden Canyon reported a phenomenal 2.10" of rain in 25 minutes.

1983 - Lightning hit an A-frame building at a Nephi recreational campground area, starting a blaze that charred attic beams. The surge of electricity caused damage to TV's and broke light bulbs all over the campground.

1986 - Fruitland (Duchesne County) was hit by 1" diameter hail.

1993 - It was "hail-of-a-day" across central and southern portions of the Salt Lake Valley due to severe thunderstorms. Many areas were clobbered with large hail, including: Herriman ½" to 1¼" diameter hail up to 3" deep, South Sandy ½" to 1½" diameter hail up to 2" deep, Midvale ¾" to 1½" diameter hail, and Murray ½" to 1½" diameter hail. Some of the more intense rainfall amounts were: South Sandy 1.25" in 20 minutes (1.50" total), Sandy .72" in 10 minutes, and Midvale .60" in 10 minutes.

AUGUST 8-11

1929 - An unusual storm began over Pine Valley in southwest Utah, and continued intermittently for four days. The town was flooded on three different days as the river rose to a record height. Local observers estimated total rainfall at 7.00".

AUGUST 9

1920 - One of Utah's most severe hailstorms occurred at Lehi, causing over $50,000 in damage. Most of the hailstones ranged between 3" and 4" in circumference, with some up to 6.5" in circumference. Hundreds of chickens and some rabbits perished. One man was struck by a hailstone which partially tore off his ear. An estimated 7,000 window panes were broken, and a large greenhouse was all but destroyed.

1926 - Hailstones nearly 1" in diameter fell at Watson (Uinta County) in northeast Utah, damaging trees shrubbery, window panes, and roofs of buildings.

1941 - Hundreds of acres of crops were flattened or completely destroyed by hail and rainfall in Vernal. At Plymouth, located in extreme northern Box Elder County, an emergency airfield was eroded by runoff when 1.36" fell in a short period of time.

1953 - At 5:15 AM in Provo, a "maroon ball of lightning one foot in diameter" struck a "silver leaf polar tree" and split the three foot thick, 75-foot tall tree in half, cracking open the ground surrounding the tree.

1983 - Intense lightning storms over northern Utah produced 15,000 cloud-to-ground strikes and 50,000 total lightning strikes in a five hour period. The lightning zapped several trees in residential areas of Utah County.

1994 - Tropical moisture spread northward across Utah producing heavy rains in short periods of time. Some reports included: Pleasant Grove .38" in 8 minutes, Maeser .50" in 10 minutes, Carbon 1.20" in 30 minutes, and Helper 1.15" in 15 minutes.

AUGUST 10

1903 - A flash flood rushed down Dry Creek at Toquerville (Washington County) in southwest Utah, trapping and drowning a man who was unable to escape.

1955 - A monstrous flash flood hit St. George, pouring a five foot wall of water one mile wide over numerous farms. Another flash flood in nearby Barracks Canyon, located 18 miles northwest of Kanab, marooned 150 members of a motion picture company for two hours. Many pieces of film equipment were swept away by the flood.

1968 - One of the worst rainstorms ever to hit Tooele dropped 1.16" of rain in 20 minutes. Several business establishments and a number of homes were flooded. A small car floated down a city street.

1981 - Iron County experienced severe weather as golf ball-sized hail piled up one foot deep in some areas.

1993 - A 72 year old male patient at a nursing home in Sandy was struck by lightning while in his bed. The lightning left a "yolk size" red mark on his cheek. The man was knocked unconscious for three to four minutes and was blinded for 10 minutes. Ironically, the patient was in intense pain just prior to the strike and was pain free for 24 hours thereafter. Heavy thunderstorms dumped 1.03" of rain in 15 minutes at Lehi in Utah County. Other intense rainfall amounts were: American Fork Canyon .80" in 15 minutes with pea-size hail, Alpine .49" in 12 minutes, and Riverton .70" in 15 minutes. The UHP reported 6" of hail on the ground at the top of Huntington Canyon.

1995 - Microburst winds gusted to 92 mph at the top of the Kimball Tower on the BYU campus in Provo.

AUGUST 11

1927 - Hailstones "the size of small bird eggs" cut a path one-half mile wide in the town of Price.

1929 - A heavy cloudburst over Bingham Canyon in Salt Lake County lasted over two hours, demolishing many houses and sending a 50,000-ton copper drum down the mountainside, barely missing several dozen people.

1982 - A flash flood produced a wall of water estimated at 60 feet wide and four feet deep near Bonanza (Uintah County) in northeast Utah. Five cars were lost, 11 cars damaged, and two people were injured.

1995 - The town of Ferron got a summer bath as 1.72" of rain fell in 45 minutes.

AUGUST 12

1882 - A violent rain and hailstorm over St. George damaged roads, blew down trees, and knocked "fruit by the ton" off orchard trees.

1956 - Lightning started a fire at a welding shop in Coalville (Summit County) in northern Utah. The shop and its contents were lost.

1986 - Hail struck from the Point of the Mountain through northern Utah County. The hail brought traffic at the Point of the Mountain to a standstill. Hail ½" in diameter was reported at Provo and Alpine.

1987 - Thunderstorms produced 1.75" of rain in 45 minutes in an area seven miles northwest of Cedar City; and 1.13" of rain in two hours at Kanab.

1995 - Golf ball size hail bombarded the Bluffdale/Draper area in the Salt Lake Valley. The UHP reported numerous traffic accidents on I-15 due to this storm.

AUGUST 13

1906 - At Tropic (Garfield County) in southern Utah, 2.00" of rain fell in two hours. Torrents of water rushed through the streets and walnut-sized hailstones stripped leaves from standing corn. The same flood struck Cannonville, four miles downstream from Tropic, as a five foot crest of water, carrying rocks and timber, bore down on the town.

1923 - One of Utah's most disastrous and deadly floods caused hundreds of thousands of dollars damage to Farmington, Centerville, and Willard. A family of six camping in Farmington Canyon perished in the flood. Observers in Farmington Canyon reported flood crests 75-100 feet high and 200 feet wide. Patrons at the nearby Lagoon amusement park were rescued from trees and roofs as they sought refuge from the rapidly rising waters. At Willard, four dwellings were destroyed and two women died when their house was demolished. In Salt Lake City, 1.05" of rain fell in 30 minutes.

1943 - Hail and rain fell on Salina and Salina Canyon. Half-dollar-sized hailstones fell for about 20 minutes. A torrential rain fell for about one hour. After the storm passed, fish of every size lined the banks of Salina Creek.

1978 - Destructive hail and wind ravaged crops in the Willard area of northern Utah, causing $1,000,000 in damage to the almost ripe fruit crop. Salt Lake City was on the southern edge of this storm and reported a wind gust of 74 mph.

AUGUST 14

1896 - A flood caused by a cloudburst and hailstorm washed out a sawmill and carried trees, boulders, and trash into Fillmore (Millard County). Some of the trees carried into town were three feet in diameter.

1924 - Heavy hail hit Roosevelt (Duchesne County), with hailstones reported ½" to 1" in diameter that covered an area one-half mile wide and four miles long. At Benmore (Tooele County), hailstones up to 1" in diameter killed a few chickens.

1968 - Rain and hail dumped 1.15" of rain on Moab, flooding homes and roads, and depositing six to ten inches of mud and sand on streets throughout the town.

1934 - In Eureka .85" of rain fell in 22 minutes and sent four feet of water into the town, flooding many buildings and causing automobiles to "float" down Main Street.

1955 - A flash flood that raged through a processing plant in Nephi killed nearly 8,000 turkeys.

AUGUST 15

1984 - On I-15 between Nephi and Levan, cars were washed off the highway as flash flooding sent a wave of water up to three feet high across the road.

1987 - A cold front moved across northern Utah, producing heavy rain and hail. Hailstones measured nearly 1" in diameter at Sandy, and 1" diameter hail piled up two inches deep in Emigration Canyon.

AUGUST 16

1928 - A sheep rancher drowned when torrential rains at Price's Nine Mile Canyon caused heavy floodwaters to cover his automobile. His daughter who was riding with him escaped by clinging to brush and crawling to safety.

1936 - Hail that was five to six inches deep gave a "Christmas in August" illusion to Beaver in southwest Utah. The vicious hailstorm destroyed numerous crops and deposited 1.56" of precipitation in just one hour.

1958 - An incredible 5.00" of rain fell in one hour in Morgan, setting new state high intensity precipitation records for one, two, and three-hour periods. The cloudburst blocked the highway with boulders and mud four feet deep and about 40 feet wide across the road. City streets in Morgan were described as "rivers." In the Goshen/Elberta area (Utah County) of central Utah, rain, wind, and hail damaged crops, flooded homes, and stalled cars. Nearly 2.00" of rain fell in one hour.

1983 - More than 1.00" of rain fell in a 25-minute period, causing extensive flooding in downtown Provo. Damage was reported at 15 businesses. Water was four feet deep on some roads and eight buildings on the BYU campus were also flooded.

1990 - Monsoonal moisture set the stage for thunderstorms that produced heavy rain across much of Utah. Some of the more intense rainfall amounts included: Moab 1.00" in 20 minutes, Liberty 1.00" in 30 minutes, and Provo .60" in 10 minutes.

AUGUST 17

1959 - Gale force winds and a cloudburst hit the Provo area. A baby had to be evacuated out a window when three feet of water blocked the doors of the home.

1965 - Annabella and Glenwood (Sevier County) were hit hard by flash flooding. Mud from four to six inches deep piled up in fields. Buildings and roads in Annabella received substantial damage.

1969 - A brief but strong storm dropped 2.00" of rain over the Salt Lake Valley, causing heavy flooding and doing $5,000-$10,000 in damage to a number of houses. An earth-filled dam in the southern part of the valley gave way, sending a wall of water into several basements.

1989 - Strong winds ripped into the northern part of the state about dinner time with a peak gust to 67 mph at the Salt Lake City International Airport, 65 mph at Dugway, and 61 mph at Ogden.

1994 - Orderville, in southern Utah, picked up .85" of rain in 10 minutes.

AUGUST 17-18

1979 - An estimated 2.50" of rain fell over Box Elder and Weber Counties overfilling a canal with water, debris, and mud in North Ogden. The canal later broke, flooding many homes and causing $500,000 in damages.

AUGUST 18

1965 - Cloudbursts over canyons near Cedar City caused floods that wreaked havoc in government lands and damaged the city cemetery and golf course.

1977 - A long, narrow band of heavy rain from the remnants of Hurricane Doreen moved through the Cache Valley in northern Utah. Rain fell all day, with 20-foot deep gullies created along the bench areas of River Heights. Within 20 hours, 3.84" of rain fell at Utah State University in Logan, with over 4.00" reported in other nearby areas.

1991 - A cloudburst at Richfield produced 1.25" of rain in a 30 minute period.

1994 - A heavy shower deposited .71" of rain in 10 minutes at Torrey.

AUGUST 18 - SEPTEMBER 31

1886 - Four successive cloudbursts hit Kanab. The largest of the four produced hailstones 1½" in diameter. Crops and dams were considerably damaged.

AUGUST 19

1945 - In the aftermath of a furious wind, rain, and hailstorm at Salt Lake City, one eyewitness stated, "The Salt Lake [City Municipal] Airport was literally destroyed by the storm. Planes stood on the runways with wings broken off and their fuselages dotted with holes from the hail." Nearly 50 fabric-covered airplanes were badly damaged, and nearly 700 windows were broken in hangars and other buildings in and around the airport. Record size hailstones, 2" in diameter, were measured at the airport. Piles of hail 14" deep were deposited on roofs of buildings in Salt Lake City. Wind gusts up to 70 mph were recorded. At the Salt Lake Cemetery, headstones were overturned and cracked and floodwaters split open some graves, exposing bodies and washing away caskets. For the first time in modern history, City Creek flooded, sending water down State Street, uprooting entire sections of pavement, moving parked cars for several blocks, and sweeping pedestrians off their feet. Logs 30 feet long and one foot wide, and 300-400 pound boulders rolled down the streets of Salt Lake City. Storm damage approached $500,000.

1963 - A cloudburst of heavy rain, hail and lightning swept across Utah County, sending mud, rocks, and limbs cascading across Diamond Fork above Spanish Fork Canyon. In southwest Utah, Cedar City received over 2.00" of rain in four hours, flooding a number of basements.

1966 - 70 mph winds hit the Milford Airport during the afternoon, destroying three light planes and blowing a roof off a hangar, carrying it onto the highway. The roof sheared several power and telephone poles.

1989 - Hailstones 1" in diameter fell at both Price in Carbon County and at Yost in Box Elder County.

1994 - Golf ball size hail and .60" of rain in 10 minutes struck Monticello in southeast Utah.

AUGUST 20

1957 - Flash floods trapped hundreds of people in southern and eastern Utah. Near Kanab, 225 persons were stranded due to heavy flooding at two separate locations. At Moab, heavy rainfall also trapped several people.

1963 - A severe lightning and hailstorm struck Duchesne in northeast Utah. Hailstones up to 1.5" in diameter fell for 20 minutes, stripping corn, flattening grain and alfalfa, ripping holes in tomatoes, and breaking windows and neon signs.

1986 - Severe thunderstorms hit the Wasatch Front. Nearly 2.00" of rain fell, causing widespread urban flooding in Salt Lake, with some flooding reported to buildings at the University of Utah. Strong winds tore the roof off a house in Orem.

AUGUST 21

1932 - Escalante and Antimony (Garfield County) received "the greatest floods known." Antimony received 2.78" of rain in two hours.

1975 - A driving hailstorm hit Washington County, damaging crops, roadways, canals, and homes. Many crops were destroyed and windows were broken by ¾" diameter hail. Conservative estimates placed damage above $100,000.

1983 - Golf ball-sized hail pelted areas of northern Utah. Fifteen windshields were broken in cars traveling on I-15. Widespread reports of hail 1" to 1¼" in diameter were noted.

1992 - Strong winds gusted to 63 mph at Kearns shortly after midnight. That day microburst winds gusted to 76 mph at Provo BYU. A cement truck driver got the jolt of his life in Sandy when lightning struck the truck's chute, knocking the driver 20-30 feet into the bushes. When bystanders brought the man inside he was breathing erratically and was "white as a ghost".

1995 - Heavy rains were reported and noted on Doppler Radar in the Scofield Mine area. One weather observer in Torrey (Wayne County) recorded 2.90" of rain in about a two hour period.

AUGUST 22

1962 - A bolt of lightning struck an 11 year-old boy playing football in Holladay in the Salt Lake Valley. The lightning shredded his tennis shoes and burned his trouser zipper.

AUGUST 23

1921 - Helper and Price (Carbon County), received 2.00" of rain in one hour, causing local canyon floods and heavy damage.

1937 - At Tropic (Garfield County), heavy rain and 1½" diameter hailstones were observed.

1995 - An intense thunderstorm cell moved over Flaming Gorge, producing a deluge of 2.25" of rain in one hour at the Dutch John site near the dam. The storm total amounted to 2.50". In the early evening a wild thunderstorm struck Tooele with .92" of rain in 15 minutes, with 1.05" total for the storm. The winds also gusted to 72 mph in Tooele as the storm blasted through.

AUGUST 24

1905 - A cloudburst over the Virgin River in southwest Utah, caused the largest flood in St. George history. Price Dam was entirely swept away, animals were killed, and crop land was flooded.

1913 - The "annual August flood" in Ephraim (Sanpete County) broke all previous property damage records. Cellars were filled with mud, lawns were destroyed, and 25 cubic-foot boulders rolled into town.

1991 - A tremendous complex of thunderstorm cells moved into the Wasatch Front of northern Utah. The visibility was lowered to 1/8 of a mile at South

Jordan and the Point of the Mountain due to dust. Winds gusted to 61 mph at the Provo Airport and Provo BYU. Approximately 20,000 lightning strikes were noted over Utah from the morning of the 24th to the morning of the 25th.

1994 - Strong "microburst" winds were reported at Maeser, near Vernal. An eyewitness observed the winds pick up his picnic table and splinter it, and his hay barn lifted five feet in the air before the roof was torn off. The barn was made of welded oil castings which were very heavy. The roof blew 240 feet and damaged a neighbor's shed and motor home before finally landing in the driveway. There was also damage to a 1,000 pound router saw table which had taken eight men to move.

AUGUST 25

1955 - A flash flood at Lapoint in eastern Utah washed out a half dozen bridges. The waters were two feet deep around one house, with boulders half as big as a car strewn over the yard.

1957 - At Kanab (Kane County), a thunderstorm produced hail 2" deep in 10 minutes. Gardens were flattened, several roofs damaged, and some flooding occurred when the hail melted.

1965 - A wall of water "between 15 and 25 feet deep" roared down Little Bear Canyon near Huntington. Damage to the Huntington City water works included the destruction of 1,400 feet of pipeline.

1984 - Hail piled up 6" deep at Dugway (Tooele County) in Utah's west desert.

1989 - It was a cold morning across much of Utah. Some readings included: Randolph 23°F, Coalville 31°F, Providence 33°F, and Wellsville, Logan, Richfield, Flaming Gorge 34°F.

AUGUST 25-26

1993 - Tropical moisture from Hurricane Hillary dumped incredible amounts of rain across portions of southwest Utah. At the Goldstrike Mine, six miles northwest of Gunlock, 4.14" of rain was recorded in less than three hours. A weather observer at Santa Clara reported 1.75" of rain in 30 minutes, along with ½" diameter hail. Elsewhere across the state, 1.00" of rain fell in 30 minutes four miles west of Price.

AUGUST 26

1913 - Heavy rain sent water, sand, gravel, and boulders cascading down the foothills of Mayfield (Sanpete County). In some areas the debris covered the land so completely that the cost to clear the area was more than the value of the land.

1952 - A man was killed when a sudden cloudburst flooded a tunnel he was working in at Buckhorn Wash Proving Ground, 15 miles south of Castle Dale.

1985 - A wind speed of 70 mph was clocked in Sandy in the Salt Lake Valley. The Great Salt Lake Minerals plant reported a peak wind gust of 69 mph. The strong microburst winds, caused by high-based thunderstorms, also damaged six planes at Salt Lake Airport II in West Jordan.

1988 - Heavy thunderstorms developed across much of central and western Utah. Rainfall amounts included: Fairview 1.94" in one hour, Loa 1.42" in one hour, Henrieville 1.25" in 48 minutes, and Beaver 1.01" in 20 minutes.

AUGUST 27

1925 - A damaging flash flood struck near Woodside (Emery County). Nine bridges were washed out, including one that was 112 feet long and another bridge 85 feet in length. Storm damage approached $150,000.

1953 - After one hour of heavy rain, Arches National Monument experienced a flash flood that submerged nearly 50 feet of road under three feet of water. The rain forced the closure of the monument entrance, stranding 25 persons for six hours.

1985 - Strong thunderstorms produced microburst winds up to 72 mph at the Great Salt Lake Minerals plant.

1988 - Heavy rains drenched southwest Utah. Leeds picked up 1.82" in one hour and St. George received 1.00" in 30 minutes.

AUGUST 28

1971 - Heavy rains and local flash flooding caused 15 vehicle accidents and two fatalities across the state. Near Ephraim and Manti (Sanpete County), the floods washed out water systems, killed 22 lambs, and destroyed hay crops. Lightning knocked over a church steeple in Salt Lake City.

AUGUST 29

1957 - Thunderstorms produced winds of 75 mph in Salt Lake County, destroying a portion of the Saltair Beach roller coaster structure.

1969 - Moab received 6.25" of rain in seven days, with 1.21" of that falling on this date. The rains ruined rural roads.

1982 - Lightning blew a one-foot by two-foot, two-inch deep hole in the blacktop at the Salt Lake City International Airport. The strike was within 200 yards of the National Weather Service Forecast Office.

1986 - After a thunderstorm dumped 1.30" of rain in 40 minutes, rocks and boulders washed down the canyon at the Hole-in-the-Rock area in southeast Utah.

1994 - A huge thunderstorm with a beautiful anvil top moved over Utah County and produced hailstones ¼" to 1" in diameter and six to nine inches deep in the American Fork-Pleasant Grove-Lehi areas. The hail shattered the window of a police car. Water amounts from this storm were: Pleasant Grove .58" in 10 minutes and American Fork .55" in 10 minutes.

AUGUST 30

1977 - An extremely heavy storm hit the community of Pine Valley (Washington County) in southwest Utah, dropping nearly 5.20" of rain in a National Forest Service rain gauge east of Pine Valley.

1986 - Hailstones 1¾" in diameter hailstones were measured at Boulder (Garfield County) in south central Utah, during a 10 minute hailstorm. Hail covered the ground to a depth of one inch.

1993 - Frost was reported in the Cache Valley and several other locations. Some of the cold low temperatures recorded were: Randolph 23°F, Smithfield and Wellsville 31°F, and Coalville, Trenton, and Laketown 32°F.

AUGUST 30 - SEPTEMBER 1

1909 - The weather observer at Emery measured a three day total of 4.09" of water. One small house was carried away and several small animals were drowned. An observer in Washington County reported 4.20" of precipitation during August 30-31.

AUGUST 31

1931 - Intense rainfall of .40" in five minutes sent nearly one foot of water through streets of North Salt Lake. Debris measuring 13 feet deep and 350 feet long blocked the road between Salt Lake and Ogden.

1936 - Minersville (Beaver County), experienced a "cloudburst of unusual violence." Heavy rain covered the streets with two to five feet of water. Nearly 2,000 acres of farmland was inundated under two feet of water. A number of livestock were killed. At Oak City (Millard County), hail caused $20,000 in damage.

1963 - A heavy rainstorm hit southeast Salt Lake City. Up to 1.80" of rain fell in 24 hours, with 1.25" falling in 10 minutes. Hailstones were measured from ½" to 1¼" in diameter. In northwest Salt Lake County, a devastating rain and hailstorm hit the Magna area. Streams were several feet deep in many places along Main Street. Homes and businesses were flooded. The storm was billed by residents as "the heaviest storm for the longest length of time in over 20 years."

1977 - Lightning struck a herd of sheep near Orangeville (Emery County), killing 14 lambs.

SEPTEMBER 1

1939 - Lightning hit and killed 835 sheep that had been bedded down for the night on the top of Pine Canyon in the Raft River Mountains of Box Elder County in northwestern Utah. Rain from a passing thunderstorm wet the ground and sheep, causing the lightning's electrical discharge to move completely through the herd of female sheep and lambs. The next morning, fifteen sheep (out of 850) were found alive but in a dazed condition. The sheepherder was knocked temporarily unconscious, but escaped death because he was in a tent. However, burned spots on his canvas tent revealed he probably missed the fate of the sheep by only a slim margin.

1953 - An early morning thunderstorm over Tooele produced hailstones 1½" in diameter. The hail fell for 20 minutes, shattering 160 panes of glass in a greenhouse and destroying several plants.

1992 - A thunderstorm near Castle Rock in northeast Utah dropped .52" of rain in five minutes and a total of .92" in 30 minutes.

SEPTEMBER 2

1935 - Campers and fishermen in a canyon near Oak City (Millard County) narrowly escaped drowning in a flash flood. Floodwaters carried one car with five passengers several hundred feet before lodging them against a tree.

1945 - A large flood hit Fruita (Wayne County) in southern Utah. An observer reported that "the biggest flood known in Sulphur Creek crested at 15 feet and destroyed orchards." At Bryce Canyon, four inches of hail piled up in 13 minutes.

1972 - An intense lightning and windstorm in Magna toppled trees, knocked out power and telephone lines, set fires, and produced zero visibility, resulting in several traffic accidents.

1990 - A somewhat late monsoon drenched portions of southeast Utah. At Hole-in-the-Rock, south of Moab, 3.75" of rain was.

SEPTEMBER 3

1921 - Heavy rainfall broke the Hanksville Dam. The stone dam was 25 feet high by 100 feet long. The collapse of the dam isolated residents of Hanksville, Gibbs, Caineville, and Notom. At the time of the dam failure approximately 15 feet of water was pouring over it. The lives of several automobile passengers were endangered when 10 to 12 feet of water swept down a highway. No fatalities or injuries were reported.

1983 - Severe thunderstorms produced golf ball-sized hail over the Salt Lake Valley. Hailstones up to 1½" in diameter damaged homes and cars in the Holladay and Cottonwood areas. Heavy rain associated with the hail set a Utah state precipitation record with a downpour of 1.53" of water in 15 minutes at West Valley City. In Utah County, a boy was killed when wind blew a tree onto a tent in Hobble Creek Canyon.

1995 - St. George recorded its hottest September temperature: 109°F.

SEPTEMBER 3-4

1958 - Nearly 2.50" of rain fell at Kanab (Kane County), washing out water mains in Three Lakes

Canyon, filling basements in south Kanab, and flooding U.S. Highway 89.

SEPTEMBER 4-6

1970 - Moist tropical air from Pacific Storm Norma collided with a cold front from the northwest. The record-breaking Labor Day weekend rains in southeast Utah produced flash floods that destroyed roads and bridges and damaged ranches near Bluff, Montezuma Creek, and Aneth. Bug Point, located east of Monticello near the Colorado border received 6.00" of rain.

SEPTEMBER 5

1960 - A torrential rainstorm near Glenwood and Sigurd (Sevier County) in southwest Utah, caused one of the worst recorded flash floods in the area. Sections of road were stripped away by rushing water, stranding 350 automobiles. In the four square mile area of the storm, rainfall was estimated at 1.50" to 2.00" in less than 30 minutes.

1966 - A severe thunderstorm swept across Utah. Lightning struck the roof of a church house in Ogden, resulting in a fire that caused $100,000 in damage. In Cache County, lightning-caused fires destroyed barns and stored crops.

1987 - Greenville, approximately five miles west of Beaver, reported 1.33" of rain and ½" diameter hail in 30 minutes.

SEPTEMBER 5-6

1965 - One of the most treacherous floods to ever hit southern Utah raged down Zion Park Narrows at the north fork of the Virgin River in Zion National Park. Forty-two trapped hikers escaped certain death by hanging onto vines, ledges, and trees, and by climbing into crevices. The next day a second deluge caused the floodwaters to increase in height, causing the hikers to climb even higher to safety.

SEPTEMBER 6

1982 - Marble size hail fell in Layton and in the Rock Creek area of the Uinta Mountains. Hail piled up to a depth of several inches.

1994 - Three Salt Lake Buzz baseball players got "buzzed" when they were struck by lightning while playing golf in Riverton. The lightning knocked them to the ground, but they were not injured.

1995 - Heavy rains and flash flooding hit parts of southern Utah, especially in Washington County. A cloudburst let loose in the area of Snow Canyon State Park/Padre Canyon and the Tuachan Amphitheater during the early afternoon and sent a flash flood of water, red mud, and debris up to five feet deep and 75 feet wide through the theater. Doorways were filled halfway up with muck. Ironically the theater was built to re-create the

historic 1862 Santa Clara River flood. Rainfall estimates from the Las Vegas Doppler Radar indicated two to three inches of rain could have fallen in a short period of time. In addition, lightning hit an apartment complex in St. George and blew a hole through a wall into a bathroom. Just north of Blanding, 1.00" of rain fell in 20 minutes along with marble size hail.

SEPTEMBER 7

1991 - A new six-hour high intensity rainfall record was set at North Ogden: 5.50". In addition, huge amounts of water flooded through the towns of North Ogden and Harrisville. By 8:00 PM, the prolonged intense rains loosened tons of rock, mud, and debris that rolled into subdivisions along the bench areas of North Ogden, flooding hundreds of basements in both North Ogden and Harrisville. There was a "loud roar" before the debris flow hit. Luckily, no one was killed or injured. Damage totaled approximately six million dollars, as about 640 homes received some kind of damage. One house was totally destroyed and eight homes received major damage. Elsewhere across Utah, heavy rains struck the Price area, with water up to a foot deep in northern Price.

SEPTEMBER 7-8

1986 - Microburst winds from dry but intense thunderstorms hit the Wasatch Front. Wind gusts up to 64 mph were measured at Provo BYU. The strong winds in Utah County blew a roof off a house and downed power lines that started a fire in some dried grass. Other strong wind gusts included: West Kearns 63 mph, West Valley City 58 mph, and South Salt Lake 57 mph. The blustery dry winds blew down a tent at the Utah State Fair.

1991 - From 6:00 AM on the 7th to 6:00 AM on the 8th, North Ogden set a new Utah 24-hour rainfall record with a whopping 8.40". The previous 24-hour record was 6.00" at Bug Point on September 5, 1970.

SEPTEMBER 7-9

1927 - Three days of heavy rain caused flash flooding at Price, Kenilworth, and Roosevelt. Damage included livestock drowned, bridges washed away, farm lands flooded with debris, rail tracks washed out, boulders four feet in diameter washed into streets, 200 stands of bees destroyed, many crops lost, and property damage up to $200,000.

SEPTEMBER 8

1949 - St. George experienced heavy thunderstorms that caused "the worst damage from a cloudburst in 20 years." A heavy downpour over the Red Hills north of town sent muddy water through the business district, flooding basements and main floors of numerous stores and houses. Floodwater in one store was 14 feet deep.

SEPTEMBER 9

1953 - An intense thunderstorm over Bryce Canyon National Park dropped 3.36" of precipitation, including four inches of hail and slush in about two hours. A steer and four horses were killed by lightning.

1969 - A nocturnal cloudburst at Huntington (Emery County) in east central Utah dumped 6" of hail within one hour.

1991 - Strong thunderstorm winds hit the Provo and Orem areas of Utah County with winds clocked to 90 mph at the BYU campus in Provo. Damage was extensive with many large trees uprooted or damaged. A roof was lifted off an apartment complex, an aluminum roof on a carport was lifted off and carried 100 yards, and power lines were blown down.

SEPTEMBER 9-10

1986 - A funnel cloud was reported in the Ogden area. Hail up to 1" in diameter fell at Roy and Eagle Range. The hail cracked the windshield of a flying F-16 airplane. Lightning hit a taxi-way at the Salt Lake City International Airport, creating a hole 6" across and 6" deep.

SEPTEMBER 10

1972 - Winds up to 70 mph tore the roofs off houses and downed power lines at Smithfield and Logan in the Cache Valley. Power supplies to North Logan were cut off for nearly one hour.

1982 - Santaquin (Utah County) reported 2.00" of rain in one hour. Orem received 2.10" of rain and Bountiful reported a storm total of 1.79".

1984 - Heavy rain and hail hit Zion National Park, forcing the evacuation of some campers along the Virgin River. Over 2.00" of rain fell in 90 minutes.

SEPTEMBER 11

1926 - Hailstones ¾" in diameter damaged windows, awnings, and automobiles at Manti in central Utah.

1988 - A trace of snow was reported at Milford in southwest Utah. This was the second earliest snowfall ever at Milford.

SEPTEMBER 12

1927 - Water three feet deep roared down Price's Main Street. Flooding in the area was enhanced by melting mountain snow. One observer noted that "more rain fell in a week than usually falls in a year."

1988 - Winter came early to portions of southern Utah. Bryce Canyon received 6" of snow and Koosharem picked up 2" of snow.

1992 - A male in Orem was playing Nintendo in his home when a bolt of lightning struck a 30-foot Cottonwood tree in his yard. The lightning arced to a water meter on the side of the home and traveled through pipes into the living room. The electrical charge started a small fire in the carpet. Seconds before the bolt hit, electricity filled the air inside the home. "My hair was standing on end," said the Nintendo player.

SEPTEMBER 12-13

1927 - Heavy rains caused flooding across parts of southern Utah. Some amounts included: Escalante (Garfield County) 3.20", Price (Carbon County) 3.07", Alton (Kane County) 2.90", Kanab (Kane County) 2.50", and Green River (Emery County) 2.35" of rain.

SEPTEMBER 13

1940 - Heavy rain caused flooding at Price and Helper in central Utah. Basements were flooded and several houses were moved by floodwaters. One house was moved 50 feet.

1963 - Heavy rains and golf ball-sized hailstones hit Washington County, causing a flash flood that tore out Utah Highway 17 near the Berry Springs Bridge and disrupted traffic for two hours on U.S. Highway 91.

SEPTEMBER 14

1959 - Lightning started fires that destroyed a warehouse and an alfalfa mill at separate locations in Ogden.

SEPTEMBER 15

1984 - Strong thunderstorm winds at Lake Powell sunk several boats. No injuries were reported.

1985 - Thunderstorms dumped one inch diameter hail and 1.00" of rain in 15 minutes at East Carbon. Vigorous early morning thunderstorms across the state produced 700 lightning strikes during a 30-minute period.

SEPTEMBER 16

1946 - The earliest snowfall ever at Salt Lake City was recorded with a "trace" measured.

SEPTEMBER 16-19

1966 - One of the state's earliest heavy snowstorms damaged power lines, trees, shrubs, crops, and buildings across Utah. Crop damage alone was estimated at over $1,000,000 in northern Utah.

SEPTEMBER 17

1965 - An early season snowstorm hit the northern Rockies, bringing 2.2" of snow to Salt Lake City.

1961 - A hiking party of 26 persons were caught in a flash flood in a narrow canyon of the Virgin River at Zion National Park. Five members of that party were drowned. The flood resulted from 1.50" of rain falling in a short period of time. The crest of the flood reached 14 feet in some narrow gorges. At Glen Canyon, a girl was swept away by floodwaters in Wahweap Creek.

SEPTEMBER 18

1925 - Modena picked up 2.56" of rain in less than 12 hours.

SEPTEMBER 20

1983 - Cold morning low temperatures were felt across northern Utah. The Bear River Reporting Station's thermometer dipped to 10°F, Tabiona dropped to 17°F, and Smithfield recorded 21°F.

SEPTEMBER 21

1988 - One inch diameter hail fell at Clawson, ¾" diameter hail at Castledale, and ½" diameter hail at Huntington in central Utah.

SEPTEMBER 21-22

1941 - Violent winds occurred from Cache County to Davis County. Damages reached $300,000. Ogden received the brunt of the damage. An airplane hangar at the old Municipal Airport, a number of small airplane stores in the hangar, and a small brick apartment under construction were badly damaged. A municipal firehouse in North Ogden was partly destroyed.

SEPTEMBER 22-25

1967 - Four days and four nights of storms brought 4.00" of rain to Cedar City and swelled Coal Creek to near capacity. Damages to the municipal airport were estimated at $1,000.

SEPTEMBER 22-26

1986 - Cold moist air collided with warm moist air from the remnants of Tropical Storm Madeline to give Utah a taste of winter-like weather. Some valley locations received up to 3.00" of water from the storm, while up to three feet of snow fell over the higher mountains.

SEPTEMBER 23

1959 - Lightning struck a house in Ogden, shattering two bedroom windows and injuring a woman as she was talking on the telephone.

1992 - A line of thunderstorms (or squall line) rumbled across northern Utah with a lot of lightning and widespread microburst winds. Some of the wind gusts reported were: Wendover 76 mph, Lakeside 75 mph, Salt Lake Tower 74 mph, Bountiful 70 mph, University of Utah 69 mph, Taylorsville/Bennion 59 mph, and Grantsville 58 mph.

SEPTEMBER 25

1990 - A wild day across northern Utah as large hail fell in many locations. Hailstone ½" to 1½" in diameter fell in the northern and western portions of Salt Lake County. Golf ball size hailstones were reported at Park City.

SEPTEMBER 26-30

1983 - The remnants of Tropical Storm Olivia produced heavy rainfall over a large portion of Utah. Unprecedented rains caused widespread flooding in Salt Lake County. Two to four inches of rain fell on the 26th, and by the 30th over six inches was recorded. Also, heavy snow down to the 5,500 foot level created hazardous driving in the mountains, and precipitation records were set at many reporting stations.

SEPTEMBER 27

1911 - In Moab nearly 100 fruit trees were washed down canyon streams during heavy rains.

SEPTEMBER 28

1949 - A localized severe thunderstorm with heavy hail was reported at Alton. Rainfall measured 2.25". Hail fell for about one hour and measured up to two inches in diameter.

SEPTEMBER 29

1951 - One of the heaviest hailstorms ever to hit the United States passed five miles south of Emery. Hailstones larger than half-dollars covered a strip of land 300 feet wide. After 18 hours, five foot deep stacks of hail the size of cherries were found. The hailstorm completely flattened fences and gates.

SEPTEMBER 30

1971 - An early winter storm deposited 2-8" of snow along the Wasatch Front. The heavy, wet snow broke limbs off trees that were still covered with leaves.

OCTOBER 1

1984 - Lightning hit a tree in southwest Provo, causing the tree to explode into pieces. One of the large fragments went through the front window of a nearby house, showering the living room with thousands of pieces of glass.

1986 - The earliest ski season in Utah's history got under way as Powder Mountain Ski Resort opened for night skiing.

1992 - An all time record high temperature for the month of October was set at Delta with 92°F. The old record was 89°F, previously set on October 7, 1989.

OCTOBER 1-3

1916 - Heavy rains inundated parts of northern Utah. Rainfall amounts included: Farmington 4.51", Provo 2.91", Logan 2.77", and Morgan 2.72" of precipitation.

OCTOBER 2

1984 - Clawson (Emery County) received 3.55" of precipitation, including 2" of hail in a 30-hour period.

1986 - In a two-hour period during the afternoon, 450 cloud-to-ground lightning strikes were detected around the state.

OCTOBER 3

1989 - A rain cloud sat over Wendover, depositing .64" of rain. Wendover's normal annual rainfall is only 5.39".

1994 - Vernal picked up 1.26" of rain, Roosevelt received 1.12", and Spanish Fork had 1.04".

OCTOBER 4

1984 - The strongest wind gust ever measured in October at Salt Lake City occurred on this date. The record gust of 71 mph was just shy of hurricane velocity (74 mph).

OCTOBER 5

1994 - Around commute time severe thunderstorms developed over northern Utah, with many areas along the Wasatch Front pelted by hail. The Salt Lake City International Airport reported ¾" to 1¼" diameter hailstones which caused damage in the amount of $330,000 to roofs of the McDonnell Douglas Hangars. A spokesman said "it was pouring down rain inside the buildings." The Cottonwood Mall on the east side of the Salt Lake Valley received storm damage from hail 1" in diameter. The amount of the damage was 1.3 million dollars. Cottonwood Heights 1" diameter hail 10 inches deep in some gutters, with extensive tree damage.

OCTOBER 5-9

1985 - A major fall storm dumped copious amounts of rain in the valleys and snow in the mountains of southern Utah. A few areas experienced pea-size to ¼" inch diameter hail.

1993 - A major dump of moisture occurred in portions of Utah due to the remnants of Tropical Storm Norma clashing with cold air pouring out of Canada. The top of the tram at Snowbird Ski Resort received 12-18" of snow. The areas that were hit the hardest were in southern Utah and along the Wasatch Front of northern Utah. Some precipitation amounts from this storm were: Ogden Bench 3.49", Bountiful 2.71", Val Verda 2.25", Arches and four miles south of Moab 2.24", Kanab 1.73", Brigham City 1.53", and Vernal 1.47".

OCTOBER 6

1916 - Escalante (Garfield County) received a whopping 3.39" of precipitation, while Teasdale (Wayne County) reported an impressive 2.21" of rain that caused flooding and washouts.

OCTOBER 7

1975 - A major autumn storm burst into Utah. Strong winds along the Wasatch Front caused extensive damage to buildings, breaking windows, destroying signs, and toppling many trees. At Salt Lake City, winds gusted to 49 mph, but exceeded 60 mph elsewhere in the Salt Lake Valley.

OCTOBER 7-9

1960 - High temperatures dropped more than 40°F in three days along the Wasatch Front. The following temperatures were recorded highs in Salt Lake City: October 7, 83°F, October 8, 60°F, and October 9, 41°F.

OCTOBER 8

1954 - Very heavy thunderstorms caused extensive damage in Kane and Washington Counties. An observer at Orderville measured 2.10" of precipitation in one hour and fifteen minutes, and reported the worst hailstorm and flood in years. Hail was washed into piles against obstructions to the depth of several feet in some places.

OCTOBER 10

1920 - October General Conference of the Church of Jesus Christ of Latter-day Saints, held in Salt Lake City, is usually much drier than it April General Conference. Only 44% of all October conferences have received measurable precipitation. However, on this date in 1920, Salt Lake City received 1.15" of rain.

OCTOBER 11-12

1984 - Heavy rain in the valleys and very wet snow in the mountains fell over many areas of northern Utah. Nearly 2.00" of rain fell in some valleys, while a foot of heavy wet snow (with a water content of 2.00") fell at Alta Ski Resort.

OCTOBER 11-12

1986 - Easterly canyon winds whipped through the western slopes of the Wasatch Mountains. This canyon wind episode produced the following peak wind speeds: Centerville 84 mph, Farmington 75 mph, and Hill Air Force Base and Logan 61 mph.

OCTOBER 13

1987 - In Wendover, 1.15" of rain fell in 24 hours, setting a new daily record for October. Never before had this much rainfall been recorded on any day during the month of October.

OCTOBER 13-14

1983 - An inch of rain fell across Davis and Salt Lake Counties. Winds at Wahweap in southern Utah reached 55 mph.

OCTOBER 15

1994 - The snow-level dropped to near 5,000 feet over most of the state. Brian Head Ski Resort received 16" of snow, Monticello 8-10", Cedar City 7", Fillmore 6", and Tooele 5".

OCTOBER 15-16

1981 - Monroe (Sevier County) picked up 1.20" of rain in 90 minutes. Price, located in central Utah, reported 1.15" of precipitation and 4-5" of snow. Monticello, in southeast, Utah reported marble size hail.

OCTOBER 16

1991 - Salt Lake City reached a record high temperature of 85°F, which was the warmest temperature ever recorded for so late in the Fall season.

1994 - Snow continued in earnest over portions of southern Utah. Kanosh received a total of 17" of snowfall and Fillmore picked up 6". In the north, the top of the tram at Snowbird Ski Resort received 27" of snow.

OCTOBER 17-18

1938 - Heavy rains fell across Weber County in northern Utah. Amounts included Ogden with 2.56" and Riverdale with 2.55".

1984 - A "once-in-50-years lake effect snowstorm" dumped incredible snowfall amounts in the Salt Lake Valley. Salt Lake City picked up almost 1/3 of its annual snowfall as a record-breaking 18.4" of snow fell. Other incredible amounts included: Holladay 27", University of Utah 24", Cottonwood Heights 20", South Salt Lake 17", Murray 16", Sandy 15", and Kearns 6" of snow. An estimated 500,000 trees were damaged due to the weight of the snow. A 50-car pileup occurred on I-15 near Farmington. Many schools and businesses were forced to close. Damage from the storm totaled more than $1,000,000.

OCTOBER 19

1958 - Winds over 80 mph blasted through the Provo area, toppling trees, blowing over brick walls, damaging light planes, and causing considerable property damage.

OCTOBER 21

1957 - Hail up to 1¾" in diameter fell at Mexican Hat (San Juan County) in extreme southeast Utah. The hail caused damage to trailer homes, cars, and buildings.

1961 - A fast-moving cold front followed by winds over 90 mph destroyed one mile of high-tension cable in Provo. The winds broke 65-foot cedar poles six to eight feet above ground and carried them through the air like they were paper.

1985 - Strong gusty south winds preceding a cold front howled across northern Utah. A wind gust of 71 mph was reported at Lakeside on the west side of the Great Salt Lake.

OCTOBER 22

1995 - The first significant valley snowfall of the winter fell in portions of Davis, Salt Lake, and Utah counties. Snowfall amounts generally ranged from 1-3". Higher snowfall amounts occurred in parts of Utah County. Springville picked up 7", Lehi and North Orem 5", and Pleasant Grove 4".

OCTOBER 22-23

1953 - Winds gusting between 75 and 85 mph damaged schools, churches, radio and transmitting towers, and caused several traffic accidents and serious injuries in northern Utah. On the 22nd, Hill Air Force Base personnel abandoned the control tower at 4:05 PM, when wind gusts reached 85 mph.

1991 - Wellsville recorded 2.33" of precipitation from a storm that pounded many areas of Utah. Some other amounts included: Youngward 2.00", Logan Historic Farm 1.84", Liberty 1.68", Hyrum 1.60", Ogden 1.55", Milford 1.44", Richfield 1.26", and Midway 1.24".

OCTOBER 23

1956 - A pre-season winter snowstorm dumped 19" of snow at Alta and 24" at Tooele.

1991 - Early in the afternoon lightning hit the main communications antenna at the Millard County public safety building in Fillmore. The lightning bolt knocked out all power in the building, exploded plastic circuit relay casings, and welded stainless steel plates together.

OCTOBER 25-26

1989 - A major storm clobbered the northern part of Utah with thunderstorms, strong winds, rain, snow, and impressive storm precipitation totals. At the top of the tram at Snowbird Ski Resort, 24" of snow accumulated. Olympus Cove and Manti both picked up four inches of snow and Meadow received three inches of the white stuff. Some of the storm totals were: Holladay 1.95", Sandy 1.87", West Valley City 1.80", Bountiful 1.62", Hooper 1.60", Stansbury 1.57", North Salt Lake 1.53", Tooele 1.49", Wellsville 1.35", Nephi 1.31", Ogden 1.30", Alpine 1.10", and Provo BYU .84".

OCTOBER 26

1982 - Moisture from Tropical Storm Sergio collided with a cold front over northern Utah, producing heavy rains and urban flooding in some areas. Flooding was enhanced by leaves and debris that clogged storm sewers. Mudslides were reported in Parleys and Big Cottonwood Canyon.

OCTOBER 26-28

1991 - A major storm affected the entire state with phenomenal amounts of snow in the mountains and copious amounts of water in many areas. Alta Ski Resort reported a whopping 52" of snow, while Brian Head Ski Resort in southern Utah picked up an amazing 42" of powder. Most valley locations across the state received four to eight of snow with up to 10" reported at Cedar City, Tooele, and Olympus Cove. The water amounts from the storm were impressive: Stansbury 2.45", Olympus Cove 2.31", Tooele 2.27", Taylorsville 2.07", Centerville 1.94", Ogden 1.56", Cedar City 1.36", Flaming Gorge 1.23", Logan 1.21", Orem 1.17" and, Parowan 1.02".

OCTOBER 27

1992 - An 8th grader living in Salem was talking on the telephone when lightning struck a nearby transformer which sent a power surge of electricity through the telephone. The telephone was burned and the girl sustained minor injuries to her ear and hearing. In Spanish Fork, lightning struck a trampoline leaving a large hole and shattered the windows of a house.

OCTOBER 28-29

1946 - Heavy precipitation occurred throughout Utah. Two day totals included: Alta 5.68", New Harmony 4.30", Deer Creek 4.14", Santaquin 4.04", Provo 3.31", Alpine 3.24", Eureka 3.21", Delta 3.17", and Midway 3.11".

OCTOBER 28-30

1971 - A heavy snowstorm in northern Utah stranded hunters in the mountains and collapsed carport roofs on top of cars. In addition, strong canyon winds between Bountiful and Farmington covered roads with up to eight feet of drifted snow. Three campers, two trailers, and one semi-truck trailer were overturned by high winds.

OCTOBER 28-31

1992 - A large storm system hung around for days, depositing substantial amounts of water to favored northern Utah areas that do well in a southwest flow. Some of the highest precipitation amounts included: Liberty 4.60", North Ogden 4.48", Deer Creek 4.18", and Ogden 3.30".

OCTOBER 29

1959 - Wind gusts up to 90 mph occurred between Salt Lake City and Brigham City. In Centerville a filling station blew down, windows were blown out, and roofs were damaged. On a highway near Farmington, 11 semi-trailers and a small car were overturned. Estimated damages totaled $5,000,000.

1964 - Winds over 70 mph destroyed the doors and roofs of several Provo Airport hangars, and damaged three aircraft.

1988 - Thunderstorms struck Cedar City with .51" of rain, most of which fell in 20 minutes. Also, ¼" to 5/8" diameter hail blanketed the ground. It hailed for 16 minutes and the temperature dropped from 68°F down to 44°F.

OCTOBER 30

1959 - Violent winds estimated at over 100 mph ripped through Wasatch Front canyons causing several million dollars in damage to properties and structures.

1991 - The coldest day ever for any October day at a few locations. Brigham City only reached a high of 36°F which eclipsed the old record of 40°F set on October 19, 1984. Duchesne barely made it up to 24°F during the day, breaking the old record of 26°F set on October 19, 1984. Vernal only reached 27°F for a high temperature, breaking the old record of 29°F set on October 31, 1972.

OCTOBER 31

1991 - Brrrr!!! What a cold morning across the state of Utah. Many new record low temperatures were set. Randolph experienced the coldest October morning ever with a bone chilling -1°F.

OCTOBER 31 - NOVEMBER 1

1936 - Two inches of rain fell over many areas of northern Utah.

NOVEMBER 1

1963 - The Great Salt Lake reached an all-time low of 4,191.35 feet, some 20 feet lower than the all-time high set in 1986.

1986 - Hurricane-force easterly canyon winds hit Davis and Weber Counties. Wind speeds reached 81 mph at Bountiful and 74 mph at Farmington. Power lines, trees, and signs were downed.

1995 - Heavy rains fell across portions of Washington and Kane Counties in southwest Utah. Rainfall amounts for the day were: Hurricane 2.23", La Verkin 2.10", Kanab 1.74", and Virgin 1.43".

NOVEMBER 2

1994 - The first major winter storm of the season struck the valley locations of northern Utah. Power outages caused by the weight of the snow kept power crews busy. Parleys Canyon was closed for about two hours during the evening due to numerous accidents. Snowfall amounts from the storm generally ranged from three to seven inches from the Cache Valley southward to Nephi. A few spots received even higher amounts, such as North Salt Lake with 10" and Mapleton and Laketown with 9".

NOVEMBER 3

1957 - A late fall cloudburst hit areas near Castle Dale and Green River in east-central Utah. Rain fell in the valleys with snow in the mountains. Some nearby areas were isolated by flooding, with several washouts reported along the swollen Green River.

1994 - The same major winter storm that hit northern Utah on the 2nd reached southern Utah on the 3rd, bringing large amounts of snowfall to an area from Fillmore to Modena. Snowfall amounts included: Kanosh 24", Modena 18", Milford and Meadow 12", Fillmore 11", and Cedar City 10" (4" in one hour). Later in the day the storm moved into the Uintah Basin dropping 6" of snow at Vernal.

NOVEMBER 7

1986 - Lake effect snows piled up south of the Great Salt Lake. Tooele picked up 16" of snow, while South Jordan received 10" of the white stuff.

NOVEMBER 7-8

1983 - A winter storm, enhanced by the Great Salt Lake, dumped heavy snow in portions of the Salt Lake Valley. Over 12" of snow was reported from Sandy westward to West Valley City.

NOVEMBER 8

1986 - Utah's highest wind gust was recorded at Hidden Peak at Snowbird Ski Resort: 124 mph.

NOVEMBER 8-9

1984 - Alta Ski Resort received 39" of snow in a 30-hour period.

NOVEMBER 9

1985 - An early winter snowstorm unloaded snow across extreme northern Utah. Wellsville received 8" of snow.

NOVEMBER 10

1955 - Lightning damaged the Loa Elementary School at Loa (Wayne County) in southern Utah.

1982 - In southern Utah 10" of snow fell at the Long Valley Junction in Wayne County.

NOVEMBER 11

1978 - Strong easterly canyon winds along the Wasatch Front blew the roofs off buildings and homes, and blew down power lines, signs, and trees. Storm damage reached $300,000. The state's highest wind gust for a bench location was recorded on the Bountiful Bench at 120 mph.

1983 - A peak wind gust of 105 mph was reported on the top of the gondola at Park City Ski Resort.

NOVEMBER 12

1973 - Winds gusted over 75 mph at Salt Lake, Ogden, and Tooele, causing damage to mobile homes and construction sites. Trees were uprooted and power lines were downed, resulting in power outages throughout northern Utah.

NOVEMBER 14

1955 - A motorist who wandered away from his stalled car a few miles from Fairfield (Utah County), was eventually found lying on the road and nearly frozen to death.

NOVEMBER 14-16

1958 - Up to three feet of snow fell in the mountains and 15" at lower elevations, blocking northern Utah highways and downing utility lines.

1991 - A vigorous storm system moved into southern Utah with heavy snow. Bryce Canyon picked up 26" of snowfall, Enterprise received a whopping 18-20", and Panguitch had 13".

NOVEMBER 15-16

1964 - One of the worst windstorms ever recorded in Utah caused over $1,000,000 in damage. Wind speeds over 80 mph toppled a church spire in

Logan. Several aircraft were seriously damaged in Box Elder County. Schools were closed in Weber County because broken windows caused rapid heat loss. Highways between Ogden and Salt Lake were closed for hours after large trucks and trailers were overturned. Power outages occurred throughout northern Utah.

NOVEMBER 16-19

1994 - A massive snow storm began in northern Utah on the 16th and continued into the 17th, and spread into southern Utah on the 18th and 19th. Snowfall totals included: Alta 48", Brighton 43", Park City Ski Resort 37", Duck Creek 36", Enterprise 24", Cedar City 21", Midway 20", Fillmore 19", New Harmony 16", Spanish Fork 14", Springville and Coalville 13", Tooele and Manti 12", Provo BYU 11", Monticello, Ogden, Escalante, Heber, and Kanab 10".

NOVEMBER 18

1983 - Lake Effect hit the southern end of the Salt Lake Valley, dropping 12" of snow fell on Herriman and Bluffdale.

1985 - Infrequent winter thunderstorms developed off the Great Salt Lake. Lightning even hit a swamp cooler in the Salt Lake Valley. As much as 6" of snow fell along the Wasatch Front.

NOVEMBER 19

1982 - Strong wind gusts up to 70 mph occurred at Tooele and Bountiful in northern Utah.

NOVEMBER 19-20

1992 - A major winter storm clobbered the Wasatch Front and most of northern Utah making the morning commute a really true adventure. A 15-20 minute junket to work turned out to be a 90 minute ordeal with Mother Nature. Some snowfall amounts were: Olympus Cove and Bountiful Bench 16", SLC Avenues and Layton Bench 10-12", Scofield and Salem 12", Highland Park 11", Payson 10", Tooele and downtown Salt Lake City 9", Taylorsville 7", and Coalville 5".

NOVEMBER 20

1902 - "Red snow amounting to one inch" fell at Tropic (Garfield County) in south central Utah. The red color of the snow was due to the red sand which had been picked up by the winds. The area has large formations of red sandstone rock.

NOVEMBER 20-23

1983 - A broad storm system unloaded snow all across Utah. Snow reports of over 12" in valley locations were common. The Great Salt Lake "lake effect" dumped two feet of snow on Tooele. Areas from Kaysville to North Ogden reported up to 12" of snow. Gusty winds blew and drifted the snow, reducing surface visibilities to near zero in some areas.

NOVEMBER 21

1977 - Winds gusting to more than 100 mph ripped through Little Cottonwood Canyon. Sustained winds of

75 mph with gusts of over 100 mph were reported at Snowbird Ski Resort. The winds created deep snow drifts.

NOVEMBER 22-24

1992 - Alta set a new 24-hour snowfall record for a mountain location with 45" of snow from 11:30 AM on the 22nd to 11:30 AM on the 23rd. This eclipsed the previous record of 38" set at this same location on December 1-2, 1982. In addition, heavy snow fell along many bench locations of the Wasatch Front. The Bountiful Bench received 17-21" of snow from this same storm.

NOVEMBER 24

1952 - After 134 days without measurable precipitation, Delle, located 50 miles west of Salt Lake City, ended its drought that began on July 12.

1980 - A hefty snowstorm permitted some ski areas to open early. The mountains of northern Utah received over 12" of "the greatest snow on earth."

NOVEMBER 25

1983 - The 3rd winter storm of the month gave many areas of Utah a real taste of winter. Snowfall amounts included: Tooele 12", Kanosh 11", Monticello 7", and Vernal 5".

NOVEMBER 25-26

1984 - A localized lake effect storm dropped 20" of snow in the South Jordan/Copper City area of the Salt Lake Valley. Kearns reported 13" of snow and Tooele picked up 12".

NOVEMBER 25-27

1988 - A series of winter storms pounded the northern Utah mountains with 50" of powder falling at Alta and 41" at Snowbird. The Spruces in Big Cottonwood Canyon picked up 33" of snow.

1989 - A block buster snowstorm coupled with lake effect enhancement dumped an incredible 60" of snow at Alta in the northern Utah mountains. Solitude recorded 56" of powder and Park City received 23". Midway received the most snow for a valley location with 14" of the white stuff. Water amounts were very impressive in the mountains with 6.61" of water recorded at Alta.

NOVEMBER 25-29

1994 - A storm that lasted for four days came in several surges and combined with the warm waters of the Great Salt Lake to produce the DLE—Dreaded Lake Effect—across northern Utah. Massive amounts of snow fell in the Wasatch Mountains. The Alta Guard (UDOT location) received an incredible 92" of snow, while Snowbird reported 64" of snow. Valley snowfall amounts were substantial as well: Bountiful Bench 17", Snyderville and Midway 16", Sugarhouse 15", Holladay 14", Spanish Fork 12", Sandy 11", Salt Lake City International Airport and Heber 10".

NOVEMBER 26

1993 - Brrrr!!! A very cold morning with low temperatures well below zero at many locations: Woodruff -26°F, Randolph -25°F, Snyderville -13°F, and Trenton, Alta and Park City -6°F.

NOVEMBER 27-30

1981 - Cold weather produced heavy snow in southern Utah. Six inches of snow fell at Kanab and Monticello.

NOVEMBER 28-29

1975 - A major winter storm caused $350,000 in damages across northern Utah. A cross-country skier caught in the storm froze to death. Snowfall totals of 12" were common in the valleys, with higher amounts along the bench areas.

NOVEMBER 29-30

1983 - The Cache Valley received nearly 18" of snow. Cold Canadian air followed behind the front. Minimum temperatures came in as follows: Randolph -21°F, Woodruff -20°F, and Smithfield -17°F.

NOVEMBER 30

1982 - St. George received a near-record of .98" rain in 24-hours.

1995 - Record high temperatures were set for the day at over 20 stations across the state. The Salt Lake City International Airport set a new record with a maximum temperature of 68.1°F. This is the warmest reading ever for so late in November, and November 1995 was the warmest November on record at Salt Lake City.

DECEMBER 1

1995 - The warmest December day ever for many locations across Utah. The following locations broke all-time high temperatures for the month of December: Brigham City and Ogden 66°F, Delta, Nephi, and Tooele 70°F, Heber 68°F, Logan 67°F, Midway and Vernal 65°F, Park City 57°F, Provo BYU 72°F, Richfield 68°F, Salt Lake City 69°F, and Zion NP 74°F.

DECEMBER 1-2

1982 - The atmospheric pressure at Salt Lake City fell to an all-time low of 29.01 inches of mercury. This broke the record of 29.04 inches recorded on January 12, 1932. Heavy snow fell throughout northern Utah, with Bountiful Bench receiving 17" and Salt Lake City 9". Major traffic tie-ups occurred and schools closed.

DECEMBER 3

1983 - Strong winds preceded a vigorous cold front in northern Utah. Tooele reported a peak wind gust of 72 mph, while Park City Ski Resort reported a gust of 100 mph at the top of the gondola.

DECEMBER 3-10

1902 - Fog prevailed over the Salt Lake Valley for eight consecutive days.

DECEMBER 4-6

1966 - Record-breaking rainfall over southwest Utah caused the Virgin River to rise 12 feet in the Zion Narrows. A new campground and amphitheater at Zion National Park were washed out. Springdale was briefly isolated and several miles of Highway 15 were washed out. During the deluge the following rainfall amounts included: Grassy Flat 12.60", Duck Creek 11.39", and Pine Valley 11.00".

DECEMBER 5

1952 - Extreme winds estimated over 100 mph toppled and completely destroyed KSL-TV's tower. (the tallest in the country) located atop 9,200-foot Coon Peak in the Oquirrh Mountains, 17 miles southwest of Salt Lake City. The falling tower narrowly missed the operators' quarters. The tower, designed to withstand much stronger winds, fell because of a faulty section.

1966 - Winds over 58 mph blasted through Milford (Beaver County) in southwest Utah. The winds damaged trailers, cinderblock walls, and offices at the Milford Airport. Power was out at the airport weather station for nearly six hours.

DECEMBER 6

1978 - Powerful easterly canyon winds up to 85 mph blew along I-15 between Bountiful and Hill Field in northern Utah. The winds overturned many large trailers and trailer trucks.

1985 - Dense fog resulted in a multi-car accident at Beck Street in North Salt Lake.

DECEMBER 6-7

1957 - Blizzard conditions dumped up to 16" of snow in the Uinta Basin of northeast Utah. Several canyon roads were closed along the Wasatch Range. A number of people were injured in Weber County.

DECEMBER 7-8

1982 - Cedar City residents in southwest Utah were the recipients of 15" of snow. Winds created large snowdrifts and caused zero visibility in the Farmington area of northern Utah. Strong winds blew cars into guard rails in Parleys Canyon.

DECEMBER 8-9

1985 - A strong winter storm dumped up to 24" of snow in the valleys of the Wasatch Front and up to 48" of snow in the mountains.

DECEMBER 10

1982 - Freezing rain fell across central Utah, causing serious travel problems in and around Delta and Fillmore.

1985 - Canyon winds hit northern Utah with peak wind gusts as follows: Centerville 74 mph, Smithfield 72 mph, Bountiful 70 mph, and Utah State University in Logan 68 mph.

1990 - A strong temperature inversion only allowed the high temperature to reach 45°F at Salt Lake City. Meanwhile the inversion broke in Provo, allowing the high temperature to climb to 65°F.

DECEMBER 11

1973 - Winds gusting to 75 mph swept across northern Utah. Power outages occurred and trucks and mobile homes were toppled in Tooele County.

DECEMBER 12

1958 - Winds gusting over 60 mph in southwest Utah caused dust that reduced visibilities to near zero.

DECEMBER 13

1983 - A strong winter storm hit northern Utah, producing 12" of snow along the Provo Bench.

DECEMBER 13-14

1990 - A fast moving cold front blasted the western half of Utah with heavy snow, 30-40 mph winds, and lightning/thunder (a rare Utah occurrence in December). Some snowfall amounts for the three to four hour period following the front included: Brighton 23", Snowbird 20", and generally 3-6" across the northwest valleys and 4-8" across the southwest valleys.

DECEMBER 14-15

1988 - A "severe canyon wind episode" happened in Davis, Weber, and Salt Lake Counties, and the Cache Valley. The winds reached hurricane force late on the 14th until mid-afternoon on the 15th. The damage produced was phenomenal. Semis were overturned between Farmington/Kaysville on I-15, closing the roadway for a period of time. At one time, 50,000 UP&L customers were without power. Trees were uprooted, windows blown out, trailers moved off their foundations and one overturned. A house under construction in Layton was destroyed, a roof was blown off of a house in Centerville, schools were closed throughout Davis and Weber Counties, and several businesses were closed. Wind-chill temperatures dropped to -40°F. Some of the wind reports were: Centerville 104 mph (the highest the anemometer reads), KVNU Radio in Logan 90-100 mph, South Ogden 92 mph, Logan and Smithfield 84 mph, Hill AFB 74 mph, Kaysville 67 mph, Randolph 64 mph, and Taylorsville 59 mph.

DECEMBER 14-20

1969 - Persistent dense fog and smoke settled over the valleys of Wasatch Front. Limited visibility caused one traffic death and two aircraft deaths.

DECEMBER 15-21

1957 - A week-long dense fog episode in the Salt Lake Valley severely reduced visibility.

DECEMBER 16-17

1970 - Old Man Winter delivered record snowfall along the Wasatch Front and northern Utah mountains. Up to 24" of snow fell in valley locations, with two deaths attributed to the storm. Roofs collapsed under the weight of the snow.

DECEMBER 17-20

1990 - On the 17th, strong south winds howled ahead of an approaching monster winter storm that was taking aim on the state. As the storm deepened strong south winds developed in Box Elder County and in the Cache Valley, resulting in blowing and drifting snow. On the 18th, Cedar City reported a wind gust of 66 mph from the south. A cold front (with some lightning flashes) moved along the Wasatch Front during the evening. On the 19th and 20th, the main storm system clobbered the entire state with heavy snow. Some snowfall amounts included: Duck Creek 32", Brighton 27", Elk Meadows and Powder Mountain 24", Park City 20", Pleasant Grove 14", Long Valley Junction 12-16", Orem 13", Springville 12", Monticello 11", and Meadow and Fillmore 10".

DECEMBER 19-20

1984 - Enterprise, in southwest Utah, received 17" of snow.

DECEMBER 20-26

1916 - The heaviest snows "for 50 years" piled high in northern Utah. Severe blizzards occurred in many places as many correspondents reported the snow was the "heaviest ever known."

DECEMBER 22

1981 - A mammoth snowstorm hit the Salt Lake Valley. Bench areas received over a foot of snow, with 19" reported at Olympus Cove.

1990 - The high temperature of 2°F at the Salt Lake City International Airport established a new all-time record low maximum temperature. Brrrr!!!

DECEMBER 22-23

1987 - A "big-time" snow storm walloped all of Utah, especially the mountains and western half of the state. The storm came just in time to give most of Utah a White Christmas. Some snowfall totals included: Alta. 37", Snowbird 35", Elk Meadows 30", Fillmore 21", Kanosh 18", Park City and Olympus Cove 17", Meadow 14", Tooele 12", Cache Valley, Cedar City, and Springville 10".

DECEMBER 23

1955 - Locally heavy rains caused a sharp increase in the water flow of many streams in northern Utah. Several thousand acres of farmland in Morgan County were flooded when creeks overflowed their banks. Roads along the Weber River were covered with two feet of water. One concrete bridge was washed out near Mountain Green, stranding five families. Unofficial rainfall estimates of up to 3.00" were given.

1990 - An Arctic chill had a firm grip on Utah with many new record cold temperatures observed. All-time record lows for any time/any month were set at: Milford -35°F, previously -34°F on 1/9/37; Delta -30°F, previously -27°F on 2/7/89; Nephi -21°F, previously -18°F on 1/29/49; and 2/6/82 Tooele -16°F, previously -16°F also on 2/10/33. In addition, some other cold low temperatures were: Middle Sink (up Logan Canyon) -57°F, Woodruff -44°F, Flowell -43°F, Roosevelt -40°F, and Richfield -32°F. St. George tied for the coldest December morning on record with 3°F.

DECEMBER 24

1990 - The all time record low temperature for the Cache Valley was tied at the Historic Farm with -44°F. Previously this temperature was reached at Lewiston on 1/21/37.

DECEMBER 24-25

1983 - "I'm dreaming of a White Christmas," became a reality across the state. Many areas received heavy snow on Christmas day. At Logan, canyon winds gusted to 62 mph, causing severe blizzard conditions.

1988 - A "White Christmas" developed across Utah as an intense winter storm moved through the state. Snowfall amounts were phenomenal with 6-12" common in the lower valleys and 18-22" on some bench locations, with about 24" in the mountains. Some snowfall storm totals included: Glendale 24", Olympus Cove 22", Sandy 21", Bountiful 17-20", Kearns and Brigham City 17", Centerville 16", Tremonton and Holladay 15", Fruit Heights, Smithfield, and Clarkston 14", and Monticello, Kanab, and Springville 12".

DECEMBER 25

1990 - Many towns across Utah experienced their coldest high temperature on record: Brigham City 16°F, Fillmore 10°F, Logan 0°F, Ogden 14°F, Spanish Fork 12°F, St. George 37°F, and Tooele 21°F.

DECEMBER 26

1984 - Under a strong temperature inversion, Salt Lake City reported a high temperature of only 27°F. In comparison, Provo BYU reported a balmy high temperature of 51°F.

DECEMBER 27

1988 - A very dense patch of fog along the Jordan River at around 5400 South and 1100 West caused a 67 car pileup on I-215.

DECEMBER 28

1983 - The first sunny day in the Salt Lake Valley in 50 days.

DECEMBER 28-29

1972 - A heavy snowstorm accompanied by strong winds deposited a record-breaking 18.1" of snow in 24 hours at Salt Lake City, closing the Salt Lake City International Airport for 20 hours. Winds piled up heavy snow on the roof of a new mall in Salt Lake County, causing the collapse of a 250 foot section.

DECEMBER 29-30

1973 - Massive avalanches caused damages in excess of $250,000 to automobiles and resort buildings at Snowbird and Alta Ski Resorts.

DECEMBER 30

1985 - Five deaths were attributed to extremely hazardous weather conditions, as "the worst" freezing rain episode "in recent memory," occurred from Utah County to Sevier County.

DECEMBER 30-31

1975 - A major winter storm produced near blizzard conditions across northwest Utah, resulting in numerous vehicle accidents and damages estimated at $300,000.

January-July 1996
by
William J. Alder

JANUARY 1996

An "elephantine" amount of snow descended on the Salt Lake City International Airport during the month of January 1996 to the tune of 45.0 inches. This was the second greatest amount of snow for January (the record being 50.3 inches in 1993) and the second greatest for any month.

JANUARY 23-26, 1996

A "super snow storm" moved into Utah with very heavy amounts of snow and winds up to 50 mph. Due to the heavy snowfall making roads nearly impassable, there were numerous school closures. Some valley and mountain locations measured snowfall in the feet. The snowfall amounts in Davis and Salt Lake Counties were enhanced by the Great Salt Lake "lake effect."

JANUARY 26, 1996

Many avalanches occurred in the Wasatch Mountains on the 26 and 27. This was due to the heavy amounts of snow and very strong "snow loading" winds in the mountains. One catastrophic avalanche occurred in Big Cottonwood Canyon in the Argenta Area on the 26th. It was about 2 miles long, covered 800 feet of the roadway, and was 15-20 feet deep. The last time an avalanche crossed the road in this area was in 1947. Big Cottonwood Canyon was closed for over 18 hours due to avalanche concerns.

JANUARY 31, 1996

A massive avalanche occurred early on the 31st in the Bridal Veil Falls area of Provo Canyon, and the tremendous amount of snow it released closed both Provo and American Fork Canyons. The avalanche moved down the north facing slope, across the river, and up onto the highway where snow blocked the road in both directions. The snow and debris created a dam across the Provo River about 40 feet high as measured from the river bottom. It was 150 yards across the river and about 40 yards up the down the river. The Provo River was damned for a time, but the majority of the water was diverted around the blockage. The water finally cut through around the slide and concerns for a catastrophic failure were averted. The majority of the Bridal Veil tram system and gift/snack shop were destroyed. Damage estimates were between $500,000 and $1,000,000.

FEBRUARY 2, 1996

A ski patrolman at Solitude Ski Resort was killed in an avalanche. He and another patrolman were triggering slides to assess the safety of Solitude Ski Resort's Honeycomb Canyon when a massive avalanche ripped down a northeast-facing slope. The victim and his partner lobbed a charge from the ridge and stepped to what was believed to be a safe spot while the 90-second fuse burned. The explosion apparently unleashed an interconnected series of snow layers that reached over the ridge to where the patrollers stood. The avalanche sucked everything off the ridge as well as both patrolmen. The one grabbed a tree and was able to hang on while the victim tumbled hundreds of feet through trees and over rocks. He was buried 16 minutes before other ski patrol personnel got him out. He was rushed to the hospital where he was listed in critical/unstable condition. Unfortunately, he died on February 18th.

FEBRUARY 22, 1996

A cold front moved through the Wasatch Front during the morning hours of the 22nd, laced with strong winds. Snowfall was enhanced in portions of Davis and Weber Counties due to "lake effect" squalls off the Great Salt Lake. A major 20-car pileup and another 8-car pileup occurred on I-15 in the Clearfield area about noon due to one of these heavy bursts of snow. Also, another pileup involving several cars occurred on I-80 near State Street.

FEBRUARY 24-26, 1996

Two major onslaughts of snow occurred during the period with heavy amounts of snow in several valley locations. On the 26th, a tremendous pileup of various types of vehicles occurred on I-215 during the afternoon and involved about 65-70 vehicles. Also, another significant wreck involving 24 vehicles occurred in the Farmington area on I-15.

MARCH 27, 1996

A cross-country skier was killed by an avalanche in Maybird Gulch in Little Cottonwood Canyon (just down from Snowbird). The fatality was a 50-year-old male who was caught in a small avalanche which carried him into a tree.

APRIL 16-20, 1996

A series of storms moved through northern Utah with rain, heavy snow, lightning and thunder, snow pellets and gusty winds. Lightning struck a B-757 airplane on the 17th and a B-727 on the 18th as they were departing from the Salt Lake City International Airport. Neither planes were damaged, but one returned to the airport.

MAY 28, 1996

At 9:45 AM, a small short-lived tornado was observed southeast of Delta and northwest of Holden near McCornick. It was in an open field with no associated damaged.

MAY 29, 1996

At 5:20 PM, a small short-lived tornado touched down in a Syracuse subdivision just north of Antelope

Drive. The intersection of 1000 West and 1575 South was hardest hit with numerous mature trees blown down. Only minor damage occurred to homes in this area. Eyewitnesses at this location saw the funnel.

MAY 29, 1996

At 5:25 PM, the Freeport Center and Americold Incorporated Warehouse in Clearfield was hit with microbursts winds between 70-80 mph. Two large pine trees were blown over at the entrance to the Freeport Center. A parked trailer was blown over and the roof overhang of a warehouse loading dock was ripped off. Americold lost 450 feet of roofing and 8 loading dock doors were blown in. Less than an eighth of a mile further east, three large mature pine tress were blown over at two residences.

MAY 29, 1996

At 5:30 PM, an F1 tornado set down on the west side of Washington Boulevard at 2100 North in North Ogden. (An F1 tornado has winds of 73-112 mph.) The tornado path was very narrow (100 feet) and traveled east along the north side of 2100 North for approximately 1¼ miles. The tornado path ended roughly ½ mile from the abrupt rise of the mountains. Two homes sustained major damage from trees falling on them. Automobiles in the parking lot at the Health Spa on Washington Boulevard were pushed sideways by the force of the wind and at least one vehicle sustained major damage from flying debris at that location. One home near the end of the tornado path lost 12-14 fully mature pine trees and numerous other mature trees were lost at a commercial trout fishing pond at the end of the tornado path. Amazingly, only one person (a woman) sustained slight injuries to her face from flying glass. Estimates of damage along the entire path of the tornado totaled about $500,000.

JUNE 1996

It was a very stressful month for fire fighters, as wildfires took a tremendous toll on acreage across the state. Scattered thunderstorms, lightning, winds, hot temperatures and low humidities acerbated the fire situation. The most notable fire was the Little Sahara Fire in Juab County that consumed about 50,000 acres. Other major wildfires consumed over 24,000 acres.

JUNE 21, 1996

One-inch diameter hail dented vehicles and destroyed crops in and around Duchesne.

JULY 1996

The dry conditions that "reigned" during the majority of July contributed to the preponderance of wildfires, resulting in a tremendous amount of acreage being burned--like about 150,500 acres! Of the 10 major wildfires, nine were caused by lightning and the other by human activity.

JULY 9, 1996

A cloudburst scored a direct hit on Monticello, with copious rains and pea to marble size hail that piled up two to three inches deep in town and up to four feet deep around clogged storm drains. The rain occurred between 12:05 PM and 1:25 PM, with the heaviest falling in about one hour. A National Weather Service spotter with a wedge rain gauge reported 2.00 inches in 40 minutes, 2:30 inches in 60 minutes, and 2.64 inches in 80 minutes. Basements were flooded and some businesses in town received water and extensive debris.

JULY 16, 1996

Severe thunderstorms moved into portions of the Wasatch Front during the afternoon and evening. A strong wind gust blew out a third-floor window at the State Capitol during a meeting. One legislator receiving minor injuries from flying glass.

At about 10:00 PM, on July 18, 1918, two large bolts of lightning struck and killed 654 head of sheep on Mill Canyon Peak in American Fork Canyon. According to one historical account: "Forked lightning had struck twice and split down two sides of the peak. ...There was about a seventy-five foot swath in between the dead sheep and where not a one was injured. ...The dead sheep all had to be moved to the opposite side of the canyon so as to be off the 'water shed.' [Men] counted them as they were moved, six-hundred and fifty-four sheep had been killed." (Photo by the U.S. Forest Service. Historical information provided by Darlene Hagberg of Salt Lake City.)

On September 1, 1939, lightning hit and killed 835 sheep that had been bedded down for the night on the top of Pine Canyon in the Raft River Mountains of Box Elder County in northwestern Utah. Rain from a passing thunderstorm wet the ground and sheep, causing the lightning's electrical discharge to move completely through the herd of female sheep and lambs. The next morning, fifteen sheep (out of 850) were found alive but in a dazed condition. The sheepherder was knocked temporarily unconscious, but escaped death because he was in a tent. However, burned spots on his canvas tent revealed he probably missed the fate of the sheep by only a slim margin. (Photo courtesy of National Weather Service.)

At about 3:00 AM, on August 12, 1985, a large lightning strike hit the southwestern part of the Salt Lake Valley. This picture was taken from Blue Fox Circle (at 6075 South and 3686 West) in Kearns. (Photo by Mike Rogers)

In June 1996, four major wildfires consumed 74,700 acres in Utah. In addition, numerous smaller fires also took their toll. These two pictures show a lightning strike in mid-June that started a small fire at the Point of the Mountain. Note the bolt of lightning on the left, and the resultant fire (or bright spot on the hillside) on the right. (Photo by Dave Fulghum.)

On August 13, 1923, flood waters caused extensive damage in Willard. This is the Main Street of Willard after the flood had happened. (Photo by L.M. Winsor.)

During the rapid spring thaw of 1952, 1300 South Street in Salt Lake City became a river of water with dirt and sandbag boundaries. (Photo courtesy of National Weather Service.)

On September 29, 1982, floodwaters destroyed portions of the road near the Storm Mountain area of Big Cottonwood Canyon east of Salt Lake City. The flooding occurred after several days of heavy rains brought on by tropical moisture that moved into the state from dying hurricane Olivia and the energy supplied from an active cold front. (Photo by David Carpenter.)

In the Spring of 1983, rapid warming during the last week of May and the first part of June caused rivers to rise dramatically throughout Utah. In Salt Lake City, several major streets were turned into rivers with sandbag boundaries. This is a picture of the intersection of State Street and 100 South. The Federal Building is in the background. (Photo courtesy of the National Weather Service.)

In the Spring of 1983, rapid warming during the last week of May and the first part of June caused rivers to rise dramatically throughout Utah. In Salt Lake City, several major streets were turned into rivers with sandbag boundaries. This is a picture of State Street at 300 South. The State Capitol is in the far background. (Photo by Jim Duthie.)

In the Spring of 1983, rapid warming during the last week of May and the first part of June caused rivers to rise dramatically throughout Utah. In Salt Lake City, several major streets were turned into rivers with sandbag boundaries. This is a picture of 1300 South Street at 700 West. (Photo courtesy of the National Weather Service.)

On June 23, 1983, billions of gallons of water broke through the DMAD Dam northeast of Delta and spread across low laying lands and roads--including this road located two miles northwest of Delta--and flooded the towns of Deseret and Oasis with several feet of water. The spillway of the earthen DMAD Dam was destroyed by heavy rains and rapid spring runoff. (Photo courtesy of National Weather Service.)

During the past 149 years, the Great Salt Lake has peaked three times at 4,211 feet above sea level: 4,211.60 feet in June 1873, 4,211.50 feet in June 1986, and 4,211.60 feet in June 1987. This picture of the Saltair Resort on the southeast shore of the Great Salt Lake was taken during the flood years of the 1980's. Large pumps were installed on the west side of the Great Salt Lake (at a cost of $60 million) and began pumping water into the west desert in 1987. These pumps now make it possible for man to control the level of the lake. (Photo courtesy of the National Weather Service.)

On August 9, 1920, hail one to two inches in diameter killed hundreds of birds and chickens and knocked out windows and damaged roofs of homes in Lehi. The hail injured several people--including one man who had an ear partially torn off by the falling hailstones. (Photo by Zelda Kirkham.)

On August 19, 1945, towering thunderstorms pounded the Salt Lake Airport with high winds, heavy rain, and two-inch diameter hailstones. Nearly 50 fabric-covered airplanes were badly damaged, and hundreds of windows were broken in buildings in and around the airport. (Photo courtesy of the National Weather Service.)

On September 3, 1983, thunderstorms produced ½" to 1½" diameter hail throughout the Salt Lake Valley, destroying gardens, denting cars, and damaging roofs. (Photo courtesy of National Weather Service.)

On October 5, 1994, severe thunderstorms produced ¼" to 1" diameter hail that pelted many areas along the Wasatch Front. This picture shows hail collected at the Salt Lake City International Airport. The hail caused $330,000 in damage to McDonnell Douglas Hangers. Hail piled up two inches deep in parts of Cottonwood Heights, Holladay and Millcreek. (Photo courtesy of the National Weather Service.)

During the Winter of 1948-1949, heavy snow, severe cold and high winds caused serious problems throughout Utah. This picture shows the road to the Salt Lake Airport clogged by drifting snow during February 1949. (Photo by Phil Williams.)

At about 7:00 PM on January 10, 1964, forty mile-per-hour winds caused newly fallen snow to roll up like a lady's hand muff, creating an army of "snow rollers" that marched through Sugarhouse Park in Salt Lake City. (Photo by L.V. McNeely.)

On October 18, 1984, a "lake effect" snowstorm dropped 22 inches of snow in 24 hours on the east benches of the Salt Lake Valley. The man in this photo is Paul R. Rich of Holladay. (Photo by of the Salt Lake Tribune.)

On January 11, 1993, a record snow depth of 26 inches was measured at the Salt Lake City International Airport (the previous record being 23 inches in January 1949). On the morning of January 11th, William J. Alder, Meteorologist-in-charge of the Salt Lake City National Weather Service Forecast Office, took this picture of snow that had accumulated in front of his home in Holladay. (Photo by William J. Alder.)

On March 4, 1993, up to fourteen feet of snow covered the ground at Duck Creek Village east of Cedar City. (Photo by Mel Aldrich.)

On February 13, 1885, a snowslide at Alta (that was then a mining town) killed 16 people. This photograph was taken on July 3, 1885. (Photo by C.R. Savage.)

On December 23, 1988, a cold front produced heavy snow over the Wasatch Front, with up to five inches reported in some valleys, eight inches along the benches, and two to three feet in the mountains. Several avalanches occurred up Little Cottonwood Canyon. This bus was caught in a snowslide at White Pine in Little Cottonwood Canyon. (Photos courtesy of the National Weather Service.)

On February 20, 1971, canyon winds gusting to 88 mph flipped over house trailers in the Golden Bell Trailer Court near Farmington. (Photo by the Deseret News.)

On April 4-6, 1983, strong canyon winds created havoc along the Wasatch Front. Wind speeds gusted over 70 mph in many locations, and Hill Air Force Base recorded a gust to 104 mph. Hundreds of trees were uprooted, numerous windows were blown out, and several semi trucks were blown over. The train in this picture was derailed near Lagoon. Total damage from the winds was estimated at eight million dollars. (Photo by Ogden Standard Examiner.)

At 3:12 PM (MDT), on July 24, 1981, a tornado touched down about three miles north of the Hanksville Airport. The tornado lasted for about 15 minutes, took on a red color (from the red dirt and soil it picked up), and uprooted some fence posts. (Photo by Barbara J. Ekker.)

On August 25, 1987, a cold-air funnel type tornado touched down briefly west of Plymouth, then receded back into the clouds. (Photo courtesy of Christine Caldwell. Picture taken from a hill above the Hampton Ford Historical Site at about 3500 West 15200 North, Collinston, Utah.)

On May 21, 1992, a 45-foot wide tornado was spotted about 10 miles west of Beaver by a person driving south on I-15. After the person spotted the tornado, it quickly lifted back into the clouds. The tornado occurred in open country, and caused no damage. (Photo courtesy of National Weather Service.)

In August 1994, a controlled burning of vegetation on the southeast shore of Yuba Lake produced a towering firewhirl. (Photo by Jim Hanks.)

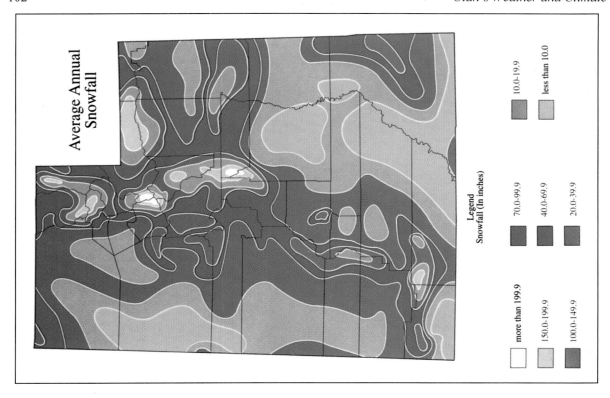

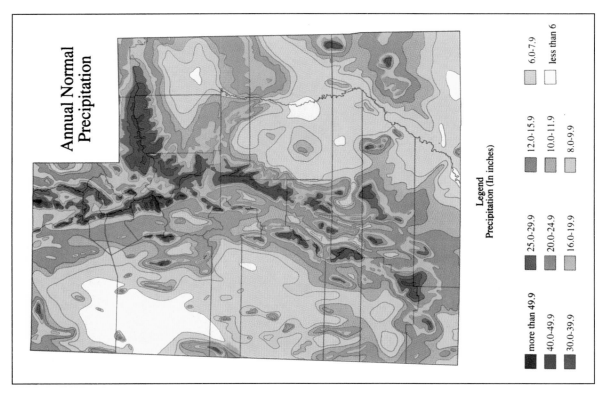

These climatic charts have been reproduced from the book *Utah Climate* (1992), courtesy of the Utah Climate Center at Utah State University.

Utah Climate Center

by
Donald T. Jensen and Gaylen L. Ashcroft

The Utah Climate Center houses all of the climate and weather data for Utah. It is a responsive group of people dedicated to using archived data to link yesterday with today and tomorrow. Located on Utah State University campus, the Utah Climate Center has a three-fold mission:

1.) Research climate and its affects on living organisms.

2.) Provide workshops and materials for weather and climate education of Utah's residents.

3.) Collect, archive, analyze and distribute quality climate data.

Research and Publication

Climate and bioclimate research conducted at the Utah Climate Center includes: methods of screening for data errors, thunderstorm research, spatial interpolation of climate data, mapping techniques, orchard heating studies, and studies of effects of weather on poison plant ingestion by range cattle. We have produced several books, including *Utah Climate*, and are currently doing *World Climate Atlas for Agriculture*. We also produce a weekly climate bulletin.

Education in Utah

An interactive computer program called *The Climate Time Machine* has been developed to retrieve, manipulate, graph, and display climate data. The program has been distributed on CD-ROM to all Utah elementary schools. The ROM also contains world climate data, a tutorial, and lesson plans to help teachers utilize *The Climate Time Machine* in teaching, science, mathematics, and social studies. We also host tours for elementary and secondary school students.

Collecting and Archiving Data

There are 22 climate or weather networks collecting data throughout Utah. These networks include:

Cooperative Observer - exceeds 700 stations
Manual stations in populated areas
RAWS - exceeds 170 stations
Automated stations in forest and range
SNOTEL - exceeds 150 stations
Automated stations in high mountains
Utah Climate Center - exceeds 40 stations
Automated agriculture stations
Storage Gages - exceeds 40 stations
Manual, remote mountain stations

Data for individual stations are archived for the period of record. Records include observations taken the late 1800's.

Distributing Data

Cooperative observers record daily maximum and minimum temperature and precipitation. Most also record snowfall and depth of snow on the ground. A limited number also record daily pan-evaporation data and/or soil temperatures.

Most automated stations record hourly values for: air and soil temperature, precipitation, wind speed and direction, humidity, and solar radiation. A limited number of stations record hourly values of barometric pressure, soil moisture, and ultraviolet radiation in the UVb band.

Data are made available as hourly, daily, 10-day, monthly, seasonal, or annual values. The data can be distributed in digital form via FTP or computer disk and in hard copy by fax or mail. There is a charge for data. The price depends on the type, amount, and distribution format of the data.

Utah Climate Center also provides calculated climate data such as heating degree days, cooling degree days, growing degree days, free-water-surface evaporation, pan evaporation, evapotranspiration, plant hardiness zone, drought indices, moisture adequacy, spring and fall freeze data, and length of freeze-free season.

In addition, to supplying measured and calculated climate data, Utah Climate Center can provide summaries for hourly, daily, 10-day, monthly, seasonal, or annual data. The summaries include tables (such as those in this book), graphs, charts, and maps (gray scale or color up to 36 inches wide and any length). Utah Climate Center provides raw climate data and climate products to meet client specifications.

For more information, see Utah Climate Center Home Page on the Internet, or contact the Utah Climate Center at one of the following:

Home page: http://climate.usu.edu/

Mail: Utah Climate Center
Utah State University
Logan, Utah, 84322-4825

Phone: (801) 797-2190

Fax: (801) 797-2117

Climatic Tables

by

Donald T. Jensen and Gaylen L. Ashcroft

Climate data from several dozen stations of the Cooperative Observer Network are presented in this book. The Cooperative Observer Network consists of volunteers who make observations of maximum and minimum temperatures and precipitation at the same time each day--usually 8:00 AM or 6:00 PM. Most volunteers also record snowfall and depth of snow on the ground.

Those perusing climate data tables for the first time frequently bump into unfamiliar terms. To enlighten the novice and refresh the memory of the occasional data user, we have defined some terms and described how mission data were handled in some of the analyses.

The data are summarized in three different types of tables--*Monthly Climate Summary, Daily Climate Summary*, and *Freeze Dates and Freeze-free Season*. Term definitions are grouped under the title of the table in which the term appears.

Monthly Climate Summary

In the *Monthly Climate Summary*, both normal and average values are given. Normals are 30-year averages and are re-computed each 10 years. The 1961-1990 monthly normals and their standard deviations are calculated and printed for each station that has data for 1961 through 1990.

The tables also give averages. Average monthly values and their standard deviations are calculated using all available data. The amount of data available varies from just a few years for some stations to more than 100 years for others.

An example shows how average values are obtained. For a station with 40 years of observations, 40 average monthly-maximum-temperature values can be calculated for January-- one value for each year. These 40 values are then averaged to provide the January average monthly-maximum-temperature value printed in the table.

Standard deviation is a measure of the variability of the climate at a station. For example, if the 40 average monthly-maximum-temperature values are quite different from year to year, the standard deviation will be larger. If the average monthly-maximum-temperature values are quite similar for all years--i.e., the yearly values are only a few degrees above or below the mean--then the standard deviation will be smaller.

The tables also give monthly extremes. For temperatures, the monthly extremes are the highest and lowest monthly **averages**. For precipitation, the extremes are the highest and lowest monthly totals. Tables also contain daily extremes and the number of days with temperatures or precipitation amounts exceeding or lower than selected threshold values.

Heating degree days and cooling degree days are based on a threshold temperature of 65°F. Average heating-degree-day values are used to estimate the average amount of energy required to heat buildings. Average cooling-degree-day values are used to estimate the average amount of energy that is required to air condition buildings.

Growing degree days, base 40, are calculated with a lower threshold of 40°F, and an upper threshold of 77°F. Base-40 values are used to estimate the rate of growth for temperate-region crops such as small grains and alfalfa.

For growing degree days, base 50, the lower and upper thresholds are 50°F and 86°F, respectively. Base-50 values are used to model the growth of tropical region plants such as corn.

Daily Climate Summary

The data for each month are presented in two tables on a single page. One table contains temperature data for each day of the month. The other presents precipitation information for each day of the month. Temperature and precipitation values in the table are calculated using all available data.

Freeze Dates and Freeze-free Season

The last Spring freeze for a given year is considered to be the latest occurrence of a 32°F or lower temperature prior to July 24. The first Fall freeze is the earliest occurrence of 32°F subsequent to July 24. The length of a freeze-free season for a given year is the number of days between the last Spring and the first Fall freeze.

Missing data can distort values. However, deleting all years with one or more minimum-temperature value missing would leave little data for analysis. As a compromise, the following procedure is used when data are missing. The date of the last 32°F in the Spring is determined. If there are 10 or more days missing between the Spring date and July 24, the year is eliminated from the analysis. The same criterion is applied between July 24 and the date of the first Fall freeze. For length of the freeze-free season, a year is eliminated from analysis if either the Spring-date criterion or the Fall-date criterion is not met.

Map of Utah Climate Locations

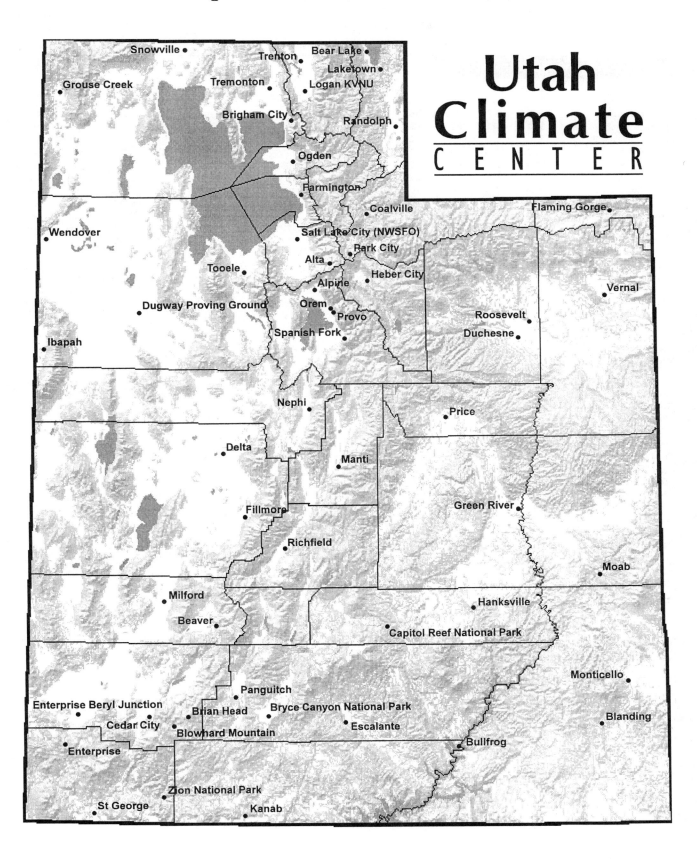

Location: Alpine   County: Utah   Latitude: 40.450   Longitude:-111.783

Elevation: 4900 feet   Period of Record: 1899-1996

ALPINE
Monthly Data Summary

Maximum Temperature in °F

	Jan	Feb	Mar	Apr	May	Jun	Jul	Aug	Sep	Oct	Nov	Dec	Annual
Monthly normal	37.2	43.8	52.1	63.0	71.0	83.6	91.7	88.7	79.3	66.4	49.9	39.9	63.9
Standard deviation	8.4	9.7	9.5	10.7	10.4	9.1	5.8	6.1	9.4	10.1	10.5	9.1	9.1
Average monthly	38.0	44.3	52.5	62.6	71.3	83.1	91.1	88.7	79.5	66.2	49.4	40.4	63.9
Standard deviation	8.5	9.7	9.4	10.6	10.4	9.3	6.2	5.9	9.1	9.9	10.6	9.0	9.0
High monthly average	44.8	53.8	59.9	71.6	77.4	90.4	97.5	92.9	86.1	75.4	57.0	44.7	97.5
Year of occurrence	1994	1995	1986	1987	1994	1988	1989	1988	1979	1988	1995	1981	1989
Low monthly average	28.9	36.1	47.7	52.2	65.1	76.3	84.6	81.9	72.5	57.4	42.1	31.3	28.9
Year of occurrence	1984	1984	1975	1975	1995	1995	1993	1965	1986	1984	1994	1985	1984
Record high daily	61	70	78	87	92†	100†	104	105	96	87†	72†	66	105
Day of occurrence	27	25	28	20	30	19	20	4	7	3	1	1	4
Year of occurrence	1987	1986	1986	1989	1984	1989	1989	1979	1979	1988	1988	1995	1979
Record low daily	12†	0	0	36	41	51	62	65	42	40†	25	17†	0†
Day of occurrence	17	1	1	1	11	7	5	14	18	29	25	27	1
Year of occurrence	1984	1900	1900	1975	1983	1993	1982	1978	1978	1989	1993	1988	1900
Days w/max >= 100	0.0	0.0	0.0	0.0	0.0	0.1	1.4	0.6	0.0	0.0	0.0	0.0	2.1
Days w/max >= 90	0.0	0.0	0.0	0.0	0.3	8.2	20.4	14.6	2.8	0.0	0.0	0.0	45.8
Days w/max <= 32	7.6	2.6	0.3	0.0	0.0	0.0	0.0	0.0	0.0	0.0	1.6	5.9	19.6

Minimum Temperature in °F

	Jan	Feb	Mar	Apr	May	Jun	Jul	Aug	Sep	Oct	Nov	Dec	Annual
Monthly normal	16.4	19.8	28.0	34.4	40.3	47.8	55.4	53.5	45.4	35.4	26.1	19.1	35.1
Standard deviation	11.1	10.8	7.4	7.8	6.9	6.7	5.4	6.0	7.5	6.5	8.2	9.4	7.8
Average monthly	17.5	20.4	28.3	34.6	40.8	47.9	54.9	53.7	45.5	35.4	25.9	19.7	35.4
Standard deviation	11.0	10.8	7.4	7.6	6.9	6.7	5.5	5.9	7.4	6.5	8.5	9.5	7.8
High monthly average	25.2	29.8	33.0	38.6	45.7	52.6	57.6	57.5	49.2	40.3	33.0	27.2	57.6
Year of occurrence	1978	1995	1986	1989	1993	1988	1988	1983	1981	1988	1995	1995	1988
Low monthly average	9.0	11.3	22.2	29.7	36.5	44.1	50.8	49.2	42.0	30.5	20.8	13.8	9.0
Year of occurrence	1975	1984	1976	1975	1975	1975	1993	1975	1978	1976	1979	1978	1975
Record high daily	42†	45	47	58	58	66	70	70	63	50†	48	44	70†
Day of occurrence	21	18	25	26	15	25	16	7	6	29	11	11	7
Year of occurrence	1969	1986	1989	1981	1984	1988	1977	1975	1993	1987	1980	1995	1975
Record low daily	-15	-20†	5†	12	24	30	39	32	25†	17	-1	-7†	-20
Day of occurrence	31	6	4	7	9	30	11	31	30	25	26	27	6
Year of occurrence	1979	1989	1989	1983	1990	1968	1983	1965	1985	1975	1993	1988	1989
Days w/min <= 32	28.6	25.2	22.4	12.0	3.8	0.3	0.0	0.1	1.4	10.3	23.9	28.4	163.6
Days w/min <= 0	2.5	1.1	0.0	0.0	0.0	0.0	0.0	0.0	0.0	0.0	0.1	0.9	4.8
Days w/min <= -20	0.0	0.1	0.0	0.0	0.0	0.0	0.0	0.0	0.0	0.0	0.0	0.0	0.1

Mean Temperature in °F

	Jan	Feb	Mar	Apr	May	Jun	Jul	Aug	Sep	Oct	Nov	Dec	Annual
Monthly normal	26.8	31.8	40.0	48.7	55.7	65.7	73.5	71.1	62.3	50.9	38.0	29.5	49.5
Standard deviation	9.1	9.5	7.5	8.3	7.7	7.1	4.4	5.0	7.4	7.3	8.5	8.4	7.5
Average monthly	27.8	32.3	40.4	48.6	56.0	65.5	73.0	71.2	62.5	50.8	37.6	30.0	49.6
Standard deviation	9.0	9.5	7.4	8.1	7.8	7.2	4.7	4.8	7.2	7.1	8.7	8.4	7.5
High monthly average	34.1	41.8	46.4	54.4	60.6	71.5	77.5	74.3	66.7	57.8	45.0	35.6	77.5
Year of occurrence	1994	1995	1986	1987	1993	1988	1989	1986	1979	1988	1995	1977	1989
Low monthly average	19.9	23.7	35.6	41.0	51.2	60.6	67.7	66.2	57.6	45.0	32.5	23.3	19.9
Year of occurrence	1984	1984	1976	1975	1975	1975	1993	1965	1986	1984	1957	1985	1984

† Also occurred on earlier date(s).

ALPINE
Monthly Data Summary

Precipitation in Inches

	Jan	Feb	Mar	Apr	May	Jun	Jul	Aug	Sep	Oct	Nov	Dec	Annual
Monthly normal	1.55	1.48	1.74	1.92	1.81	1.04	0.69	1.02	1.32	1.65	1.52	1.82	17.56
Standard deviation	0.13	0.13	0.14	0.16	0.18	0.13	0.09	0.12	0.16	0.16	0.14	0.15	0.14
Average monthly	1.57	1.52	1.70	1.81	1.80	0.87	0.70	0.99	1.03	1.51	1.29	1.64	16.44
Standard deviation	0.15	0.15	0.16	0.16	0.18	0.12	0.11	0.12	0.13	0.16	0.13	0.15	0.14
High monthly total	4.58	5.10	5.83	4.71	6.99	4.50	3.03	3.77	6.61	5.81	3.61	8.37	8.37
Year of occurrence	1996	1980	1978	1974	1908	1969	1911	1906	1982	1946	1994	1983	1983
Low monthly total	0.00†	0.00	0.00	0.03	0.00	0.00†	0.00†	0.00†	0.00†	0.00†	0.00	0.06	0.00†
Year of occurrence	1961	1912	1900	1934	1934	1994	1978	1974	1974	1958	1904	1976	1904
Record high daily	2.20	2.60	2.40	2.13	2.30	1.50	2.30	1.75	1.62	2.07	1.60	1.70	2.60
Day of occurrence	20	1	24	20	3	2	29	30	17	28	18	13	1
Year of occurrence	1903	1905	1916	1904	1908	1944	1911	1907	1978	1946	1900	1983	1905
Days w/pcp >= .01	6.9	6.6	7.3	7.2	6.4	4.1	3.5	4.5	4.2	5.0	5.6	6.7	68.3
Days w/pcp >= .10	4.7	4.6	5.0	5.2	4.5	2.4	2.0	2.8	2.8	3.8	3.8	4.8	46.6
Days w/pcp >= .50	0.7	0.8	0.9	1.0	1.1	0.4	0.3	0.5	0.6	1.0	0.7	0.9	8.9

Snow and Sleet in Inches

	Jan	Feb	Mar	Apr	May	Jun	Jul	Aug	Sep	Oct	Nov	Dec	Annual
Monthly normal	7.2	7.1	2.9	0.4	0.0	0.0	0.0	0.0	0.0	0.2	3.4	4.7	25.9
Standard deviation	0.8	1.0	0.5	0.2	0.0	0.0	0.0	0.0	0.0	0.1	0.7	0.7	0.3
Average monthly	11.0	6.7	3.3	1.1	0.0	0.0	0.0	0.0	0.0	0.1	2.7	6.4	31.3
Standard deviation	1.3	1.1	0.8	0.5	0.0	0.0	0.0	0.0	0.0	0.1	0.6	1.0	0.4
High monthly total	61.0	41.0	38.0	19.0	1.0	0.0†	0.0†	0.0†	0.0†	4.0	23.5	48.0	61.0
Year of occurrence	1929	1922	1924	1917	1993	1995	1995	1995	1995	1929	1994	1931	1929
Low monthly total	0.0†	0.0†	0.0†	0.0†	0.0†	0.0†	0.0†	0.0†	0.0†	0.0†	0.0†	0.0†	0.0†
Year of occurrence	1981	1977	1994	1994	1995	1995	1995	1995	1995	1995	1982	1986	1986
Record high daily	16.0	18.0	24.0	12.0	1.0	0.0†	0.0†	0.0†	0.0†	4.0	11.0	12.0	24.0
Day of occurrence	24	22	24	5	8	30	31	31	30	28	12	29	24
Year of occurrence	1929	1922	1916	1929	1993	1995	1995	1995	1995	1929	1985	1931	1916
Days w/snow >= .1	3.7	2.5	1.2	0.4	0.0	0.0	0.0	0.0	0.0	0.1	1.2	2.4	10.5
Days w/snow >= 5	0.6	0.4	0.2	0.1	0.0	0.0	0.0	0.0	0.0	0.0	0.1	0.4	1.6
Days w/snow >= 10	0.1	0.1	0.0	0.0	0.0	0.0	0.0	0.0	0.0	0.0	0.0	0.0	0.3

Degree Days

	Jan	Feb	Mar	Apr	May	Jun	Jul	Aug	Sep	Oct	Nov	Dec	Annual
Heating normal	1168	931	770	487	294	75	3	11	127	435	802	1088	6197
Heating average	1141	916	760	490	285	79	5	10	122	439	814	1074	6141
Cooling normal	0	0	0	1	8	97	268	199	48	0	0	0	624
Cooling average	0	0	0	1	10	95	254	201	49	0	0	0	612
Growing 40 normal	32	83	193	352	493	645	811	775	606	413	163	54	4625
Growing 40 average	37	88	200	348	501	645	803	779	610	410	158	57	4640
Growing 50 normal	3	21	76	204	325	489	638	604	440	259	65	9	3137
Growing 50 average	3	23	79	198	330	485	629	608	446	254	61	10	3132

† Also occurred on earlier date(s).

Location: Alta   County: Salt Lake   Latitude: 40.600   Longitude: -111.633
Elevation: 8730 feet   Period of Record: 1941-1995

ALTA
Monthly Data Summary

Maximum Temperature in °F

	Jan	Feb	Mar	Apr	May	Jun	Jul	Aug	Sep	Oct	Nov	Dec	Annual
Monthly normal	30.2	31.3	33.8	40.7	50.8	62.9	71.0	70.0	60.6	48.8	37.0	30.6	47.3
Standard deviation	10.6	10.1	9.7	10.5	10.3	10.1	6.0	5.4	9.4	10.9	10.8	10.9	9.6
Average monthly	30.2	31.6	34.1	41.2	50.9	62.5	71.0	70.0	61.4	49.1	36.9	31.6	47.5
Standard deviation	10.3	10.3	9.6	10.3	10.1	9.9	6.3	5.3	8.9	10.8	11.3	10.3	9.5
High monthly average	39.5	40.3	41.8	51.6	60.5	69.8	78.8	73.6	69.3	57.5	50.7	41.6	78.8
Year of occurrence	1981	1991	1972	1942	1969	1988	1945	1994	1979	1988	1949	1980	1945
Low monthly average	23.6	22.6	27.5	31.2	40.5	50.4	65.5	65.9	53.3	40.0	28.7	24.9	22.6
Year of occurrence	1949	1985	1955	1970	1983	1951	1986	1951	1986	1984	1959	1983	1985
Record high daily	57	57	60	70	72†	89	94	83†	79	70†	71	59	94
Day of occurrence	23	9	15	21	31	20	27	5	7	1	5	14	27
Year of occurrence	1981	1947	1994	1942	1994	1945	1945	1994	1983	1992	1945	1952	1945
Record low daily	-4†	-4	4	11	23	33†	41	45	28	12	-5	-8	-8
Day of occurrence	12	1	3	4	12	15	6	20	25	24	16	22	22
Year of occurrence	1963	1985	1966	1955	1983	1981	1982	1980	1984	1975	1955	1990	1990
Days w/max >= 100	0.0	0.0	0.0	0.0	0.0	0.0	0.0	0.0	0.0	0.0	0.0	0.0	0.0
Days w/max >= 90	0.0	0.0	0.0	0.0	0.0	0.0	0.1	0.0	0.0	0.0	0.0	0.0	0.1
Days w/max <= 32	18.9	15.1	13.5	6.4	1.5	0.0	0.0	0.0	0.1	2.8	11.0	16.0	108.3

Minimum Temperature in °F

	Jan	Feb	Mar	Apr	May	Jun	Jul	Aug	Sep	Oct	Nov	Dec	Annual
Monthly normal	12.7	14.2	16.5	23.4	31.9	41.1	48.7	47.5	39.4	30.0	19.9	13.6	28.3
Standard deviation	10.6	9.4	9.2	9.0	7.6	7.5	4.8	5.1	7.7	9.1	9.7	10.3	8.3
Average monthly	12.6	14.1	16.5	23.5	32.3	39.2	49.0	47.9	39.2	29.8	19.2	14.6	28.2
Standard deviation	10.2	9.7	9.3	8.9	7.4	11.3	5.6	5.7	8.8	9.3	10.4	9.9	8.9
High monthly average	21.3	22.4	24.8	32.0	37.6	46.0	60.1	52.5	45.2	37.2	29.8	22.8	60.1
Year of occurrence	1986	1995	1992	1992	1969	1988	1945	1967	1990	1988	1949	1950	1945
Low monthly average	3.4	3.9	8.9	17.9	28.0	15.3	42.7	42.4	27.2	20.6	12.5	6.1	3.4
Year of occurrence	1949	1955	1955	1983	1975	1947	1993	1976	1947	1946	1947	1990	1949
Record high daily	35†	38†	46	48	52	64	70	64	57†	51	43†	36†	70
Day of occurrence	30	5	10	21	27	22	21	2	1	1	6	4	21
Year of occurrence	1986	1963	1989	1989	1988	1945	1945	1945	1995	1953	1975	1987	1945
Record low daily	-26	-19	-8†	0†	12†	0†	31†	0†	0†	-1	-16	-25	-26
Day of occurrence	12	2	2	30	2	18	6	24	16	30	16	23	12
Year of occurrence	1963	1985	1971	1948	1988	1947	1982	1946	1947	1971	1955	1990	1963
Days w/min <= 32	30.7	27.9	30.2	23.9	14.3	5.7	0.1	0.3	6.4	17.8	26.6	30.5	250.3
Days w/min <= 0	4.2	2.6	1.6	0.1	0.0	1.4	0.0	0.1	0.4	0.3	1.5	2.8	18.9
Days w/min <= -20	0.0	0.0	0.0	0.0	0.0	0.0	0.0	0.0	0.0	0.0	0.0	0.1	0.1

Mean Temperature in °F

	Jan	Feb	Mar	Apr	May	Jun	Jul	Aug	Sep	Oct	Nov	Dec	Annual
Monthly normal	21.5	22.8	25.2	32.3	41.5	52.1	60.0	58.8	50.0	39.6	28.6	22.2	37.9
Standard deviation	10.1	9.2	8.9	9.3	8.6	8.4	4.8	4.8	8.1	9.6	9.8	10.1	8.5
Average monthly	21.4	22.8	25.3	32.3	41.9	51.1	60.1	59.0	50.2	39.4	28.1	23.2	37.9
Standard deviation	9.6	9.4	8.7	9.2	8.3	9.1	5.4	4.9	7.9	9.5	10.3	9.5	8.5
High monthly average	29.7	30.9†	32.3	41.0	49.0	57.9	69.4	62.3	56.1	47.4	40.0	31.9	69.4
Year of occurrence	1981	1995	1986	1992	1969	1988	1945	1967	1979	1988	1949	1980	1945
Low monthly average	13.5	13.5	18.2	25.5	34.2	37.8	54.4	55.5	43.9	30.3	20.9	15.6	13.5
Year of occurrence	1949	1955	1955	1983	1983	1947	1993	1975	1986	1946	1959	1990	1949

† Also occurred on earlier date(s).

ALTA
Monthly Data Summary

Precipitation in Inches

	Jan	Feb	Mar	Apr	May	Jun	Jul	Aug	Sep	Oct	Nov	Dec	Annual
Monthly normal	7.26	6.84	7.39	6.29	4.20	1.86	1.95	1.72	3.04	4.20	6.45	7.26	58.46
Standard deviation	0.46	0.42	0.43	0.42	0.33	0.20	0.19	0.16	0.30	0.36	0.44	0.47	0.35
Average monthly	7.21	6.57	7.39	5.45	4.29	1.77	1.78	2.09	2.61	4.43	6.00	6.94	56.53
Standard deviation	0.48	0.42	0.43	0.40	0.33	0.19	0.18	0.19	0.27	0.37	0.45	0.46	0.35
High monthly total	16.70	13.73	15.09	13.09	10.15	7.02	4.49	6.36	13.47	13.08	13.79	25.45	25.45
Year of occurrence	1980	1980	1982	1986	1981	1984	1987	1983	1982	1946	1983	1983	1983
Low monthly total	0.00	0.00	0.00	0.00†	0.00	0.11	0.00	0.09	0.06	0.29	0.00	0.00†	0.00†
Year of occurrence	1942	1942	1942	1945	1969	1994	1971	1985	1979	1967	1976	1976	1976
Record high daily	3.63	2.88	2.90	2.61	2.74	1.62	1.87	1.73	3.43	4.32	5.59	3.55	5.59
Day of occurrence	28	15	9	12	9	25	21	5	27	28	16	24	16
Year of occurrence	1956	1980	1986	1982	1986	1985	1987	1991	1982	1946	1955	1955	1955
Days w/pcp >= .01	12.7	12.0	13.8	9.4	10.0	5.8	6.7	8.8	6.9	8.4	10.4	11.8	123.3
Days w/pcp >= .10	10.8	10.5	12.1	8.3	8.0	3.7	3.8	5.3	5.1	6.8	8.9	9.9	100.9
Days w/pcp >= .50	5.3	5.2	5.5	4.2	2.9	1.3	1.2	1.2	1.7	3.5	4.4	5.2	46.6

Snow and Sleet in Inches

	Jan	Feb	Mar	Apr	May	Jun	Jul	Aug	Sep	Oct	Nov	Dec	Annual
Monthly normal	79.2	74.1	84.0	60.3	27.8	4.4	0.1	0.0	6.0	27.0	70.1	85.7	518.6
Standard deviation	4.6	4.5	4.6	4.1	2.7	0.7	0.1	0.0	1.2	2.5	4.7	5.3	2.9
Average monthly	81.3	73.5	81.3	54.4	27.8	4.7	0.1	0.0	4.4	29.7	66.9	78.5	502.7
Standard deviation	4.8	4.6	4.4	4.0	2.8	0.8	0.1	0.0	1.0	2.8	4.6	4.8	2.9
High monthly total	168.0	155.0	164.0	135.6	88.9	25.0	2.0	0.0†	45.0	98.0	143.5	244.5	244.5
Year of occurrence	1967	1960	1982	1986	1986	1984	1982	1995	1982	1946	1983	1983	1983
Low monthly total	1.0	10.4	6.8	0.0†	0.0†	0.0†	0.0†	0.0†	0.0†	0.0†	2.0	8.3	0.0†
Year of occurrence	1961	1942	1966	1952	1992	1994	1995	1995	1994	1989	1944	1986	1989
Record high daily	36.0	32.0	31.0	30.0	20.5	8.0†	2.0	0.0†	15.0	22.0†	37.0	38.0	38.0
Day of occurrence	6	7	25	4	9	7	6	31	30	22	27	2	2
Year of occurrence	1994	1990	1983	1983	1986	1993	1982	1995	1982	1995	1988	1982	1982
Days w/snow >= .1	13.0	12.1	13.7	8.8	5.1	1.8	0.0	0.0	1.1	5.6	10.2	12.3	99.6
Days w/snow >= 5	6.3	6.0	6.6	4.6	2.1	0.3	0.0	0.0	0.3	2.6	5.3	6.4	48.9
Days w/snow >= 10	2.5	2.6	2.8	2.1	0.9	0.0	0.0	0.0	0.1	0.8	2.4	2.8	20.6

Degree Days

	Jan	Feb	Mar	Apr	May	Jun	Jul	Aug	Sep	Oct	Nov	Dec	Annual
Heating normal	1344	1188	1234	971	718	386	162	194	449	788	1092	1318	9851
Heating average	1347	1187	1230	944	708	416	162	188	443	793	1092	1288	9805
Cooling normal	0	0	0	0	0	1	7	2	0	0	0	0	11
Cooling average	0	0	0	0	0	1	12	3	0	0	0	0	18
Growing 40 normal	15	13	24	73	190	395	617	583	353	169	48	17	2504
Growing 40 average	14	16	24	72	195	393	613	587	362	168	48	18	2516
Growing 50 normal	0	0	2	18	74	208	348	324	174	60	8	1	1222
Growing 50 average	0	1	1	17	76	207	350	325	181	59	9	1	1232

† Also occurred on earlier date(s).

Location: Bear Lake State Park County: Rich   Latitude: 41.967   Longitude: -111.400
Elevation: 6000 feet   Period of Record: 1989-1995

BEAR LAKE STATE PARK
Monthly Data Summary

Maximum Temperature in °F

	Jan	Feb	Mar	Apr	May	Jun	Jul	Aug	Sep	Oct	Nov	Dec	Annual
Monthly normal													
Standard deviation													
Average monthly	32.4	36.2	46.2	57.9	66.5	75.3	83.8	84.5	75.0	60.7	43.3	34.0	58.0
Standard deviation	7.8	7.8	7.3	9.4	9.0	8.7	5.7	5.9	7.5	9.9	9.3	8.6	8.1
High monthly average	36.9	40.1	50.4	64.5	72.2	80.7	87.3	87.5	79.4	64.4	52.3	40.4	87.5
Year of occurrence	1994	1995	1992	1992	1992	1994	1994	1992	1990	1992	1995	1995	1992
Low monthly average	27.7	28.8	42.3	52.4	60.7	70.1	77.0	81.3	71.1	57.6	38.0	26.1	26.1
Year of occurrence	1993	1993	1993	1993	1995	1993	1993	1991	1991	1994	1992	1990	1990
Record high daily	54†	53	62†	81	81†	92	97	96	94	80†	67	63	97
Day of occurrence	10	20	16	21	31	30	18	13	2	3	8	1	18
Year of occurrence	1990	1991	1994	1994	1994	1990	1994	1992	1995	1992	1995	1995	1994
Record low daily	12	12	21	40	39	53	61	69†	60†	26	19†	-5†	-5
Day of occurrence	21	16	1	29	5	9	23	24	23	30	25	23	23
Year of occurrence	1991	1993	1993	1990	1993	1995	1993	1992	1995	1991	1993	1990	1990
Days w/max >= 100	0.0	0.0	0.0	0.0	0.0	0.0	0.0	0.0	0.0	0.0	0.0	0.0	0.0
Days w/max >= 90	0.0	0.0	0.0	0.0	0.0	1.5	3.8	6.8	1.5	0.0	0.0	0.0	12.0
Days w/max <= 32	15.8	8.7	1.0	0.0	0.0	0.0	0.0	0.0	0.0	0.4	3.6	13.6	46.0

Minimum Temperature in °F

	Jan	Feb	Mar	Apr	May	Jun	Jul	Aug	Sep	Oct	Nov	Dec	Annual
Monthly normal													
Standard deviation													
Average monthly	13.0	14.2	23.1	30.3	36.7	42.6	48.5	50.2	41.7	31.9	22.0	14.5	30.7
Standard deviation	9.9	10.1	7.9	5.9	5.8	5.3	5.6	5.4	6.2	6.2	9.9	10.4	7.4
High monthly average	18.2	19.2	25.7	33.0	39.6	44.2	51.7	51.9†	46.1	33.3	28.0	24.0	51.9
Year of occurrence	1990	1995	1992	1992	1992	1994	1989	1994	1990	1992	1995	1995	1994
Low monthly average	6.8	5.5	19.3	27.3	34.1	40.4	42.1	48.2	38.8	29.1	15.7	5.2	5.2
Year of occurrence	1991	1993	1993	1991	1989	1993	1993	1989	1992	1995	1993	1990	1990
Record high daily	38	34	38	46	51	60	64	80	79	46	41	47	80
Day of occurrence	10	20	11	22	21	21	22	11	6	10	9	1	11
Year of occurrence	1990	1992	1995	1994	1993	1994	1989	1995	1994	1989	1989	1995	1995
Record low daily	-15	-10†	-7†	16	22†	28	33	32†	28	14	-12	-25	-25
Day of occurrence	29	28	2	8	22	21	6	26	23	30	25	22	22
Year of occurrence	1991	1993	1993	1991	1989	1989	1993	1992	1995	1991	1993	1990	1990
Days w/min <= 32	30.5	27.8	28.5	18.9	6.4	1.3	0.0	0.4	2.0	16.6	26.7	30.1	205.0
Days w/min <= 0	2.8	2.5	0.8	0.0	0.0	0.0	0.0	0.0	0.0	0.0	0.7	2.0	9.3
Days w/min <= -20	0.0	0.0	0.0	0.0	0.0	0.0	0.0	0.0	0.0	0.0	0.0	0.4	0.5

Mean Temperature in °F

	Jan	Feb	Mar	Apr	May	Jun	Jul	Aug	Sep	Oct	Nov	Dec	Annual
Monthly normal													
Standard deviation													
Average monthly	22.7	25.2	34.6	44.2	51.6	59.0	66.2	67.3	58.3	46.3	32.7	24.3	44.4
Standard deviation	8.5	8.5	6.9	7.1	6.5	6.4	5.1	4.9	5.8	7.3	9.0	9.2	7.1
High monthly average	27.1	29.7	38.0	48.8	55.9	62.5	69.0	69.6	62.8	48.9	40.2	32.2	69.6
Year of occurrence	1994	1995	1992	1992	1992	1994	1989	1994	1990	1992	1995	1995	1994
Low monthly average	17.6	17.1	30.8	40.4	48.0	55.3	59.6	65.3	56.0	44.5	28.1	15.6	15.6
Year of occurrence	1993	1993	1993	1993	1995	1993	1993	1989	1991	1995	1993	1990	1990

† Also occurred on earlier date(s).

BEAR LAKE STATE PARK
Monthly Data Summary

Precipitation in Inches

	Jan	Feb	Mar	Apr	May	Jun	Jul	Aug	Sep	Oct	Nov	Dec	Annual
Monthly normal													
Standard deviation													
Average monthly	1.31	1.01	1.58	1.70	2.02	1.39	0.68	0.93	0.88	1.24	1.52	1.17	15.43
Standard deviation	0.12	0.11	0.14	0.14	0.15	0.14	0.09	0.11	0.09	0.16	0.13	0.12	0.12
High monthly total	2.34	2.12	2.17	2.23	3.58	2.72	1.34	2.13	1.68	2.15	3.48	3.03	3.58
Year of occurrence	1990	1995	1994	1993	1995	1995	1993	1991	1991	1994	1991	1995	1995
Low monthly total	0.54	0.07	0.58	1.22	0.83	0.42	0.19	0.30	0.12	0.61	0.55	0.35	0.07
Year of occurrence	1991	1991	1992	1995	1992	1994	1989	1994	1993	1989	1993	1991	1991
Record high daily	0.94	1.13	1.02	1.28	0.90	1.00	0.65	0.80	0.65	1.38	1.00	0.91	1.38
Day of occurrence	8	14	22	28	1	4	23	31	19	23	29	4	23
Year of occurrence	1990	1995	1994	1990	1995	1989	1993	1992	1990	1991	1991	1995	1991
Days w/pcp >= .01	7.5	7.7	10.5	12.4	13.3	8.6	7.1	6.1	6.8	7.4	8.9	6.6	114.7
Days w/pcp >= .10	4.2	3.8	4.7	5.1	5.9	3.7	1.4	2.4	3.0	2.9	4.7	3.3	50.0
Days w/pcp >= .50	0.5	0.2	0.7	0.4	0.9	0.9	0.4	0.6	0.3	0.4	0.7	0.6	7.3

Snow and Sleet in Inches

	Jan	Feb	Mar	Apr	May	Jun	Jul	Aug	Sep	Oct	Nov	Dec	Annual
Monthly normal													
Standard deviation													
Average monthly	11.0	7.0	4.8	0.4	0.4	0.0	0.0	0.0	0.0	0.0	9.4	7.5	40.5
Standard deviation	1.1	0.7	0.7	0.2	0.2	0.0	0.0	0.0	0.0	0.0	1.5	1.0	0.5
High monthly total	19.5	16.0	12.5	2.0	3.0	0.0†	0.0†	0.0†	0.0†	0.0†	35.0	21.0	35.0
Year of occurrence	1993	1993	1991	1989	1991	1995	1995	1995	1995	1995	1991	1992	1991
Low monthly total	5.0	1.0	0.0†	0.0†	0.0†	0.0†	0.0†	0.0†	0.0†	0.0†	0.0	0.0	0.0†
Year of occurrence	1995	1992	1995	1995	1995	1995	1995	1995	1995	1995	1995	1995	1995
Record high daily	7.0	3.0†	6.0	2.0	3.0	0.0†	0.0†	0.0†	0.0†	0.0†	17.0	8.0	17.0
Day of occurrence	7	22	22	11	3	30	31	31	30	31	29	9	29
Year of occurrence	1992	1993	1994	1989	1991	1995	1995	1995	1995	1995	1991	1992	1991
Days w/snow >= .1	4.3	3.8	2.3	0.3	0.1	0.0	0.0	0.0	0.0	0.0	3.4	3.3	18.2
Days w/snow >= 5	0.7	0.0	0.2	0.0	0.0	0.0	0.0	0.0	0.0	0.0	0.6	0.3	1.8
Days w/snow >= 10	0.0	0.0	0.0	0.0	0.0	0.0	0.0	0.0	0.0	0.0	0.1	0.0	0.2

Degree Days

	Jan	Feb	Mar	Apr	May	Jun	Jul	Aug	Sep	Oct	Nov	Dec	Annual
Heating normal													
Heating average	1312	1113	941	618	392	199	42	31	212	574	970	1262	7670
Cooling normal													
Cooling average	0	0	0	0	0	18	86	103	13	0	0	0	222
Growing 40 normal													
Growing 40 average	11	19	109	264	406	544	671	728	544	322	84	16	3724
Growing 50 normal													
Growing 50 average	0	0	20	130	248	376	510	542	374	177	20	1	2404

† Also occurred on earlier date(s).

Location: Beaver   County: Beaver   Latitude:38.300   Longitude:-112.650
Elevation: 5940 feet   Period of Record: 1889-1993

BEAVER
Monthly Data Summary

Maximum Temperature in °F

	Jan	Feb	Mar	Apr	May	Jun	Jul	Aug	Sep	Oct	Nov	Dec	Annual
Monthly normal	42.4	46.4	52.2	60.6	70.9	81.8	88.4	85.8	77.6	66.4	52.6	43.8	64.1
Standard deviation	9.5	9.6	10.4	10.3	9.7	8.0	5.2	5.4	7.8	10.3	10.4	10.0	8.9
Average monthly	41.6	45.0	52.0	61.0	70.7	80.8	87.4	85.1	77.7	66.1	52.7	43.3	63.6
Standard deviation	9.8	9.8	9.7	10.2	9.5	8.1	5.4	5.6	8.0	10.0	10.7	10.0	8.9
High monthly average	61.5	67.3	62.4	69.3	81.8	88.8	94.5	93.0	85.8	77.4	65.8	63.3	94.5
Year of occurrence	1907	1907	1972	1954	1925	1918	1931	1915	1956	1891	1904	1906	1931
Low monthly average	22.5	31.3	43.3	49.2	62.3	73.3	83.1	78.5	62.0	48.6	33.8	32.0	22.5
Year of occurrence	1949	1893	1948	1993	1933	1908	1914	1938	1931	1931	1931	1892	1949
Record high daily	68†	75	78	85	93	102†	102†	101†	97	93	85	73	102†
Day of occurrence	11	19	11	28	29	23	7	2	3	4	11	19	7
Year of occurrence	1990	1907	1892	1890	1925	1954	1989	1954	1950	1964	1890	1906	1989
Record low daily	-2	14†	22†	30	37	44	65†	61	34	23	16	3	-2
Day of occurrence	22	27	28	1	1	1	5	24	24	29	24	10	22
Year of occurrence	1937	1962	1975	1975	1915	1891	1982	1921	1931	1971	1931	1972	1937
Days w/max >= 100	0.0	0.0	0.0	0.0	0.0	0.0	0.2	0.0	0.0	0.0	0.0	0.0	0.3
Days w/max >= 90	0.0	0.0	0.0	0.0	0.1	3.9	11.6	6.7	0.8	0.0	0.0	0.0	23.0
Days w/max <= 32	5.1	2.9	0.5	0.1	0.0	0.0	0.0	0.0	0.0	0.0	1.2	4.4	14.1

Minimum Temperature in °F

	Jan	Feb	Mar	Apr	May	Jun	Jul	Aug	Sep	Oct	Nov	Dec	Annual
Monthly normal	13.5	18.6	23.2	29.0	36.3	44.1	51.4	49.4	40.8	30.7	22.0	15.1	31.2
Standard deviation	10.9	10.0	8.6	7.4	6.9	7.3	5.9	5.8	7.8	7.4	8.8	10.0	8.1
Average monthly	13.4	18.0	23.5	29.4	36.3	43.3	50.8	49.6	40.7	30.5	21.2	15.3	31.0
Standard deviation	11.2	10.6	8.3	7.6	6.9	7.1	6.1	6.0	8.1	7.7	8.6	10.4	8.2
High monthly average	24.6	29.1	33.0	42.0	42.1	52.3	62.4	58.0	50.3	37.5	33.0	30.3	62.4
Year of occurrence	1911	1907	1910	1907	1910	1968	1968	1944	1910	1889	1910	1889	1968
Low monthly average	-2.1	-0.4	14.5	22.0	28.1	33.9	39.8	40.7	26.7	20.1	11.6	3.2	-2.1
Year of occurrence	1949	1933	1913	1975	1916	1905	1949	1913	1912	1913	1952	1913	1949
Record high daily	44	44†	52	55	61	70†	74	72	69	57	50	44	74
Day of occurrence	13	11	31	25	29	27	18	24	3	15	1	3	18
Year of occurrence	1980	1962	1907	1907	1968	1970	1968	1944	1927	1918	1904	1926	1968
Record low daily	-31†	-34	-9	3†	13	20	30	29	14†	6†	-16	-25	-34
Day of occurrence	9	10	2	11	1	30	6	31	25	21	27	13	10
Year of occurrence	1937	1933	1966	1933	1972	1968	1905	1962	1913	1913	1984	1932	1933
Days w/min <= 32	29.7	26.3	26.9	19.7	9.1	1.8	0.0	0.2	4.8	18.8	26.7	29.3	195.0
Days w/min <= 0	4.2	2.0	0.4	0.0	0.0	0.0	0.0	0.0	0.0	0.0	0.4	2.8	10.0
Days w/min <= -20	0.1	0.1	0.0	0.0	0.0	0.0	0.0	0.0	0.0	0.0	0.0	0.0	0.2

Mean Temperature in °F

	Jan	Feb	Mar	Apr	May	Jun	Jul	Aug	Sep	Oct	Nov	Dec	Annual
Monthly normal	28.0	32.5	37.7	44.8	53.6	62.9	69.9	67.6	59.2	48.6	37.3	29.5	47.6
Standard deviation	9.0	8.5	8.1	7.6	7.2	6.6	4.0	4.3	6.6	7.5	8.3	8.7	7.2
Average monthly	27.4	31.6	37.7	45.2	53.5	62.1	69.1	67.3	59.1	48.3	36.9	29.3	47.3
Standard deviation	9.4	9.0	7.7	7.6	7.1	6.4	4.2	4.1	6.7	7.3	8.2	8.9	7.2
High monthly average	42.1	48.2	46.7	53.9	60.5	68.4	75.2	73.2	65.0	55.0	44.3	44.9	75.2
Year of occurrence	1907	1907	1907	1907	1925	1918	1968	1944	1944	1988	1910	1906	1968
Low monthly average	9.9	18.4	30.6	36.2	46.8	56.1	62.6	63.3	46.0	35.4	25.2	20.6	9.9
Year of occurrence	1949	1933	1913	1975	1933	1908	1949	1927	1931	1931	1931	1892	1949

† Also occurred on earlier date(s).

BEAVER
Monthly Data Summary

Precipitation in Inches

	Jan	Feb	Mar	Apr	May	Jun	Jul	Aug	Sep	Oct	Nov	Dec	Annual
Monthly normal	0.75	0.82	1.10	1.16	1.04	0.65	1.11	1.52	1.17	0.83	0.89	0.85	11.89
Standard deviation	0.08	0.09	0.09	0.12	0.11	0.08	0.11	0.15	0.14	0.10	0.10	0.09	0.11
Average monthly	0.78	0.94	1.05	1.08	1.00	0.60	1.15	1.48	0.96	0.87	0.71	0.79	11.39
Standard deviation	0.08	0.10	0.09	0.12	0.11	0.09	0.12	0.15	0.13	0.11	0.09	0.09	0.11
High monthly total	2.55	2.52	2.56	2.89	3.03	2.53	5.76	4.21	3.74	3.20	2.15	2.51	5.76
Year of occurrence	1978	1962	1981	1993	1947	1936	1936	1955	1982	1941	1983	1941	1936
Low monthly total	0.00†	0.00	0.00†	0.06	0.00	0.00†	0.02	0.05	0.00†	0.00†	0.00†	0.00†	0.00†
Year of occurrence	1942	1961	1972	1977	1974	1979	1958	1960	1979	1988	1956	1989	1989
Record high daily	1.20	0.90	1.20	1.70	2.09	1.20	2.03	2.00	2.17	1.90	1.70	1.50	2.17
Day of occurrence	1	21	21	5	30	5	31	2	30	4	26	7	30
Year of occurrence	1907	1921	1918	1921	1937	1949	1936	1922	1911	1918	1919	1919	1911
Days w/pcp >= .01	4.9	5.8	6.6	5.8	5.6	3.2	6.0	7.3	4.3	4.2	4.0	4.3	62.3
Days w/pcp >= .10	2.8	3.3	3.8	3.2	3.0	1.9	3.4	4.1	2.5	2.5	2.3	2.7	35.6
Days w/pcp >= .50	0.2	0.3	0.3	0.5	0.4	0.2	0.6	0.8	0.6	0.5	0.2	0.3	4.9

Snow and Sleet in Inches

	Jan	Feb	Mar	Apr	May	Jun	Jul	Aug	Sep	Oct	Nov	Dec	Annual
Monthly normal	8.0	5.5	4.9	3.2	1.4	0.0	0.0	0.0	0.2	0.7	5.2	5.4	34.4
Standard deviation	0.9	0.9	0.9	1.0	0.5	0.0	0.0	0.0	0.1	0.3	1.1	0.8	0.5
Average monthly	8.4	6.5	4.8	2.6	0.9	0.1	0.0	0.0	0.1	0.7	4.0	5.2	33.3
Standard deviation	1.0	1.0	0.8	0.7	0.4	0.1	0.0	0.0	0.1	0.3	0.9	0.8	0.5
High monthly total	33.5	26.5	22.1	21.0	11.0	4.4	0.0†	1.0	4.1	6.5	27.5	31.4	33.5
Year of occurrence	1949	1944	1945	1985	1933	1941	1989	1932	1978	1932	1983	1968	1949
Low monthly total	0.0†	0.0†	0.0†	0.0†	0.0†	0.0†	0.0†	0.0†	0.0†	0.0†	0.0†	0.0†	0.0†
Year of occurrence	1989	1984	1981	1990	1990	1989	1989	1989	1989	1989	1988	1989	1989
Record high daily	12.0	10.0†	12.0	18.0	13.0	4.4	0.0†	1.0	4.1	11.9	18.0	12.2	18.0†
Day of occurrence	1	6	16	20	10	7	31	28	18	10	25	7	25
Year of occurrence	1907	1948	1988	1985	1922	1941	1989	1932	1978	1920	1983	1919	1983
Days w/snow >= .1	3.5	2.6	1.9	0.9	0.2	0.0	0.0	0.0	0.0	0.2	1.4	1.9	11.9
Days w/snow >= 5	0.4	0.4	0.2	0.1	0.1	0.0	0.0	0.0	0.0	0.0	0.2	0.2	1.7
Days w/snow >= 10	0.0	0.0	0.0	0.0	0.0	0.0	0.0	0.0	0.0	0.0	0.0	0.0	0.1

Degree Days

	Jan	Feb	Mar	Apr	May	Jun	Jul	Aug	Sep	Oct	Nov	Dec	Annual
Heating normal	1143	904	830	600	353	111	6	24	188	505	825	1097	6592
Heating average	1146	926	826	578	350	123	11	22	186	506	826	1091	6599
Cooling normal	0	0	0	0	1	49	155	104	14	0	0	0	326
Cooling average	0	0	0	0	1	37	137	94	13	0	0	0	284
Growing 40 normal	78	110	195	309	474	591	738	714	565	405	197	95	4476
Growing 40 average	71	95	190	312	468	582	728	707	556	397	198	89	4397
Growing 50 normal	15	33	84	172	323	454	579	550	414	259	85	23	2996
Growing 50 average	13	26	77	175	316	445	567	540	409	250	87	22	2932

† Also occurred on earlier date(s).

Location: Blanding   County: San Juan   Latitude: 37.617   Longitude:-109.483
Elevation: 6040 feet   Period of Record: 1904-1996

BLANDING
Monthly Data Summary

Maximum Temperature in °F

	Jan	Feb	Mar	Apr	May	Jun	Jul	Aug	Sep	Oct	Nov	Dec	Annual
Monthly normal	38.5	45.2	52.0	61.6	72.4	83.7	89.0	86.0	77.7	65.5	50.9	40.8	63.6
Standard deviation	8.1	8.2	9.4	9.5	8.8	7.6	4.7	5.4	7.6	9.4	8.8	7.9	7.9
Average monthly	38.5	44.5	52.2	61.9	71.7	82.9	88.2	85.9	78.0	65.8	51.3	40.9	63.5
Standard deviation	7.9	8.4	9.1	9.4	8.6	7.6	5.4	5.8	7.5	9.2	8.6	8.0	8.0
High monthly average	48.9	57.6	63.1	71.6	78.7	91.6	95.3	97.0	86.1	76.2	62.0	51.4	97.0
Year of occurrence	1981	1995	1934	1992	1984	1994	1905	1905	1928	1905	1909	1980	1905
Low monthly average	27.1	34.4	42.9	50.1	61.3	74.1	74.6	77.8	70.0	56.6	44.3	30.2	27.1
Year of occurrence	1937	1933	1924	1928	1917	1916	1916	1923	1923	1969	1972	1924	1937
Record high daily	62	71	86	88†	92	110	109	106	100	99†	74	65	110
Day of occurrence	1	28	31	10	27	22	19	18	1	17	4	3	22
Year of occurrence	1918	1906	1906	1906	1951	1905	1905	1905	1905	1905	1905	1929	1905
Record low daily	10†	10	26	31	35	48	65†	65†	48	34†	21	10†	10†
Day of occurrence	7	8	1	2	1	8	27	31	27	29	23	27	27
Year of occurrence	1971	1933	1971	1947	1915	1979	1916	1992	1936	1991	1931	1924	1924
Days w/max >= 100	0.0	0.0	0.0	0.0	0.0	0.2	0.1	0.2	0.0	0.0	0.0	0.0	0.6
Days w/max >= 90	0.0	0.0	0.0	0.0	0.2	5.7	14.2	8.5	1.2	0.1	0.0	0.0	30.0
Days w/max <= 32	6.8	2.1	0.3	0.0	0.0	0.0	0.0	0.0	0.0	0.0	0.5	4.7	14.6

Minimum Temperature in °F

	Jan	Feb	Mar	Apr	May	Jun	Jul	Aug	Sep	Oct	Nov	Dec	Annual
Monthly normal	16.1	22.1	27.2	33.3	41.8	50.7	57.5	55.8	47.8	37.8	27.2	18.8	36.4
Standard deviation	9.2	7.9	6.6	6.5	6.3	6.4	3.8	4.3	6.1	6.7	6.9	8.3	6.6
Average monthly	16.3	21.8	27.3	34.1	41.6	50.2	57.4	55.7	47.8	37.5	26.3	18.7	36.2
Standard deviation	9.3	8.7	6.7	7.1	6.6	6.8	4.2	4.5	6.3	7.0	7.2	8.4	6.9
High monthly average	27.3	31.0	33.1	49.8	49.1	58.5	63.2	65.6	59.2	49.5	35.5	27.8	65.6
Year of occurrence	1927	1927	1918	1938	1925	1994	1925	1926	1926	1926	1926	1922	1926
Low monthly average	-1.8	3.1	21.9	25.7	32.5	44.2	53.5	47.5	37.4	28.7	16.3	7.0	-1.8
Year of occurrence	1937	1933	1909	1909	1909	1907	1928	1922	1922	1908	1932	1931	1937
Record high daily	39	42	47	70	62	90	79†	75	81	59	53	40†	90
Day of occurrence	24	27	23	19	31	27	17	4	3	13	25	3	27
Year of occurrence	1916	1927	1990	1906	1926	1994	1925	1938	1931	1929	1933	1906	1994
Record low daily	-20	-23	-3	10	15	28†	36	38	20†	10	-7	-13	-23
Day of occurrence	12	8	28	24	16	13	15	23	27	30	25	23	8
Year of occurrence	1963	1933	1975	1913	1910	1947	1934	1968	1908	1971	1931	1990	1933
Days w/min <= 32	30.5	26.4	24.4	12.5	2.9	0.2	0.0	0.0	0.4	7.1	24.3	30.0	158.5
Days w/min <= 0	2.0	0.8	0.0	0.0	0.0	0.0	0.0	0.0	0.0	0.0	0.1	0.9	3.8
Days w/min <= -20	0.0	0.0	0.0	0.0	0.0	0.0	0.0	0.0	0.0	0.0	0.0	0.0	0.0

Mean Temperature in °F

	Jan	Feb	Mar	Apr	May	Jun	Jul	Aug	Sep	Oct	Nov	Dec	Annual
Monthly normal	27.3	33.7	39.6	47.4	57.1	67.2	73.2	70.9	62.8	51.7	39.1	29.8	50.0
Standard deviation	8.1	7.3	7.3	7.4	7.0	6.5	3.5	4.1	6.2	7.3	7.2	7.5	6.6
Average monthly	27.4	33.2	39.8	48.0	56.7	66.6	72.8	70.8	62.9	51.7	38.8	29.9	49.9
Standard deviation	8.0	7.8	7.1	7.5	7.0	6.5	3.9	4.3	6.0	7.3	7.1	7.4	6.6
High monthly average	36.0	44.2	47.1	56.9	62.6	75.0	77.5	77.2	69.0	59.5	46.3	39.4	77.5
Year of occurrence	1981	1995	1910	1992	1984	1994	1994	1926	1926	1926	1926	1980	1994
Low monthly average	12.6	18.8	33.0	39.4	50.1	61.2	66.3	65.6	56.6	44.6	32.4	19.4	12.6
Year of occurrence	1937	1933	1948	1928	1917	1907	1916	1968	1922	1969	1952	1931	1937

† Also occurred on earlier date(s).

BLANDING
Monthly Data Summary

Precipitation in Inches

	Jan	Feb	Mar	Apr	May	Jun	Jul	Aug	Sep	Oct	Nov	Dec	Annual
Monthly normal	1.25	0.91	0.95	0.75	0.62	0.46	1.32	1.43	1.28	1.36	1.08	1.18	12.60
Standard deviation	0.14	0.10	0.09	0.10	0.08	0.08	0.15	0.20	0.15	0.15	0.12	0.14	0.13
Average monthly	1.36	1.18	1.04	0.85	0.73	0.46	1.18	1.39	1.24	1.42	1.03	1.38	13.28
Standard deviation	0.15	0.13	0.11	0.11	0.09	0.09	0.13	0.17	0.15	0.18	0.14	0.17	0.13
High monthly total	5.31	3.87	3.72	4.35	2.62	2.84	3.55	4.95	4.80	7.01	4.17	6.84	7.01
Year of occurrence	1993	1913	1906	1926	1926	1948	1914	1968	1927	1916	1905	1909	1916
Low monthly total	0.00	0.00†	0.00†	0.00†	0.00†	0.00†	0.00	0.03	0.00†	0.00†	0.00†	0.00†	0.00†
Year of occurrence	1972	1972	1972	1937	1972	1994	1920	1985	1957	1995	1989	1989	1989
Record high daily	1.49	1.50	1.13	1.33	1.26	1.40	1.74	4.48	1.85	2.00†	2.79	3.50	4.48
Day of occurrence	15	3	1	4	25	28	21	1	29	31	27	23	1
Year of occurrence	1978	1908	1970	1987	1994	1938	1985	1968	1905	1928	1919	1909	1968
Days w/pcp >= .01	5.9	5.5	5.6	4.5	4.1	2.5	6.1	7.2	4.8	4.8	4.2	5.2	60.6
Days w/pcp >= .10	3.6	3.3	3.4	2.3	2.2	1.2	3.3	3.8	3.1	3.2	2.7	3.4	35.4
Days w/pcp >= .50	0.8	0.6	0.5	0.5	0.3	0.3	0.6	0.7	0.9	0.9	0.6	0.8	7.4

Snow and Sleet in Inches

	Jan	Feb	Mar	Apr	May	Jun	Jul	Aug	Sep	Oct	Nov	Dec	Annual
Monthly normal	13.0	8.0	6.8	2.6	0.2	0.0	0.0	0.0	0.0	0.3	3.6	10.1	44.5
Standard deviation	1.3	1.1	0.8	0.5	0.1	0.0	0.0	0.0	0.0	0.1	0.6	1.3	0.5
Average monthly	11.4	7.5	4.6	1.9	0.2	0.0	0.0	0.0	0.0	0.3	3.3	10.4	39.7
Standard deviation	1.2	1.0	0.7	0.5	0.1	0.0	0.0	0.0	0.1	0.1	0.7	1.4	0.5
High monthly total	46.9	39.7	17.9	15.2	4.0	0.0†	2.5	0.0†	3.5	6.0	19.0	55.0	55.0
Year of occurrence	1979	1913	1970	1957	1978	1995	1906	1995	1905	1984	1931	1909	1909
Low monthly total	0.0†	0.0†	0.0†	0.0†	0.0†	0.0†	0.0†	0.0†	0.0†	0.0†	0.0†	0.0†	0.0†
Year of occurrence	1972	1991	1994	1993	1994	1995	1995	1995	1995	1995	1995	1995	1995
Record high daily	14.0	12.0†	9.0	160.6	4.0	0.0†	2.5	0.0†	3.5	3.0†	9.0	36.0	160.6
Day of occurrence	15	8	10	3	5	30	29	31	25	24	24	23	3
Year of occurrence	1978	1966	1909	1911	1978	1995	1906	1995	1905	1935	1908	1909	1911
Days w/snow >= .1	4.7	3.4	2.3	1.0	0.2	0.0	0.0	0.0	0.0	0.2	1.4	3.6	16.6
Days w/snow >= 5	0.6	0.3	0.2	0.1	0.0	0.0	0.0	0.0	0.0	0.0	0.2	0.7	2.1
Days w/snow >= 10	0.1	0.0	0.0	0.0	0.0	0.0	0.0	0.0	0.0	0.0	0.0	0.1	0.2

Degree Days

	Jan	Feb	Mar	Apr	May	Jun	Jul	Aug	Sep	Oct	Nov	Dec	Annual
Heating normal	1165	884	787	526	253	51	0	5	110	414	778	1090	6069
Heating average	1159	896	780	503	264	57	1	6	103	411	783	1084	6051
Cooling normal	0	0	0	0	8	118	255	188	42	0	0	0	614
Cooling average	0	0	0	0	7	105	242	185	42	0	0	0	584
Growing 40 normal	39	91	191	330	534	702	844	814	638	417	170	56	4830
Growing 40 average	37	85	193	333	523	692	838	811	637	418	175	56	4805
Growing 50 normal	4	20	76	183	350	520	661	619	431	246	61	5	3181
Growing 50 average	3	18	75	185	337	510	651	613	435	248	62	6	3149

† Also occurred on earlier date(s).

Location: Blowhard Mountain Radar County: Iron Latitude: 37.583 Longitude:-112.850
Elevation: 10700   feet   Period of Record: 1964-1996

BLOWHARD MOUNTAIN RADAR
Monthly Data Summary

Maximum Temperature in °F

	Jan	Feb	Mar	Apr	May	Jun	Jul	Aug	Sep	Oct	Nov	Dec	Annual
Monthly normal													
Standard deviation													
Average monthly	27.6	28.0	30.2	37.1	45.4	56.1	62.3	60.3	53.7	44.1	33.5	28.1	42.2
Standard deviation	9.6	9.1	8.2	8.5	8.0	7.4	4.9	5.2	6.6	9.1	9.2	9.9	8.0
High monthly average	35.5	34.1	39.2	44.7	52.2	62.8	66.2	64.2	58.3	51.3	43.7	38.1	66.2
Year of occurrence	1986	1991	1972	1989	1984	1974	1972	1994	1979	1988	1995	1980	1972
Low monthly average	20.6	22.1	23.3	28.5	39.4	48.9	59.0	54.0	46.5	34.0	26.8	21.7	20.6
Year of occurrence	1979	1993	1991	1967	1977	1965	1982	1968	1986	1984	1972	1971	1979
Record high daily	55	51	53	58	68	73	75†	72†	67†	63†	57	54†	75
Day of occurrence	18	25	31	23	25	26	7	1	4	2	11	16	7
Year of occurrence	1977	1986	1966	1969	1983	1970	1989	1993	1995	1980	1989	1980	1989
Record low daily	-9	-1†	3	12	18	29	44	40	27	9	8	-13	-13
Day of occurrence	3	6	3	7	1	8	22	19	28	30	19	22	22
Year of occurrence	1971	1989	1966	1975	1967	1995	1986	1979	1982	1972	1994	1990	1990
Days w/max >= 100	0.0	0.0	0.0	0.0	0.0	0.0	0.0	0.0	0.0	0.0	0.0	0.0	0.0
Days w/max >= 90	0.0	0.0	0.0	0.0	0.0	0.0	0.0	0.0	0.0	0.0	0.0	0.0	0.0
Days w/max <= 32	20.8	18.1	18.1	7.9	2.3	0.1	0.0	0.0	0.4	3.7	13.2	19.6	106.2

Minimum Temperature in °F

	Jan	Feb	Mar	Apr	May	Jun	Jul	Aug	Sep	Oct	Nov	Dec	Annual
Monthly normal													
Standard deviation													
Average monthly	12.6	12.8	15.1	21.2	29.6	40.3	47.3	45.3	38.7	29.3	18.8	13.3	27.0
Standard deviation	9.9	9.2	9.1	9.6	8.8	8.4	4.8	5.0	7.4	9.5	9.6	10.2	8.5
High monthly average	21.5	20.2	22.3	29.2	36.4	46.9	51.1	49.2	43.0	36.5	29.6	21.8	51.1
Year of occurrence	1986	1991	1972	1992	1984	1994	1994	1994	1979	1988	1995	1980	1994
Low monthly average	3.2	5.6	8.5	11.5	23.2	33.8	43.7	40.9	32.7	20.3	11.8	6.5	3.2
Year of occurrence	1979	1966	1977	1967	1980	1965	1992	1968	1965	1984	1992	1971	1979
Record high daily	35†	36	39	44	51	60	62	62	54†	47	41	35†	62†
Day of occurrence	11	25	17	30	29	22	29	9	11	1	5	1	9
Year of occurrence	1990	1986	1972	1977	1984	1974	1995	1975	1990	1974	1975	1995	1975
Record low daily	-20	-18	-13	-4	2	16	29	23	13†	-3	-11	-23	-23
Day of occurrence	4	1	28	2	2	8	2	31	19	30	28	8	8
Year of occurrence	1971	1985	1975	1975	1967	1979	1992	1964	1978	1971	1976	1978	1978
Days w/min <= 32	29.4	26.9	29.0	24.8	17.3	5.8	0.1	0.3	5.2	17.4	26.7	29.3	215.6
Days w/min <= 0	3.6	2.8	1.6	0.2	0.0	0.0	0.0	0.0	0.0	0.1	0.7	3.2	12.6
Days w/min <= -20	0.0	0.0	0.0	0.0	0.0	0.0	0.0	0.0	0.0	0.0	0.0	0.1	0.1

Mean Temperature in °F

	Jan	Feb	Mar	Apr	May	Jun	Jul	Aug	Sep	Oct	Nov	Dec	Annual
Monthly normal													
Standard deviation													
Average monthly	20.1	20.4	22.7	29.2	37.5	48.2	54.8	52.8	46.2	36.7	26.2	20.7	34.6
Standard deviation	9.1	8.5	8.1	8.5	8.0	7.6	4.6	4.8	6.7	9.0	8.8	9.5	7.8
High monthly average	28.5	27.2	30.8	36.6	44.3	54.5	58.5	56.7	50.6	43.9	36.6	29.9	58.5
Year of occurrence	1986	1991	1972	1989	1984	1974	1994	1994	1979	1988	1995	1980	1994
Low monthly average	11.9	14.1	17.0	20.0	31.9	41.3	51.4	47.5	39.6	27.2	19.6	14.0	11.9
Year of occurrence	1979	1966	1977	1967	1971	1965	1992	1968	1986	1984	1972	1971	1979

† Also occurred on earlier date(s).

BLOWHARD MOUNTAIN RADAR
Monthly Data Summary

Precipitation in Inches

	Jan	Feb	Mar	Apr	May	Jun	Jul	Aug	Sep	Oct	Nov	Dec	Annual
Monthly normal													
Standard deviation													
Average monthly	2.99	3.17	4.51	3.10	1.82	0.83	2.16	2.84	1.45	1.73	2.43	2.74	29.77
Standard deviation	0.27	0.29	0.35	0.28	0.20	0.12	0.21	0.22	0.16	0.17	0.27	0.27	0.24
High monthly total	7.85	8.19	9.52	10.36	5.12	2.87	6.59	6.80	5.00	5.98	7.64	7.52	10.36
Year of occurrence	1980	1969	1982	1965	1965	1967	1975	1971	1967	1972	1965	1965	1965
Low monthly total	0.40	0.23	0.35	0.20	0.00†	0.00†	0.12	0.07	0.05	0.00†	0.02	0.00	0.00†
Year of occurrence	1972	1972	1972	1989	1984	1980	1972	1985	1979	1995	1995	1989	1989
Record high daily	3.60	2.65	2.97	2.84	2.31	1.63	2.72	1.68	1.95	1.51	3.06	3.04	3.60
Day of occurrence	25	10	19	2	25	6	13	5	24	23	25	30	25
Year of occurrence	1967	1978	1982	1967	1965	1993	1973	1967	1967	1975	1965	1965	1967
Days w/pcp >= .01	7.4	7.6	9.5	7.1	5.7	3.4	8.3	9.9	6.1	5.5	6.1	7.4	84.2
Days w/pcp >= .10	6.2	6.5	8.3	5.8	4.3	2.1	5.0	6.8	3.4	4.2	4.9	5.4	62.9
Days w/pcp >= .50	2.0	2.2	3.2	2.3	1.0	0.5	1.2	1.9	0.9	1.2	1.5	1.7	19.5

Snow and Sleet in Inches

	Jan	Feb	Mar	Apr	May	Jun	Jul	Aug	Sep	Oct	Nov	Dec	Annual
Monthly normal													
Standard deviation													
Average monthly	35.6	35.0	48.3	30.4	13.9	2.3	0.0	0.1	2.0	11.4	27.1	34.5	240.6
Standard deviation	3.2	3.2	3.5	2.8	1.6	0.6	0.0	0.0	0.5	1.4	2.9	3.2	1.9
High monthly total	85.5	102.5	91.5	94.0	39.0	17.5	0.0†	1.0†	25.0	36.0	69.0	71.0	102.5
Year of occurrence	1982	1969	1979	1965	1981	1967	1995	1992	1986	1971	1982	1982	1969
Low monthly total	7.0	3.5	7.0	2.5†	0.0†	0.0†	0.0†	0.0†	0.0†	0.0†	0.0	0.0	0.0†
Year of occurrence	1972	1972	1966	1992	1994	1994	1995	1994	1995	1995	1995	1989	1989
Record high daily	36.0	28.0	26.0†	26.0	18.0	14.0	0.0†	1.0	7.0	18.0	30.0	30.0	36.0
Day of occurrence	25	6	15	2	20	6	31	23	25	27	12	1	25
Year of occurrence	1967	1969	1987	1967	1981	1993	1995	1992	1986	1991	1985	1982	1967
Days w/snow >= .1	7.3	7.5	9.4	6.9	4.6	1.1	0.0	0.1	0.9	3.7	6.0	7.2	54.8
Days w/snow >= 5	2.6	2.7	3.7	2.4	1.0	0.1	0.0	0.0	0.1	0.7	2.0	2.3	17.5
Days w/snow >= 10	0.9	1.0	1.5	0.9	0.3	0.0	0.0	0.0	0.0	0.2	0.7	1.0	6.5

Degree Days

	Jan	Feb	Mar	Apr	May	Jun	Jul	Aug	Sep	Oct	Nov	Dec	Annual
Heating normal													
Heating average	1333	1195	1230	1013	811	477	306	357	534	832	1121	1312	10527
Cooling normal													
Cooling average	0	0	0	0	0	0	0	0	0	0	0	0	0
Growing 40 normal													
Growing 40 average	6	3	6	29	106	281	445	385	229	97	18	6	1617
Growing 50 normal													
Growing 50 average	0	0	0	1	18	105	197	159	71	17	0	0	573

† Also occurred on earlier date(s).

Location: Brian Head County: Iron   Latitude: 37.683   Longitude: -112.833
Elevation: 9770 feet   Period of Record: 1991-1995

BRIAN HEAD
Monthly Data Summary

Maximum Temperature in °F

	Jan	Feb	Mar	Apr	May	Jun	Jul	Aug	Sep	Oct	Nov	Dec	Annual
Monthly normal													
Standard deviation													
Average monthly	29.3	33.8	37.4	44.5	48.2	59.6	67.7	66.9	59.8	46.1	32.8	27.8	46.2
Standard deviation	7.2	7.8	7.7	9.4	8.4	8.8	5.8	5.5	5.3	9.9	10.9	7.7	7.9
High monthly average	31.7	39.4	42.6	49.8	53.6	67.6	72.2	69.6	60.9	50.3	43.6	30.6	72.2
Year of occurrence	1992	1991	1993	1992	1993	1994	1994	1995	1995	1995	1995	1991	1994
Low monthly average	27.4	28.7	32.5	41.9	42.5	54.0	65.0	64.2	58.8	43.2	26.7	24.6	24.6
Year of occurrence	1995	1993	1991	1995	1991	1995	1992	1992	1991	1994	1992	1992	1992
Record high daily	45	50†	55	60	64	77†	79	80	73	64	50†	46	80
Day of occurrence	31	21	22	29	30	25	1	4	3	15	25	5	4
Year of occurrence	1992	1995	1993	1992	1994	1994	1994	1994	1995	1991	1995	1991	1994
Record low daily	13	12	19	23†	20	37†	50	51†	45†	11	7	10	7
Day of occurrence	31	19	26	20	11	9	1	31	30	30	20	13	20
Year of occurrence	1994	1991	1995	1995	1991	1995	1992	1992	1995	1991	1994	1992	1994
Days w/max >= 100	0.0	0.0	0.0	0.0	0.0	0.0	0.0	0.0	0.0	0.0	0.0	0.0	0.0
Days w/max >= 90	0.0	0.0	0.0	0.0	0.0	0.0	0.0	0.0	0.0	0.0	0.0	0.0	0.0
Days w/max <= 32	21.5	14.4	8.8	4.8	1.2	0.0	0.0	0.0	0.0	2.6	13.4	22.8	105.2

Minimum Temperature in °F

	Jan	Feb	Mar	Apr	May	Jun	Jul	Aug	Sep	Oct	Nov	Dec	Annual
Monthly normal													
Standard deviation													
Average monthly	9.9	10.7	13.8	18.2	26.0	33.9	40.7	42.1	34.2	24.2	12.8	8.9	23.0
Standard deviation	7.4	7.7	7.9	6.6	6.4	6.5	4.2	4.0	5.7	6.8	9.6	8.2	6.7
High monthly average	11.4	14.0	16.1	22.8	30.5	38.8	43.3	44.5	35.7	27.1	20.1	10.8	44.5
Year of occurrence	1995	1995	1992	1992	1992	1994	1994	1994	1995	1992	1995	1994	1994
Low monthly average	8.9	5.5	9.9	15.2	21.4	29.1	38.8	39.5	32.8†	21.7	6.6	5.7	5.5
Year of occurrence	1992	1994	1991	1995	1995	1995	1992	1992	1993	1994	1992	1992	1994
Record high daily	28	29	29	35	40	48	49	51	46	37	28†	24†	51
Day of occurrence	9	17	21	30	13	27	6	27	2	2	6	12	27
Year of occurrence	1995	1991	1995	1992	1994	1994	1992	1994	1994	1992	1994	1995	1994
Record low daily	-14	-12	-7	4	4	17	26†	27†	24†	0†	-13	-12	-14
Day of occurrence	31	1	30	1	7	6	3	28	22	31	25	19	31
Year of occurrence	1994	1994	1995	1995	1995	1995	1992	1992	1995	1991	1992	1992	1994
Days w/min <= 32	31.0	28.2	31.0	29.8	27.8	12.4	1.0	1.4	12.2	28.8	30.0	31.0	315.2
Days w/min <= 0	3.0	3.4	1.8	0.0	0.0	0.0	0.0	0.0	0.0	0.4	4.2	5.0	21.5
Days w/min <= -20	0.0	0.0	0.0	0.0	0.0	0.0	0.0	0.0	0.0	0.0	0.0	0.0	0.0

Mean Temperature in °F

	Jan	Feb	Mar	Apr	May	Jun	Jul	Aug	Sep	Oct	Nov	Dec	Annual
Monthly normal													
Standard deviation													
Average monthly	19.6	22.3	25.6	31.4	37.1	46.7	54.2	54.5	47.0	35.1	22.8	18.4	34.6
Standard deviation	6.0	6.4	6.5	7.1	6.4	7.1	4.5	3.9	4.8	7.8	9.9	7.0	6.5
High monthly average	20.3†	26.2	28.5	36.3	40.1	53.2	57.7	56.9	48.3	37.5	31.9	20.5	57.7
Year of occurrence	1994	1991	1993	1992	1993	1994	1994	1994	1995	1995	1995	1991	1994
Low monthly average	18.4	18.1	21.2	28.5	33.1	41.5	51.9	51.8	46.3	32.4	16.6	15.2	15.2
Year of occurrence	1993	1994	1991	1995	1995	1995	1992	1992	1993	1994	1992	1992	1992

† Also occurred on earlier date(s).

BRIAN HEAD
Monthly Data Summary

Precipitation in Inches

	Jan	Feb	Mar	Apr	May	Jun	Jul	Aug	Sep	Oct	Nov	Dec	Annual
Monthly normal													
Standard deviation													
Average monthly	5.33	4.63	5.48	3.58	1.83	1.41	0.85	3.15	1.27	3.21	2.70	3.02	36.47
Standard deviation	0.35	0.32	0.35	0.24	0.13	0.15	0.08	0.25	0.17	0.32	0.22	0.23	0.24
High monthly total	9.51	8.65	11.12	6.11	3.41	2.09	1.36	4.62	2.51	5.63	5.57	5.47	11.12
Year of occurrence	1993	1993	1995	1995	1995	1993	1992	1992	1994	1991	1994	1992	1995
Low monthly total	1.65	0.95	2.13	1.24	0.53	0.35	0.38	1.48	0.27	0.00	0.14	1.35	0.00
Year of occurrence	1994	1991	1994	1992	1994	1994	1993	1993	1992	1995	1995	1991	1995
Record high daily	1.82	1.31	2.42	1.04	0.71	1.18	0.62	1.58	1.22	1.98	1.20	1.52	2.42
Day of occurrence	31	12	12	10	11	1	18	13	30	28	12	30	12
Year of occurrence	1993	1994	1995	1994	1991	1991	1995	1994	1994	1991	1993	1992	1995
Days w/pcp >= .01	12.0	10.8	14.4	9.5	11.6	7.4	8.0	13.4	5.2	6.8	9.4	11.8	143.0
Days w/pcp >= .10	8.8	7.6	10.4	7.8	5.8	3.8	3.0	6.4	2.6	5.0	6.2	7.0	88.0
Days w/pcp >= .50	4.2	4.2	3.0	3.0	0.8	0.8	0.2	1.8	0.8	2.2	2.2	2.0	29.8

Snow and Sleet in Inches

	Jan	Feb	Mar	Apr	May	Jun	Jul	Aug	Sep	Oct	Nov	Dec	Annual
Monthly normal													
Standard deviation													
Average monthly	79.8	63.5	70.9	41.8	11.7	9.1	0.0	0.1	0.9	24.2	41.3	51.1	394.4
Standard deviation	5.1	4.6	4.2	2.9	1.1	1.4	0.0	0.0	0.3	3.1	3.0	3.7	2.5
High monthly total	117.5	123.0	142.0	78.5	29.5	20.0	0.0†	0.5	3.0	61.5	91.0	89.5	142.0
Year of occurrence	1995	1993	1995	1995	1995	1991	1995	1992	1993	1991	1994	1992	1995
Low monthly total	42.0	18.0	28.5	11.5	3.0	0.0	0.0†	0.0†	0.0†	0.0	1.5	20.3	0.0†
Year of occurrence	1994	1991	1994	1992	1992	1994	1995	1995	1995	1995	1995	1991	1995
Record high daily	29.0	29.0	26.0†	11.5	8.0	15.0	0.0†	0.5	3.0	21.0†	19.0	24.5	29.0†
Day of occurrence	16	12	25	10	11	1	31	23	18	30	18	13	12
Year of occurrence	1995	1994	1995	1994	1991	1991	1995	1992	1993	1991	1994	1992	1994
Days w/snow >= .1	12.0	10.8	14.2	9.0	6.2	3.0	0.0	0.2	0.4	4.4	9.0	11.8	96.0
Days w/snow >= 5	6.2	4.6	5.8	3.5	0.4	0.4	0.0	0.0	0.0	1.4	3.8	3.0	34.0
Days w/snow >= 10	3.0	2.4	2.6	1.2	0.0	0.2	0.0	0.0	0.0	1.0	1.0	1.6	15.2

Degree Days

	Jan	Feb	Mar	Apr	May	Jun	Jul	Aug	Sep	Oct	Nov	Dec	Annual
Heating normal													
Heating average	1407	1205	1221	1009	864	547	333	325	541	925	1266	1444	11092
Cooling normal													
Cooling average	0	0	0	0	0	0	0	0	0	0	0	0	0
Growing 40 normal													
Growing 40 average	2	14	30	103	140	303	461	460	302	122	21	2	1965
Growing 50 normal													
Growing 50 average	0	0	1	20	37	157	274	261	148	31	0	0	933

† Also occurred on earlier date(s).

Location: Brigham City County: Box Elder   Latitude: 41.483   Longitude:-112.033
Elevation: 4340 feet   Period of Record: 1899-1974

BRIGHAM CITY
Monthly Data Summary

Maximum Temperature in °F

	Jan	Feb	Mar	Apr	May	Jun	Jul	Aug	Sep	Oct	Nov	Dec	Annual
Monthly normal													
Standard deviation													
Average monthly	35.7	41.6	51.0	61.6	72.7	81.8	91.8	89.5	78.8	65.9	49.6	38.5	63.2
Standard deviation	9.0	8.9	9.7	10.0	10.0	9.6	5.6	5.9	9.0	9.8	9.4	8.7	8.8
High monthly average	47.5	52.1	62.8	72.9	83.7	90.7	97.9	96.2	87.3	75.6	57.7	47.7	97.9
Year of occurrence	1953	1963	1934	1934	1934	1933	1931	1969	1938	1933	1914	1917	1931
Low monthly average	20.5	28.9	38.8	51.9	62.1	71.9	84.5	82.7	70.9	56.1	40.2	28.3	20.5
Year of occurrence	1949	1933	1917	1920	1917	1945	1913	1968	1965	1920	1938	1930	1949
Record high daily	62	68	78	86	96	105	108	105	96†	89†	74	64	108
Day of occurrence	31	5	28	19	25	20	24	2	12	3	9	11	24
Year of occurrence	1971	1963	1943	1962	1967	1913	1931	1969	1963	1963	1958	1939	1931
Record low daily	6†	5	21	33†	40	50	67	62†	37	33	12	4	4
Day of occurrence	23	10	1	3	2	21	13	22	17	29	16	19	19
Year of occurrence	1937	1933	1922	1955	1964	1916	1918	1968	1965	1971	1955	1924	1924
Days w/max >= 100	0.0	0.0	0.0	0.0	0.0	0.3	2.0	0.8	0.0	0.0	0.0	0.0	3.2
Days w/max >= 90	0.0	0.0	0.0	0.0	0.7	7.0	21.9	16.7	2.7	0.0	0.0	0.0	49.9
Days w/max <= 32	10.6	4.2	0.6	0.0	0.0	0.0	0.0	0.0	0.0	0.0	0.8	7.4	23.6

Minimum Temperature in °F

	Jan	Feb	Mar	Apr	May	Jun	Jul	Aug	Sep	Oct	Nov	Dec	Annual
Monthly normal													
Standard deviation													
Average monthly	17.0	22.3	28.8	37.1	45.3	53.1	60.9	58.3	48.1	38.4	28.5	20.9	38.2
Standard deviation	11.8	10.0	7.6	7.0	7.3	7.5	5.9	6.2	7.9	7.1	7.5	10.0	8.0
High monthly average	31.5	32.7	33.8	44.6	50.8	61.9	65.2	63.8	53.9	44.2	35.9	30.5	65.2
Year of occurrence	1953	1963	1921	1915	1969	1961	1971	1967	1960	1944	1953	1917	1971
Low monthly average	3.2	3.6	19.7	32.2	39.5	47.0	56.2	52.8	34.9	33.4	20.0	7.2	3.2
Year of occurrence	1949	1933	1917	1970	1933	1929	1962	1939	1942	1919	1930	1932	1949
Record high daily	46	48	55	64	72	80	86	78†	79	64†	53	55	86
Day of occurrence	6	5	25	30	26	28	28	1	1	1	21	22	28
Year of occurrence	1965	1963	1956	1965	1969	1963	1971	1964	1945	1951	1921	1964	1971
Record low daily	-23	-27	0	9	25	30	39†	37†	19†	17	-13	-24	-27
Day of occurrence	22	10	1	2	6	2	3	30	27	29	16	25	10
Year of occurrence	1930	1933	1939	1936	1965	1929	1921	1964	1942	1917	1955	1924	1933
Days w/min <= 32	28.5	24.9	21.4	8.1	1.2	0.0	0.0	0.0	0.6	6.3	21.1	28.1	140.8
Days w/min <= 0	3.2	1.0	0.0	0.0	0.0	0.0	0.0	0.0	0.0	0.0	0.0	1.3	5.7
Days w/min <= -20	0.1	0.0	0.0	0.0	0.0	0.0	0.0	0.0	0.0	0.0	0.0	0.1	0.1

Mean Temperature in °F

	Jan	Feb	Mar	Apr	May	Jun	Jul	Aug	Sep	Oct	Nov	Dec	Annual
Monthly normal													
Standard deviation													
Average monthly	26.3	31.9	39.9	49.3	59.0	67.4	76.4	73.9	63.4	52.1	39.1	29.7	50.7
Standard deviation	9.9	8.8	8.0	7.9	7.9	7.8	4.8	5.1	7.5	7.5	7.6	8.8	7.6
High monthly average	39.5	42.4	48.1	57.9	66.1	75.8	80.5	79.5	69.5	58.5	46.4	39.1	80.5
Year of occurrence	1953	1963	1934	1915	1934	1961	1971	1967	1938	1963	1953	1917	1971
Low monthly average	11.8	16.2	29.3	42.5	52.5	61.9	71.9	68.9	55.9	45.4	31.6	18.1	11.8
Year of occurrence	1949	1933	1917	1920	1916	1945	1913	1968	1942	1946	1938	1930	1949

† Also occurred on earlier date(s).

BRIGHAM CITY
Monthly Data Summary

Precipitation in Inches

	Jan	Feb	Mar	Apr	May	Jun	Jul	Aug	Sep	Oct	Nov	Dec	Annual
Monthly normal													
Standard deviation													
Average monthly	1.89	1.66	1.83	2.19	1.68	1.42	0.47	0.75	1.26	1.69	1.72	1.90	18.46
Standard deviation	0.16	0.15	0.16	0.18	0.16	0.18	0.08	0.11	0.16	0.18	0.17	0.16	0.16
High monthly total	4.55	4.12	5.37	5.67	4.30	5.94	2.15	3.70	4.48	4.58	3.49	5.43	5.94
Year of occurrence	1914	1936	1973	1967	1962	1944	1914	1968	1915	1916	1970	1921	1944
Low monthly total	0.00	0.00	0.00	0.48	0.00†	0.00†	0.00†	0.00†	0.00†	0.00†	0.00	0.14	0.00†
Year of occurrence	1961	1974	1943	1961	1974	1951	1971	1967	1956	1958	1939	1962	1939
Record high daily	2.02	1.40	1.89	2.19	1.95	2.07	1.24	1.61	1.90	1.64	2.32	2.15	2.32
Day of occurrence	14	2	22	13	5	5	5	29	30	14	10	19	10
Year of occurrence	1953	1936	1973	1972	1926	1945	1914	1971	1926	1968	1949	1921	1949
Days w/pcp >= .01	8.3	7.4	7.8	8.0	6.5	4.6	2.2	3.4	4.2	5.1	6.3	8.3	72.8
Days w/pcp >= .10	5.5	4.8	5.4	5.7	4.4	3.1	1.4	2.2	2.9	3.8	4.4	5.6	49.8
Days w/pcp >= .50	1.0	0.9	0.9	1.3	1.0	0.9	0.3	0.3	0.9	1.3	1.1	0.9	10.9

Snow and Sleet in Inches

	Jan	Feb	Mar	Apr	May	Jun	Jul	Aug	Sep	Oct	Nov	Dec	Annual
Monthly normal													
Standard deviation													
Average monthly	14.9	9.6	6.7	2.6	0.2	0.0	0.0	0.0	0.5	0.8	3.4	11.3	50.0
Standard deviation	1.5	1.2	0.9	0.6	0.1	0.0	0.0	0.0	0.3	0.4	0.6	1.2	0.6
High monthly total	48.5	38.0	26.7	15.0	5.0	0.0†	0.0†	0.0†	27.2	13.5	27.2	42.0	48.5
Year of occurrence	1949	1969	1951	1921	1915	1973	1972	1972	1942	1971	1942	1967	1949
Low monthly total	0.0†	0.0†	0.0†	0.0†	0.0†	0.0†	0.0†	0.0†	0.0†	0.0†	0.0†	0.0†	0.0†
Year of occurrence	1961	1963	1965	1965	1974	1973	1972	1972	1972	1972	1969	1962	1962
Record high daily	14.0†	12.5	10.0	8.0	4.5	0.0†	0.0†	0.0†	6.0	11.0	9.0	18.0	18.0
Day of occurrence	20	17	31	5	2	30	31	31	30	28	14	19	19
Year of occurrence	1949	1952	1936	1921	1964	1973	1972	1972	1942	1961	1955	1921	1921
Days w/snow >= .1	5.2	3.7	2.6	0.9	0.1	0.0	0.0	0.0	0.2	0.3	1.3	4.4	18.5
Days w/snow >= 5	0.9	0.6	0.3	0.1	0.0	0.0	0.0	0.0	0.0	0.1	0.2	0.5	2.5
Days w/snow >= 10	0.1	0.1	0.0	0.0	0.0	0.0	0.0	0.0	0.0	0.0	0.0	0.0	0.3

Degree Days

	Jan	Feb	Mar	Apr	May	Jun	Jul	Aug	Sep	Oct	Nov	Dec	Annual
Heating normal													
Heating average	1198	933	778	470	214	64	1	5	113	400	777	1095	6053
Cooling normal													
Cooling average	0	0	0	0	28	137	353	281	66	2	0	0	870
Growing 40 normal													
Growing 40 average	27	61	181	346	570	720	897	855	642	428	158	42	4933
Growing 50 normal													
Growing 50 average	2	11	69	185	367	518	719	674	454	253	54	5	3317

† Also occurred on earlier date(s).

Location: Bryce Canyon National Park County: Garfield   Latitude: 37.650 Longitude:-112.167
Elevation: 7910 feet   Period of Record: 1959-1996

BRYCE CANYON NATL PK HD
Monthly Data Summary

Maximum Temperature in °F

	Jan	Feb	Mar	Apr	May	Jun	Jul	Aug	Sep	Oct	Nov	Dec	Annual
Monthly normal	36.3	38.9	44.0	53.0	63.2	73.9	79.6	76.7	69.5	59.2	44.9	37.3	56.4
Standard deviation	8.9	8.8	9.2	9.7	9.0	7.5	5.0	5.5	7.5	9.4	9.7	9.5	8.3
Average monthly	35.8	38.7	44.0	53.1	62.9	73.8	79.6	76.8	69.7	59.0	44.5	36.9	56.2
Standard deviation	8.8	8.7	9.0	9.9	8.9	7.7	5.2	5.5	7.3	9.6	9.8	9.3	8.3
High monthly average	44.7	46.3	54.8	60.6	70.8	80.1	83.2	80.6	75.6	65.8	52.1	49.4	83.2
Year of occurrence	1981	1995	1972	1989	1984	1974	1959	1960	1979	1964	1995	1980	1959
Low monthly average	28.9	32.5	37.1	43.4	55.9	66.5	74.5	69.2	62.2	51.4	36.6	28.9	28.9
Year of occurrence	1979	1969	1991	1975	1995	1995	1992	1968	1986	1969	1994	1990	1979
Record high daily	59	64	67	75	82	92	95	90†	86†	79	68	60†	95
Day of occurrence	11	26	31	29	24	21	9	7	8	1	3	6	9
Year of occurrence	1986	1986	1966	1992	1984	1981	1976	1981	1977	1980	1976	1995	1976
Record low daily	0	4	14	27	30	44	56	57	38	20	16	1	0
Day of occurrence	12	6	3	12	2	7	21	24	29	31	20	23	12
Year of occurrence	1963	1989	1966	1991	1988	1993	1987	1992	1986	1991	1994	1990	1963
Days w/max >= 100	0.0	0.0	0.0	0.0	0.0	0.0	0.0	0.0	0.0	0.0	0.0	0.0	0.0
Days w/max >= 90	0.0	0.0	0.0	0.0	0.0	0.2	0.2	0.1	0.0	0.0	0.0	0.0	0.5
Days w/max <= 32	10.8	6.8	3.2	0.8	0.0	0.0	0.0	0.0	0.0	0.4	3.5	9.2	34.9

Minimum Temperature in °F

	Jan	Feb	Mar	Apr	May	Jun	Jul	Aug	Sep	Oct	Nov	Dec	Annual
Monthly normal	8.9	11.7	17.1	23.4	30.8	38.8	46.0	44.5	36.4	27.1	18.3	10.4	26.1
Standard deviation	10.1	10.1	8.8	7.5	6.5	7.2	5.2	5.5	7.0	7.2	8.5	9.7	7.8
Average monthly	8.9	11.8	17.5	23.8	31.1	39.0	46.0	44.7	36.6	27.2	18.0	10.3	26.2
Standard deviation	9.9	9.9	8.6	7.5	6.5	7.0	5.2	5.4	7.0	7.0	8.6	9.5	7.7
High monthly average	16.1	19.1	23.8	30.0	35.7	47.5	48.9	48.6	41.4	31.5†	22.3	17.9	48.9
Year of occurrence	1969	1963	1989	1989	1992	1981	1981	1994	1990	1978	1965	1980	1981
Low monthly average	2.2	4.9	8.6	17.1	27.1	34.7	42.3	40.5	32.5	22.3	13.0	1.4	1.4
Year of occurrence	1989	1966	1962	1983	1975	1965	1962	1976	1971	1982	1994	1990	1990
Record high daily	35	37†	39†	48	53	72	62	61	57	50	37†	39	72
Day of occurrence	14	19	12	21	28	21	25	9	6	3	1	6	21
Year of occurrence	1980	1986	1989	1989	1986	1981	1987	1969	1978	1967	1987	1966	1981
Record low daily	-26	-26	-11†	-3	13	21	28	23	16	0	-12	-23	-26†
Day of occurrence	13	6	4	2	18	15	6	31	19	30	17	22	6
Year of occurrence	1963	1989	1966	1975	1977	1976	1982	1962	1971	1971	1964	1990	1989
Days w/min <= 32	30.7	28.1	30.2	26.6	18.3	5.2	0.2	0.6	8.6	24.8	29.0	30.8	234.4
Days w/min <= 0	6.1	3.6	1.1	0.1	0.0	0.0	0.0	0.0	0.0	0.0	0.9	4.8	16.8
Days w/min <= -20	0.1	0.1	0.0	0.0	0.0	0.0	0.0	0.0	0.0	0.0	0.0	0.2	0.4

Mean Temperature in °F

	Jan	Feb	Mar	Apr	May	Jun	Jul	Aug	Sep	Oct	Nov	Dec	Annual
Monthly normal	22.6	25.3	30.6	38.2	47.0	56.4	62.8	60.6	53.0	43.2	31.6	23.8	41.3
Standard deviation	8.5	8.5	8.2	7.7	6.9	6.5	3.9	4.3	6.2	7.3	8.2	8.6	7.1
Average monthly	22.4	25.3	30.8	38.4	47.0	56.4	62.8	60.8	53.1	43.1	31.3	23.6	41.2
Standard deviation	8.3	8.2	7.9	7.8	6.8	6.5	4.0	4.3	6.1	7.3	8.2	8.4	7.0
High monthly average	30.1	32.1	38.7	45.3	52.2	63.2	65.6	64.1	56.4	47.9	36.6	33.6	65.6
Year of occurrence	1981	1963	1972	1989	1984	1981	1959	1994	1979	1988	1995	1980	1959
Low monthly average	16.6	18.8	23.6	30.6	43.2	51.5	59.2	56.0	48.4	37.8	24.8	15.2	15.2
Year of occurrence	1960	1966	1962	1975	1975	1965	1992	1968	1986	1969	1994	1990	1990

† Also occurred on earlier date(s).

BRYCE CANYON NATL PK HD
Monthly Data Summary

Precipitation in Inches

	Jan	Feb	Mar	Apr	May	Jun	Jul	Aug	Sep	Oct	Nov	Dec	Annual
Monthly normal	1.16	1.36	1.53	0.95	1.03	0.57	1.51	2.20	1.70	1.20	1.20	1.12	15.52
Standard deviation	0.14	0.18	0.15	0.12	0.12	0.09	0.14	0.19	0.23	0.15	0.16	0.13	0.15
Average monthly	1.37	1.54	1.56	0.88	1.10	0.56	1.34	2.26	1.60	1.26	1.16	1.15	15.76
Standard deviation	0.17	0.19	0.15	0.11	0.12	0.08	0.13	0.19	0.22	0.15	0.15	0.13	0.15
High monthly total	7.38	6.07	4.95	5.75	3.55	3.28	5.66	7.68	5.11	4.89	5.98	3.68	7.68
Year of occurrence	1993	1993	1983	1965	1992	1972	1984	1963	1986	1972	1978	1965	1963
Low monthly total	0.01	0.00†	0.05	0.00	0.00†	0.00†	0.08	0.08†	0.00	0.00†	0.13	0.00†	0.00†
Year of occurrence	1970	1972	1972	1989	1986	1980	1979	1985	1979	1995	1995	1989	1989
Record high daily	2.27	2.29	1.75	1.19	1.15	1.17	1.35	1.86	3.15	2.07	2.05	1.39	3.15
Day of occurrence	26	9	3	4	29	7	23	13	18	19	2	15	18
Year of occurrence	1995	1993	1983	1965	1990	1972	1986	1979	1963	1972	1978	1967	1963
Days w/pcp >= .01	5.4	5.6	7.2	4.9	5.7	4.4	7.6	10.2	6.1	4.7	4.8	5.4	72.8
Days w/pcp >= .10	3.2	3.6	4.1	2.2	3.1	1.7	4.2	5.6	3.2	3.1	2.6	3.0	40.1
Days w/pcp >= .50	0.8	0.9	0.9	0.4	0.7	0.2	0.6	1.2	0.9	0.8	0.7	0.7	8.9

Snow and Sleet in Inches

	Jan	Feb	Mar	Apr	May	Jun	Jul	Aug	Sep	Oct	Nov	Dec	Annual
Monthly normal	14.7	15.8	18.0	7.5	2.6	0.0	0.0	0.0	0.1	1.3	10.5	14.7	85.1
Standard deviation	1.6	1.8	1.8	1.2	0.7	0.0	0.0	0.0	0.1	0.4	1.4	1.6	0.9
Average monthly	17.4	17.8	17.4	7.2	2.3	0.0	0.0	0.0	0.1	1.9	10.6	15.0	89.7
Standard deviation	1.9	1.9	1.7	1.1	0.7	0.0	0.0	0.0	0.1	0.5	1.5	1.6	0.9
High monthly total	82.0	55.0	46.0	61.8	17.5	0.5	0.0†	0.0†	2.0	9.0†	35.2	49.5	82.0
Year of occurrence	1993	1993	1983	1965	1965	1995	1995	1995	1988	1991	1972	1984	1993
Low monthly total	1.5	0.0	0.0	0.0	0.0†	0.0†	0.0†	0.0†	0.0†	0.0†	0.5†	0.0†	0.0†
Year of occurrence	1970	1972	1972	1989	1994	1994	1995	1995	1995	1995	1995	1989	1989
Record high daily	20.0	18.0	18.0	13.0	12.0	0.5	0.0†	0.0†	2.0	7.5	16.0	18.0	20.0
Day of occurrence	26	9	17	10	6	18	31	31	13	30	16	16	26
Year of occurrence	1995	1993	1963	1965	1964	1995	1995	1995	1988	1959	1991	1984	1995
Days w/snow >= .1	5.6	5.3	6.1	2.5	0.8	0.0	0.0	0.0	0.1	0.8	3.5	5.1	30.0
Days w/snow >= 5	1.2	1.3	1.1	0.4	0.1	0.0	0.0	0.0	0.0	0.1	0.7	1.0	5.9
Days w/snow >= 10	0.3	0.2	0.2	0.1	0.0	0.0	0.0	0.0	0.0	0.0	0.2	0.2	1.4

Degree Days

	Jan	Feb	Mar	Apr	May	Jun	Jul	Aug	Sep	Oct	Nov	Dec	Annual
Heating normal	1301	1116	1062	798	557	264	88	146	360	677	987	1263	8623
Heating average	1305	1119	1057	792	556	262	89	141	355	679	999	1272	8631
Cooling normal	0	0	0	0	0	6	19	9	0	0	0	0	36
Cooling average	0	0	0	0	0	6	20	9	0	0	0	0	37
Growing 40 normal	28	41	93	202	362	518	654	617	457	301	102	37	3417
Growing 40 average	26	39	91	203	358	514	654	620	460	299	99	35	3403
Growing 50 normal	1	3	21	85	211	361	465	418	294	158	27	3	2054
Growing 50 average	1	3	20	86	207	356	465	420	296	158	25	3	2047

† Also occurred on earlier date(s).

Location: Bullfrog Basin   County: Kane Latitude: 37.517   Longitude: -110.733
Elevation: 3820 feet   Period of Record: 1967-1990

BULLFROG BASIN
Monthly Data Summary

Maximum Temperature in °F

	Jan	Feb	Mar	Apr	May	Jun	Jul	Aug	Sep	Oct	Nov	Dec	Annual
Monthly normal													
Standard deviation													
Average monthly	44.5	52.5	62.1	71.2	82.1	93.8	99.4	96.4	87.6	73.6	58.0	46.8	72.3
Standard deviation	8.0	8.6	9.0	8.9	8.7	7.4	4.8	5.2	7.3	9.2	8.5	7.3	7.7
High monthly average	52.5	58.6	72.2	77.0	89.8	98.8	102.4	·100.1	92.7	81.1	63.1	54.8	102.4
Year of occurrence	1986	1970	1972	1981	1984	1974	1988	1969	1988	1988	1989	1980	1988
Low monthly average	33.9	40.2	56.4	62.4	76.3	88.6	96.2	91.6	83.0	67.0	51.1	37.5	33.9
Year of occurrence	1973	1979	1973	1975	1975	1975	1983	1968	1985	1984	1979	1978	1973
Record high daily	67	72†	83†	93	99†	110	110†	107†	101†	93	79	69	110†
Day of occurrence	21	25	27	20	9	26	8	8	5	1	3	25	8
Year of occurrence	1986	1989	1971	1989	1989	1970	1989	1969	1989	1989	1988	1969	1989
Record low daily	22	18	34	38	52	63	79	72	59†	42	34†	24†	18
Day of occurrence	6	6	1	1	6	9	19	29	29	30	29	23	6
Year of occurrence	1971	1989	1971	1975	1978	1979	1969	1986	1986	1972	1976	1990	1989
Days w/max >= 100	0.0	0.0	0.0	0.0	0.0	6.9	16.6	9.2	0.7	0.0	0.0	0.0	33.3
Days w/max >= 90	0.0	0.0	0.0	0.0	6.1	22.3	30.0	28.3	13.3	0.6	0.0	0.0	100.1
Days w/max <= 32	2.2	0.5	0.0	0.0	0.0	0.0	0.0	0.0	0.0	0.0	0.0	1.3	4.0

Minimum Temperature in °F

	Jan	Feb	Mar	Apr	May	Jun	Jul	Aug	Sep	Oct	Nov	Dec	Annual
Monthly normal													
Standard deviation													
Average monthly	24.5	30.1	36.9	43.7	53.5	63.1	70.3	68.4	59.1	46.7	35.6	26.4	46.5
Standard deviation	7.1	7.0	6.5	7.1	7.1	6.9	4.8	5.3	6.6	6.6	6.3	6.2	6.5
High monthly average	32.2	35.1	42.8	48.7	57.5	68.1	73.1	71.3	62.7	50.6	38.8	31.9	73.1
Year of occurrence	1980	1968	1978	1981	1974	1977	1976	1977	1977	1978	1980	1976
Low monthly average	15.1	22.7	31.8	38.5	48.4	56.7	64.9	60.8	54.2	41.4	32.1	19.8	15.1
Year of occurrence	1968	1974	1987	1975	1986	1969	1969	1975	1975	1975	1979	1990	1968
Record high daily	47	50	55†	64	74	81	84	81	74†	66	52†	45	84
Day of occurrence	21	13	17	21	31	28	25	2	1	14	2	24	25
Year of occurrence	1969	1970	1974	1989	1984	1968	1988	1970	1983	1968	1987	1969	1988
Record low daily	3	4	15	21	33	42	54	46	44†	25	13	0	0
Day of occurrence	7	5	2	1	5	5	19	23	7	30	28	22	22
Year of occurrence	1971	1989	1971	1975	1975	1980	1969	1972	1981	1971	1976	1990	1990
Days w/min <= 32	27.4	17.9	7.5	1.2	0.0	0.0	0.0	0.0	0.0	0.6	9.5	26.8	91.3
Days w/min <= 0	0.0	0.0	0.0	0.0	0.0	0.0	0.0	0.0	0.0	0.0	0.0	0.0	0.0
Days w/min <= -20	0.0	0.0	0.0	0.0	0.0	0.0	0.0	0.0	0.0	0.0	0.0	0.0	0.0

Mean Temperature in °F

	Jan	Feb	Mar	Apr	May	Jun	Jul	Aug	Sep	Oct	Nov	Dec	Annual
Monthly normal													
Standard deviation													
Average monthly	34.5	41.3	49.5	57.5	67.8	78.5	84.9	82.4	73.4	60.1	46.8	36.6	59.4
Standard deviation	7.0	7.2	7.1	7.4	7.3	6.7	4.1	4.5	6.4	7.2	6.8	6.1	6.5
High monthly average	40.8	46.2	56.5	62.8	73.5	82.4	87.6	85.2	77.2	65.6	49.8	43.4	87.6
Year of occurrence	1986	1968	1972	1981	1984	1974	1988	1970	1979	1988	1967	1980	1988
Low monthly average	25.6	31.9	44.7	50.4	62.4	73.5	82.3	78.1	70.1	55.7	41.6	29.4	25.6
Year of occurrence	1973	1979	1987	1975	1975	1975	1969	1975	1973	1982	1979	1978	1973

† Also occurred on earlier date(s).

BULLFROG BASIN
Monthly Data Summary

Precipitation in Inches

	Jan	Feb	Mar	Apr	May	Jun	Jul	Aug	Sep	Oct	Nov	Dec	Annual
Monthly normal													
Standard deviation													
Average monthly	0.57	0.37	0.63	0.29	0.41	0.17	0.41	0.49	0.54	0.96	0.62	0.48	5.93
Standard deviation	0.07	0.05	0.08	0.05	0.07	0.03	0.08	0.07	0.08	0.13	0.09	0.07	0.07
High monthly total	1.98	1.27	2.35	1.47	1.89	1.03	1.75	1.63	1.55	6.53	1.97	2.37	6.53
Year of occurrence	1980	1980	1983	1975	1979	1972	1969	1989	1986	1972	1979	1978	1972
Low monthly total	0.00†	0.00†	0.00	0.00†	0.00†	0.00†	0.00	0.00	0.00†	0.00	0.00	0.00†	0.00†
Year of occurrence	1986	1974	1972	1977	1984	1987	1971	1974	1989	1990	1989	1989	1989
Record high daily	0.78	0.44	0.95	0.87	0.95	0.42	1.74	1.20	0.88	1.19	0.81	0.79	1.74
Day of occurrence	18	20	4	2	8	23	19	18	11	22	8	2	19
Year of occurrence	1980	1980	1983	1975	1979	1972	1969	1989	1977	1978	1979	1978	1969
Days w/pcp >= .01	4.4	3.8	4.5	2.6	2.8	1.7	3.1	3.8	3.2	4.2	3.5	3.4	42.0
Days w/pcp >= .10	1.9	1.3	2.1	0.9	1.2	0.8	1.2	1.6	1.8	2.5	1.7	1.7	19.0
Days w/pcp >= .50	0.1	0.0	0.2	0.0	0.2	0.0	0.1	0.1	0.2	0.6	0.4	0.1	2.2

Snow and Sleet in Inches

	Jan	Feb	Mar	Apr	May	Jun	Jul	Aug	Sep	Oct	Nov	Dec	Annual
Monthly normal													
Standard deviation													
Average monthly	1.8	0.7	0.4	0.0	0.0	0.0	0.0	0.0	0.0	0.0	0.3	2.4	5.6
Standard deviation	0.4	0.3	0.2	0.0	0.0	0.0	0.0	0.0	0.0	0.0	0.2	0.5	0.1
High monthly total	9.3	6.5	6.1	0.0†	0.0†	0.0†	0.0†	0.0†	0.0†	0.0†	5.0	16.4	16.4
Year of occurrence	1979	1979	1985	1990	1990	1989	1989	1989	1989	1990	1979	1967	1967
Low monthly total	0.0†	0.0†	0.0†	0.0†	0.0†	0.0†	0.0†	0.0†	0.0†	0.0†	0.0†	0.0†	0.0†
Year of occurrence	1986	1990	1990	1990	1990	1989	1989	1989	1989	1990	1990	1989	1989
Record high daily	8.0	5.0	6.0	0.0†	0.0†	0.0†	0.0†	0.0†	0.0†	0.0†	4.5	6.5	8.0
Day of occurrence	5	1	28	30	31	30	31	31	30	31	19	29	5
Year of occurrence	1974	1979	1985	1990	1990	1989	1989	1989	1989	1990	1979	1974	1974
Days w/snow >= .1	1.3	0.4	0.2	0.0	0.0	0.0	0.0	0.0	0.0	0.0	0.2	1.1	3.0
Days w/snow >= 5	0.1	0.0	0.0	0.0	0.0	0.0	0.0	0.0	0.0	0.0	0.0	0.1	0.2
Days w/snow >= 10	0.0	0.0	0.0	0.0	0.0	0.0	0.0	0.0	0.0	0.0	0.0	0.0	0.0

Degree Days

	Jan	Feb	Mar	Apr	May	Jun	Jul	Aug	Sep	Oct	Nov	Dec	Annual
Heating normal													
Heating average	941	663	473	236	55	1	0	0	10	181	543	878	3986
Cooling normal													
Cooling average	0	0	0	14	142	404	614	538	259	30	0	0	2005
Growing 40 normal													
Growing 40 average	92	185	357	508	744	894	1039	1012	831	595	282	118	6662
Growing 50 normal													
Growing 50 average	17	67	190	320	540	722	871	840	642	379	130	21	4745

† Also occurred on earlier date(s).

Location: Capitol Reef National Park   County: Wayne   Latitude: 38.283 Longitude: -111.267
Elevation: 5500 feet   Period of Record: 1938-1995

CAPITOL REEF NATL PARK
Monthly Data Summary

Maximum Temperature in °F

	Jan	Feb	Mar	Apr	May	Jun	Jul	Aug	Sep	Oct	Nov	Dec	Annual
Monthly normal	40.2	47.6	57.3	66.2	76.3	87.5	92.4	89.6	81.8	68.3	53.1	41.9	66.9
Standard deviation	9.7	9.2	9.0	8.9	8.4	7.8	5.4	5.6	7.3	9.5	9.2	8.1	8.2
Average monthly	40.6	47.3	57.3	66.3	76.3	86.4	92.1	89.3	81.8	68.4	52.7	42.1	66.7
Standard deviation	9.3	8.9	8.6	9.2	8.0	8.0	5.3	5.5	7.1	9.2	9.2	8.3	8.1
High monthly average	50.6	54.7†	66.9	77.8	83.1	92.9	95.9	93.2	89.1	75.1	59.8	53.5	95.9
Year of occurrence	1943	1995	1972	1943	1984	1974	1979	1969	1979	1979	1942	1942	1979
Low monthly average	30.4	38.0	50.9	58.4	68.4	79.2	87.8	83.4	74.1	60.5	45.1	34.7	30.4
Year of occurrence	1979	1939	1973	1975	1995	1995	1987	1968	1940	1969	1994	1978	1979
Record high daily	69†	71	80	91	95†	104	104	102†	98†	91†	77†	69	104†
Day of occurrence	30	26	28	29	30	26	5	1	7	7	8	7	5
Year of occurrence	1971	1986	1943	1943	1984	1970	1985	1979	1977	1980	1980	1977	1985
Record low daily	9	16†	27	39	48	58	72†	72†	54	35	27	13	9
Day of occurrence	7	7	1	5	8	9	2	13	28	30	28	23	7
Year of occurrence	1971	1989	1971	1983	1979	1995	1995	1968	1986	1971	1976	1990	1971
Days w/max >= 100	0.0	0.0	0.0	0.0	0.0	0.8	1.4	0.5	0.0	0.0	0.0	0.0	2.9
Days w/max >= 90	0.0	0.0	0.0	0.1	1.0	12.0	22.8	16.0	4.6	0.1	0.0	0.0	58.9
Days w/max <= 32	6.0	1.3	0.0	0.0	0.0	0.0	0.0	0.0	0.0	0.0	0.2	3.9	11.0

Minimum Temperature in °F

	Jan	Feb	Mar	Apr	May	Jun	Jul	Aug	Sep	Oct	Nov	Dec	Annual
Monthly normal	18.3	24.6	31.8	38.5	47.4	56.9	63.3	61.8	53.6	42.5	30.1	20.9	40.8
Standard deviation	8.3	8.3	7.1	7.3	7.1	7.0	4.4	4.8	6.9	7.7	7.5	7.5	7.0
Average monthly	18.7	24.4	31.7	38.6	47.3	55.9	63.1	61.7	53.8	43.2	29.3	21.0	40.7
Standard deviation	7.9	8.2	7.0	7.1	6.8	7.0	4.6	4.9	6.5	7.5	7.4	7.1	6.8
High monthly average	27.1	33.8	39.3	46.7	52.7	62.0	67.4	65.7	57.8	51.1	35.3	28.7	67.4
Year of occurrence	1981	1995	1986	1992	1984	1986	1941	1941	1990	1939	1967	1980	1941
Low monthly average	11.1	14.1	22.4	31.6	42.5	49.6	59.0	57.4	48.6	37.1	22.6	13.4	11.1
Year of occurrence	1973	1939	1941	1975	1942	1945	1944	1968	1942	1969	1938	1990	1973
Record high daily	45†	43	59	59	65†	76	76	76†	72	62	51	45	76†
Day of occurrence	25	27	14	28	8	30	1	3	5	6	3	7	3
Year of occurrence	1975	1986	1972	1992	1989	1990	1990	1977	1941	1942	1941	1977	1977
Record low daily	-9	-7	10†	18†	28	35	44	44	32	17	5	-7	-9
Day of occurrence	7	6	5	1	6	1	1	23	21	30	28	24	7
Year of occurrence	1971	1989	1976	1980	1968	1988	1968	1968	1978	1971	1976	1990	1971
Days w/min <= 32	30.0	23.9	16.6	6.1	0.4	0.0	0.0	0.0	0.0	2.7	20.0	29.6	126.9
Days w/min <= 0	0.4	0.2	0.0	0.0	0.0	0.0	0.0	0.0	0.0	0.0	0.0	0.1	0.7
Days w/min <= -20	0.0	0.0	0.0	0.0	0.0	0.0	0.0	0.0	0.0	0.0	0.0	0.0	0.0

Mean Temperature in °F

	Jan	Feb	Mar	Apr	May	Jun	Jul	Aug	Sep	Oct	Nov	Dec	Annual
Monthly normal	29.3	36.1	44.6	52.4	61.9	72.2	77.9	75.7	67.7	55.4	41.6	31.4	53.8
Standard deviation	8.5	8.3	7.5	7.7	7.3	7.0	4.2	4.6	6.7	8.2	7.9	7.3	7.1
Average monthly	29.7	35.8	44.5	52.5	61.8	71.2	77.6	75.5	67.8	55.8	41.0	31.6	53.7
Standard deviation	8.0	8.1	7.2	7.7	6.9	7.1	4.2	4.5	6.3	7.9	7.7	7.1	6.9
High monthly average	38.8	44.2	52.9	60.4	67.9	76.5	80.0	79.3	73.3	62.0	46.4	40.8	80.0
Year of occurrence	1981	1995	1972	1943	1984	1974	1988	1969	1979	1988	1967	1980	1988
Low monthly average	20.9	26.1	39.5	45.0	56.1	65.2	74.6	70.4	62.9	48.8	34.7	24.4	20.9
Year of occurrence	1973	1939	1969	1975	1995	1944	1944	1968	1986	1969	1994	1990	1973

† Also occurred on earlier date(s).

CAPITOL REEF NATL PARK
Monthly Data Summary

Precipitation in Inches

	Jan	Feb	Mar	Apr	May	Jun	Jul	Aug	Sep	Oct	Nov	Dec	Annual
Monthly normal	0.40	0.35	0.66	0.44	0.65	0.43	1.08	1.14	0.74	0.70	0.60	0.21	7.40
Standard deviation	0.08	0.08	0.10	0.06	0.08	0.08	0.11	0.12	0.11	0.09	0.10	0.05	0.09
Average monthly	0.48	0.41	0.66	0.51	0.63	0.45	0.88	1.16	0.77	0.84	0.58	0.35	7.73
Standard deviation	0.09	0.07	0.10	0.06	0.08	0.08	0.10	0.12	0.11	0.11	0.10	0.09	0.09
High monthly total	2.32	2.13	2.25	1.78	2.08	2.29	2.81	3.28	3.00	3.96	2.84	2.15	3.96
Year of occurrence	1993	1993	1981	1941	1992	1969	1985	1982	1980	1941	1978	1947	1941
Low monthly total	0.00†	0.00†	0.00†	0.00†	0.00†	0.00†	0.05	0.09	0.00†	0.00†	0.00†	0.00†	0.00†
Year of occurrence	1981	1974	1994	1984	1974	1978	1939	1978	1979	1995	1976	1989	1989
Record high daily	1.12	0.90	1.45	0.75	0.85	1.14	1.39	1.45	1.73	1.23	1.68	2.15	2.15
Day of occurrence	19	20	4	11	14	17	17	12	10	19	12	1	1
Year of occurrence	1980	1971	1983	1941	1989	1969	1985	1945	1980	1972	1972	1947	1947
Days w/pcp >= .01	3.1	3.0	3.9	4.4	4.6	3.1	6.4	7.2	4.7	4.1	2.9	2.6	51.0
Days w/pcp >= .10	1.2	1.3	1.8	1.8	1.8	1.4	3.0	3.3	2.1	2.3	1.6	0.9	23.0
Days w/pcp >= .50	0.3	0.2	0.4	0.1	0.3	0.2	0.3	0.5	0.3	0.3	0.3	0.1	3.4

Snow and Sleet in Inches

	Jan	Feb	Mar	Apr	May	Jun	Jul	Aug	Sep	Oct	Nov	Dec	Annual
Monthly normal	5.7	2.4	3.6	0.7	0.1	0.0	0.0	0.0	0.0	0.7	2.2	2.4	17.6
Standard deviation	0.9	0.7	0.8	0.3	0.1	0.0	0.0	0.0	0.0	0.4	0.6	0.4	0.3
Average monthly	5.9	2.0	3.5	0.6	0.1	0.0	0.0	0.0	0.0	0.6	2.2	2.4	17.3
Standard deviation	1.0	0.6	0.8	0.3	0.1	0.0	0.0	0.0	0.0	0.4	0.5	0.4	0.3
High monthly total	23.3	13.2	16.5	6.0	2.5	0.0†	0.0†	0.0†	0.0†	10.1	13.7	8.2	23.3
Year of occurrence	1982	1975	1985	1968	1979	1995	1995	1995	1995	1971	1972	1979	1982
Low monthly total	0.0†	0.0†	0.0†	0.0†	0.0†	0.0†	0.0†	0.0†	0.0†	0.0†	0.0†	0.0†	0.0†
Year of occurrence	1991	1995	1994	1994	1995	1995	1995	1995	1995	1995	1995	1995	1995
Record high daily	15.0	10.0	14.0	6.0	2.5	0.0†	0.0†	0.0†	0.0†	10.1	8.5	10.0	15.0
Day of occurrence	20	20	28	18	8	30	31	31	30	29	12	12	20
Year of occurrence	1945	1971	1985	1968	1979	1995	1995	1995	1995	1971	1972	1940	1945
Days w/snow >= .1	2.7	0.9	1.2	0.4	0.1	0.0	0.0	0.0	0.0	0.1	0.8	1.7	7.8
Days w/snow >= 5	0.3	0.1	0.2	0.0	0.0	0.0	0.0	0.0	0.0	0.0	0.1	0.1	0.9
Days w/snow >= 10	0.1	0.0	0.0	0.0	0.0	0.0	0.0	0.0	0.0	0.0	0.0	0.0	0.2

Degree Days

	Jan	Feb	Mar	Apr	May	Jun	Jul	Aug	Sep	Oct	Nov	Dec	Annual
Heating normal	1107	815	633	382	145	20	0	0	48	307	702	1039	5203
Heating average	1089	821	627	375	138	26	0	0	42	290	707	1025	5146
Cooling normal	0	0	0	2	48	237	397	332	128	10	0	0	1157
Cooling average	0	0	0	3	41	211	387	322	124	10	0	0	1102
Growing 40 normal	62	123	276	421	637	802	931	909	740	498	203	65	5673
Growing 40 average	62	116	273	417	629	785	925	901	736	496	194	68	5607
Growing 50 normal	11	37	129	247	428	616	755	725	532	294	82	9	3870
Growing 50 average	11	33	127	247	420	595	748	717	529	291	77	10	3811

† Also occurred on earlier date(s).

Location: Cedar City FAA Airport County: Iron   Latitude: 37.700 Longitude:-113.100
Elevation: 5610 feet   Period of Record: 1948-1996

CEDAR CITY FAA AIRPORT
Monthly Data Summary

Maximum Temperature in °F

	Jan	Feb	Mar	Apr	May	Jun	Jul	Aug	Sep	Oct	Nov	Dec	Annual
Monthly normal	41.8	47.0	52.9	61.5	71.9	83.7	90.2	87.4	79.0	67.1	52.7	43.0	64.8
Standard deviation	9.7	10.2	10.3	10.1	9.6	8.2	5.3	5.7	8.2	10.3	10.5	10.7	9.1
Average monthly	41.8	46.7	53.0	62.0	71.7	83.4	90.0	87.5	79.9	67.4	52.7	43.4	65.0
Standard deviation	9.8	10.1	9.9	10.0	9.5	8.3	5.2	5.6	7.9	10.4	10.8	10.1	9.0
High monthly average	51.4	58.9	64.4	70.3	80.9	89.5	94.1	91.3	87.0	77.1	63.6	54.4	94.1
Year of occurrence	1986	1995	1972	1989	1984	1994	1981	1958	1979	1952	1949	1958	1981
Low monthly average	24.4	36.4	43.6	53.4	64.2	76.7	86.4	79.0	70.8	58.0	43.1	32.9	24.4
Year of occurrence	1949	1949	1973	1975	1953	1995	1965	1968	1986	1972	1972	1967	1949
Record high daily	70	73	77	83†	96	101†	105	100†	97	87	75	68	105
Day of occurrence	9	25	31	28	29	25	7	6	1	2	8	3	7
Year of occurrence	1990	1986	1966	1992	1984	1981	1989	1981	1950	1979	1976	1977	1989
Record low daily	4	11	23	34†	38	47	67	65	43	23	23†	3	3
Day of occurrence	12	5	1	1	7	3	24	22	18	29	14	22	22
Year of occurrence	1963	1989	1971	1975	1965	1949	1965	1968	1965	1971	1964	1990	1990
Days w/max >= 100	0.0	0.0	0.0	0.0	0.0	0.2	0.5	0.0	0.0	0.0	0.0	0.0	0.8
Days w/max >= 90	0.0	0.0	0.0	0.0	0.2	7.1	17.3	12.3	2.4	0.0	0.0	0.0	39.7
Days w/max <= 32	5.1	2.3	0.7	0.0	0.0	0.0	0.0	0.0	0.0	0.1	0.9	4.2	13.4

Minimum Temperature in °F

	Jan	Feb	Mar	Apr	May	Jun	Jul	Aug	Sep	Oct	Nov	Dec	Annual
Monthly normal	17.3	22.2	27.2	33.5	41.2	49.7	58.1	56.6	47.1	36.3	26.7	18.3	36.2
Standard deviation	11.2	10.3	8.1	7.1	6.8	7.0	4.8	5.1	7.7	7.5	8.5	10.7	7.9
Average monthly	17.2	21.7	26.9	33.4	41.1	49.5	57.8	56.5	47.4	36.1	25.5	18.1	35.9
Standard deviation	11.5	10.5	8.1	7.3	6.9	7.0	4.9	5.0	7.6	7.5	9.0	10.6	8.0
High monthly average	26.7	29.9	34.4	39.0	45.5	56.3	62.6	60.3	51.2†	42.3	31.1	26.6	62.6
Year of occurrence	1980	1983	1978	1992	1976	1994	1981	1982	1981	1963	1981	1977	1981
Low monthly average	-1.2	7.1	20.5	28.1	34.9	44.8	54.1	53.1	41.5	30.2	14.9	6.9	-1.2
Year of occurrence	1949	1949	1964	1970	1953	1995	1993	1968	1965	1969	1956	1990	1949
Record high daily	43†	45	51	56	60	70	73	71	67†	58	48†	49	73
Day of occurrence	13	18	26	28	30	30	6	17	4	19	14	23	6
Year of occurrence	1980	1980	1971	1987	1984	1976	1981	1962	1995	1979	1981	1955	1981
Record low daily	-26	-24	-1†	6	21	30†	40†	36	23	-7	-7	-23	-26
Day of occurrence	31	6	9	2	2	6	2	23	18	30	20	23	31
Year of occurrence	1951	1989	1958	1975	1988	1982	1992	1968	1965	1971	1956	1990	1951
Days w/min <= 32	28.8	24.6	23.4	14.1	3.5	0.2	0.0	0.0	1.0	9.5	23.6	28.8	159.6
Days w/min <= 0	2.7	1.2	0.1	0.0	0.0	0.0	0.0	0.0	0.0	0.0	0.3	1.8	6.3
Days w/min <= -20	0.0	0.1	0.0	0.0	0.0	0.0	0.0	0.0	0.0	0.0	0.0	0.1	0.2

Mean Temperature in °F

	Jan	Feb	Mar	Apr	May	Jun	Jul	Aug	Sep	Oct	Nov	Dec	Annual
Monthly normal	29.5	34.6	40.1	47.5	56.5	66.7	74.1	72.0	63.0	51.7	39.7	30.7	50.5
Standard deviation	9.6	9.3	8.2	7.7	7.4	6.9	4.0	4.4	7.1	7.8	8.5	9.8	7.6
Average monthly	29.5	34.2	40.0	47.7	56.4	66.5	73.9	72.0	63.6	51.8	39.1	30.8	50.4
Standard deviation	9.8	9.4	7.9	7.7	7.4	6.9	4.0	4.3	6.8	7.9	8.8	9.5	7.5
High monthly average	38.1	43.6	47.3	53.9†	62.5	72.9	78.3	75.3	68.9	57.6	45.5	39.3	78.3
Year of occurrence	1953	1995	1972	1992	1984	1994	1981	1958	1979	1988	1995	1977	1981
Low monthly average	11.6	21.8	33.4	42.2	49.6	60.8	70.9	66.0	57.2	45.1	30.9	20.8	11.6
Year of occurrence	1949	1949	1952	1975	1953	1995	1993	1968	1965	1969	1994	1990	1949

† Also occurred on earlier date(s).

CEDAR CITY FAA AIRPORT
Monthly Data Summary

Precipitation in Inches

	Jan	Feb	Mar	Apr	May	Jun	Jul	Aug	Sep	Oct	Nov	Dec	Annual
Monthly normal	0.69	0.89	1.36	1.10	0.84	0.43	1.09	1.47	0.98	0.95	1.00	0.70	11.50
Standard deviation	0.08	0.11	0.12	0.11	0.10	0.07	0.13	0.17	0.15	0.11	0.12	0.07	0.11
Average monthly	0.74	0.85	1.24	1.00	0.84	0.45	0.98	1.23	0.79	0.92	0.90	0.70	10.64
Standard deviation	0.08	0.10	0.11	0.11	0.10	0.07	0.12	0.15	0.13	0.11	0.11	0.08	0.11
High monthly total	2.98	2.38	2.97	3.14	2.16	1.89	4.37	4.38	4.62	3.33	2.63	1.75	4.62
Year of occurrence	1980	1980	1978	1988	1981	1995	1975	1984	1967	1972	1994	1965	1967
Low monthly total	0.04	0.00	0.00	0.07	0.00	0.00†	0.00	0.00	0.00†	0.00†	0.03†	0.00†	0.00†
Year of occurrence	1964	1972	1972	1959	1974	1978	1948	1985	1984	1995	1968	1989	1989
Record high daily	1.21	1.60	1.28	1.07	1.25	1.01	1.62	2.02	2.10	1.30†	1.02	1.07	2.10
Day of occurrence	14	6	18	2	14	7	28	19	24	27	14	13	24
Year of occurrence	1980	1965	1961	1974	1977	1970	1975	1963	1967	1991	1987	1995	1967
Days w/pcp >= .01	6.0	6.0	8.0	6.1	5.7	3.0	5.5	6.8	4.0	4.7	5.1	5.6	67.3
Days w/pcp >= .10	2.4	2.7	4.0	3.0	2.8	1.4	2.7	3.3	1.8	2.5	2.4	2.4	31.8
Days w/pcp >= .50	0.2	0.3	0.4	0.4	0.3	0.1	0.5	0.5	0.5	0.4	0.5	0.2	4.3

Snow and Sleet in Inches

	Jan	Feb	Mar	Apr	May	Jun	Jul	Aug	Sep	Oct	Nov	Dec	Annual
Monthly normal	7.7	7.9	10.1	5.8	1.6	0.0	0.0	0.0	0.1	1.4	5.2	7.8	47.8
Standard deviation	0.9	1.2	1.0	0.8	0.5	0.0	0.0	0.0	0.1	0.4	0.8	1.0	0.6
Average monthly	8.4	7.9	8.4	4.8	1.2	0.1	0.0	0.0	0.1	1.7	5.2	7.2	45.1
Standard deviation	0.9	1.1	0.9	0.7	0.4	0.1	0.0	0.0	0.1	0.5	0.9	1.0	0.5
High monthly total	36.9	34.2	28.1	23.7	8.9	2.6	0.0†	0.6	2.0	18.8	32.5	23.4	36.9
Year of occurrence	1949	1971	1961	1964	1975	1993	1995	1992	1965	1991	1994	1972	1949
Low monthly total	0.0†	0.0†	0.0	0.0†	0.0†	0.0†	0.0†	0.0†	0.0†	0.0†	0.0†	0.0†	0.0†
Year of occurrence	1970	1977	1972	1992	1995	1995	1995	1995	1995	1995	1995	1989	1989
Record high daily	9.0	13.1	9.6	7.0	8.9	2.0	0.0†	0.6	2.0	9.6	14.1	14.9	14.9
Day of occurrence	21	4	10	1	20	6	31	25	18	27	18	7	7
Year of occurrence	1974	1989	1952	1973	1975	1993	1995	1992	1965	1991	1994	1982	1982
Days w/snow >= .1	4.5	3.8	4.5	2.4	0.6	0.1	0.0	0.0	0.1	0.7	2.6	3.7	23.2
Days w/snow >= 5	0.4	0.4	0.3	0.2	0.0	0.0	0.0	0.0	0.0	0.1	0.2	0.4	2.0
Days w/snow >= 10	0.0	0.1	0.0	0.0	0.0	0.0	0.0	0.0	0.0	0.0	0.0	0.0	0.2

Degree Days

	Jan	Feb	Mar	Apr	May	Jun	Jul	Aug	Sep	Oct	Nov	Dec	Annual
Heating normal	1097	858	772	523	270	62	1	5	113	413	758	1063	5941
Heating average	1096	870	776	518	275	63	1	5	101	410	777	1060	5957
Cooling normal	0	0	0	0	7	113	284	222	54	0	0	0	683
Cooling average	0	0	0	0	7	108	276	222	59	0	0	0	675
Growing 40 normal	74	120	210	333	523	686	852	828	639	434	202	93	5001
Growing 40 average	74	116	210	341	521	684	847	827	647	438	202	94	5006
Growing 50 normal	14	38	90	185	343	512	673	639	452	271	88	23	3335
Growing 50 average	15	36	89	191	340	509	669	639	465	277	90	23	3348

† Also occurred on earlier date(s).

Location: Coalville   County: Summit   Latitude: 40.917   Longitude: -111.400
Elevation: 5550 feet   Period of Record: 1948-1995

COALVILLE
Monthly Data Summary

Maximum Temperature in °F

	Jan	Feb	Mar	Apr	May	Jun	Jul	Aug	Sep	Oct	Nov	Dec	Annual
Monthly normal	36.7	42.0	49.6	59.8	69.4	78.4	86.1	84.4	75.6	65.7	50.2	38.6	61.4
Standard deviation	9.3	9.4	9.5	10.3	9.7	8.6	5.0	5.7	8.8	10.4	11.1	10.3	9.0
Average monthly	37.1	42.2	49.8	60.1	69.5	78.3	86.0	84.6	76.7	66.0	50.2	39.4	61.7
Standard deviation	9.0	9.2	9.4	10.1	9.6	8.5	5.1	5.4	8.6	10.2	11.1	9.4	8.8
High monthly average	47.5	51.2	58.6	69.1	76.8	85.1	90.3	89.2	84.3	77.1	61.0	47.6	90.3
Year of occurrence	1953	1954	1986	1949	1969	1988	1988	1967	1979	1952	1949	1962	1988
Low monthly average	29.0	33.2	39.6	50.6	62.7	72.8	80.2	78.2	68.2	55.4	40.7	29.4	29.0
Year of occurrence	1984	1989	1952	1975	1953	1970	1993	1968	1965	1984	1994	1990	1984
Record high daily	60†	68†	76†	84	91	99	97	97†	95	85†	77	65	99
Day of occurrence	31	25	29	29	29	23	5	26	3	1	1	21	23
Year of occurrence	1971	1986	1986	1992	1984	1954	1973	1985	1950	1992	1965	1969	1954
Record low daily	7	3†	22	36	41†	49†	60	59	40	26	18†	-2	-2
Day of occurrence	2	6	10	4	11	19	5	14	29	29	30	22	22
Year of occurrence	1974	1989	1969	1983	1983	1975	1982	1978	1982	1971	1979	1990	1990
Days w/max >= 100	0.0	0.0	0.0	0.0	0.0	0.0	0.0	0.0	0.0	0.0	0.0	0.0	0.0
Days w/max >= 90	0.0	0.0	0.0	0.0	0.1	1.8	7.4	5.7	0.7	0.0	0.0	0.0	16.3
Days w/max <= 32	8.9	3.8	0.7	0.0	0.0	0.0	0.0	0.0	0.0	0.1	1.9	6.0	22.3

Minimum Temperature in °F

	Jan	Feb	Mar	Apr	May	Jun	Jul	Aug	Sep	Oct	Nov	Dec	Annual
Monthly normal	10.7	14.2	21.3	28.1	34.4	40.5	46.5	44.6	36.5	28.0	21.1	12.7	28.2
Standard deviation	13.9	12.6	9.1	6.6	6.2	5.9	6.1	6.6	7.7	7.0	9.4	12.1	8.6
Average monthly	10.8	14.3	21.4	27.9	34.4	39.9	45.5	43.9	36.1	27.7	20.3	12.9	27.9
Standard deviation	13.9	12.6	9.1	6.7	6.0	5.7	6.2	6.7	7.5	6.9	10.1	11.9	8.6
High monthly average	21.7	23.4	27.7	32.2	37.8	44.7	49.7	51.2	41.3	33.2	25.5	22.1	51.2
Year of occurrence	1953	1986	1983	1965	1981	1988	1985	1983	1990	1963	1991	1950	1983
Low monthly average	0.9	3.6	7.7	22.8	30.1	34.6	39.2	36.7	30.7	22.4	12.3	2.2	0.9
Year of occurrence	1955	1952	1964	1955	1953	1950	1993	1950	1951	1976	1952	1990	1955
Record high daily	38†	42	50	51†	57	65	66	66	67	51†	47	47	67
Day of occurrence	13	11	21	12	27	27	4	1	4	12	28	27	4
Year of occurrence	1980	1962	1995	1992	1982	1981	1986	1964	1950	1995	1949	1967	1950
Record low daily	-30	-33†	-20	10†	15	26†	31†	24†	14	5	-17	-27	-33
Day of occurrence	12	7	7	20	1	19	19	27	30	31	16	10	7
Year of occurrence	1963	1989	1964	1982	1972	1973	1987	1992	1985	1991	1955	1972	1989
Days w/min <= 32	29.3	26.8	27.3	22.3	11.6	2.5	0.2	0.8	10.2	23.6	25.8	28.2	212.9
Days w/min <= 0	7.1	4.2	0.8	0.0	0.0	0.0	0.0	0.0	0.0	0.0	1.1	4.0	17.9
Days w/min <= -20	0.5	0.2	0.0	0.0	0.0	0.0	0.0	0.0	0.0	0.0	0.0	0.2	1.1

Mean Temperature in °F

	Jan	Feb	Mar	Apr	May	Jun	Jul	Aug	Sep	Oct	Nov	Dec	Annual
Monthly normal	23.7	28.0	35.6	43.9	51.9	59.4	66.4	64.5	56.0	46.7	35.4	25.9	44.8
Standard deviation	10.6	10.0	7.8	6.8	6.3	5.8	3.5	4.3	6.3	6.6	8.6	10.0	7.2
Average monthly	23.9	28.2	35.7	44.0	52.0	59.1	65.8	64.2	56.4	46.8	35.1	26.3	44.8
Standard deviation	10.5	9.9	7.8	6.7	6.2	5.6	3.8	4.2	6.1	6.3	9.0	9.4	7.1
High monthly average	34.6	35.9	43.1	50.0	56.6	64.9	69.1	67.7	60.2	51.7	42.2	33.7	69.1
Year of occurrence	1953	1963	1986	1992	1969	1988	1953	1969	1990	1963	1967	1950	1953
Low monthly average	16.1	19.6	24.0	38.3	46.4	55.1	59.7	60.6	50.6	41.5	28.1	15.8	15.8
Year of occurrence	1989	1952	1964	1975	1953	1951	1993	1950	1965	1984	1979	1990	1990

† Also occurred on earlier date(s).

COALVILLE
Monthly Data Summary

Precipitation in Inches

	Jan	Feb	Mar	Apr	May	Jun	Jul	Aug	Sep	Oct	Nov	Dec	Annual
Monthly normal	1.08	1.12	1.54	1.98	1.79	1.15	0.93	1.05	1.41	1.51	1.59	1.27	16.42
Standard deviation	0.10	0.11	0.12	0.16	0.15	0.12	0.11	0.13	0.16	0.15	0.14	0.13	0.13
Average monthly	1.20	1.10	1.55	1.75	1.85	1.11	0.93	0.98	1.19	1.40	1.52	1.25	15.82
Standard deviation	0.10	0.11	0.12	0.14	0.15	0.13	0.12	0.12	0.14	0.14	0.14	0.13	0.13
High monthly total	4.37	2.86	3.73	4.69	3.75	3.25	2.25	3.71	6.13	3.61	3.51	4.33	6.13
Year of occurrence	1980	1980	1952	1963	1967	1983	1995	1986	1982	1981	1988	1964	1982
Low monthly total	0.00	0.34	0.15	0.14	0.16	0.03	0.00†	0.00	0.00†	0.00†	0.05	0.01	0.00†
Year of occurrence	1961	1953	1956	1949	1972	1994	1978	1985	1974	1978	1976	1976	1978
Record high daily	0.98	1.45	1.02	1.49	1.72	1.60	2.06	2.60	1.59	1.43	1.30	1.65	2.60
Day of occurrence	31	7	16	2	10	29	30	21	26	17	15	23	21
Year of occurrence	1963	1950	1987	1974	1985	1959	1969	1986	1982	1969	1958	1964	1986
Days w/pcp >= .01	9.4	8.5	10.3	9.1	9.9	5.7	5.8	6.1	6.0	6.2	8.0	7.9	94.9
Days w/pcp >= .10	4.0	3.7	4.9	5.1	5.4	3.2	2.6	2.9	3.0	3.5	4.6	3.8	47.7
Days w/pcp >= .50	0.4	0.3	0.6	0.7	0.8	0.5	0.3	0.3	0.6	0.9	0.7	0.5	6.7

Snow and Sleet in Inches

	Jan	Feb	Mar	Apr	May	Jun	Jul	Aug	Sep	Oct	Nov	Dec	Annual
Monthly normal	12.7	13.5	11.5	4.7	2.0	0.0	0.0	0.0	0.1	2.1	10.8	15.0	72.3
Standard deviation	1.6	1.6	1.5	1.0	0.7	0.0	0.0	0.0	0.1	0.7	1.6	1.8	0.9
Average monthly	15.9	13.0	10.6	3.7	1.4	0.0	0.0	0.0	0.1	1.3	8.8	12.8	67.7
Standard deviation	1.6	1.5	1.4	0.8	0.6	0.0	0.0	0.0	0.1	0.5	1.4	1.6	0.8
High monthly total	44.0	32.0	44.0	20.0	26.0	0.0†	0.0†	0.0†	3.0	16.0	38.6	78.0	78.0
Year of occurrence	1993	1959	1952	1986	1975	1995	1995	1995	1965	1984	1985	1983	1983
Low monthly total	0.0	0.0†	0.0†	0.0†	0.0†	0.0†	0.0†	0.0†	0.0†	0.0†	0.0†	0.0†	0.0†
Year of occurrence	1961	1963	1993	1992	1994	1995	1995	1995	1995	1995	1977	1976	1976
Record high daily	24.0	12.0	12.0†	10.0†	10.0	0.0†	0.0†	0.0†	3.0	12.0	18.0	16.0†	24.0
Day of occurrence	29	11	21	13	11	30	31	31	17	28	15	24	29
Year of occurrence	1980	1973	1980	1986	1983	1995	1995	1995	1965	1971	1958	1983	1980
Days w/snow >= .1	4.6	3.6	2.7	1.1	0.2	0.0	0.0	0.0	0.0	0.3	2.2	3.4	16.9
Days w/snow >= 5	1.1	0.9	0.9	0.3	0.1	0.0	0.0	0.0	0.0	0.1	0.6	0.9	4.5
Days w/snow >= 10	0.1	0.1	0.2	0.1	0.0	0.0	0.0	0.0	0.0	0.0	0.2	0.2	0.9

Degree Days

	Jan	Feb	Mar	Apr	May	Jun	Jul	Aug	Sep	Oct	Nov	Dec	Annual
Heating normal	1230	1021	868	608	400	163	22	57	263	543	852	1129	7162
Heating average	1239	1024	881	616	400	172	33	61	257	549	876	1142	7257
Cooling normal	0	0	0	0	0	12	64	41	2	0	0	0	121
Cooling average	0	0	0	0	0	9	57	39	3	0	0	0	110
Growing 40 normal	32	63	154	285	445	508	636	643	504	378	158	45	3859
Growing 40 average	34	66	158	294	448	512	630	636	517	390	164	48	3902
Growing 50 normal	2	13	55	154	298	390	515	519	374	238	65	7	2636
Growing 50 average	3	13	56	159	301	395	516	518	393	247	68	6	2680

† Also occurred on earlier date(s).

Location: Delta   County: Millard   Latitude: 39.333   Longitude:-112.583
Elevation: 4620 feet   Period of Record: 1938-1996

DELTA
Monthly Data Summary

Maximum Temperature in °F

	Jan	Feb	Mar	Apr	May	Jun	Jul	Aug	Sep	Oct	Nov	Dec	Annual
Monthly normal	36.8	45.3	54.4	63.6	73.7	85.1	93.1	90.6	80.1	67.7	51.3	38.5	65.0
Standard deviation	10.1	10.8	10.7	10.8	10.8	9.2	5.4	6.0	9.3	10.7	11.2	10.7	9.6
Average monthly	37.8	45.0	54.2	64.0	73.8	84.5	93.4	91.2	81.3	67.9	50.9	40.1	65.3
Standard deviation	10.0	10.5	10.4	10.7	10.4	9.3	5.5	5.7	9.1	10.7	10.9	10.0	9.4
High monthly average	50.5	56.2	64.5	73.0	80.8	92.3	98.1	95.9	89.1	76.7	61.4	49.6	98.1
Year of occurrence	1953	1995	1972	1943	1958	1974	1942	1938	1938	1952	1949	1939	1942
Low monthly average	20.1	30.6	44.2	56.7	67.0	77.6	86.7	87.9	73.0	58.3	41.3	29.0	20.1
Year of occurrence	1949	1949	1952	1975	1995	1945	1993	1993	1961	1946	1938	1972	1949
Record high daily	64	74	81	89	94[†]	106	109	110	101	92	77	70	110
Day of occurrence	9	28	28	28	30	23	30	1	27	1	6	1	1
Year of occurrence	1953	1972	1986	1987	1994	1954	1938	1938	1938	1992	1980	1995	1938
Record low daily	4	7	23	33	37	48	59	66	39	24	22	2[†]	2
Day of occurrence	29	7	3	1	20	17	5	24	25	29	21	23	23
Year of occurrence	1949	1989	1966	1945	1975	1939	1982	1989	1961	1971	1964	1990	1990
Days w/max >= 100	0.0	0.0	0.0	0.0	0.0	0.8	3.4	1.5	0.0	0.0	0.0	0.0	5.8
Days w/max >= 90	0.0	0.0	0.0	0.0	1.0	10.1	24.7	20.6	5.2	0.0	0.0	0.0	62.8
Days w/max <= 32	8.6	3.2	0.4	0.0	0.0	0.0	0.0	0.0	0.0	0.0	1.5	6.7	21.1

Minimum Temperature in °F

	Jan	Feb	Mar	Apr	May	Jun	Jul	Aug	Sep	Oct	Nov	Dec	Annual
Monthly normal	11.9	19.1	26.0	32.3	41.2	49.5	57.2	55.0	45.0	34.2	23.9	14.3	34.1
Standard deviation	12.4	10.6	8.0	7.1	7.1	6.7	5.3	5.9	7.8	7.6	8.8	11.2	8.2
Average monthly	13.2	19.3	26.1	33.3	41.9	49.6	57.7	56.0	45.9	34.9	23.2	15.8	34.7
Standard deviation	12.4	10.8	7.9	7.3	7.0	6.7	5.4	6.0	8.0	7.4	9.1	10.7	8.2
High monthly average	24.8	27.9[†]	32.3	39.0	46.4	57.8	61.9	61.2	51.8	41.5	29.4	24.6	61.9
Year of occurrence	1953	1958	1978	1943	1963	1961	1961	1963	1960	1963	1965	1950	1961
Low monthly average	-7.9	-0.4	18.5	27.5	35.7	45.2	52.5	49.3	39.3	27.9	11.3	2.6	-7.9
Year of occurrence	1949	1949	1976	1975	1975	1995	1993	1976	1970	1970	1938	1990	1949
Record high daily	43	45	47	56	61[†]	70	72[†]	72	68	57[†]	49[†]	46	72[†]
Day of occurrence	13	18	28	26	21	29	30	14	8	9	14	24	14
Year of occurrence	1980	1986	1967	1946	1958	1957	1964	1944	1955	1963	1981	1955	1944
Record low daily	-25[†]	-27	-8	13[†]	21	25	37	35	24[†]	-2	-6	-30	-30
Day of occurrence	6	7	4	2	2	14	2	27	19	30	13	23	23
Year of occurrence	1971	1989	1966	1982	1967	1976	1992	1992	1988	1971	1938	1990	1990
Days w/min <= 32	30.1	26.1	24.8	14.1	3.1	0.2	0.0	0.0	1.5	12.0	25.6	29.6	170.5
Days w/min <= 0	5.1	1.9	0.1	0.0	0.0	0.0	0.0	0.0	0.0	0.0	0.3	2.2	9.9
Days w/min <= -20	0.3	0.1	0.0	0.0	0.0	0.0	0.0	0.0	0.0	0.0	0.0	0.2	0.6

Mean Temperature in °F

	Jan	Feb	Mar	Apr	May	Jun	Jul	Aug	Sep	Oct	Nov	Dec	Annual
Monthly normal	24.3	32.2	40.2	48.0	57.5	67.3	75.1	72.8	62.5	50.9	37.6	26.4	49.6
Standard deviation	10.6	9.9	8.3	7.9	8.1	7.2	4.2	4.9	7.6	8.0	9.0	10.1	8.0
Average monthly	25.5	32.2	40.1	48.6	57.9	67.1	75.6	73.6	63.6	51.4	37.1	27.9	50.0
Standard deviation	10.5	9.8	8.1	8.0	7.9	7.2	4.5	4.9	7.6	7.9	9.0	9.5	7.9
High monthly average	37.7	40.1	47.0	56.0	63.3	74.3	79.0	76.8	68.9	57.5	43.1	34.8	79.0
Year of occurrence	1953	1986	1986	1943	1958	1961	1960	1938	1990	1950	1949	1977	1960
Low monthly average	6.1	15.1	32.9	42.1	52.2	61.5	69.6	68.6	56.9	45.0	26.3	16.0	6.1
Year of occurrence	1949	1949	1948	1975	1975	1995	1993	1976	1965	1970	1938	1972	1949

† Also occurred on earlier date(s).

DELTA
Monthly Data Summary

Precipitation in Inches

	Jan	Feb	Mar	Apr	May	Jun	Jul	Aug	Sep	Oct	Nov	Dec	Annual
Monthly normal	0.50	0.56	0.85	0.79	0.90	0.47	0.53	0.57	0.81	0.81	0.71	0.62	8.11
Standard deviation	0.05	0.07	0.08	0.09	0.10	0.07	0.08	0.08	0.10	0.10	0.09	0.08	0.08
Average monthly	0.56	0.58	0.84	0.79	0.92	0.49	0.40	0.53	0.63	0.83	0.58	0.61	7.75
Standard deviation	0.06	0.07	0.08	0.09	0.10	0.07	0.06	0.07	0.09	0.11	0.07	0.09	0.08
High monthly total	1.75	2.21	2.79	2.30	3.46	1.75	2.04	2.30	4.18	4.54	2.00	3.77	4.54
Year of occurrence	1993	1962	1980	1941	1957	1984	1984	1965	1982	1946	1978	1951	1946
Low monthly total	0.00†	0.00	0.00	0.00	0.00	0.00†	0.01†	0.00†	0.00†	0.00†	0.00†	0.01†	0.00†
Year of occurrence	1972	1974	1972	1992	1974	1994	1964	1956	1974	1995	1995	1976	1995
Record high daily	0.61	0.89	0.96†	1.22	1.21	1.08	1.05	1.25	1.09	2.59	1.04	1.60	2.59
Day of occurrence	25	12	29	22	11	17	8	2	5	28	25	31	28
Year of occurrence	1954	1949	1979	1957	1947	1939	1982	1982	1970	1946	1978	1951	1946
Days w/pcp >= .01	5.8	5.3	6.9	6.2	6.0	3.5	3.4	4.3	4.3	4.8	4.9	5.3	61.4
Days w/pcp >= .10	2.1	2.1	3.0	2.4	2.8	1.3	1.3	1.8	1.9	2.4	1.8	1.9	25.1
Days w/pcp >= .50	0.0	0.1	0.2	0.2	0.3	0.1	0.1	0.2	0.3	0.3	0.2	0.2	2.2

Snow and Sleet in Inches

	Jan	Feb	Mar	Apr	May	Jun	Jul	Aug	Sep	Oct	Nov	Dec	Annual
Monthly normal	6.1	3.6	4.9	1.5	1.0	0.0	0.0	0.0	0.4	0.7	3.2	5.3	26.6
Standard deviation	0.7	0.6	0.7	0.3	0.6	0.0	0.0	0.0	0.2	0.2	0.7	0.7	0.4
Average monthly	6.4	4.0	4.2	1.3	0.5	0.0	0.0	0.0	0.2	0.6	2.7	4.5	24.4
Standard deviation	0.8	0.7	0.6	0.3	0.4	0.0	0.0	0.0	0.2	0.2	0.6	0.6	0.4
High monthly total	27.9	17.7	25.9	6.6	18.0	0.0†	0.0†	0.0†	7.0	5.7	19.8	23.0	27.9
Year of occurrence	1949	1990	1980	1991	1975	1995	1995	1995	1978	1991	1994	1948	1949
Low monthly total	0.0†	0.0†	0.0†	0.0†	0.0†	0.0†	0.0†	0.0†	0.0†	0.0†	0.0†	0.0†	0.0†
Year of occurrence	1959	1983	1994	1993	1995	1995	1995	1995	1995	1995	1995	1995	1995
Record high daily	13.0	9.0	7.5	5.2	16.0	0.0†	0.0†	0.0†	5.0	5.4	12.0	7.0	16.0
Day of occurrence	25	12	13	12	20	30	31	31	18	24	25	27	20
Year of occurrence	1954	1949	1944	1983	1975	1995	1995	1995	1978	1954	1978	1948	1975
Days w/snow >= .1	3.9	2.4	2.4	0.9	0.2	0.0	0.0	0.0	0.1	0.4	1.7	2.7	14.6
Days w/snow >= 5	0.1	0.1	0.2	0.0	0.0	0.0	0.0	0.0	0.0	0.0	0.1	0.1	0.8
Days w/snow >= 10	0.0	0.0	0.0	0.0	0.0	0.0	0.0	0.0	0.0	0.0	0.0	0.0	0.1

Degree Days

	Jan	Feb	Mar	Apr	May	Jun	Jul	Aug	Sep	Oct	Nov	Dec	Annual
Heating normal	1260	926	768	511	249	59	1	6	129	437	820	1194	6366
Heating average	1224	927	770	491	239	61	1	4	110	422	838	1142	6235
Cooling normal	0	0	0	0	16	127	314	248	54	0	0	0	762
Cooling average	0	0	0	0	18	123	327	270	69	1	0	0	811
Growing 40 normal	39	105	230	356	535	682	833	804	611	432	185	53	4871
Growing 40 average	44	100	226	364	543	681	843	817	629	435	179	61	4928
Growing 50 normal	5	33	107	212	370	513	662	633	452	279	79	10	3360
Growing 50 average	7	30	103	217	372	510	672	647	472	282	75	11	3401

† Also occurred on earlier date(s).

Location: Duchesne   County: Duchesne   Latitude: 40.167   Longitude: -110.440

Elevation: 5520 feet   Period of Record: 1906-1996

DUCHESNE
Monthly Data Summary

Maximum Temperature in °F

	Jan	Feb	Mar	Apr	May	Jun	Jul	Aug	Sep	Oct	Nov	Dec	Annual
Monthly normal	31.3	38.4	50.0	62.0	72.7	81.6	88.1	86.0	76.3	63.5	47.0	33.3	60.8
Standard deviation	10.9	11.1	10.6	9.4	9.0	8.4	4.8	5.3	8.3	9.2	9.2	10.5	8.9
Average monthly	30.8	37.5	49.6	61.7	71.5	80.6	87.1	85.0	76.5	63.4	46.7	33.8	60.3
Standard deviation	10.3	10.5	9.9	9.6	9.0	8.4	5.2	5.4	7.9	9.2	9.5	10.1	8.8
High monthly average	43.2	51.4	61.3	70.2	79.4	87.8	91.8	91.1	82.2†	72.7	57.0	47.1	91.8
Year of occurrence	1981	1954	1934	1992	1934	1961	1964	1970	1956	1952	1949	1917	1964
Low monthly average	12.7	25.4	36.3	54.5	60.5	72.8	81.6	79.2	68.7	54.4	37.3	19.0	12.7
Year of occurrence	1937	1973	1952	1929	1917	1967	1912	1968	1965	1908	1971	1909	1937
Record high daily	61	73	76	83†	99	99	100	101	93†	85	73	61	101
Day of occurrence	31	25	30	30	7	21	5	4	13	5	7	7	4
Year of occurrence	1971	1986	1966	1992	1987	1961	1985	1970	1990	1947	1980	1958	1970
Record low daily	-19	-6	16	24	36	49	61	60	37	24†	12	-7	-19
Day of occurrence	20	5	1	16	26	1	12	30	17	30	27	22	20
Year of occurrence	1948	1989	1962	1948	1950	1936	1936	1932	1965	1991	1919	1990	1948
Days w/max >= 100	0.0	0.0	0.0	0.0	0.0	0.0	0.0	0.0	0.0	0.0	0.0	0.0	0.0
Days w/max >= 90	0.0	0.0	0.0	0.0	0.2	4.2	10.9	6.3	0.5	0.0	0.0	0.0	22.2
Days w/max <= 32	17.2	8.8	1.3	0.0	0.0	0.0	0.0	0.0	0.0	0.1	2.1	13.1	42.8

Minimum Temperature in °F

	Jan	Feb	Mar	Apr	May	Jun	Jul	Aug	Sep	Oct	Nov	Dec	Annual
Monthly normal	5.5	12.5	23.2	31.5	39.3	47.8	54.3	52.8	42.9	32.6	21.5	8.8	31.1
Standard deviation	11.7	12.0	8.0	6.8	6.6	5.9	4.6	5.4	6.8	6.9	8.1	10.8	7.8
Average monthly	3.7	10.7	22.2	30.4	38.0	45.1	52.1	50.4	41.2	31.1	19.4	8.6	29.4
Standard deviation	12.5	12.7	8.3	7.1	6.5	6.4	5.4	5.9	7.1	7.1	8.7	12.0	8.3
High monthly average	16.1	24.3	31.0	37.7	44.9	51.4	56.9	56.8	49.5	38.5	27.3	19.6	56.9
Year of occurrence	1995	1958	1986	1990	1992	1988	1918	1970	1990	1963	1965	1917	1918
Low monthly average	-18.2	-8.8	12.2	24.8	32.0	38.6	46.3	44.7	33.7	25.3	8.2	-9.6	-18.2
Year of occurrence	1937	1933	1952	1933	1933	1923	1915	1924	1912	1935	1930	1930	1937
Record high daily	41	38†	43†	59	60	66	73	73	62	52	48	43	73†
Day of occurrence	30	25	11	28	30	24	30	2	1	12	14	8	2
Year of occurrence	1965	1954	1995	1928	1913	1959	1918	1918	1991	1971	1906	1938	1918
Record low daily	-43	-40	-16	4	0	25†	35†	26	16	4	-17	-39	-43
Day of occurrence	9	10	2	3	26	3	5	31	25	29	24	9	9
Year of occurrence	1937	1933	1922	1945	1950	1929	1912	1908	1926	1917	1931	1919	1937
Days w/min <= 32	30.7	27.8	28.7	18.4	6.2	0.6	0.0	0.1	3.4	17.9	28.3	30.4	194.8
Days w/min <= 0	12.2	6.2	0.5	0.0	0.0	0.0	0.0	0.0	0.0	0.0	0.7	7.5	27.5
Days w/min <= -20	1.1	0.4	0.0	0.0	0.0	0.0	0.0	0.0	0.0	0.0	0.0	0.5	2.0

Mean Temperature in °F

	Jan	Feb	Mar	Apr	May	Jun	Jul	Aug	Sep	Oct	Nov	Dec	Annual
Monthly normal	18.4	25.4	36.6	46.8	56.0	64.7	71.2	69.4	59.6	48.1	34.2	21.1	46.0
Standard deviation	10.8	11.1	8.6	7.1	6.9	6.4	3.4	4.5	6.7	7.1	7.9	10.1	7.5
Average monthly	17.3	24.1	35.9	46.1	54.7	62.9	69.6	67.7	58.8	47.2	33.0	21.2	44.9
Standard deviation	10.8	11.0	8.2	7.2	6.7	6.3	4.0	4.3	6.2	6.9	8.1	10.3	7.5
High monthly average	29.5	36.8	46.0	53.5	61.2	69.5	73.7	74.0	64.3	54.5	39.5	33.3	74.0
Year of occurrence	1981	1958	1986	1992	1969	1961	1964	1970	1990	1988	1965	1917	1970
Low monthly average	-2.7	8.9	24.3	40.3	47.9	57.3	65.1	63.5	51.4	40.1	24.7	5.1	-2.7
Year of occurrence	1937	1933	1952	1933	1933	1908	1912	1927	1912	1908	1930	1909	1937

† Also occurred on earlier date(s).

DUCHESNE
Monthly Data Summary

Precipitation in Inches

	Jan	Feb	Mar	Apr	May	Jun	Jul	Aug	Sep	Oct	Nov	Dec	Annual
Monthly normal	0.43	0.50	0.64	0.84	0.91	0.90	0.97	1.00	1.17	0.94	0.52	0.73	9.55
Standard deviation	0.06	0.08	0.07	0.09	0.09	0.09	0.10	0.08	0.12	0.11	0.06	0.08	0.09
Average monthly	0.54	0.58	0.70	0.71	0.85	0.77	0.96	1.19	1.05	0.97	0.51	0.60	9.43
Standard deviation	0.08	0.08	0.09	0.08	0.10	0.09	0.10	0.11	0.12	0.12	0.07	0.08	0.09
High monthly total	2.55	3.35	2.15	3.06	3.24	3.14	2.54	3.21	4.60	3.49	2.31	2.81	4.60
Year of occurrence	1937	1927	1939	1986	1987	1965	1987	1952	1940	1981	1906	1951	1940
Low monthly total	0.00†	0.00	0.00†	0.00†	0.00†	0.00†	0.00	0.00	0.00†	0.00†	0.00†	0.00	0.00†
Year of occurrence	1966	1924	1956	1927	1927	1942	1928	1950	1951	1952	1956	1930	1930
Record high daily	2.00	1.00†	1.10	1.08	1.72	1.28	1.08	1.73	1.69	1.65	1.30	1.67	2.00
Day of occurrence	1	19	3	16	30	7	23	23	1	12	3	30	1
Year of occurrence	1937	1927	1927	1920	1937	1941	1985	1995	1909	1928	1957	1951	1937
Days w/pcp >= .01	4.1	4.5	5.0	5.0	5.4	4.9	6.6	7.8	5.4	4.7	3.7	4.4	61.7
Days w/pcp >= .10	1.9	2.0	2.2	2.6	2.6	2.4	3.0	3.9	3.0	2.9	1.6	2.3	30.6
Days w/pcp >= .50	0.1	0.2	0.2	0.2	0.3	0.3	0.3	0.4	0.5	0.5	0.1	0.2	3.4

Snow and Sleet in Inches

	Jan	Feb	Mar	Apr	May	Jun	Jul	Aug	Sep	Oct	Nov	Dec	Annual
Monthly normal	4.0	3.6	3.2	0.5	0.0	0.0	0.0	0.0	0.0	1.0	1.2	6.0	19.6
Standard deviation	0.6	0.8	0.6	0.2	0.0	0.0	0.0	0.0	0.0	0.4	0.4	0.9	0.3
Average monthly	5.6	5.6	3.7	0.7	0.2	0.0	0.0	0.0	0.0	0.6	2.3	5.6	24.3
Standard deviation	0.8	0.8	0.7	0.3	0.2	0.0	0.0	0.0	0.0	0.3	0.5	0.8	0.4
High monthly total	28.0†	34.0	23.0	15.0	8.0	0.0†	0.0†	0.0†	0.0†	13.0	15.4	34.5	34.5
Year of occurrence	1949	1927	1936	1931	1912	1995	1995	1995	1995	1906	1906	1951	1951
Low monthly total	0.0†	0.0†	0.0†	0.0†	0.0†	0.0†	0.0†	0.0†	0.0†	0.0†	0.0†	0.0†	0.0†
Year of occurrence	1981	1991	1995	1994	1995	1995	1995	1995	1995	1995	1995	1995	1995
Record high daily	15.0	10.0†	10.0	7.0	6.0	0.0†	0.0†	0.0†	0.0†	9.0	9.0	19.5	19.5
Day of occurrence	1	3	17	23	3	30	31	31	30	21	3	30	30
Year of occurrence	1937	1989	1930	1931	1912	1995	1995	1995	1995	1906	1922	1951	1951
Days w/snow >= .1	3.2	3.2	1.9	0.4	0.1	0.0	0.0	0.0	0.0	0.3	1.2	3.2	13.3
Days w/snow >= 5	0.2	0.2	0.2	0.0	0.0	0.0	0.0	0.0	0.0	0.0	0.1	0.2	1.0
Days w/snow >= 10	0.0	0.0	0.0	0.0	0.0	0.0	0.0	0.0	0.0	0.0	0.0	0.0	0.1

Degree Days

	Jan	Feb	Mar	Apr	May	Jun	Jul	Aug	Sep	Oct	Nov	Dec	Annual
Heating normal	1443	1115	880	544	282	82	2	13	176	521	921	1339	7325
Heating average	1469	1152	901	565	320	110	8	22	195	549	957	1342	7596
Cooling normal	0	0	0	0	4	73	193	148	15	0	0	0	436
Cooling average	0	0	0	0	2	46	149	104	10	0	0	0	314
Growing 40 normal	18	48	170	333	515	646	793	766	566	370	123	21	4373
Growing 40 average	14	41	162	327	492	610	758	728	555	362	121	23	4201
Growing 50 normal	1	9	65	186	352	469	613	583	396	215	37	1	2931
Growing 50 average	0	6	59	184	333	454	584	554	398	210	35	2	2824

† Also occurred on earlier date(s).

Utah's Weather and Climate

Location: Dugway   County: Tooele   Latitude: 40.183   Longitude: -112.917
Elevation: 4340 feet   Period of Record: 1950-1995

DUGWAY
Monthly Data Summary

Maximum Temperature in °F

	Jan	Feb	Mar	Apr	May	Jun	Jul	Aug	Sep	Oct	Nov	Dec	Annual
Monthly normal	36.5	45.1	53.1	62.5	72.9	84.7	94.4	91.3	79.9	65.9	50.5	38.2	64.6
Standard deviation	9.8	10.2	10.1	11.1	11.0	10.4	5.7	6.7	10.3	10.6	10.2	10.0	9.7
Average monthly	37.4	45.2	53.3	62.9	73.3	84.7	94.3	91.7	81.0	66.8	50.3	39.1	65.0
Standard deviation	9.8	10.4	10.1	10.8	10.8	10.2	5.9	6.5	9.9	10.6	10.4	9.4	9.6
High monthly average	51.1	57.4	61.0	73.6	80.5	92.3	100.8	96.5	88.0	76.2	61.3	47.5	100.8
Year of occurrence	1953	1995	1989	1992	1992	1974	1989	1995	1979	1950	1995	1977	1989
Low monthly average	24.7	29.3	42.3	53.0	67.1†	76.0	88.1	83.1	73.4	58.5	42.6	29.6	24.7
Year of occurrence	1984	1984	1952	1975	1975	1963	1993	1968	1986	1984	1994	1985	1984
Record high daily	66	71†	80†	88†	98	107	109	108	102†	89†	78	69	109
Day of occurrence	10	24	26	29	27	23	19	11	1	1	12	1	19
Year of occurrence	1953	1995	1971	1992	1974	1954	1989	1972	1995	1992	1973	1995	1989
Record low daily	6	12	24	36†	40	48	61	60	44	27	20†	9†	6
Day of occurrence	12	7	28	27	20	1	1	22	29	29	17	24	12
Year of occurrence	1963	1989	1975	1970	1975	1955	1992	1968	1982	1971	1958	1990	1963
Days w/max >= 100	0.0	0.0	0.0	0.0	0.0	1.4	5.6	2.3	0.1	0.0	0.0	0.0	9.6
Days w/max >= 90	0.0	0.0	0.0	0.0	1.1	11.0	25.4	21.6	6.3	0.0	0.0	0.0	65.4
Days w/max <= 32	10.0	3.3	0.4	0.0	0.0	0.0	0.0	0.0	0.0	0.1	1.0	7.8	22.5

Minimum Temperature in °F

	Jan	Feb	Mar	Apr	May	Jun	Jul	Aug	Sep	Oct	Nov	Dec	Annual
Monthly normal	14.9	22.9	28.7	35.4	44.2	53.2	61.9	59.3	48.2	36.2	26.7	17.3	37.4
Standard deviation	12.5	10.6	7.9	7.6	7.6	7.4	6.2	6.8	8.8	7.9	8.6	11.1	8.6
Average monthly	15.6	22.8	28.6	35.7	44.4	53.3	61.5	59.6	48.4	36.3	25.9	17.9	37.5
Standard deviation	12.4	10.5	7.9	7.6	7.5	7.4	6.3	6.7	8.8	7.9	9.1	10.6	8.6
High monthly average	28.7	31.6	36.4	41.0	49.5	59.7	66.3	65.0	54.2	44.5	35.7	30.3	66.3
Year of occurrence	1953	1986	1978	1965	1969	1961	1966	1963	1963	1963	1965	1950	1966
Low monthly average	0.4	7.2	21.5	29.2	38.9	47.7	53.5	52.6	41.6	28.5	16.4	1.2	0.4
Year of occurrence	1989	1984	1977	1970	1953	1995	1993	1974	1974	1995	1993	1990	1989
Record high daily	47	50†	52	59†	65†	73	79	79	73†	64†	54†	52	79†
Day of occurrence	20	18	10	12	25	27	28	4	9	1	16	23	4
Year of occurrence	1969	1986	1995	1992	1964	1964	1961	1970	1979	1953	1966	1964	1970
Record low daily	-25	-29	-6	13	21	31†	37	33†	22	9	-8	-27	-29
Day of occurrence	18	7	3	1	1	15	1	27	26	30	27	23	7
Year of occurrence	1984	1989	1952	1970	1972	1976	1968	1992	1970	1971	1952	1990	1989
Days w/min <= 32	28.6	23.9	21.5	10.5	1.6	0.1	0.0	0.0	1.1	10.0	23.6	28.7	150.5
Days w/min <= 0	3.7	0.9	0.0	0.0	0.0	0.0	0.0	0.0	0.0	0.0	0.2	1.7	6.5
Days w/min <= -20	0.1	0.1	0.0	0.0	0.0	0.0	0.0	0.0	0.0	0.0	0.0	0.1	0.3

Mean Temperature in °F

	Jan	Feb	Mar	Apr	May	Jun	Jul	Aug	Sep	Oct	Nov	Dec	Annual
Monthly normal	25.7	34.0	40.9	49.0	58.6	69.0	78.2	75.3	64.0	51.0	38.6	27.7	51.0
Standard deviation	10.4	9.6	8.0	8.2	8.4	8.0	4.7	5.5	8.5	8.0	8.5	9.5	8.1
Average monthly	26.5	34.0	41.0	49.3	58.9	69.0	77.9	75.6	64.6	51.5	38.1	28.5	51.2
Standard deviation	10.4	9.6	7.9	8.1	8.2	7.9	4.9	5.4	8.2	7.9	8.8	9.1	8.0
High monthly average	39.9	41.5	47.6	56.4	64.9	75.0	81.0	78.9	69.5	58.6	46.2	35.5†	81.0
Year of occurrence	1953	1958	1978	1992	1969	1961	1989	1952	1979	1963	1965	1977	1989
Low monthly average	14.8	18.3	33.7	41.4	53.0	63.5	70.8	69.9	58.0	46.2	31.1	17.2	14.8
Year of occurrence	1984	1984	1952	1975	1953	1975	1993	1968	1970	1984	1993	1990	1984

† Also occurred on earlier date(s).

DUGWAY
Monthly Data Summary

Precipitation in Inches

	Jan	Feb	Mar	Apr	May	Jun	Jul	Aug	Sep	Oct	Nov	Dec	Annual
Monthly normal	0.46	0.57	0.84	0.81	1.06	0.53	0.57	0.61	0.72	0.81	0.59	0.59	8.16
Standard deviation	0.05	0.07	0.09	0.09	0.11	0.08	0.09	0.10	0.10	0.09	0.08	0.07	0.08
Average monthly	0.51	0.57	0.79	0.77	1.01	0.49	0.53	0.58	0.58	0.71	0.55	0.57	7.65
Standard deviation	0.06	0.07	0.09	0.08	0.11	0.07	0.08	0.09	0.09	0.09	0.07	0.07	0.08
High monthly total	1.54	1.58	2.44	2.14	2.96	2.35	1.89	1.89	3.16	2.00	1.86	2.33	3.16
Year of occurrence	1980	1980	1986	1986	1982	1967	1983	1983	1982	1981	1973	1983	1982
Low monthly total	0.00†	0.00	0.00	0.04	0.00	0.00†	0.00†	0.00†	0.00†	0.00†	0.00	0.00†	0.00†
Year of occurrence	1970	1967	1956	1992	1969	1994	1971	1966	1979	1959	1959	1986	1986
Record high daily	0.98	0.84	1.34	0.95	1.24	0.74	1.11	1.46	1.17	1.02	0.95	1.01	1.46
Day of occurrence	31	25	8	15	31	12	31	6	17	9	15	31	6
Year of occurrence	1983	1958	1986	1969	1994	1967	1983	1988	1961	1961	1963	1959	1988
Days w/pcp >= .01	5.1	5.0	6.1	5.9	6.2	3.2	3.8	3.6	3.4	4.4	4.4	5.2	56.3
Days w/pcp >= .10	2.0	1.9	2.9	2.4	3.2	1.6	1.5	1.6	1.7	2.2	1.9	2.0	24.8
Days w/pcp >= .50	0.1	0.2	0.2	0.2	0.4	0.2	0.2	0.2	0.2	0.4	0.2	0.1	2.5

Snow and Sleet in Inches

	Jan	Feb	Mar	Apr	May	Jun	Jul	Aug	Sep	Oct	Nov	Dec	Annual
Monthly normal	3.8	2.2	2.2	0.9	0.4	0.0	0.0	0.0	0.0	0.1	1.9	4.5	16.0
Standard deviation	0.5	0.4	0.4	0.2	0.2	0.0	0.0	0.0	0.0	0.1	0.4	0.6	0.2
Average monthly	4.0	2.7	2.4	0.8	0.3	0.0	0.0	0.0	0.0	0.1	1.9	3.7	15.9
Standard deviation	0.5	0.4	0.4	0.2	0.1	0.0	0.0	0.0	0.0	0.1	0.4	0.5	0.2
High monthly total	13.9	11.8	21.2	7.8	6.4	0.1	0.0†	0.0†	0.0†	1.7	8.8	15.6	21.2
Year of occurrence	1993	1955	1952	1970	1965	1951	1995	1995	1995	1956	1985	1968	1952
Low monthly total	0.0†	0.0†	0.0†	0.0†	0.0†	0.0†	0.0†	0.0†	0.0†	0.0†	0.0†	0.0†	0.0†
Year of occurrence	1994	1992	1993	1994	1995	1995	1995	1995	1995	1995	1993	1995	1995
Record high daily	7.0	5.1	4.8	3.5	3.7	0.1	0.0†	0.0†	0.0†	1.3	6.0	9.0	9.0
Day of occurrence	29	28	31	27	8	22	31	31	30	31	15	17	17
Year of occurrence	1980	1955	1958	1970	1965	1951	1995	1995	1995	1956	1963	1970	1970
Days w/snow >= .1	3.7	2.6	1.9	0.8	0.2	0.0	0.0	0.0	0.0	0.2	1.6	3.0	14.0
Days w/snow >= 5	0.0	0.0	0.0	0.0	0.0	0.0	0.0	0.0	0.0	0.0	0.0	0.1	0.1
Days w/snow >= 10	0.0	0.0	0.0	0.0	0.0	0.0	0.0	0.0	0.0	0.0	0.0	0.0	0.0

Degree Days

	Jan	Feb	Mar	Apr	May	Jun	Jul	Aug	Sep	Oct	Nov	Dec	Annual
Heating normal	1208	860	738	475	230	52	0	5	117	429	790	1148	6058
Heating average	1187	863	738	468	221	51	1	4	105	416	805	1127	5989
Cooling normal	0	0	0	2	30	171	404	322	87	2	0	0	1020
Cooling average	0	0	0	2	32	170	398	332	94	3	0	0	1032
Growing 40 normal	37	99	210	348	555	723	901	862	643	414	173	49	5019
Growing 40 average	43	102	214	357	562	727	898	870	653	427	171	51	5082
Growing 50 normal	5	27	88	197	366	536	729	686	466	252	67	9	3433
Growing 50 average	6	30	91	203	372	540	726	694	481	267	67	9	3490

† Also occurred on earlier date(s).

Location: Enterprise Beryl Junction   County: Iron   Latitude: 37.767   Longitude:-113.650
Elevation: 5150 feet   Period of Record: 1948-1996

ENTERPRISE BERYL JUNCTION
Monthly Data Summary

Maximum Temperature in °F

	Jan	Feb	Mar	Apr	May	Jun	Jul	Aug	Sep	Oct	Nov	Dec	Annual
Monthly normal	41.2	46.8	54.8	63.8	73.2	83.5	89.8	87.2	78.8	67.9	53.2	42.6	65.2
Standard deviation	10.0	10.2	10.2	9.9	9.3	8.1	5.3	5.8	7.9	9.8	10.5	10.7	9.0
Average monthly	41.6	47.1	55.0	64.0	73.2	83.6	89.9	87.7	79.7	68.3	53.1	42.9	65.5
Standard deviation	9.9	10.1	9.9	9.8	9.1	8.2	5.4	5.7	7.8	9.9	10.7	10.5	8.9
High monthly average	53.5	59.2	66.2	73.3	80.5	90.8	94.1	91.8	85.8	76.6	63.9	51.5	94.1
Year of occurrence	1986	1995	1972	1989	1984	1956	1960	1986	1955	1988	1995	1980	1960
Low monthly average	31.6	37.7	46.4	55.9	64.9	76.7	86.5	79.3	71.8	60.4	42.3	32.9	31.6
Year of occurrence	1973	1985	1973	1975	1977	1995	1992	1968	1965	1969	1994	1972	1973
Record high daily	70	77	78†	86†	97	102	104†	102†	98	88	76	72	104
Day of occurrence	11	26	30	21	30	21	6	6	16	1	5	1	6
Year of occurrence	1990	1986	1986	1994	1983	1961	1985	1981	1955	1988	1983	1995	1985
Record low daily	11	7†	25	37†	39†	53	68	68	43	26	25†	0†	0
Day of occurrence	23	7	1	2	21	1	23	21	18	29	20	24	24
Year of occurrence	1962	1989	1971	1984	1975	1991	1984	1975	1965	1971	1994	1990	1990
Days w/max >= 100	0.0	0.0	0.0	0.0	0.0	0.2	0.8	0.2	0.0	0.0	0.0	0.0	1.3
Days w/max >= 90	0.0	0.0	0.0	0.0	0.4	7.5	17.1	12.4	2.3	0.0	0.0	0.0	39.3
Days w/max <= 32	5.3	1.7	0.3	0.0	0.0	0.0	0.0	0.0	0.0	0.1	0.9	4.5	13.1

Minimum Temperature in °F

	Jan	Feb	Mar	Apr	May	Jun	Jul	Aug	Sep	Oct	Nov	Dec	Annual
Monthly normal	11.4	17.7	22.5	27.5	35.4	42.5	50.5	49.7	40.1	29.6	20.5	12.8	30.0
Standard deviation	12.6	11.2	8.2	7.4	7.1	6.8	6.7	6.7	7.9	8.0	8.8	11.9	8.6
Average monthly	12.1	18.1	22.9	27.6	35.4	42.6	49.9	49.5	40.0	29.4	19.9	12.9	30.0
Standard deviation	12.4	10.9	8.2	7.4	7.0	6.8	6.7	6.8	7.9	7.8	9.2	11.6	8.6
High monthly average	24.1	27.1	30.3	31.7	39.4	49.1	55.0	55.3	45.6	36.7	25.0	23.5	55.3
Year of occurrence	1995	1968	1978	1978	1974	1981	1981	1969	1981	1972	1965	1955	1969
Low monthly average	-1.1	8.5	16.4	21.1	30.7	38.1	43.5	44.5	33.3	23.7	9.5	1.8	-1.1
Year of occurrence	1989	1964	1976	1991	1983	1965	1956	1976	1993	1995	1956	1990	1989
Record high daily	43	45	50	52	60	70	72	69	59†	60	49	46	72
Day of occurrence	13	19	26	11	16	29	29	9	5	3	12	6	29
Year of occurrence	1980	1986	1971	1982	1971	1956	1980	1969	1972	1967	1973	1966	1980
Record low daily	-26	-33	-8	8	10	26	29	30	18†	-5	-13	-34†	-34
Day of occurrence	30	7	1	25	21	6	19	27	19	30	20	24	24
Year of occurrence	1979	1989	1962	1960	1975	1982	1987	1992	1988	1971	1956	1990	1990
Days w/min <= 32	29.4	26.3	27.4	22.5	10.7	1.4	0.0	0.2	5.5	21.1	27.2	29.7	204.1
Days w/min <= 0	5.5	1.7	0.2	0.0	0.0	0.0	0.0	0.0	0.0	0.0	0.6	3.5	11.8
Days w/min <= -20	0.2	0.2	0.0	0.0	0.0	0.0	0.0	0.0	0.0	0.0	0.0	0.3	0.7

Mean Temperature in °F

	Jan	Feb	Mar	Apr	May	Jun	Jul	Aug	Sep	Oct	Nov	Dec	Annual
Monthly normal	26.3	32.3	38.6	45.7	54.3	63.0	70.2	68.5	59.5	48.7	36.9	27.7	47.6
Standard deviation	9.9	9.2	7.2	6.9	6.8	6.2	4.3	4.7	6.4	7.1	8.0	9.9	7.2
Average monthly	26.9	32.6	38.9	45.8	54.3	63.1	69.9	68.6	59.8	48.9	36.5	27.9	47.8
Standard deviation	9.7	9.1	7.1	6.9	6.7	6.3	4.3	4.7	6.4	7.1	8.3	9.6	7.2
High monthly average	36.3	40.8	44.1	51.2	58.6	68.1	73.2	72.5	63.4	53.2	40.7	37.2	73.2
Year of occurrence	1956	1995	1978	1992	1984	1981	1981	1986	1960	1988	1967	1955	1981
Low monthly average	16.4	23.9	34.1	40.4	50.5	57.5	66.7†	64.3	53.4	43.4	27.9	18.9	16.4
Year of occurrence	1989	1985	1964	1983	1977	1965	1983	1968	1965	1984	1994	1972	1989

† Also occurred on earlier date(s).

ENTERPRISE BERYL JUNCTION
Monthly Data Summary

Precipitation in Inches

	Jan	Feb	Mar	Apr	May	Jun	Jul	Aug	Sep	Oct	Nov	Dec	Annual
Monthly normal	0.68	0.83	1.10	0.90	0.66	0.46	1.18	1.18	0.94	0.81	0.86	0.62	10.21
Standard deviation	0.09	0.10	0.11	0.10	0.08	0.10	0.13	0.15	0.13	0.10	0.11	0.07	0.11
Average monthly	0.73	0.80	1.17	0.81	0.73	0.51	0.98	1.09	0.77	0.85	0.81	0.60	9.85
Standard deviation	0.09	0.10	0.12	0.10	0.10	0.10	0.12	0.14	0.12	0.11	0.11	0.07	0.11
High monthly total	3.03	2.85	4.96	2.85	2.90	2.81	3.93	3.70	2.86	2.29	2.42	1.92	4.96
Year of occurrence	1980	1969	1992	1988	1977	1982	1984	1968	1982	1991	1963	1965	1992
Low monthly total	0.02	0.00	0.00	0.00	0.00†	0.00†	0.02	0.00†	0.02	0.00†	0.00	0.00†	0.00†
Year of occurrence	1972	1972	1972	1977	1974	1986	1979	1985	1974	1995	1956	1989	1989
Record high daily	1.15	1.10	1.35	0.90	1.30	2.50	1.54	2.27	1.76	1.26	1.31	1.00	2.50
Day of occurrence	18	10	28	24	16	18	29	8	17	27	7	23	18
Year of occurrence	1988	1978	1979	1990	1993	1982	1975	1968	1961	1991	1963	1987	1982
Days w/pcp >= .01	5.0	4.8	6.7	4.8	4.9	3.1	5.3	5.8	4.0	4.1	4.0	4.3	56.8
Days w/pcp >= .10	2.3	2.4	3.7	2.3	2.1	1.5	2.6	3.0	1.9	2.3	2.2	1.9	28.4
Days w/pcp >= .50	0.2	0.2	0.4	0.4	0.2	0.1	0.4	0.5	0.5	0.5	0.3	0.1	4.0

Snow and Sleet in Inches

	Jan	Feb	Mar	Apr	May	Jun	Jul	Aug	Sep	Oct	Nov	Dec	Annual
Monthly normal	6.5	5.6	5.9	2.9	0.9	0.0	0.0	0.0	0.1	0.6	3.9	5.7	32.1
Standard deviation	0.9	0.8	0.7	0.5	0.4	0.0	0.0	0.0	0.1	0.2	0.7	0.8	0.4
Average monthly	6.4	5.0	5.1	2.5	0.7	0.0	0.0	0.0	0.1	0.7	4.3	5.1	29.9
Standard deviation	0.9	0.8	0.7	0.5	0.3	0.0	0.0	0.0	0.1	0.3	0.9	0.7	0.4
High monthly total	26.0	19.0	19.5	10.5	12.5	0.0†	0.0†	0.0†	2.5	10.0	29.5	17.0	29.5
Year of occurrence	1974	1969	1987	1973	1975	1995	1995	1995	1982	1971	1994	1972	1994
Low monthly total	0.0†	0.0†	0.0†	0.0†	0.0†	0.0†	0.0†	0.0†	0.0†	0.0†	0.0†	0.0†	0.0†
Year of occurrence	1970	1995	1993	1993	1995	1995	1995	1995	1995	1995	1995	1995	1995
Record high daily	9.0	10.0	6.0†	6.0	10.0	0.0†	0.0†	0.0†	2.5	5.0	12.0	11.0	12.0
Day of occurrence	21	27	25	10	20	30	31	31	30	28	18	23	18
Year of occurrence	1974	1993	1977	1965	1975	1995	1995	1995	1982	1971	1994	1987	1994
Days w/snow >= .1	2.8	2.5	2.8	1.2	0.4	0.0	0.0	0.0	0.1	0.4	1.7	2.7	14.4
Days w/snow >= 5	0.3	0.2	0.2	0.1	0.0	0.0	0.0	0.0	0.0	0.0	0.3	0.2	1.2
Days w/snow >= 10	0.0	0.0	0.0	0.0	0.0	0.0	0.0	0.0	0.0	0.0	0.1	0.0	0.2

Degree Days

	Jan	Feb	Mar	Apr	May	Jun	Jul	Aug	Sep	Oct	Nov	Dec	Annual
Heating normal	1184	915	815	579	331	108	8	23	180	499	834	1151	6631
Heating average	1169	907	806	574	329	107	9	22	173	496	847	1145	6590
Cooling normal	0	0	0	0	2	49	167	130	15	0	0	0	366
Cooling average	0	0	0	0	2	49	161	133	19	0	0	0	366
Growing 40 normal	70	117	233	355	498	599	737	723	562	428	207	87	4621
Growing 40 average	73	119	236	357	499	598	727	721	568	433	206	89	4632
Growing 50 normal	15	37	107	214	356	480	591	568	425	280	92	20	3190
Growing 50 average	16	38	108	215	357	480	586	570	436	287	93	22	3214

† Also occurred on earlier date(s).

Location: Escalante   County: Garfield   Latitude: 37.767   Longitude: -111.600
Elevation: 5810 feet   Period of Record: 1901-1996

ESCALANTE
Monthly Data Summary

Maximum Temperature in °F

	Jan	Feb	Mar	Apr	May	Jun	Jul	Aug	Sep	Oct	Nov	Dec	Annual
Monthly normal	41.0	47.2	54.5	63.7	73.8	84.5	89.9	86.6	78.4	67.2	53.0	42.8	65.2
Standard deviation	8.7	8.6	9.2	9.1	8.6	7.5	5.1	5.7	7.4	9.0	8.9	8.2	8.0
Average monthly	39.8	45.3	53.9	63.0	72.3	83.0	88.1	85.2	78.1	66.5	52.5	41.9	64.1
Standard deviation	8.5	9.3	9.2	9.3	8.7	7.8	5.8	6.0	7.3	8.9	9.1	8.5	8.2
High monthly average	50.5	62.3	66.1	71.6	80.4	92.1	95.3	91.7	84.3	73.5	61.7	54.0	95.3
Year of occurrence	1956	1912	1910	1992	1974	1974	1994	1994	1955	1952	1954	1917	1994
Low monthly average	25.7	32.4†	40.4	52.6	62.9	75.4	82.4	78.4	68.2	56.9	43.4	31.2	25.7
Year of occurrence	1937	1949	1924	1941	1933	1923	1937	1923	1941	1946	1947	1909	1937
Record high daily	68	84	80†	85†	92	103	102†	101	96	87†	78	69†	103
Day of occurrence	18	4	29	29	30	24	29	9	8	1	2	5	24
Year of occurrence	1971	1912	1911	1992	1910	1994	1995	1969	1955	1978	1937	1995	1994
Record low daily	10†	12	19	27	40†	45	60	60	47	33	26	10	10†
Day of occurrence	12	7	30	7	2	6	11	29	21	30	14	25	25
Year of occurrence	1963	1933	1924	1928	1935	1934	1930	1951	1941	1971	1928	1926	1926
Days w/max >= 100	0.0	0.0	0.0	0.0	0.0	0.2	0.3	0.1	0.0	0.0	0.0	0.0	0.6
Days w/max >= 90	0.0	0.0	0.0	0.0	0.2	5.9	13.9	7.5	1.1	0.0	0.0	0.0	28.7
Days w/max <= 32	5.8	2.2	0.3	0.0	0.0	0.0	0.0	0.0	0.0	0.0	0.4	4.4	13.4

Minimum Temperature in °F

	Jan	Feb	Mar	Apr	May	Jun	Jul	Aug	Sep	Oct	Nov	Dec	Annual
Monthly normal	14.1	20.9	26.3	32.4	39.9	47.6	54.7	52.8	44.5	35.1	25.4	16.5	34.2
Standard deviation	9.4	8.3	6.9	6.3	5.8	6.2	4.5	4.8	6.3	6.3	7.3	8.6	6.7
Average monthly	13.4	19.9	25.9	32.3	39.6	46.8	53.9	52.3	43.8	34.6	23.9	16.0	33.5
Standard deviation	9.8	9.1	6.7	6.5	5.8	6.0	4.8	5.0	6.5	6.4	7.2	9.0	6.9
High monthly average	21.7†	28.4	32.0	38.9	47.7	53.7	57.9	57.3	51.1	40.2	28.8	25.4	57.9
Year of occurrence	1978	1995	1972	1992	1901	1918	1936	1994	1990	1963	1995	1977	1936
Low monthly average	-6.4	2.5	18.3	22.4	33.5	38.7	46.0	41.3	31.3	23.9	11.0	0.2	-6.4
Year of occurrence	1937	1933	1924	1933	1933	1923	1916	1916	1924	1924	1924	1924	1937
Record high daily	43	42	47	58	66	70	69†	69	65	58	46	50	70
Day of occurrence	7	1	5	28	7	9	25	9	16	11	10	28	9
Year of occurrence	1962	1963	1991	1990	1901	1902	1987	1960	1990	1934	1955	1948	1902
Record low daily	-22	-21	2†	10	23	25	38	32†	16	10†	-3	-20	-22
Day of occurrence	22	10	3	10	2	14	4	20	22	30	25	18	22
Year of occurrence	1937	1933	1965	1933	1967	1932	1902	1916	1924	1971	1931	1924	1937
Days w/min <= 32	30.4	26.7	26.2	14.7	3.7	0.2	0.0	0.0	1.3	10.5	26.5	30.0	172.2
Days w/min <= 0	3.3	1.1	0.0	0.0	0.0	0.0	0.0	0.0	0.0	0.0	0.1	1.6	6.3
Days w/min <= -20	0.0	0.0	0.0	0.0	0.0	0.0	0.0	0.0	0.0	0.0	0.0	0.0	0.1

Mean Temperature in °F

	Jan	Feb	Mar	Apr	May	Jun	Jul	Aug	Sep	Oct	Nov	Dec	Annual
Monthly normal	27.6	34.0	40.4	48.0	56.8	66.1	72.3	69.7	61.5	51.1	39.2	29.6	49.7
Standard deviation	8.3	7.6	7.2	6.9	6.5	6.2	3.5	4.2	6.0	6.8	7.3	7.5	6.5
Average monthly	26.7	32.6	39.9	47.6	55.9	65.0	71.0	68.8	60.9	50.6	38.2	29.0	48.8
Standard deviation	8.3	8.4	7.0	7.0	6.4	6.2	4.1	4.2	5.8	6.6	7.2	7.8	6.6
High monthly average	35.5	44.3	48.3	55.3	62.5	72.1	75.5	74.5	65.8	56.0	45.1	38.5	75.5
Year of occurrence	1956	1912	1972	1992	1901	1994	1994	1994	1990	1988	1995	1980	1994
Low monthly average	9.6	18.2	29.4	39.1	48.2	57.0	64.9	61.8	53.1	42.9	30.6	17.4	9.6
Year of occurrence	1937	1933	1924	1922	1933	1923	1924	1916	1923	1924	1924	1909	1937

† Also occurred on earlier date(s).

ESCALANTE
Monthly Data Summary

Precipitation in Inches

	Jan	Feb	Mar	Apr	May	Jun	Jul	Aug	Sep	Oct	Nov	Dec	Annual
Monthly normal	0.78	0.64	0.90	0.50	0.68	0.41	1.06	1.51	1.04	0.98	0.83	0.70	10.04
Standard deviation	0.10	0.10	0.10	0.09	0.09	0.06	0.12	0.15	0.13	0.13	0.12	0.09	0.11
Average monthly	0.98	0.79	0.88	0.55	0.60	0.47	1.24	1.74	1.10	1.03	0.68	0.86	10.93
Standard deviation	0.14	0.12	0.12	0.09	0.10	0.09	0.16	0.18	0.16	0.16	0.12	0.13	0.13
High monthly total	4.44	3.06	3.46	3.30	2.50	2.50	5.41	4.50	5.70	5.57	4.65	3.76	5.70
Year of occurrence	1993	1993	1918	1941	1928	1927	1932	1923	1927	1916	1978	1947	1927
Low monthly total	0.00†	0.00†	0.00†	0.00†	0.00†	0.00†	0.00	0.07†	0.00†	0.00†	0.00†	0.00†	0.00†
Year of occurrence	1976	1977	1972	1989	1974	1980	1920	1985	1956	1995	1995	1989	1989
Record high daily	2.26	1.82	1.90	1.60	2.11	1.26	3.24	4.40	3.20	3.39	1.60	2.08	4.40
Day of occurrence	22	24	19	29	29	22	12	31	12	6	19	1	31
Year of occurrence	1943	1944	1902	1957	1934	1918	1932	1921	1927	1916	1940	1932	1921
Days w/pcp >= .01	3.2	3.3	3.5	2.7	3.0	2.3	5.4	7.2	3.8	3.2	2.3	2.8	42.8
Days w/pcp >= .10	2.4	2.3	2.4	1.5	1.7	1.2	3.1	4.4	2.4	2.3	1.6	2.0	27.4
Days w/pcp >= .50	0.6	0.5	0.4	0.2	0.3	0.3	0.6	1.0	0.7	0.7	0.4	0.5	6.4

Snow and Sleet in Inches

	Jan	Feb	Mar	Apr	May	Jun	Jul	Aug	Sep	Oct	Nov	Dec	Annual
Monthly normal	8.8	4.4	5.7	1.5	0.1	0.0	0.0	0.0	0.0	0.3	3.1	6.6	30.4
Standard deviation	1.2	0.8	0.9	0.5	0.0	0.0	0.0	0.0	0.0	0.2	0.7	1.1	0.5
Average monthly	9.0	3.9	3.6	0.7	0.0	0.0	0.1	0.0	0.0	0.1	2.1	6.3	25.9
Standard deviation	1.3	0.8	0.8	0.4	0.0	0.0	0.1	0.0	0.0	0.1	0.7	1.2	0.5
High monthly total	33.0	21.5	20.0	20.0	1.5	0.0†	5.0	0.0†	0.0†	4.0	18.5	34.0	34.0
Year of occurrence	1993	1993	1949	1965	1965	1995	1932	1995	1995	1986	1906	1936	1936
Low monthly total	0.0†	0.0†	0.0†	0.0†	0.0†	0.0†	0.0†	0.0†	0.0†	0.0†	0.0†	0.0†	0.0†
Year of occurrence	1976	1995	1994	1995	1995	1995	1995	1995	1995	1995	1995	1995	1995
Record high daily	14.0†	14.0	19.0	10.0	1.5	0.0†	5.0	0.0†	0.0†	4.0	15.0	17.8	19.0
Day of occurrence	5	27	19	4	7	30	12	31	30	31	23	28	19
Year of occurrence	1974	1907	1902	1965	1965	1995	1932	1995	1995	1986	1906	1936	1902
Days w/snow >= .1	2.4	1.3	0.9	0.2	0.0	0.0	0.0	0.0	0.0	0.0	0.5	1.6	6.9
Days w/snow >= 5	0.6	0.2	0.2	0.1	0.0	0.0	0.0	0.0	0.0	0.0	0.2	0.5	1.8
Days w/snow >= 10	0.1	0.0	0.0	0.0	0.0	0.0	0.0	0.0	0.0	0.0	0.0	0.1	0.4

Degree Days

	Jan	Feb	Mar	Apr	May	Jun	Jul	Aug	Sep	Oct	Nov	Dec	Annual
Heating normal	1160	874	760	508	258	60	1	9	134	426	773	1096	6066
Heating average	1178	902	775	516	282	73	4	14	140	440	793	1105	6227
Cooling normal	0	0	0	0	6	93	227	154	29	0	0	0	510
Cooling average	0	0	0	0	3	72	188	128	21	0	0	0	416
Growing 40 normal	60	114	227	358	527	662	800	762	602	422	198	75	4813
Growing 40 average	49	96	218	345	504	642	776	746	585	410	190	68	4634
Growing 50 normal	9	32	98	210	367	505	624	579	428	267	80	11	3215
Growing 50 average	6	25	92	199	341	485	597	559	417	255	76	10	3069

† Also occurred on earlier date(s).

Location: Farmington   County: Davis   Latitude: 40.983   Longitude:-111.900
Elevation: 4270 feet   Period of Record: 1900-1995

FARMINGTON
Monthly Data Summary

Maximum Temperature in °F

	Jan	Feb	Mar	Apr	May	Jun	Jul	Aug	Sep	Oct	Nov	Dec	Annual
Monthly normal	37.6	45.3	50.8	62.0	72.5	82.2	93.2	93.1	81.0	70.3	52.3	40.3	65.0
Standard deviation	9.0	10.2	10.0	10.4	10.2	10.3	4.3	5.3	9.1	9.9	9.0	8.9	8.9
Average monthly	37.9	43.6	52.3	62.8	72.7	82.3	91.5	89.2	79.0	66.3	51.0	40.0	64.1
Standard deviation	8.5	9.0	9.2	9.7	9.7	9.2	5.5	5.6	9.1	9.7	9.1	8.4	8.6
High monthly average	49.5	54.1	63.2	72.8	83.5	90.5	96.8	96.5	86.9	74.8	61.7	49.5	96.8
Year of occurrence	1953	1995	1934	1934	1934	1918	1931	1961	1956	1952	1959	1939	1931
Low monthly average	25.4	28.8	40.6	55.0	65.2	73.1	87.2	83.9	69.9	52.8	43.1	29.2	25.4
Year of occurrence	1949	1903	1917	1922	1953	1907	1902	1907	1912	1919	1947	1930	1949
Record high daily	62	72	79†	86†	96	102†	106	102†	99	90	77	68	106
Day of occurrence	12	10	25	18	20	19	24	7	1	3	1	6	24
Year of occurrence	1953	1951	1956	1962	1954	1940	1931	1960	1948	1963	1947	1946	1931
Record low daily	4	12	27	35	43	41	64	62	44	36	22†	10	4
Day of occurrence	21	14	1	4	2	1	4	30	26	31	14	26	21
Year of occurrence	1937	1903	1922	1955	1964	1908	1902	1932	1908	1919	1916	1924	1937
Days w/max >= 100	0.0	0.0	0.0	0.0	0.0	0.2	1.6	0.5	0.0	0.0	0.0	0.0	2.4
Days w/max >= 90	0.0	0.0	0.0	0.0	0.8	7.0	21.7	16.0	3.3	0.0	0.0	0.0	48.5
Days w/max <= 32	7.8	2.9	0.2	0.0	0.0	0.0	0.0	0.0	0.0	0.0	0.6	5.6	17.6

Minimum Temperature in °F

	Jan	Feb	Mar	Apr	May	Jun	Jul	Aug	Sep	Oct	Nov	Dec	Annual
Monthly normal	17.1	24.5	27.7	36.7	45.0	52.3	59.3	59.7	48.6	40.9	29.6	22.8	38.7
Standard deviation	10.7	10.4	7.4	6.7	7.6	7.4	5.4	6.3	7.1	7.8	6.6	8.9	7.7
Average monthly	19.0	24.1	29.9	36.9	43.9	50.8	58.3	56.5	47.0	37.9	28.4	22.1	37.9
Standard deviation	10.5	9.4	7.5	7.1	7.1	7.1	6.0	5.9	7.5	7.1	7.6	9.4	7.7
High monthly average	28.2	32.5	40.8	42.6	49.9	60.3	63.5	62.3	52.6	45.0	38.4	32.5	63.5
Year of occurrence	1953	1934	1918	1915	1934	1918	1960	1901	1960	1901	1901	1917	1960
Low monthly average	3.4	8.9	21.3	31.9	36.5	42.3	50.1	50.1	40.0	30.9	22.0	10.9	3.4
Year of occurrence	1949	1933	1917	1958	1908	1904	1904	1907	1903	1906	1930	1932	1949
Record high daily	47	49	58	67	69	84	87	77	76	68	55	55	87
Day of occurrence	30	10	29	30	23	13	23	9	4	3	9	10	23
Year of occurrence	1911	1962	1943	1934	1926	1918	1947	1932	1931	1922	1927	1929	1947
Record low daily	-20	-20	4	12	26†	30†	36	36	23	16	-8	-17	-20†
Day of occurrence	21	10	4	2	7	3	3	21	25	28	16	12	10
Year of occurrence	1937	1933	1923	1936	1965	1908	1921	1904	1926	1919	1955	1932	1933
Days w/min <= 32	28.2	23.6	19.8	8.4	1.4	0.0	0.0	0.0	0.5	7.0	21.6	27.1	139.7
Days w/min <= 0	1.5	0.5	0.0	0.0	0.0	0.0	0.0	0.0	0.0	0.0	0.0	0.5	2.7
Days w/min <= -20	0.0	0.0	0.0	0.0	0.0	0.0	0.0	0.0	0.0	0.0	0.0	0.0	0.0

Mean Temperature in °F

	Jan	Feb	Mar	Apr	May	Jun	Jul	Aug	Sep	Oct	Nov	Dec	Annual
Monthly normal	27.3	34.9	39.3	49.4	59.8	67.2	76.2	76.4	64.8	55.6	41.0	31.5	51.9
Standard deviation	9.1	9.8	8.0	7.9	7.5	8.3	4.0	5.0	7.0	7.9	6.8	8.2	7.5
Average monthly	28.5	33.9	41.1	49.9	58.3	66.6	74.9	72.9	63.0	52.1	39.7	31.0	51.0
Standard deviation	8.9	8.6	7.6	7.7	7.6	7.3	4.8	4.8	7.3	7.4	7.5	8.3	7.3
High monthly average	38.9	42.2	49.9	57.2	66.7	75.4	80.0	79.2	69.0	58.5	46.0	40.1	80.0
Year of occurrence	1953	1934	1934	1934	1934	1918	1960	1961	1960	1963	1901	1917	1960
Low monthly average	14.2	19.1	31.0	43.6	51.8	58.0	69.8	67.0	55.1	42.4	33.2	20.8	14.2
Year of occurrence	1949	1903	1917	1922	1908	1907	1902	1907	1912	1919	1938	1930	1949

† Also occurred on earlier date(s).

FARMINGTON
Monthly Data Summary

Precipitation in Inches

	Jan	Feb	Mar	Apr	May	Jun	Jul	Aug	Sep	Oct	Nov	Dec	Annual
Monthly normal	1.40	1.56	2.70	3.55	2.21	1.63	0.57	0.75	1.62	1.48	1.70	1.26	20.41
Standard deviation	0.14	0.12	0.22	0.24	0.21	0.22	0.13	0.08	0.20	0.17	0.17	0.14	0.17
Average monthly	2.18	2.02	2.21	2.39	2.15	1.19	0.60	0.97	1.08	1.62	1.78	1.89	20.08
Standard deviation	0.18	0.18	0.18	0.20	0.21	0.15	0.11	0.14	0.15	0.18	0.17	0.16	0.17
High monthly total	5.90	5.26	5.26	5.69	5.56	4.76	2.33	4.76	3.26	5.59	4.30	5.72	5.90
Year of occurrence	1918	1907	1904	1963	1995	1963	1914	1945	1918	1916	1927	1924	1918
Low monthly total	0.00	0.17	0.20	0.28	0.02	0.00†	0.00†	0.00†	0.00†	0.00†	0.00†	0.08	0.00†
Year of occurrence	1961	1946	1956	1907	1934	1960	1963	1962	1932	1958	1939	1962	1939
Record high daily	2.60	1.44	1.55	2.37	1.93	2.01	1.67	2.24	2.42	2.73	1.46	1.60	2.73
Day of occurrence	14	2	14	23	28	21	20	29	30	1	16	19	1
Year of occurrence	1953	1905	1938	1957	1946	1948	1922	1916	1926	1916	1954	1913	1916
Days w/pcp >= .01	9.3	8.4	8.6	8.4	7.3	4.1	2.9	3.9	4.2	5.3	6.3	8.2	78.3
Days w/pcp >= .10	6.2	5.7	6.0	5.7	4.6	2.7	1.5	2.3	2.6	3.6	4.4	5.3	51.6
Days w/pcp >= .50	1.1	1.2	1.2	1.6	1.5	0.7	0.3	0.6	0.6	1.2	1.2	0.9	12.3

Snow and Sleet in Inches

	Jan	Feb	Mar	Apr	May	Jun	Jul	Aug	Sep	Oct	Nov	Dec	Annual
Monthly normal	5.1	7.0	14.4	0.6	1.6	0.0	0.0	0.0	0.0	1.7	3.0	6.4	39.7
Standard deviation	0.7	1.1	1.5	0.1	0.5	0.0	0.0	0.0	0.0	0.5	0.5	0.9	0.5
Average monthly	18.5	11.6	10.4	3.6	0.3	0.0	0.0	0.0	0.0	0.8	5.1	13.3	63.7
Standard deviation	1.6	1.3	1.2	0.9	0.2	0.0	0.0	0.0	0.0	0.4	0.8	1.4	0.7
High monthly total	56.9	33.9	46.0	28.0	7.0	1.9	0.0†	0.0†	0.0†	10.0	23.5	51.1	56.9
Year of occurrence	1918	1917	1952	1953	1964	1914	1963	1963	1963	1946	1906	1948	1918
Low monthly total	0.0†	0.0†	0.0†	0.0†	0.0†	0.0†	0.0†	0.0†	0.0†	0.0†	0.0†	0.0†	0.0†
Year of occurrence	1963	1963	1959	1964	1963	1995	1963	1963	1963	1963	1963	1962	1962
Record high daily	22.0	13.2	11.5	26.0	6.0	1.9	0.0†	0.0†	0.0†	10.0	11.4	16.0	26.0
Day of occurrence	20	3	11	9	2	6	31	31	30	29	24	19	9
Year of occurrence	1955	1915	1952	1953	1964	1914	1963	1963	1963	1946	1908	1913	1953
Days w/snow >= .1	6.6	4.5	3.4	1.2	0.2	0.0	0.0	0.0	0.0	0.2	2.0	4.7	23.4
Days w/snow >= 5	1.1	0.6	0.6	0.2	0.0	0.0	0.0	0.0	0.0	0.1	0.3	0.6	3.6
Days w/snow >= 10	0.1	0.0	0.0	0.0	0.0	0.0	0.0	0.0	0.0	0.0	0.0	0.1	0.4

Degree Days

	Jan	Feb	Mar	Apr	May	Jun	Jul	Aug	Sep	Oct	Nov	Dec	Annual
Heating normal	1140	853	790	470	191	71	0	3	84	293	713	945	5558
Heating average	1113	874	735	454	229	67	3	6	118	401	755	1037	5797
Cooling normal	0	0	0	1	28	140	348	356	77	11	0	0	964
Cooling average	0	0	0	1	23	114	309	246	59	2	0	0	757
Growing 40 normal	36	106	174	347	591	685	871	878	658	496	187	54	5089
Growing 40 average	37	80	199	362	554	688	852	818	621	425	175	50	4867
Growing 50 normal	3	30	69	189	387	491	700	706	476	322	73	8	3460
Growing 50 average	4	17	77	200	361	501	679	641	444	255	63	7	3253

† Also occurred on earlier date(s).

Location: Fillmore   County: Millard   Latitude: 38.950   Longitude: -112.317
Elevation: 5120 feet   Period of Record: 1898-1996

FILLMORE
Monthly Data Summary

Maximum Temperature in °F

	Jan	Feb	Mar	Apr	May	Jun	Jul	Aug	Sep	Oct	Nov	Dec	Annual
Monthly normal	39.4	46.1	54.1	62.8	72.9	83.9	91.6	89.1	80.1	67.4	51.9	40.2	65.0
Standard deviation	10.0	10.2	10.0	10.0	9.7	8.3	4.7	5.4	8.4	10.3	10.9	10.4	9.0
Average monthly	39.6	45.8	54.2	63.9	73.5	84.1	92.2	90.0	81.5	68.4	52.1	41.4	65.6
Standard deviation	10.0	9.9	9.7	10.3	9.7	8.7	5.4	5.5	8.3	10.4	11.2	10.3	9.1
High monthly average	53.0	54.4	66.1	74.1	83.6	92.0	99.1	97.5	90.1	78.2	61.9	54.4	99.1
Year of occurrence	1953	1995	1934	1898	1934	1974	1931	1898	1898	1952	1949	1939	1931
Low monthly average	23.7	35.6	45.7	55.0	65.3	76.4	87.4	82.3	73.2	59.1	41.0	28.3	23.7
Year of occurrence	1949	1949	1952	1975	1995	1995	1993	1968	1986	1969	1994	1930	1949
Record high daily	88	72†	78†	91	93†	104	107†	106	99†	89	90	70	107
Day of occurrence	17	25	28	26	3	14	23	12	4	9	7	10	23
Year of occurrence	1929	1986	1986	1898	1947	1974	1937	1898	1934	1954	1898	1939	1937
Record low daily	3	6†	28	34	37	50	70	66	45	25	17	-2	-2
Day of occurrence	22	8	27	11	7	4	10	30	18	29	22	23	23
Year of occurrence	1937	1989	1975	1991	1965	1936	1930	1932	1965	1971	1931	1990	1990
Days w/max >= 100	0.0	0.0	0.0	0.0	0.0	0.3	2.4	1.0	0.0	0.0	0.0	0.0	3.7
Days w/max >= 90	0.0	0.0	0.0	0.0	0.6	8.4	22.4	17.5	4.6	0.0	0.0	0.0	54.3
Days w/max <= 32	7.1	2.5	0.1	0.0	0.0	0.0	0.0	0.0	0.0	0.0	1.3	5.8	17.0

Minimum Temperature in °F

	Jan	Feb	Mar	Apr	May	Jun	Jul	Aug	Sep	Oct	Nov	Dec	Annual
Monthly normal	16.4	22.3	28.2	34.8	42.5	50.9	59.2	57.4	48.3	37.3	27.3	18.1	36.9
Standard deviation	10.9	9.8	8.7	8.4	8.1	8.1	5.5	6.0	8.8	8.2	8.8	10.6	8.5
Average monthly	17.3	22.3	28.7	35.8	43.2	51.6	59.9	58.6	49.5	38.2	26.8	19.5	37.6
Standard deviation	10.6	9.9	8.2	8.3	8.1	8.1	5.6	5.8	8.4	8.3	8.6	10.1	8.3
High monthly average	28.0	32.3	37.3	43.2	51.3	58.7	64.5	66.3	56.5	45.3	33.9	28.0	66.3
Year of occurrence	1953	1934	1986	1930	1934	1933	1933	1937	1937	1988	1965	1946	1937
Low monthly average	-0.3	9.3	16.5	26.1	31.7	43.3	50.4	50.5	38.7	21.8	18.7	7.8	-0.3
Year of occurrence	1949	1933	1898	1970	1898	1898	1898	1976	1898	1898	1898	1972	1949
Record high daily	44	81	52†	63	73	76	77	75†	71†	66	50†	45	81
Day of occurrence	13	8	19	22	27	27	24	30	14	18	3	4	8
Year of occurrence	1980	1930	1994	1939	1948	1970	1953	1981	1955	1942	1988	1946	1930
Record low daily	-23	-21	-6	12	0	23	32	35	19	1	-3	-19†	-23
Day of occurrence	9	10	2	2	14	4	2	23	18	30	24	23	9
Year of occurrence	1937	1933	1971	1975	1931	1898	1898	1968	1965	1971	1931	1990	1937
Days w/min <= 32	29.3	24.4	21.0	11.1	3.2	0.2	0.0	0.0	0.9	7.4	22.5	28.3	150.1
Days w/min <= 0	2.3	0.7	0.0	0.0	0.0	0.0	0.0	0.0	0.0	0.0	0.0	1.5	4.5
Days w/min <= -20	0.0	0.0	0.0	0.0	0.0	0.0	0.0	0.0	0.0	0.0	0.0	0.0	0.0

Mean Temperature in °F

	Jan	Feb	Mar	Apr	May	Jun	Jul	Aug	Sep	Oct	Nov	Dec	Annual
Monthly normal	27.9	34.2	41.1	48.8	57.7	67.4	75.4	73.3	64.2	52.3	39.6	29.2	50.9
Standard deviation	9.7	9.3	8.6	8.5	8.2	7.6	4.3	4.9	7.9	8.5	9.1	9.8	8.0
Average monthly	28.4	34.1	41.5	49.9	58.3	67.9	76.1	74.3	65.5	53.4	39.4	30.5	51.6
Standard deviation	9.7	9.2	8.2	8.6	8.3	7.7	4.6	4.8	7.6	8.5	9.1	9.5	8.0
High monthly average	40.5	42.6	50.7	57.9	67.5	74.8	81.4	81.0	70.7	60.4	46.1	40.4	81.4
Year of occurrence	1953	1934	1934	1934	1934	1933	1931	1937	1937	1952	1950	1939	1931
Low monthly average	11.7	22.7	34.2	41.8	50.2	61.8	71.0	67.6	58.2	44.6	31.3	18.2	11.7
Year of occurrence	1949	1933	1898	1975	1898	1995	1993	1968	1965	1969	1994	1930	1949

† Also occurred on earlier date(s).

FILLMORE
Monthly Data Summary

Precipitation in Inches

	Jan	Feb	Mar	Apr	May	Jun	Jul	Aug	Sep	Oct	Nov	Dec	Annual
Monthly normal	1.27	1.26	2.08	1.82	1.43	0.90	0.75	0.87	1.21	1.38	1.46	1.50	15.93
Standard deviation	0.13	0.13	0.17	0.17	0.15	0.14	0.09	0.09	0.16	0.15	0.16	0.15	0.14
Average monthly	1.36	1.42	1.92	1.61	1.45	0.80	0.73	0.89	0.86	1.26	1.38	1.29	14.97
Standard deviation	0.14	0.15	0.17	0.17	0.15	0.13	0.09	0.10	0.12	0.15	0.16	0.14	0.14
High monthly total	3.18	3.64	3.89	4.49	4.44	4.48	4.14	4.62	5.05	4.85	4.79	4.07	5.05
Year of occurrence	1974	1955	1945	1957	1898	1936	1936	1945	1982	1946	1983	1966	1982
Low monthly total	0.10	0.06	0.05	0.02	0.00†	0.00†	0.00†	0.02†	0.00†	0.00†	0.10	0.14	0.00†
Year of occurrence	1931	1970	1956	1898	1940	1979	1978	1980	1974	1995	1939	1980	1995
Record high daily	1.90	2.06	2.32	2.21	2.08	2.15	1.11	1.62	1.74	1.60	1.85	2.00	2.32
Day of occurrence	6	3	11	22	20	11	1	4	27	9	20	29	11
Year of occurrence	1937	1955	1940	1957	1975	1990	1980	1945	1982	1973	1947	1972	1940
Days w/pcp >= .01	6.4	6.9	7.8	6.6	6.1	3.5	4.4	5.4	4.2	5.2	5.2	5.9	68.5
Days w/pcp >= .10	3.9	4.1	5.0	4.1	3.6	2.0	2.1	2.9	2.4	3.2	3.2	3.7	40.5
Days w/pcp >= .50	0.8	0.6	1.1	0.8	0.9	0.4	0.3	0.3	0.4	0.8	1.0	0.7	8.0

Snow and Sleet in Inches

	Jan	Feb	Mar	Apr	May	Jun	Jul	Aug	Sep	Oct	Nov	Dec	Annual
Monthly normal	14.9	11.7	16.6	8.2	3.0	0.1	0.0	0.0	0.6	2.8	11.2	16.1	85.1
Standard deviation	1.5	1.4	1.7	1.1	1.0	0.1	0.0	0.0	0.4	0.7	1.5	1.8	0.9
Average monthly	15.5	12.6	13.9	6.5	2.1	0.1	0.0	0.0	0.3	2.1	9.7	13.0	75.7
Standard deviation	1.6	1.6	1.7	1.1	0.7	0.1	0.0	0.0	0.3	0.6	1.4	1.6	0.9
High monthly total	42.3	40.0	42.9	25.8	31.6	4.0	0.0†	0.0†	11.0	32.7	36.5	43.5	43.5
Year of occurrence	1974	1959	1973	1972	1975	1990	1995	1995	1965	1971	1983	1972	1972
Low monthly total	0.0	0.0†	0.0†	0.0†	0.0†	0.0†	0.0†	0.0†	0.0†	0.0†	0.0†	0.0†	0.0†
Year of occurrence	1956	1970	1993	1993	1994	1995	1995	1995	1995	1995	1995	1986	1986
Record high daily	22.0	16.0	23.0	14.0	21.8	4.0	0.0†	0.0†	11.0	12.0	16.0	21.0	23.0
Day of occurrence	6	3	11	10	20	1	31	31	17	28	18	23	11
Year of occurrence	1937	1955	1940	1945	1975	1990	1995	1995	1965	1971	1941	1987	1940
Days w/snow >= .1	4.7	3.9	3.8	1.9	0.5	0.0	0.0	0.0	0.0	0.7	2.7	3.9	22.4
Days w/snow >= 5	1.2	0.8	1.0	0.5	0.2	0.0	0.0	0.0	0.0	0.1	0.7	0.8	5.6
Days w/snow >= 10	0.1	0.2	0.2	0.0	0.0	0.0	0.0	0.0	0.0	0.0	0.2	0.1	0.9

Degree Days

	Jan	Feb	Mar	Apr	May	Jun	Jul	Aug	Sep	Oct	Nov	Dec	Annual
Heating normal	1134	856	724	477	244	62	1	6	104	387	754	1103	5855
Heating average	1123	867	721	450	231	59	1	3	83	360	761	1066	5730
Cooling normal	0	0	0	1	20	134	318	258	80	3	0	0	817
Cooling average	0	0	0	2	25	144	341	290	98	4	0	0	908
Growing 40 normal	56	109	222	356	544	698	858	829	647	441	191	63	5020
Growing 40 average	56	106	225	376	560	710	876	855	674	462	195	74	5175
Growing 50 normal	9	33	98	200	361	524	687	654	469	273	82	12	3406
Growing 50 average	10	30	98	217	372	534	703	679	496	290	85	16	3536

† Also occurred on earlier date(s).

Location: Flaming Gorge   County: Daggett   Latitude: 40.933   Longitude: -109.417
Elevation: 6270 feet   Period of Record: 1957-1995

FLAMING GORGE
Monthly Data Summary

Maximum Temperature in °F

	Jan	Feb	Mar	Apr	May	Jun	Jul	Aug	Sep	Oct	Nov	Dec	Annual
Monthly normal	34.6	39.7	46.0	56.3	67.3	77.8	85.6	83.3	73.9	61.7	45.4	35.4	58.9
Standard deviation	9.9	9.4	9.7	10.6	9.6	9.0	5.1	5.7	9.1	10.7	10.4	9.9	9.1
Average monthly	34.7	39.5	46.4	56.4	67.3	77.9	85.3	83.3	74.2	61.8	45.2	36.0	59.0
Standard deviation	9.6	9.6	9.6	10.6	9.6	8.8	5.4	5.8	9.0	10.8	10.5	9.7	9.1
High monthly average	42.7	46.5†	55.4	65.7	74.8	85.4	90.1	87.5	80.6	70.5	53.2	46.6	90.1
Year of occurrence	1981	1995	1986	1989	1969	1977	1989	1969	1979	1988	1995	1980	1989
Low monthly average	22.9	29.1	38.9	48.1	58.4	70.4	80.5	76.5	64.9	49.7	36.6	27.9	22.9
Year of occurrence	1979	1960	1964	1975	1995	1967	1993	1968	1965	1969	1971	1978	1979
Record high daily	59	66	74	80†	88	96†	100	98	91	83	75	64	100
Day of occurrence	22	25	30	30	30	26	8	5	13	1	14	1	8
Year of occurrence	1981	1986	1966	1992	1994	1994	1989	1979	1990	1980	1967	1995	1989
Record low daily	2	3	15†	29	36	43	62	58	28	18	12	-9	-9
Day of occurrence	12	7	10	5	20	11	24	27	17	31	27	21	21
Year of occurrence	1963	1989	1969	1983	1959	1970	1993	1977	1965	1972	1976	1990	1990
Days w/max >= 100	0.0	0.0	0.0	0.0	0.0	0.0	0.0	0.0	0.0	0.0	0.0	0.0	0.0
Days w/max >= 90	0.0	0.0	0.0	0.0	0.0	2.1	7.0	4.2	0.1	0.0	0.0	0.0	13.6
Days w/max <= 32	11.9	6.3	2.3	0.2	0.0	0.0	0.0	0.0	0.1	0.3	3.6	10.6	36.5

Minimum Temperature in °F

	Jan	Feb	Mar	Apr	May	Jun	Jul	Aug	Sep	Oct	Nov	Dec	Annual
Monthly normal	8.7	12.8	19.9	28.0	35.5	43.2	50.4	48.0	39.5	30.1	20.6	11.3	29.0
Standard deviation	13.0	12.2	9.6	7.7	6.5	6.5	5.8	6.2	7.7	7.7	9.8	11.7	8.7
Average monthly	8.5	12.6	20.4	28.2	35.8	43.3	49.8	48.0	39.6	30.0	20.5	11.5	29.0
Standard deviation	12.7	12.2	9.5	7.6	6.4	6.4	5.9	6.2	7.9	7.7	10.1	11.5	8.7
High monthly average	18.0	20.1	25.9	32.1	39.2	47.7	52.8	54.0	44.8	36.1	27.1	20.3	54.0
Year of occurrence	1978	1963	1986	1962	1963	1988	1966	1963	1963	1963	1970	1980	1963
Low monthly average	-1.1	0.7	9.5	22.5	31.0	38.1	42.5	41.5	35.5	25.5	13.5	3.1	-1.1
Year of occurrence	1979	1993	1969	1982	1975	1975	1993	1987	1971	1970	1971	1990	1979
Record high daily	40	42	47†	57	55	65†	69	70	63	56	47	42	70
Day of occurrence	30	11	21	22	17	25	22	4	1	3	13	3	4
Year of occurrence	1965	1962	1995	1960	1988	1988	1963	1970	1960	1967	1995	1980	1970
Record low daily	-38	-31	-14	-2	14	26	30	26	11	-4	-13	-36	-38
Day of occurrence	12	5	10	1	1	3	4	26	18	30	26	22	12
Year of occurrence	1963	1982	1969	1958	1972	1990	1993	1992	1965	1971	1992	1990	1963
Days w/min <= 32	30.4	27.5	28.8	22.0	9.7	1.5	0.1	0.2	5.5	20.1	27.0	30.2	209.2
Days w/min <= 0	7.9	4.7	1.2	0.0	0.0	0.0	0.0	0.0	0.0	0.1	1.1	5.3	20.9
Days w/min <= -20	0.6	0.2	0.0	0.0	0.0	0.0	0.0	0.0	0.0	0.0	0.0	0.2	1.1

Mean Temperature in °F

	Jan	Feb	Mar	Apr	May	Jun	Jul	Aug	Sep	Oct	Nov	Dec	Annual
Monthly normal	21.6	26.2	32.9	42.2	51.4	60.5	68.0	65.6	56.7	45.9	33.0	23.4	44.0
Standard deviation	10.6	9.8	8.6	7.9	6.9	6.7	3.9	4.7	7.2	7.8	9.0	10.0	7.8
Average monthly	21.6	26.0	33.4	42.3	51.5	60.6	67.5	65.7	56.9	45.9	32.8	23.8	44.0
Standard deviation	10.3	9.9	8.4	7.9	6.9	6.6	4.3	4.7	7.2	7.8	9.2	9.7	7.7
High monthly average	28.4	33.3	40.6	48.8	56.7	66.3	70.8	69.3	61.9	52.8	38.4	33.4	70.8
Year of occurrence	1981	1963	1986	1989	1969	1988	1964	1969	1963	1963	1962	1980	1964
Low monthly average	10.9	15.0	24.4	36.4	46.5	54.9	61.5	60.4	50.4	38.1	25.1	16.9	10.9
Year of occurrence	1979	1993	1969	1970	1995	1975	1993	1968	1965	1969	1971	1978	1979

† Also occurred on earlier date(s).

FLAMING GORGE
Monthly Data Summary

Precipitation in Inches

	Jan	Feb	Mar	Apr	May	Jun	Jul	Aug	Sep	Oct	Nov	Dec	Annual
Monthly normal	0.43	0.52	1.07	1.63	1.58	1.21	1.20	1.12	1.07	1.20	0.77	0.70	12.50
Standard deviation	0.05	0.07	0.10	0.16	0.16	0.14	0.13	0.13	0.12	0.17	0.10	0.08	0.12
Average monthly	0.46	0.58	1.05	1.51	1.64	1.13	1.11	1.10	1.07	1.27	0.82	0.60	12.36
Standard deviation	0.06	0.07	0.10	0.15	0.16	0.13	0.12	0.13	0.12	0.17	0.10	0.07	0.12
High monthly total	1.46	1.86	2.51	4.08	4.20	3.73	2.60	2.85	4.02	4.84	2.61	2.38	4.84
Year of occurrence	1962	1959	1983	1986	1995	1970	1985	1978	1982	1994	1983	1964	1994
Low monthly total	0.07	0.05	0.20	0.17†	0.02	0.13	0.15	0.01	0.07	0.00†	0.03	0.02†	0.00
Year of occurrence	1961	1973	1966	1987	1974	1971	1971	1985	1979	1988	1976	1986	1988
Record high daily	0.89	0.98	1.17	1.93	2.05	1.77	1.29	2.17	1.72	3.37	1.47	0.80†	3.37
Day of occurrence	21	25	7	18	20	11	17	14	27	8	13	20	8
Year of occurrence	1962	1970	1983	1973	1975	1970	1974	1978	1982	1961	1978	1968	1961
Days w/pcp >= .01	4.9	5.3	7.3	7.6	8.3	7.0	7.1	7.2	6.8	5.4	5.3	5.4	79.4
Days w/pcp >= .10	1.6	2.0	3.7	4.1	4.6	2.9	3.6	3.1	3.2	3.1	2.8	1.9	37.4
Days w/pcp >= .50	0.0	0.2	0.3	0.8	0.7	0.6	0.4	0.4	0.4	0.7	0.2	0.2	5.2

Snow and Sleet in Inches

	Jan	Feb	Mar	Apr	May	Jun	Jul	Aug	Sep	Oct	Nov	Dec	Annual
Monthly normal	8.7	7.6	12.3	8.5	1.2	0.3	0.0	0.0	0.2	5.0	7.5	9.4	60.7
Standard deviation	1.0	1.1	1.3	1.4	0.4	0.2	0.0	0.0	0.2	1.4	1.1	1.2	0.8
Average monthly	9.4	8.7	10.9	7.4	1.1	0.3	0.0	0.0	0.1	4.4	7.9	8.8	58.9
Standard deviation	1.1	1.1	1.3	1.3	0.4	0.2	0.0	0.0	0.1	1.3	1.1	1.1	0.8
High monthly total	31.0	29.5	30.7	26.0	10.0	6.0	0.0†	0.0†	4.8	35.0	30.7	29.2	35.0
Year of occurrence	1993	1959	1977	1973	1988	1990	1995	1994	1984	1971	1983	1983	1971
Low monthly total	0.0†	0.0	0.0	0.0†	0.0†	0.0†	0.0†	0.0†	0.0†	0.0†	0.0†	0.0†	0.0†
Year of occurrence	1987	1964	1966	1995	1995	1995	1995	1994	1995	1992	1987	1986	1986
Record high daily	18.0	12.0†	18.0	22.5	8.0	6.0	0.0†	0.0†	4.8	24.0	12.0	14.2	24.0
Day of occurrence	21	5	10	18	2	1	31	31	24	8	3	15	8
Year of occurrence	1962	1976	1988	1973	1988	1990	1995	1994	1984	1961	1973	1983	1961
Days w/snow >= .1	4.5	4.0	4.8	2.2	0.4	0.1	0.0	0.0	0.1	1.1	3.1	4.0	24.1
Days w/snow >= 5	0.4	0.4	0.6	0.4	0.1	0.0	0.0	0.0	0.0	0.2	0.4	0.5	3.0
Days w/snow >= 10	0.1	0.1	0.1	0.1	0.0	0.0	0.0	0.0	0.0	0.1	0.1	0.1	0.6

Degree Days

	Jan	Feb	Mar	Apr	May	Jun	Jul	Aug	Sep	Oct	Nov	Dec	Annual
Heating normal	1343	1092	994	685	422	163	15	47	254	588	959	1287	7854
Heating average	1345	1098	980	681	417	160	22	47	250	589	964	1276	7835
Cooling normal	0	0	0	0	0	28	107	67	5	0	0	0	209
Cooling average	0	0	0	0	0	28	101	69	7	0	0	0	206
Growing 40 normal	25	49	116	252	431	570	731	693	522	345	113	29	3881
Growing 40 average	23	49	121	252	433	573	719	694	527	346	111	31	3883
Growing 50 normal	1	6	34	124	272	414	562	525	363	198	34	2	2540
Growing 50 average	1	6	36	124	272	418	552	525	367	199	33	2	2540

† Also occurred on earlier date(s).

Location: Green River Aviation   County: Emery   Latitude: 39.000   Longitude:-110.167
Elevation: 4070 feet   Period of Record: 1893-1996

GREEN RIVER AVIATION
Monthly Data Summary

Maximum Temperature in °F

	Jan	Feb	Mar	Apr	May	Jun	Jul	Aug	Sep	Oct	Nov	Dec	Annual
Monthly normal	36.9	47.7	58.6	69.2	79.3	90.6	96.7	93.6	84.1	70.7	54.6	41.0	68.6
Standard deviation	10.4	10.3	9.2	9.4	9.2	8.2	5.0	5.7	8.2	9.4	8.3	8.8	8.5
Average monthly	37.6	47.6	60.0	70.5	80.5	91.5	97.6	94.8	85.6	71.6	54.9	41.2	69.5
Standard deviation	10.3	10.3	9.1	9.4	9.1	8.2	5.5	5.9	8.0	9.3	8.5	8.8	8.5
High monthly average	59.0	64.8	77.6	79.0†	90.5	100.1	103.5	100.7	94.8	87.5	67.0	51.9	103.5
Year of occurrence	1900	1907	1904	1992	1902	1902	1901	1901	1901	1903	1903	1980	1901
Low monthly average	20.5	30.9	50.9	61.8	63.8	83.6	89.3	87.2	75.7	61.5	47.0	24.8	20.5
Year of occurrence	1937	1955	1952	1975	1905	1967	1918	1968	1961	1969	1948	1909	1937
Record high daily	70	86	90	98	102	110†	112†	110†	103†	97	81	74	112
Day of occurrence	15	15	14	22	31	18	12	3	2	6	2	1	12
Year of occurrence	1900	1907	1904	1902	1910	1940	1939	1902	1947	1903	1899	1899	1939
Record low daily	-8	10	30	40	44	55	69	66	44	35	17	11†	-8
Day of occurrence	1	5	11	9	1	3	21	30	29	29	27	31	1
Year of occurrence	1919	1979	1979	1922	1915	1944	1991	1957	1900	1991	1919	1972	1919
Days w/max >= 100	0.0	0.0	0.0	0.0	0.1	4.8	12.4	6.8	0.4	0.0	0.0	0.0	24.4
Days w/max >= 90	0.0	0.0	0.0	0.3	4.9	19.7	28.6	25.8	10.4	0.3	0.0	0.0	89.7
Days w/max <= 32	9.8	2.3	0.0	0.0	0.0	0.0	0.0	0.0	0.0	0.0	0.2	4.7	17.3

Minimum Temperature in °F

	Jan	Feb	Mar	Apr	May	Jun	Jul	Aug	Sep	Oct	Nov	Dec	Annual
Monthly normal	8.7	17.8	27.6	35.6	45.0	52.9	60.5	57.9	47.3	35.4	23.9	13.5	35.5
Standard deviation	12.1	10.3	7.9	7.4	6.9	7.0	5.8	6.6	7.2	7.8	8.0	9.5	8.0
Average monthly	9.2	18.1	27.7	35.9	44.8	52.4	60.3	58.0	47.3	35.0	22.2	13.2	35.3
Standard deviation	12.3	11.2	7.9	7.7	6.9	7.0	6.1	6.4	7.7	7.9	8.3	10.1	8.3
High monthly average	23.9	44.5	37.5	42.5	50.0	62.9	66.9	63.5	53.0	43.7	30.8	23.8†	66.9
Year of occurrence	1907	1907	1904	1992	1984	1910	1910	1994	1933	1972	1928	1941	1910
Low monthly average	-10.9	-6.0	21.2	28.7	38.5	45.8	54.2	51.5	40.0	27.5	10.4	-2.7	-10.9
Year of occurrence	1919	1903	1956	1975	1918	1917	1958	1918	1912	1917	1894	1909	1919
Record high daily	40†	62	54	61†	71	76†	80†	85	73	68	55	44	85
Day of occurrence	22	15	26	22	31	29	20	3	7	12	16	14	3
Year of occurrence	1943	1907	1910	1994	1910	1970	1906	1985	1931	1910	1907	1893	1985
Record low daily	-42	-32	4	9	23	30	40	37	25†	10	-6	-23†	-42
Day of occurrence	22	8	18	2	6	1	6	27	21	31	28	16	22
Year of occurrence	1937	1933	1923	1936	1975	1923	1982	1992	1978	1935	1976	1931	1937
Days w/min <= 32	30.5	26.5	22.7	9.8	1.2	0.0	0.0	0.0	0.9	12.2	26.6	30.2	161.9
Days w/min <= 0	7.8	2.1	0.0	0.0	0.0	0.0	0.0	0.0	0.0	0.0	0.1	2.9	13.2
Days w/min <= -20	0.4	0.1	0.0	0.0	0.0	0.0	0.0	0.0	0.0	0.0	0.0	0.1	0.7

Mean Temperature in °F

	Jan	Feb	Mar	Apr	May	Jun	Jul	Aug	Sep	Oct	Nov	Dec	Annual
Monthly normal	22.8	32.7	43.1	52.4	62.1	71.7	78.6	75.8	65.7	53.1	39.2	27.2	52.0
Standard deviation	10.4	9.2	7.0	7.0	6.8	6.5	3.8	4.7	6.3	7.1	7.0	8.1	7.0
Average monthly	23.4	32.9	43.8	53.2	62.7	72.0	79.0	76.4	66.5	53.3	38.6	27.2	52.4
Standard deviation	10.4	9.7	7.0	7.1	6.7	6.4	4.3	4.7	6.3	6.9	6.9	8.3	7.1
High monthly average	39.0	54.7	57.5	60.7	68.5	79.7	83.2	81.5	71.8	59.3	45.1	36.1	83.2
Year of occurrence	1907	1907	1904	1992	1934	1903	1910	1901	1947	1903	1899	1893	1910
Low monthly average	4.9	13.5	36.6	45.3	55.3	65.8	72.5	69.7	59.1	47.2	31.6	11.0	4.9
Year of occurrence	1919	1955	1917	1975	1905	1975	1918	1918	1912	1899	1938	1909	1919

† Also occurred on earlier date(s).

GREEN RIVER AVIATION
Monthly Data Summary

Precipitation in Inches

	Jan	Feb	Mar	Apr	May	Jun	Jul	Aug	Sep	Oct	Nov	Dec	Annual
Monthly normal	0.40	0.32	0.59	0.50	0.61	0.41	0.57	0.74	0.71	0.87	0.41	0.39	6.52
Standard deviation	0.05	0.05	0.07	0.07	0.09	0.06	0.08	0.10	0.10	0.11	0.06	0.06	0.08
Average monthly	0.41	0.39	0.48	0.48	0.58	0.33	0.48	0.80	0.64	0.77	0.44	0.37	6.16
Standard deviation	0.06	0.06	0.07	0.07	0.08	0.06	0.07	0.11	0.10	0.11	0.08	0.05	0.08
High monthly total	1.79	1.42	2.55	3.50	2.12	2.94	2.75	3.40	3.41	4.39	2.38	1.37	4.39
Year of occurrence	1993	1993	1979*	1906	1973	1914	1986	1921	1961	1972	1902	1915	1972
Low monthly total	0.00†	0.00†	0.00†	0.00†	0.00†	0.00†	0.00†	0.00	0.00†	0.00†	0.00†	0.00†	0.00†
Year of occurrence	1981	1974	1974	1982	1974	1978	1917	1975	1995	1964	1989	1989	1989
Record high daily	0.75	0.65	0.84	1.00†	1.23	2.11	1.13	2.00	1.90	2.28	1.78	0.80	2.28
Day of occurrence	23	16	28	7	6	30	11	2	13	10	22	7	10
Year of occurrence	1921	1926	1979	1906	1973	1940	1936	1919	1927	1916	1902	1926	1916
Days w/pcp >= .01	3.2	3.2	3.7	3.4	3.5	2.3	3.9	4.6	3.7	3.7	2.5	3.1	41.0
Days w/pcp >= .10	1.5	1.5	1.5	1.5	1.9	1.0	1.6	2.2	1.8	2.0	1.2	1.3	19.0
Days w/pcp >= .50	0.1	0.0	0.1	0.1	0.2	0.1	0.1	0.4	0.3	0.5	0.2	0.1	2.3

Snow and Sleet in Inches

	Jan	Feb	Mar	Apr	May	Jun	Jul	Aug	Sep	Oct	Nov	Dec	Annual
Monthly normal	5.4	0.8	0.6	0.0	0.0	0.0	0.0	0.0	0.0	0.1	0.4	3.3	10.5
Standard deviation	0.8	0.3	0.3	0.0	0.0	0.0	0.0	0.0	0.0	0.1	0.2	0.6	0.2
Average monthly	3.8	1.0	0.3	0.0	0.1	0.0	0.0	0.0	0.0	0.0	0.5	2.7	8.5
Standard deviation	0.6	0.3	0.2	0.1	0.1	0.0	0.0	0.0	0.0	0.0	0.2	0.5	0.2
High monthly total	26.0	12.9	5.0†	2.5	2.5	0.0†	0.0†	0.0†	0.0†	2.0	6.8	13.0	26.0
Year of occurrence	1979	1901	1985	1921	1922	1995	1995	1995	1995	1971	1909	1984	1979
Low monthly total	0.0†	0.0†	0.0†	0.0†	0.0†	0.0†	0.0†	0.0†	0.0†	0.0†	0.0†	0.0†	0.0†
Year of occurrence	1994	1995	1994	1995	1995	1995	1995	1995	1995	1995	1995	1995	1995
Record high daily	7.0†	6.0	5.0†	2.5	2.5	0.0†	0.0†	0.0†	0.0†	2.0	4.9	8.0	8.0
Day of occurrence	17	4	28	5	10	30	31	31	30	29	20	28	28
Year of occurrence	1988	1989	1985	1921	1922	1995	1995	1995	1995	1971	1947	1972	1972
Days w/snow >= .1	2.0	0.7	0.2	0.0	0.0	0.0	0.0	0.0	0.0	0.0	0.2	1.5	4.0
Days w/snow >= 5	0.1	0.0	0.0	0.0	0.0	0.0	0.0	0.0	0.0	0.0	0.0	0.1	0.2
Days w/snow >= 10	0.0	0.0	0.0	0.0	0.0	0.0	0.0	0.0	0.0	0.0	0.0	0.0	0.0

Degree Days

	Jan	Feb	Mar	Apr	May	Jun	Jul	Aug	Sep	Oct	Nov	Dec	Annual
Heating normal	1307	911	679	379	134	16	0	0	65	371	771	1170	5809
Heating average	1287	907	656	355	122	16	0	0	56	365	792	1171	5733
Cooling normal	0	0	0	2	45	218	421	334	86	2	0	0	1111
Cooling average	0	0	0	2	50	225	432	353	100	2	0	0	1168
Growing 40 normal	43	130	291	442	622	745	891	850	656	477	221	63	5436
Growing 40 average	46	129	312	459	627	738	887	852	661	487	226	64	5493
Growing 50 normal	5	42	146	289	452	582	721	681	504	323	92	6	3848
Growing 50 average	6	41	164	308	466	579	716	683	519	336	97	8	3930

† Also occurred on earlier date(s).

Location: Grouse Creek   County: Box Elder   Latitude: 41.717   Longitude: -113.883

Elevation: 5320 feet   Period of Record: 1890-1995

GROUSE CREEK
Monthly Data Summary

Maximum Temperature in °F

	Jan	Feb	Mar	Apr	May	Jun	Jul	Aug	Sep	Oct	Nov	Dec	Annual
Monthly normal	34.7	40.5	46.9	57.5	67.3	77.0	87.7	86.0	75.6	63.1	47.6	35.5	59.9
Standard deviation	8.3	8.8	9.6	10.7	11.0	10.1	6.5	7.1	10.0	11.4	10.3	9.0	9.4
Average monthly	33.6	39.9	47.5	57.6	67.6	76.3	86.9	85.3	75.5	62.1	46.8	35.7	59.6
Standard deviation	9.7	9.2	9.5	11.0	11.0	11.4	8.2	8.6	10.6	12.5	10.7	9.7	10.2
High monthly average	43.3	49.9	56.8	67.2	76.7	84.6	92.4	92.4	84.2	73.2	57.0	45.1	92.4
Year of occurrence	1994	1963	1992	1987	1992	1961	1989	1969	1990	1988	1976	1980	1969
Low monthly average	14.9	27.1	36.1	42.5	56.4	46.6	60.7	55.5	47.8	33.0	25.5	14.2	14.2
Year of occurrence	1893	1892	1964	1892	1892	1890	1890	1890	1890	1890	1890	1891	1891
Record high daily	58	65†	75	84†	91	100	104	101	94†	86	86	63	104
Day of occurrence	20	26	31	26	12	25	21	3	13	4	4	2	21
Year of occurrence	1994	1995	1966	1977	1960	1988	1892	1992	1990	1963	1966	1995	1892
Record low daily	-5†	-8	20	27	35	32	44	46	34	24	11	-6†	-8
Day of occurrence	21	8	8	3	4	15	10	23	7	3	16	24	8
Year of occurrence	1893	1892	1964	1892	1892	1890	1890	1890	1890	1890	1890	1891	1892
Days w/max >= 100	0.0	0.0	0.0	0.0	0.0	0.0	0.3	0.1	0.0	0.0	0.0	0.0	0.4
Days w/max >= 90	0.0	0.0	0.0	0.0	0.1	2.9	12.8	10.0	1.1	0.0	0.0	0.0	26.7
Days w/max <= 32	12.3	5.4	1.5	0.2	0.0	0.0	0.0	0.0	0.0	0.6	2.6	10.0	32.7

Minimum Temperature in °F

	Jan	Feb	Mar	Apr	May	Jun	Jul	Aug	Sep	Oct	Nov	Dec	Annual
Monthly normal	9.0	15.2	22.0	27.1	35.5	42.8	49.6	46.9	38.2	28.4	20.6	10.3	28.8
Standard deviation	11.3	10.5	7.5	6.7	6.7	6.5	5.9	6.6	7.9	7.2	8.4	9.8	7.9
Average monthly	8.8	15.1	22.4	27.7	35.9	42.7	50.0	47.2	38.8	29.1	19.6	11.4	29.1
Standard deviation	11.2	10.8	7.7	6.8	6.7	6.6	7.1	6.7	7.7	7.3	9.2	9.7	8.1
High monthly average	17.9	24.8	28.8	33.2	40.5	48.1	64.4	52.8	47.4	35.9	26.0	21.4	64.4
Year of occurrence	1994	1963	1986	1990	1994	1961	1892	1961	1990	1963	1937	1890	1892
Low monthly average	-7.1	3.8	16.3	22.1	31.7	38.2	42.3	42.0	31.8	22.1	0.0	2.5	-7.1
Year of occurrence	1937	1984	1964	1970	1975	1975	1993	1974	1971	1970	1910	1990	1937
Record high daily	40	36†	41†	48	56†	63	94	68†	68	50	44	40	94
Day of occurrence	17	28	27	18	2	25	31	15	28	2	2	1	31
Year of occurrence	1982	1938	1990	1961	1939	1988	1892	1992	1938	1963	1987	1890	1892
Record low daily	-32	-18	-6	-5	15	6†	30	25	16	-1	-12	-25†	-32
Day of occurrence	21	5	1	2	5	21	1	31	29	31	25	30	21
Year of occurrence	1937	1982	1960	1936	1961	1938	1968	1965	1985	1935	1993	1990	1937
Days w/min <= 32	29.5	25.9	27.6	21.0	8.8	1.9	0.1	0.5	5.5	19.8	26.7	29.5	197.9
Days w/min <= 0	6.8	3.0	0.3	0.0	0.0	0.0	0.0	0.0	0.0	0.1	1.4	4.2	15.8
Days w/min <= -20	0.3	0.0	0.0	0.0	0.0	0.0	0.0	0.0	0.0	0.0	0.0	0.1	0.4

Mean Temperature in °F

	Jan	Feb	Mar	Apr	May	Jun	Jul	Aug	Sep	Oct	Nov	Dec	Annual
Monthly normal	21.9	27.9	34.5	42.4	51.6	59.9	68.6	66.4	57.1	45.8	34.5	22.8	44.4
Standard deviation	9.0	9.0	7.8	7.8	8.3	7.7	5.3	5.9	7.9	8.3	8.1	8.6	7.8
Average monthly	21.2	27.4	35.0	42.7	52.0	59.8	68.9	66.3	57.4	45.6	33.7	23.8	44.5
Standard deviation	9.4	9.1	7.7	8.0	8.1	7.8	6.0	6.3	7.9	8.5	8.2	8.2	7.9
High monthly average	30.6	37.3	42.6	49.2	58.3	66.3	75.0	71.5	65.8	53.7	40.0	31.4	75.0
Year of occurrence	1994	1963	1986	1992	1992	1961	1892	1967	1990	1988	1937	1980	1892
Low monthly average	7.1	17.1	26.2	34.5	44.9	53.6	60.5	52.5	45.0	32.5	24.9	15.1	7.1
Year of occurrence	1937	1984	1964	1892	1892	1892	1993	1890	1890	1890	1994	1985	1937

† Also occurred on earlier date(s).

GROUSE CREEK
Monthly Data Summary

Precipitation in Inches

	Jan	Feb	Mar	Apr	May	Jun	Jul	Aug	Sep	Oct	Nov	Dec	Annual
Monthly normal	0.96	0.85	0.80	0.85	1.29	1.34	0.85	0.75	0.71	0.84	1.10	1.03	11.36
Standard deviation	0.09	0.09	0.07	0.10	0.12	0.13	0.11	0.09	0.09	0.12	0.11	0.10	0.10
Average monthly	0.98	0.83	0.80	0.91	1.20	1.30	0.84	0.70	0.66	0.82	0.88	0.93	10.85
Standard deviation	0.09	0.09	0.08	0.10	0.11	0.13	0.12	0.09	0.10	0.11	0.10	0.09	0.10
High monthly total	2.32	2.49	2.42	2.86	4.25	4.52	3.80	2.45	3.73	4.32	2.62	3.51	4.52
Year of occurrence	1970	1986	1995	1991	1995	1913	1984	1968	1982	1972	1965	1983	1913
Low monthly total	0.15	0.00	0.00	0.00†	0.00	0.00†	0.00†	0.00†	0.00†	0.00†	0.00†	0.00†	0.00†
Year of occurrence	1992	1893	1893	1966	1893	1910	1963	1985	1987	1988	1959	1986	1986
Record high daily	1.01	1.37	1.39	0.96	1.19	1.15	1.95	1.36	2.15	1.86	1.15	0.70†	2.15
Day of occurrence	16	15	10	22	21	11	31	29	2	5	24	28	2
Year of occurrence	1893	1891	1891	1915	1985	1913	1960	1913	1960	1972	1965	1981	1960
Days w/pcp >= .01	6.2	5.9	6.3	6.1	7.2	6.4	4.4	4.5	3.6	3.8	5.3	5.4	66.1
Days w/pcp >= .10	3.6	3.0	2.9	2.7	3.7	3.7	2.3	2.0	1.8	2.3	2.9	3.4	35.0
Days w/pcp >= .50	0.3	0.2	0.1	0.4	0.5	0.7	0.3	0.3	0.3	0.3	0.3	0.3	4.0

Snow and Sleet in Inches

	Jan	Feb	Mar	Apr	May	Jun	Jul	Aug	Sep	Oct	Nov	Dec	Annual
Monthly normal	8.6	6.6	3.5	1.4	0.0	0.0	0.0	0.0	0.0	0.2	4.9	9.7	35.0
Standard deviation	1.0	0.9	0.6	0.5	0.0	0.0	0.0	0.0	0.0	0.1	0.8	1.0	0.4
Average monthly	9.7	7.0	3.0	1.6	0.2	0.1	0.0	0.0	0.0	0.2	3.5	8.7	34.0
Standard deviation	1.0	0.9	0.5	0.5	0.1	0.1	0.0	0.0	0.0	0.1	0.6	0.9	0.4
High monthly total	26.0	18.0	20.0	18.9	4.7	2.7	0.0†	0.0†	0.0†	3.0	30.0	53.0	53.0
Year of occurrence	1936	1993	1964	1912	1892	1914	1995	1995	1995	1984	1985	1983	1983
Low monthly total	0.0	0.0†	0.0†	0.0†	0.0†	0.0†	0.0†	0.0†	0.0†	0.0†	0.0†	0.0†	0.0†
Year of occurrence	1992	1992	1995	1995	1995	1994	1995	1995	1995	1995	1995	1995	1995
Record high daily	8.0	7.0†	8.0	10.0	4.7	2.7	0.0†	0.0†	0.0†	2.0†	10.5	8.0	10.5
Day of occurrence	20	13	22	23	5	5	31	31	30	17	20	24	20
Year of occurrence	1962	1986	1973	1964	1892	1914	1995	1995	1995	1984	1983	1983	1983
Days w/snow >= .1	4.5	3.5	1.5	0.7	0.1	0.1	0.0	0.0	0.0	0.2	1.8	3.8	15.4
Days w/snow >= 5	0.3	0.3	0.1	0.1	0.0	0.0	0.0	0.0	0.0	0.0	0.2	0.4	1.4
Days w/snow >= 10	0.0	0.0	0.0	0.0	0.0	0.0	0.0	0.0	0.0	0.0	0.0	0.0	0.0

Degree Days

	Jan	Feb	Mar	Apr	May	Jun	Jul	Aug	Sep	Oct	Nov	Dec	Annual
Heating normal	1235	962	895	616	389	165	24	50	226	551	838	1234	7190
Heating average	1289	1001	893	625	387	169	28	56	223	569	886	1224	7356
Cooling normal	0	0	0	0	1	28	129	89	13	0	0	0	263
Cooling average	0	0	0	0	1	29	143	95	13	0	0	0	283
Growing 40 normal	17	47	119	237	403	499	674	621	468	335	121	24	3571
Growing 40 average	16	45	128	246	416	507	697	638	484	328	120	26	3656
Growing 50 normal	1	7	37	121	259	354	525	488	342	205	43	0	2387
Growing 50 average	1	8	40	126	268	363	544	497	357	200	41	1	2452

† Also occurred on earlier date(s).

Location: Hanksville   County: Wayne   Latitude: 38.367   Longitude: -110.717
Elevation: 4310 feet   Period of Record: 1910-1996

HANKSVILLE
Monthly Data Summary

Maximum Temperature in °F

	Jan	Feb	Mar	Apr	May	Jun	Jul	Aug	Sep	Oct	Nov	Dec	Annual
Monthly normal	40.3	49.7	59.9	70.2	81.2	92.7	98.8	95.5	85.4	71.8	55.2	42.5	70.3
Standard deviation	9.9	9.3	10.3	10.4	9.9	8.9	5.9	6.5	9.2	10.2	9.4	8.6	9.0
Average monthly	40.0	49.1	60.0	70.4	80.8	92.0	97.6	94.2	85.6	72.0	55.7	43.2	70.0
Standard deviation	10.3	9.7	9.4	9.7	9.1	8.3	6.0	6.7	8.0	9.5	9.5	8.9	8.7
High monthly average	60.2	61.8	72.4	80.5	89.3	99.4	104.3	99.5	94.1	82.7	69.5	56.8	104.3
Year of occurrence	1943	1995	1934	1989	1925	1977	1989	1994	1979	1933	1927	1939	1989
Low monthly average	14.7	32.0	49.3	57.2	72.8	83.6	90.9	77.9	75.6	61.7	45.9	32.2	14.7
Year of occurrence	1919	1955	1913	1933	1933	1947	1914	1942	1932	1932	1947	1967	1919
Record high daily	69†	75	85	98	104	110†	114	110	105	95†	82†	70	114
Day of occurrence	26	27	10	19	29	26	8	5	14	1	3	4	8
Year of occurrence	1975	1918	1989	1989	1925	1994	1989	1979	1990	1978	1988	1995	1989
Record low daily	-10	16	30†	34	45	57	0	0	49	37	0	14	-10
Day of occurrence	1	1	1	3	3	8	31	31	18	30	30	26	1
Year of occurrence	1919	1949	1971	1934	1935	1984	1936	1912	1965	1971	1936	1924	1919
Days w/max >= 100	0.0	0.0	0.0	0.0	0.1	5.6	12.9	6.7	0.7	0.0	0.0	0.0	26.2
Days w/max >= 90	0.0	0.0	0.0	0.4	5.0	20.1	28.4	24.6	10.3	0.5	0.0	0.0	90.2
Days w/max <= 32	7.3	1.5	0.0	0.0	0.0	0.0	0.0	0.0	0.0	0.0	0.1	3.9	13.3

Minimum Temperature in °F

	Jan	Feb	Mar	Apr	May	Jun	Jul	Aug	Sep	Oct	Nov	Dec	Annual
Monthly normal	10.2	19.0	28.0	36.2	44.9	53.4	60.4	58.1	47.9	35.6	23.4	13.4	35.9
Standard deviation	12.3	10.7	8.3	8.1	7.7	7.7	6.2	6.9	8.4	8.9	9.0	9.8	8.7
Average monthly	9.9	18.9	27.7	35.7	44.3	52.8	60.0	57.0	47.7	35.4	22.3	13.8	35.5
Standard deviation	12.1	10.8	8.1	8.1	7.4	7.6	6.4	7.7	8.8	8.7	8.7	10.0	8.7
High monthly average	24.2	34.8	33.8	44.0	51.5	59.6	68.2	65.6	57.7	47.8	33.0	23.6	68.2
Year of occurrence	1980	1941	1967	1946	1954	1961	1954	1955	1944	1945	1965	1937	1954
Low monthly average	-15.9	0.5	17.1	26.5	35.5	44.1	51.7	34.7	23.0	25.0	12.2	2.9	-15.9
Year of occurrence	1919	1949	1917	1933	1916	1917	1918	1942	1945	1917	1979	1911	1919
Record high daily	41	49†	58	67	68†	76†	85	93	79†	68†	51	48	93
Day of occurrence	8	28	28	22	15	26	29	6	4	3	21	20	6
Year of occurrence	1962	1941	1967	1989	1974	1981	1945	1933	1944	1967	1966	1921	1933
Record low daily	-35†	-33	4	10	23	31	0	0	0	-6	-8	-24	-35
Day of occurrence	22	6	5	8	7	2	31	31	6	30	17	26	22
Year of occurrence	1937	1989	1977	1921	1968	1990	1936	1912	1945	1971	1964	1924	1937
Days w/min <= 32	30.3	26.0	22.7	10.6	1.8	0.1	0.0	0.3	1.1	11.6	26.7	29.9	162.9
Days w/min <= 0	6.5	1.6	0.0	0.0	0.0	0.0	0.0	0.0	0.0	0.0	0.3	2.7	11.5
Days w/min <= -20	0.4	0.1	0.0	0.0	0.0	0.0	0.0	0.0	0.0	0.0	0.0	0.1	0.6

Mean Temperature in °F

	Jan	Feb	Mar	Apr	May	Jun	Jul	Aug	Sep	Oct	Nov	Dec	Annual
Monthly normal	25.2	34.4	43.9	53.2	63.0	73.0	79.6	76.8	66.7	53.7	39.3	27.9	53.1
Standard deviation	10.2	8.8	7.6	7.6	7.3	6.9	4.1	4.8	7.0	7.7	8.0	8.1	7.3
Average monthly	25.0	34.0	43.8	53.1	62.5	72.4	78.8	75.6	66.7	53.7	39.0	28.5	52.8
Standard deviation	10.2	9.0	7.2	7.4	6.9	6.6	4.6	5.6	6.7	7.4	7.6	8.1	7.3
High monthly average	34.6	43.2	52.0	60.4	68.4	77.9	83.4	81.1	73.5	61.0	46.6	37.0	83.4
Year of occurrence	1943	1995	1934	1992	1925	1994	1954	1994	1944	1963	1927	1922	1954
Low monthly average	-0.6	17.0	35.0	41.9	54.4	67.4	72.7	56.1	55.1	44.6	30.6	18.2	-0.6
Year of occurrence	1919	1955	1913	1933	1916	1915	1918	1942	1945	1915	1979	1978	1919

† Also occurred on earlier date(s).

HANKSVILLE
Monthly Data Summary

Precipitation in Inches

	Jan	Feb	Mar	Apr	May	Jun	Jul	Aug	Sep	Oct	Nov	Dec	Annual
Monthly normal	0.38	0.22	0.51	0.42	0.49	0.30	0.53	0.73	0.74	0.68	0.38	0.31	5.69
Standard deviation	0.07	0.03	0.07	0.07	0.07	0.06	0.07	0.09	0.10	0.09	0.05	0.05	0.07
Average monthly	0.38	0.26	0.38	0.35	0.41	0.31	0.56	0.74	0.61	0.65	0.33	0.32	5.32
Standard deviation	0.08	0.04	0.06	0.06	0.07	0.06	0.09	0.10	0.09	0.10	0.06	0.05	0.07
High monthly total	3.74	1.50	2.64	2.38	3.11	1.85	2.92	2.96	2.73	3.58	1.67	1.65	3.74
Year of occurrence	1913	1927	1912	1957	1979	1914	1950	1952	1980	1972	1957	1918	1913
Low monthly total	0.00†	0.00†	0.00†	0.00†	0.00†	0.00†	0.00†	0.00†	0.00†	0.00†	0.00†	0.00†	0.00†
Year of occurrence	1972	1972	1994	1971	1974	1994	1952	1985	1992	1995	1995	1989	1989
Record high daily	2.00	0.83	1.15	0.78	1.35	1.00	1.74	1.80	1.20	1.25	1.10	0.75	2.00
Day of occurrence	3	28	22	6	24	1	8	14	10	2	14	18	3
Year of occurrence	1913	1927	1980	1942	1979	1914	1950	1952	1980	1933	1910	1937	1913
Days w/pcp >= .01	2.9	2.8	3.5	2.8	2.9	2.2	4.0	4.6	3.5	3.2	2.4	2.8	38.0
Days w/pcp >= .10	1.1	1.0	1.1	1.1	1.4	0.8	1.5	1.9	1.7	1.7	1.1	1.1	15.7
Days w/pcp >= .50	0.2	0.0	0.1	0.1	0.1	0.2	0.3	0.4	0.3	0.4	0.1	0.1	2.2

Snow and Sleet in Inches

	Jan	Feb	Mar	Apr	May	Jun	Jul	Aug	Sep	Oct	Nov	Dec	Annual
Monthly normal	0.7	1.0	1.1	0.1	0.0	0.0	0.0	0.0	0.0	0.3	0.7	1.8	5.7
Standard deviation	0.2	0.4	0.4	0.1	0.0	0.0	0.0	0.0	0.0	0.3	0.3	0.4	0.2
Average monthly	2.1	1.4	0.6	0.1	0.0	0.0	0.0	0.0	0.0	0.2	1.0	2.2	7.5
Standard deviation	0.4	0.4	0.2	0.1	0.0	0.0	0.0	0.0	0.0	0.2	0.3	0.4	0.2
High monthly total	13.8	11.5	8.2	4.0	2.0	0.0†	0.0†	0.0†	0.0†	7.0	12.5	17.0	17.0
Year of occurrence	1930	1911	1970	1983	1922	1995	1995	1995	1995	1971	1947	1967	1967
Low monthly total	0.0†	0.0†	0.0†	0.0†	0.0†	0.0†	0.0†	0.0†	0.0†	0.0†	0.0†	0.0†	0.0†
Year of occurrence	1994	1995	1994	1995	1995	1995	1995	1995	1995	1995	1995	1995	1995
Record high daily	8.0	7.4	6.0	4.0	2.0	0.0†	0.0†	0.0†	0.0†	7.0	6.0	8.0	8.0†
Day of occurrence	17	4	3	5	10	30	31	31	30	29	29	14	14
Year of occurrence	1933	1989	1964	1983	1922	1995	1995	1995	1995	1971	1954	1967	1967
Days w/snow >= .1	1.3	0.7	0.4	0.1	0.0	0.0	0.0	0.0	0.0	0.1	0.5	1.3	4.2
Days w/snow >= 5	0.1	0.1	0.0	0.0	0.0	0.0	0.0	0.0	0.0	0.0	0.0	0.0	0.2
Days w/snow >= 10	0.0	0.0	0.0	0.0	0.0	0.0	0.0	0.0	0.0	0.0	0.0	0.0	0.0

Degree Days

	Jan	Feb	Mar	Apr	May	Jun	Jul	Aug	Sep	Oct	Nov	Dec	Annual
Heating normal	1232	863	653	359	123	15	0	1	63	354	768	1149	5584
Heating average	1237	873	654	358	125	15	0	5	56	353	776	1126	5585
Cooling normal	0	0	0	4	62	256	450	366	112	5	0	0	1259
Cooling average	0	0	0	3	49	236	427	331	108	4	0	0	1163
Growing 40 normal	64	149	311	454	629	753	887	853	668	491	231	75	5571
Growing 40 average	62	143	312	454	618	742	880	831	673	490	238	82	5530
Growing 50 normal	11	50	167	303	472	593	716	684	517	340	103	11	3973
Growing 50 average	11	48	166	305	466	586	710	665	524	339	109	16	3951

† Also occurred on earlier date(s).

Location: Heber   County: Wasatch   Latitude: 40.500   Longitude:-111.417
Elevation: 5630 feet   Period of Record: 1892-1996

HEBER
Monthly Data Summary

Maximum Temperature in °F

	Jan	Feb	Mar	Apr	May	Jun	Jul	Aug	Sep	Oct	Nov	Dec	Annual
Monthly normal	34.0	39.6	48.0	58.3	68.6	78.2	86.5	84.7	75.7	64.6	48.2	36.2	60.2
Standard deviation	9.5	9.1	9.6	9.9	9.5	8.6	4.9	5.6	8.5	10.3	10.9	10.1	8.9
Average monthly	34.5	39.1	48.0	59.5	69.2	79.0	87.1	85.5	76.9	65.2	49.3	37.0	60.9
Standard deviation	9.1	8.9	9.3	10.1	9.6	8.8	5.4	5.5	8.4	10.1	10.9	9.7	8.8
High monthly average	46.3	51.6	61.5	70.6	80.6	88.9	94.8	91.0	82.9	75.5	59.8	48.3	94.8
Year of occurrence	1961	1934	1934	1934	1934	1918	1931	1940	1990	1933	1939	1939	1931
Low monthly average	20.8	24.7	37.6	51.1	61.7	70.1	82.1	77.5	67.2	54.2	36.8	26.1	20.8
Year of occurrence	1949	1894	1917	1975	1938	1945	1986	1968	1965	1984	1957	1909	1949
Record high daily	60†	68	74	86	91	100	105	101	97	88†	77	68	105
Day of occurrence	18	24	9	25	28	13	23	13	3	1	3	1	23
Year of occurrence	1921	1995	1972	1895	1896	1918	1931	1940	1950	1992	1924	1995	1931
Record low daily	-2	-10	22†	32†	38	46	60†	60	37	25	10†	-2†	-10
Day of occurrence	7	6	1	4	5	9	2	30	17	29	29	24	6
Year of occurrence	1913	1899	1971	1983	1938	1941	1921	1908	1965	1971	1896	1990	1899
Days w/max >= 100	0.0	0.0	0.0	0.0	0.0	0.0	0.2	0.0	0.0	0.0	0.0	0.0	0.2
Days w/max >= 90	0.0	0.0	0.0	0.0	0.0	3.1	11.3	7.8	1.0	0.0	0.0	0.0	23.5
Days w/max <= 32	12.0	5.7	1.1	0.0	0.0	0.0	0.0	0.0	0.0	0.0	1.9	9.7	30.8

Minimum Temperature in °F

	Jan	Feb	Mar	Apr	May	Jun	Jul	Aug	Sep	Oct	Nov	Dec	Annual
Monthly normal	8.5	13.0	21.9	28.6	35.3	41.7	48.3	46.6	38.2	29.3	21.6	11.7	28.7
Standard deviation	13.2	12.4	8.8	6.9	6.4	6.0	5.6	6.3	7.4	7.2	9.1	12.0	8.4
Average monthly	8.1	12.4	21.4	28.6	35.2	40.6	46.7	45.3	37.0	28.6	20.2	11.6	28.0
Standard deviation	13.8	13.3	9.3	6.9	6.2	6.0	6.0	6.5	7.6	7.4	9.4	12.5	8.7
High monthly average	20.4	26.4	29.0	33.8	39.6	45.7	51.3	51.6	45.1	35.0	27.0	23.1	51.6
Year of occurrence	1956	1934	1986	1989	1992	1988	1990	1983	1990	1972	1970	1917	1983
Low monthly average	-10.0	-5.2	8.9	24.0	30.1	35.2	39.8	39.4	30.6	23.7	9.6	-1.5	-10.0
Year of occurrence	1949	1903	1917	1970	1950	1950	1902	1950	1901	1905	1930	1930	1949
Record high daily	38†	40†	49	54†	60†	66	73	68	68	55†	45†	44	73
Day of occurrence	5	28	21	18	28	4	24	7	16	12	17	24	24
Year of occurrence	1956	1908	1995	1987	1919	1939	1929	1908	1925	1995	1986	1955	1929
Record low daily	-35	-38	-17	0†	15†	25†	27	24	12	6†	-21	-34†	-38
Day of occurrence	2	6	8	4	1	9	3	31	25	30	16	23	6
Year of occurrence	1952	1899	1964	1917	1972	1936	1921	1908	1926	1971	1955	1990	1899
Days w/min <= 32	30.5	27.6	28.6	22.0	10.5	2.5	0.2	0.6	8.9	22.4	27.5	30.2	213.0
Days w/min <= 0	9.9	5.6	1.1	0.0	0.0	0.0	0.0	0.0	0.0	0.0	1.1	6.2	24.2
Days w/min <= -20	0.9	0.5	0.0	0.0	0.0	0.0	0.0	0.0	0.0	0.0	0.0	0.4	1.7

Mean Temperature in °F

	Jan	Feb	Mar	Apr	May	Jun	Jul	Aug	Sep	Oct	Nov	Dec	Annual
Monthly normal	21.3	26.3	35.0	43.5	52.0	59.9	67.4	65.6	56.9	47.0	34.9	24.0	44.5
Standard deviation	10.6	10.0	8.0	6.9	6.6	6.1	3.7	4.4	6.4	6.9	8.6	10.3	7.4
Average monthly	21.3	25.8	34.7	44.0	52.2	59.8	66.9	65.4	57.0	46.9	34.8	24.3	44.4
Standard deviation	10.7	10.2	8.1	7.0	6.5	6.0	4.1	4.3	6.1	6.6	8.6	10.2	7.4
High monthly average	31.8	39.0	44.2	51.5	58.9	66.9	70.6	70.5	64.0	52.4	41.5	35.6	70.6
Year of occurrence	1981	1934	1934	1992	1934	1918	1994	1994	1990	1963	1995	1917	1994
Low monthly average	5.4	10.7	23.3	37.7	46.1	53.9	62.4	60.8	50.5	40.1	25.3	13.0	5.4
Year of occurrence	1949	1903	1917	1970	1953	1945	1902	1899	1912	1899	1957	1898	1949

† Also occurred on earlier date(s).

HEBER
Monthly Data Summary

Precipitation in Inches

	Jan	Feb	Mar	Apr	May	Jun	Jul	Aug	Sep	Oct	Nov	Dec	Annual
Monthly normal	1.78	1.56	1.37	1.37	1.23	0.90	0.87	0.98	1.26	1.47	1.64	1.62	16.04
Standard deviation	0.18	0.16	0.12	0.12	0.11	0.11	0.10	0.11	0.13	0.16	0.15	0.14	0.13
Average monthly	1.91	1.74	1.61	1.32	1.32	0.80	0.80	1.02	1.06	1.42	1.46	1.66	16.11
Standard deviation	0.17	0.16	0.13	0.12	0.13	0.10	0.10	0.11	0.12	0.16	0.14	0.15	0.13
High monthly total	8.81	5.85	4.30	3.71	7.04	3.55	3.35	3.11	5.55	4.59	4.42	5.40	8.81
Year of occurrence	1909	1899	1920	1963	1898	1964	1896	1906	1982	1946	1900	1964	1909
Low monthly total	0.00	0.12	0.11	0.14	0.01	0.00†	0.00†	0.00†	0.00†	0.00	0.00†	0.00	0.00†
Year of occurrence	1961	1924	1893	1949	1974	1933	1978	1962	1946	1952	1976	1897	1897
Record high daily	2.20	2.00	1.60	1.10	3.00	1.42	1.66	1.38	1.50	3.00	1.62	2.00	3.00†
Day of occurrence	14	10	12	5	3	1	17	28	8	12	14	31	12
Year of occurrence	1909	1915	1906	1929	1898	1943	1932	1925	1894	1899	1955	1892	1899
Days w/pcp >= .01	9.4	8.4	8.9	7.7	7.2	4.7	5.0	5.9	5.6	5.7	6.6	8.0	83.3
Days w/pcp >= .10	5.6	5.1	5.2	4.5	4.2	2.5	2.5	3.2	3.2	3.7	4.3	5.0	49.1
Days w/pcp >= .50	0.9	1.0	0.8	0.5	0.5	0.3	0.3	0.5	0.5	0.9	0.7	0.8	7.8

Snow and Sleet in Inches

	Jan	Feb	Mar	Apr	May	Jun	Jul	Aug	Sep	Oct	Nov	Dec	Annual
Monthly normal	17.6	13.7	6.7	3.6	1.1	0.0	0.0	0.0	0.2	1.8	8.8	14.0	67.5
Standard deviation	1.8	1.7	0.8	0.5	0.4	0.0	0.0	0.0	0.1	0.5	1.1	1.3	0.7
Average monthly	18.3	15.4	8.6	3.3	0.8	0.0	0.0	0.0	0.1	1.2	7.4	14.2	69.3
Standard deviation	1.6	1.6	1.0	0.6	0.3	0.0	0.0	0.0	0.1	0.4	1.0	1.4	0.7
High monthly total	68.0	58.5	38.5	17.0	13.0	0.0†	0.0†	1.0	3.0†	12.0†	26.5	66.0	68.0
Year of occurrence	1993	1899	1952	1929	1950	1995	1995	1954	1982	1984	1994	1916	1993
Low monthly total	0.0†	0.0†	0.0†	0.0†	0.0†	0.0†	0.0†	0.0†	0.0†	0.0†	0.0†	0.0†	0.0†
Year of occurrence	1961	1957	1994	1988	1995	1995	1995	1995	1995	1994	1976	1976	1976
Record high daily	28.0	18.0†	13.0	8.0	8.0	0.0†	0.0†	1.0	3.0	9.0	15.0	20.0	28.0
Day of occurrence	29	3	12	5	20	30	31	5	20	17	19	31	29
Year of occurrence	1980	1989	1907	1929	1975	1995	1995	1954	1924	1984	1900	1892	1980
Days w/snow >= .1	6.8	5.4	3.6	1.5	0.3	0.0	0.0	0.0	0.0	0.6	2.9	5.1	26.6
Days w/snow >= 5	1.1	1.0	0.5	0.1	0.0	0.0	0.0	0.0	0.0	0.0	0.4	0.8	3.9
Days w/snow >= 10	0.1	0.2	0.0	0.0	0.0	0.0	0.0	0.0	0.0	0.0	0.0	0.1	0.4

Degree Days

	Jan	Feb	Mar	Apr	May	Jun	Jul	Aug	Sep	Oct	Nov	Dec	Annual
Heating normal	1356	1092	931	646	404	170	17	45	246	559	903	1272	7645
Heating average	1353	1107	937	628	397	172	26	46	245	560	906	1261	7644
Cooling normal	0	0	0	0	0	18	91	65	5	0	0	0	181
Cooling average	0	0	0	0	0	16	84	59	5	0	0	0	165
Growing 40 normal	21	45	139	277	446	558	702	677	528	383	145	36	3962
Growing 40 average	20	41	138	294	451	553	679	663	532	390	158	37	3961
Growing 50 normal	1	8	47	143	291	417	555	532	386	236	56	4	2680
Growing 50 average	1	5	45	158	300	426	549	535	403	243	62	5	2737

† Also occurred on earlier date(s).

Location: Ibapah   County: Tooele   Latitude: 40.033   Longitude: -113.983
Elevation: 5280 feet   Period of Record: 1903-1995

IBAPAH
Monthly Data Summary

Maximum Temperature in °F

	Jan	Feb	Mar	Apr	May	Jun	Jul	Aug	Sep	Oct	Nov	Dec	Annual
Monthly normal	41.5	47.2	54.0	62.2	72.0	81.9	92.0	89.7	80.2	67.6	52.5	42.5	65.3
Standard deviation	9.6	9.8	10.0	10.3	10.3	9.8	5.5	6.0	9.0	11.0	10.1	10.2	9.3
Average monthly	40.7	45.4	52.9	62.0	71.1	81.0	90.8	88.9	80.1	67.1	52.6	42.2	64.6
Standard deviation	9.7	9.7	9.9	10.4	10.4	9.9	6.1	6.2	9.0	10.6	10.5	10.2	9.4
High monthly average	52.2	58.6	64.9	72.1	81.0	90.3	96.2	95.7	87.4	78.5	62.2	55.3	96.2
Year of occurrence	1909	1995	1934	1992	1992	1974	1994	1994	1994	1988	1995	1917	1994
Low monthly average	23.1	31.9	41.4	50.4	58.5	61.8	78.7	74.6	68.3	53.6	38.9	31.1	23.1
Year of occurrence	1937	1923	1917	1920	1917	1907	1907	1908	1907	1919	1906	1930	1937
Record high daily	68	75	81	88†	94†	103†	106	103†	102	91	78†	73	106
Day of occurrence	10	26	29	28	19	24	21	8	13	3	1	1	21
Year of occurrence	1990	1986	1986	1992	1992	1974	1931	1994	1990	1987	1988	1995	1931
Record low daily	5	4	23	30	34	42†	64†	60†	0	21	16	4	0
Day of occurrence	22	3	28	1	6	3	5	30	1	21	22	31	1
Year of occurrence	1937	1923	1975	1908	1965	1908	1938	1908	1906	1906	1906	1923	1906
Days w/max >= 100	0.0	0.0	0.0	0.0	0.0	0.2	1.4	0.5	0.0	0.0	0.0	0.0	2.1
Days w/max >= 90	0.0	0.0	0.0	0.0	0.3	6.4	20.6	16.3	4.0	0.1	0.0	0.0	48.6
Days w/max <= 32	6.2	2.5	0.5	0.0	0.0	0.0	0.0	0.0	0.0	0.1	0.9	5.0	15.2

Minimum Temperature in °F

	Jan	Feb	Mar	Apr	May	Jun	Jul	Aug	Sep	Oct	Nov	Dec	Annual
Monthly normal	9.6	15.9	21.4	27.1	34.3	40.2	46.4	44.8	35.4	26.8	19.1	11.1	27.7
Standard deviation	12.3	10.7	8.2	7.3	7.0	6.4	6.5	6.9	7.9	8.0	8.6	11.1	8.4
Average monthly	9.6	15.6	21.6	27.6	34.1	39.7	46.7	45.2	35.8	26.8	17.9	10.6	27.6
Standard deviation	12.7	11.7	8.4	7.2	6.9	6.6	6.8	7.1	8.2	8.1	9.6	11.9	8.8
High monthly average	25.8	24.6	30.5	33.7	38.2	46.0	51.5	51.7	43.2	33.6	26.7	20.2	51.7
Year of occurrence	1953	1907	1928	1990	1962	1918	1925	1929	1929	1918	1927	1977	1929
Low monthly average	-8.1	-6.1	14.0	19.1	28.1	32.9	39.1	36.4	25.0	18.8	4.1	-4.5	-8.1
Year of occurrence	1937	1903	1964	1955	1916	1950	1993	1956	1971	1905	1956	1930	1937
Record high daily	44	40†	45	56	68	62†	82	65†	64	55†	46	51	82
Day of occurrence	29	17	18	19	29	21	23	19	5	12	30	16	23
Year of occurrence	1965	1986	1907	1929	1936	1994	1947	1957	1903	1968	1932	1939	1947
Record low daily	-39	-32	-10†	2†	8	20†	24	20	0	-3	-18	-38	-39
Day of occurrence	21	14	1	2	6	6	1	31	1	30	16	13	21
Year of occurrence	1937	1903	1930	1982	1965	1954	1968	1917	1906	1971	1955	1932	1937
Days w/min <= 32	30.4	27.5	28.7	22.6	12.9	4.1	0.4	1.0	10.8	24.1	28.2	30.0	222.5
Days w/min <= 0	7.2	3.2	0.5	0.0	0.0	0.0	0.0	0.0	0.0	0.0	1.3	5.8	18.3
Days w/min <= -20	0.7	0.2	0.0	0.0	0.0	0.0	0.0	0.0	0.0	0.0	0.0	0.4	1.4

Mean Temperature in °F

	Jan	Feb	Mar	Apr	May	Jun	Jul	Aug	Sep	Oct	Nov	Dec	Annual
Monthly normal	25.6	31.6	37.7	44.6	53.1	61.1	69.2	67.3	57.8	47.1	35.8	26.8	46.5
Standard deviation	9.9	9.3	8.0	7.5	7.7	7.0	4.7	5.2	7.2	8.0	8.2	9.6	7.7
Average monthly	25.1	30.5	37.3	44.8	52.6	60.4	68.8	67.1	58.0	47.0	35.3	26.4	46.1
Standard deviation	10.2	9.6	7.9	7.5	7.4	7.1	5.0	5.2	7.2	7.7	8.6	10.0	7.8
High monthly average	38.1	39.5	44.9	51.5	58.9	66.0	72.9	71.6	62.7	54.0	43.6	37.6	72.9
Year of occurrence	1953	1995	1986	1990	1934	1974	1933	1958	1960	1988	1927	1917	1933
Low monthly average	7.5	14.8	29.0	37.8	45.6	48.8	62.4	60.1	50.3	38.0	26.5	13.3	7.5
Year of occurrence	1937	1903	1917	1955	1917	1907	1993	1908	1971	1919	1956	1930	1937

† Also occurred on earlier date(s).

IBAPAH
Monthly Data Summary

Precipitation in Inches

	Jan	Feb	Mar	Apr	May	Jun	Jul	Aug	Sep	Oct	Nov	Dec	Annual
Monthly normal	0.53	0.61	0.96	1.08	1.32	1.13	0.79	0.83	0.91	0.93	0.51	0.48	10.06
Standard deviation	0.08	0.09	0.11	0.12	0.14	0.15	0.10	0.11	0.15	0.14	0.08	0.08	0.11
Average monthly	0.68	0.83	1.04	1.19	1.48	0.99	0.82	0.97	0.72	0.98	0.63	0.62	10.94
Standard deviation	0.09	0.10	0.12	0.12	0.15	0.14	0.10	0.12	0.11	0.13	0.09	0.08	0.11
High monthly total	2.51	3.76	3.52	4.81	4.16	4.16	2.58	4.10	5.85	3.27	3.81	2.08	5.85
Year of occurrence	1907	1908	1907	1941	1938	1941	1973	1930	1982	1981	1906	1926	1982
Low monthly total	0.00	0.00†	0.00†	0.00†	0.00†	0.00†	0.00†	0.00†	0.00†	0.00†	0.00†	0.00†	0.00†
Year of occurrence	1963	1988	1972	1970	1969	1986	1967	1981	1987	1995	1959	1986	1986
Record high daily	1.36	1.12	1.38	1.02	2.35	2.05	1.29	1.60	3.11	1.60†	1.23	0.95	3.11
Day of occurrence	6	12	4	19	2	13	11	20	27	5	23	17	27
Year of occurrence	1988	1908	1911	1941	1938	1967	1932	1906	1982	1962	1906	1970	1982
Days w/pcp >= .01	4.2	4.8	5.3	5.4	6.0	4.4	4.5	4.7	3.3	3.6	3.2	3.5	53.0
Days w/pcp >= .10	2.2	2.6	3.1	3.7	4.2	2.6	2.4	2.8	2.2	2.5	2.1	2.0	32.3
Days w/pcp >= .50	0.3	0.4	0.5	0.6	0.8	0.5	0.5	0.5	0.3	0.6	0.3	0.3	5.5

Snow and Sleet in Inches

	Jan	Feb	Mar	Apr	May	Jun	Jul	Aug	Sep	Oct	Nov	Dec	Annual
Monthly normal	6.5	5.8	7.3	4.3	1.6	0.0	0.0	0.0	0.1	1.1	3.0	5.6	35.2
Standard deviation	1.0	1.0	1.1	0.9	0.5	0.0	0.0	0.0	0.1	0.4	0.6	0.9	0.5
Average monthly	7.6	7.7	6.6	4.4	1.7	0.1	0.0	0.0	0.1	2.0	4.3	6.4	40.9
Standard deviation	1.0	1.1	1.0	0.9	0.5	0.1	0.0	0.0	0.1	0.6	0.8	0.9	0.6
High monthly total	25.0	28.2	27.8	26.1	28.0	4.0	0.0†	0.0†	3.0	17.5	21.0†	24.0	28.2
Year of occurrence	1993	1942	1920	1922	1975	1914	1995	1995	1982	1920	1922	1966	1942
Low monthly total	0.0†	0.0†	0.0†	0.0†	0.0†	0.0†	0.0†	0.0†	0.0†	0.0†	0.0†	0.0†	0.0†
Year of occurrence	1963	1995	1994	1995	1995	1995	1995	1995	1995	1995	1991	1991	1991
Record high daily	14.5	13.0	14.0†	15.0	10.0	4.0	0.0†	0.0†	3.0	14.0	13.0†	15.0	15.0†
Day of occurrence	6	26	3	20	3	6	31	31	30	24	17	26	26
Year of occurrence	1939	1930	1985	1932	1950	1914	1995	1995	1982	1954	1941	1966	1966
Days w/snow >= .1	3.4	3.3	2.8	1.3	0.5	0.0	0.0	0.0	0.1	0.7	1.8	2.7	18.1
Days w/snow >= 5	0.4	0.4	0.4	0.3	0.1	0.0	0.0	0.0	0.0	0.1	0.2	0.4	2.7
Days w/snow >= 10	0.0	0.0	0.1	0.0	0.0	0.0	0.0	0.0	0.0	0.0	0.0	0.0	0.3

Degree Days

	Jan	Feb	Mar	Apr	May	Jun	Jul	Aug	Sep	Oct	Nov	Dec	Annual
Heating normal	1221	942	845	610	372	154	16	36	229	553	876	1184	7044
Heating average	1235	974	859	604	385	167	20	37	225	558	891	1186	7148
Cooling normal	0	0	0	0	4	36	145	107	13	0	0	0	307
Cooling average	0	0	0	0	3	29	138	101	14	0	0	0	287
Growing 40 normal	72	120	221	330	478	561	678	660	539	418	194	83	4361
Growing 40 average	65	100	206	328	466	552	680	661	543	413	198	80	4296
Growing 50 normal	14	37	98	192	341	449	568	555	437	279	83	20	3077
Growing 50 average	12	27	87	190	327	442	563	550	438	270	87	19	3017

† Also occurred on earlier date(s).

Location: Kanab   County: Kane   Latitude: 37.050   Longitude: -112.533
Elevation: 4950 feet   Period of Record: 1899-1996

KANAB
Monthly Data Summary

Maximum Temperature in °F

	Jan	Feb	Mar	Apr	May	Jun	Jul	Aug	Sep	Oct	Nov	Dec	Annual
Monthly normal	48.1	53.5	58.7	67.0	77.0	87.5	92.5	89.8	82.7	72.7	58.9	49.5	69.8
Standard deviation	8.7	9.2	9.4	9.5	8.6	7.3	5.1	5.3	6.7	9.1	9.6	9.2	8.2
Average monthly	47.0	52.1	58.8	67.8	77.1	87.3	92.6	89.7	83.7	72.3	58.8	48.6	69.7
Standard deviation	8.7	9.4	9.1	9.4	8.6	7.6	5.7	7.8	7.3	9.0	9.2	8.9	8.4
High monthly average	58.8	63.4	70.5	76.5	85.4	93.8	97.7	97.7	91.2	83.2	68.7	60.2	97.7†
Year of occurrence	1986	1954	1972	1954	1984	1961	1959	1937	1956	1952	1949	1980	1937
Low monthly average	31.3	37.1	50.3	57.3	67.9	78.1	81.2	42.3	76.6	62.7	51.4†	38.7	31.3
Year of occurrence	1937	1903	1958	1975	1917	1907	1914	1907	1986	1912	1994	1920	1937
Record high daily	72	77	83	90	97†	107	108	106	103	94	81	74	108
Day of occurrence	31	26	31	30	29	22	5	12	6	1	4	10	5
Year of occurrence	1971	1986	1966	1981	1984	1954	1985	1937	1955	1980	1924	1950	1985
Record low daily	15	0	31	38	42	54	67	30	52	35	24	20	0
Day of occurrence	6	29	1	12	8	17	8	21	29	29	23	22	29
Year of occurrence	1913	1948	1971	1912	1930	1995	1992	1907	1905	1971	1931	1990	1948
Days w/max >= 100	0.0	0.0	0.0	0.0	0.0	1.0	2.9	1.2	0.1	0.0	0.0	0.0	5.4
Days w/max >= 90	0.0	0.0	0.0	0.0	1.4	12.3	22.8	17.3	6.7	0.3	0.0	0.0	61.6
Days w/max <= 32	1.3	0.6	0.0	0.0	0.0	0.0	0.0	0.0	0.0	0.0	0.1	1.0	3.1

Minimum Temperature in °F

	Jan	Feb	Mar	Apr	May	Jun	Jul	Aug	Sep	Oct	Nov	Dec	Annual
Monthly normal	22.4	26.4	30.4	35.5	43.2	51.3	58.5	57.1	49.6	40.0	30.5	23.4	39.0
Standard deviation	8.4	7.6	6.4	6.2	6.0	6.0	4.7	4.6	5.8	6.4	6.8	8.1	6.4
Average monthly	21.7	25.5	29.7	35.6	42.8	50.3	57.9	56.4	49.9	39.5	29.8	23.2	38.5
Standard deviation	8.9	8.3	7.1	6.9	6.9	7.2	6.0	7.4	6.8	7.2	7.4	8.4	7.4
High monthly average	29.5	33.5	35.9	41.4	48.7	57.3	67.9	62.3	58.5	45.1	38.0	29.7	67.9
Year of occurrence	1956	1957	1978	1926	1958	1961	1919	1961	1925	1958	1903	1980	1919
Low monthly average	4.8	13.1	12.7	23.0	29.2	38.1	46.0	11.8	37.2	28.1	18.4	12.8	4.8
Year of occurrence	1937	1949	1917	1917	1907	1917	1904	1907	1917	1905	1904	1904	1937
Record high daily	45	46†	59	58	70	80	86	80	75	68	58†	48	86
Day of occurrence	13	19	11	6	8	24	13	17	8	4	28	6	13
Year of occurrence	1980	1986	1916	1972	1916	1922	1925	1942	1903	1918	1903	1966	1925
Record low daily	-20	-12	1†	8	16	23	39	-15	24	9	-4	-11	-20
Day of occurrence	22	14	23	2	2	1	4	3	23	9	23	30	22
Year of occurrence	1937	1949	1917	1917	1904	1917	1904	1907	1917	1906	1931	1911	1937
Days w/min <= 32	27.7	22.2	19.7	9.3	2.4	0.3	0.0	0.4	0.2	4.8	18.6	27.1	133.3
Days w/min <= 0	0.7	0.4	0.0	0.0	0.0	0.0	0.0	0.1	0.0	0.0	0.0	0.5	1.7
Days w/min <= -20	0.0	0.0	0.0	0.0	0.0	0.0	0.0	0.0	0.0	0.0	0.0	0.0	0.0

Mean Temperature in °F

	Jan	Feb	Mar	Apr	May	Jun	Jul	Aug	Sep	Oct	Nov	Dec	Annual
Monthly normal	35.2	39.9	44.5	51.2	60.1	69.4	75.5	73.4	66.2	56.4	44.7	36.4	54.4
Standard deviation	7.4	7.2	6.8	7.0	6.7	6.0	3.8	4.0	5.4	6.8	7.1	7.5	6.3
Average monthly	34.4	38.7	44.2	51.7	60.0	68.9	75.3	73.0	66.8	55.9	44.3	36.0	54.1
Standard deviation	7.7	7.7	6.9	7.2	6.9	6.5	4.7	6.7	5.9	7.1	7.2	7.5	6.8
High monthly average	43.9	46.8	52.0	58.4	66.0	75.6	80.8	79.1	72.2	63.3	51.5	45.0	80.8
Year of occurrence	1986	1954	1972	1989	1984	1961	1919	1937	1937	1952	1949	1980	1919
Low monthly average	17.6	27.1	33.0	43.4	49.0	58.3	64.7	27.2	58.0	46.8	37.4	27.7	17.6
Year of occurrence	1937	1903	1917	1917	1917	1907	1914	1907	1906	1905	1905	1932	1937

† Also occurred on earlier date(s).

KANAB
Monthly Data Summary

Precipitation in Inches

	Jan	Feb	Mar	Apr	May	Jun	Jul	Aug	Sep	Oct	Nov	Dec	Annual
Monthly normal	1.50	1.32	1.60	0.92	0.72	0.32	1.01	1.49	0.94	0.98	1.27	1.24	13.31
Standard deviation	0.16	0.15	0.15	0.11	0.09	0.05	0.11	0.14	0.13	0.12	0.15	0.17	0.13
Average monthly	1.52	1.40	1.57	0.95	0.66	0.35	1.03	1.42	1.06	0.96	1.01	1.24	13.17
Standard deviation	0.16	0.16	0.17	0.12	0.09	0.07	0.12	0.14	0.15	0.13	0.14	0.15	0.13
High monthly total	7.45	5.77	8.50	4.51	2.81	1.96	4.23	3.75	7.26	3.98	4.68	7.15	8.50
Year of occurrence	1993	1980	1906	1926	1995	1914	1917	1963	1939	1972	1978	1966	1906
Low monthly total	0.00†	0.00†	0.00†	0.00†	0.00†	0.00†	0.00†	0.00	0.00†	0.00†	0.00†	0.00†	0.00†
Year of occurrence	1976	1972	1972	1989	1970	1989	1920	1900	1993	1995	1992	1989	1989
Record high daily	2.01	1.84	2.40	1.35	1.07	1.40	1.60	1.46	2.08	1.75	2.05	2.80	2.80
Day of occurrence	25	9	12	29	13	30	22	29	3	5	20	6	6
Year of occurrence	1969	1932	1906	1917	1965	1956	1904	1951	1958	1925	1902	1966	1966
Days w/pcp >= .01	5.5	5.4	6.5	4.7	3.9	2.2	5.8	6.7	4.5	3.7	3.9	4.9	58.5
Days w/pcp >= .10	3.9	3.5	3.9	2.6	2.0	1.1	2.8	3.8	2.5	2.3	2.4	3.2	34.5
Days w/pcp >= .50	0.9	0.9	0.9	0.5	0.3	0.1	0.6	0.8	0.7	0.7	0.7	0.8	8.0

Snow and Sleet in Inches

	Jan	Feb	Mar	Apr	May	Jun	Jul	Aug	Sep	Oct	Nov	Dec	Annual
Monthly normal	7.4	4.5	3.3	1.8	0.0	0.0	0.0	0.0	0.0	0.1	1.7	5.3	24.1
Standard deviation	1.1	0.8	0.6	0.5	0.0	0.0	0.0	0.0	0.0	0.1	0.5	0.8	0.4
Average monthly	7.6	3.8	2.6	1.1	0.0	0.0	0.0	0.1	0.0	0.2	1.3	5.3	22.1
Standard deviation	1.1	0.8	0.6	0.4	0.0	0.0	0.0	0.2	0.0	0.1	0.4	0.9	0.4
High monthly total	40.1	25.5	19.5	14.8	2.0	0.0†	0.0†	13.0	0.0†	4.0	16.0	27.0	40.1
Year of occurrence	1949	1917	1964	1975	1950	1995	1995	1907	1995	1991	1985	1936	1949
Low monthly total	0.0†	0.0†	0.0†	0.0†	0.0†	0.0†	0.0†	0.0†	0.0†	0.0†	0.0†	0.0†	0.0†
Year of occurrence	1976	1995	1993	1994	1995	1995	1995	1995	1995	1995	1995	1989	1989
Record high daily	15.0	14.0	11.0	9.0	2.0	0.0†	0.0†	12.0	0.0†	3.0	10.5	15.0	15.0†
Day of occurrence	4	19	4	1	4	30	31	1	30	19	12	31	31
Year of occurrence	1973	1917	1945	1975	1950	1995	1995	1907	1995	1920	1985	1936	1936
Days w/snow >= .1	2.7	1.4	1.2	0.5	0.0	0.0	0.0	0.0	0.0	0.1	0.6	1.9	8.5
Days w/snow >= 5	0.4	0.3	0.1	0.1	0.0	0.0	0.0	0.0	0.0	0.0	0.1	0.3	1.3
Days w/snow >= 10	0.1	0.0	0.0	0.0	0.0	0.0	0.0	0.0	0.0	0.0	0.0	0.0	0.2

Degree Days

	Jan	Feb	Mar	Apr	May	Jun	Jul	Aug	Sep	Oct	Nov	Dec	Annual
Heating normal	921	703	634	413	173	26	0	0	48	273	607	885	4688
Heating average	921	721	626	390	172	33	1	15	45	278	599	876	4683
Cooling normal	0	0	0	0	21	156	322	261	83	5	0	0	852
Cooling average	0	0	0	0	22	145	310	255	98	6	0	0	840
Growing 40 normal	138	194	292	410	586	718	849	837	689	519	287	160	5683
Growing 40 average	122	173	285	412	571	683	823	798	667	500	277	144	5460
Growing 50 normal	41	80	148	258	415	550	678	656	504	352	148	53	3889
Growing 50 average	33	67	145	262	406	528	656	628	497	336	141	46	3752

† Also occurred on earlier date(s).

Location: Laketown   County: Rich   Latitude: 41.817   Longitude: -111.317
Elevation: 5980 feet   Period of Record: 1910-1996

LAKETOWN
Monthly Data Summary

Maximum Temperature in °F

	Jan	Feb	Mar	Apr	May	Jun	Jul	Aug	Sep	Oct	Nov	Dec	Annual
Monthly normal	32.0	35.0	42.1	53.6	64.6	74.2	83.1	81.1	71.4	59.2	43.7	34.0	56.1
Standard deviation	9.5	9.5	8.8	9.9	9.4	8.8	4.8	5.6	8.8	10.0	9.1	8.7	8.6
Average monthly	31.7	34.5	41.7	53.9	65.3	74.6	83.2	81.4	72.1	59.3	43.6	34.5	56.3
Standard deviation	8.8	8.7	8.6	10.0	9.4	8.8	5.3	5.4	8.3	9.8	9.2	8.2	8.4
High monthly average	41.0	44.0	53.6	64.5	75.0	83.6	90.0	87.6	78.8	68.8	53.3	46.6	90.0
Year of occurrence	1953	1963	1934	1934	1934	1919	1919	1919	1979	1952	1937	1937	1919
Low monthly average	20.1	22.4	31.0	41.7	57.6	67.6	73.7	76.0	63.7	49.5	36.5	26.7	20.1
Year of occurrence	1949	1923	1922	1922	1930	1945	1993	1968	1965	1919	1922	1985	1949
Record high daily	59[†]	60[†]	69	80	95	96[†]	97[†]	98	90[†]	82[†]	69	63	98
Day of occurrence	9	24	29	21	28	25	27	13	1	2	13	10	13
Year of occurrence	1990	1986	1986	1994	1919	1988	1931	1940	1995	1992	1937	1939	1940
Record low daily	-10	-7	5	27[†]	37	48[†]	52	58[†]	35	21	9	-9	-10
Day of occurrence	12	1	1	1	6	2	1	24	17	29	16	21	12
Year of occurrence	1963	1985	1922	1975	1965	1955	1992	1989	1965	1971	1955	1990	1963
Days w/max >= 100	0.0	0.0	0.0	0.0	0.0	0.0	0.0	0.0	0.0	0.0	0.0	0.0	0.0
Days w/max >= 90	0.0	0.0	0.0	0.0	0.0	0.7	3.0	1.3	0.0	0.0	0.0	0.0	5.0
Days w/max <= 32	16.2	10.7	4.0	0.2	0.0	0.0	0.0	0.0	0.0	0.1	3.5	12.3	47.6

Minimum Temperature in °F

	Jan	Feb	Mar	Apr	May	Jun	Jul	Aug	Sep	Oct	Nov	Dec	Annual
Monthly normal	10.7	11.0	18.2	27.1	34.5	41.3	47.7	45.8	38.0	29.5	22.1	13.6	28.3
Standard deviation	13.0	12.7	10.4	6.8	6.1	6.1	5.8	6.3	7.2	6.8	8.1	10.2	8.3
Average monthly	10.2	10.8	18.3	27.5	35.0	40.9	47.2	45.6	37.9	29.8	21.5	14.3	28.2
Standard deviation	12.7	12.9	10.5	6.9	6.1	6.2	6.1	6.5	7.1	6.8	8.7	10.2	8.4
High monthly average	24.4	24.1	28.6	33.7	39.6	47.8	52.3	51.2	45.2	35.8	31.0	23.2	52.3
Year of occurrence	1953	1934	1934	1990	1992	1918	1988	1983	1990	1988	1927	1977	1988
Low monthly average	-9.5	-3.2	5.5	20.7	30.2	34.5	39.6	36.3	31.0	25.6	13.9	4.2	-9.5
Year of occurrence	1949	1952	1952	1963	1963	1962	1962	1962	1974	1961	1952	1990	1949
Record high daily	39	39[†]	44	50	64	66	68	64	62[†]	52	45	41	68
Day of occurrence	7	1	22	22	16	13	18	3	2	3	9	23	18
Year of occurrence	1923	1995	1910	1994	1934	1934	1925	1992	1995	1922	1934	1955	1925
Record low daily	-37[†]	-34	-21	-3	16	22	29	22	13	5[†]	-17	-27	-37
Day of occurrence	22	1	8	2	1	3	5	31	25	31	16	21	22
Year of occurrence	1962	1985	1964	1936	1972	1929	1932	1962	1926	1961	1955	1990	1962
Days w/min <= 32	30.1	27.6	29.3	22.9	10.9	2.5	0.2	0.6	6.6	20.6	27.2	29.8	209.6
Days w/min <= 0	6.7	6.4	2.2	0.0	0.0	0.0	0.0	0.0	0.0	0.0	0.5	2.7	18.7
Days w/min <= -20	0.6	0.5	0.0	0.0	0.0	0.0	0.0	0.0	0.0	0.0	0.0	0.1	1.3

Mean Temperature in °F

	Jan	Feb	Mar	Apr	May	Jun	Jul	Aug	Sep	Oct	Nov	Dec	Annual
Monthly normal	21.3	23.0	30.1	40.3	49.5	57.8	65.4	63.4	54.7	44.3	32.9	23.8	42.2
Standard deviation	10.7	10.6	8.9	7.3	6.7	6.5	4.2	4.7	6.9	7.3	7.7	8.9	7.5
Average monthly	20.9	22.6	30.0	40.7	50.1	57.7	65.2	63.5	55.0	44.6	32.5	24.4	42.3
Standard deviation	10.2	10.2	8.8	7.5	6.7	6.5	4.5	4.6	6.5	7.0	8.0	8.6	7.4
High monthly average	32.7	33.6	41.1	47.6	57.2	65.1	70.0	67.8	60.3	51.0	40.2	32.7	70.0
Year of occurrence	1953	1934	1934	1943	1934	1918	1919	1919	1990	1988	1995	1937	1919
Low monthly average	5.3	10.6	20.0	32.3	44.3	52.9	57.6	58.6	49.5[†]	38.0	26.9	16.0	5.3
Year of occurrence	1949	1923	1952	1922	1953	1963	1993	1962	1965	1919	1938	1990	1949

[†] Also occurred on earlier date(s).

LAKETOWN
Monthly Data Summary

Precipitation in Inches

	Jan	Feb	Mar	Apr	May	Jun	Jul	Aug	Sep	Oct	Nov	Dec	Annual
Monthly normal	0.93	0.85	0.98	1.15	1.18	1.11	0.71	0.82	1.17	1.11	1.06	1.14	12.20
Standard deviation	0.10	0.11	0.10	0.12	0.11	0.11	0.09	0.13	0.14	0.13	0.11	0.11	0.11
Average monthly	0.92	0.81	0.94	1.12	1.16	0.99	0.62	0.80	0.98	1.20	0.93	0.88	11.36
Standard deviation	0.09	0.09	0.09	0.11	0.11	0.12	0.08	0.11	0.11	0.13	0.10	0.09	0.10
High monthly total	3.81	4.25	2.94	2.74	3.16	4.91	2.22	5.13	4.65	3.81	3.60	5.36	5.36
Year of occurrence	1911	1986	1995	1972	1980	1995	1993	1983	1982	1919	1970	1964	1964
Low monthly total	0.05	0.00[†]	0.00[†]	0.00[†]	0.00[†]	0.00[†]	0.00[†]	0.00[†]	0.00[†]	0.00[†]	0.00[†]	0.00[†]	0.00[†]
Year of occurrence	1961	1991	1933	1987	1972	1994	1988	1985	1933	1988	1976	1986	1986
Record high daily	1.80	1.08	1.05	1.10[†]	1.54	1.90[†]	0.98	2.47	1.45	1.39	1.15	1.37[†]	2.47
Day of occurrence	13	17	19	15	11	9	8	18	6	23	24	23	18
Year of occurrence	1980	1986	1994	1967	1947	1995	1926	1977	1965	1991	1965	1964	1977
Days w/pcp >= .01	6.1	5.8	6.7	6.7	7.1	5.5	3.9	4.5	4.8	5.1	5.5	5.7	68.2
Days w/pcp >= .10	3.1	2.8	3.3	3.6	3.8	3.0	2.0	2.4	3.0	3.2	3.0	3.0	36.6
Days w/pcp >= .50	0.3	0.2	0.3	0.4	0.4	0.4	0.2	0.3	0.5	0.7	0.3	0.2	4.3

Snow and Sleet in Inches

	Jan	Feb	Mar	Apr	May	Jun	Jul	Aug	Sep	Oct	Nov	Dec	Annual
Monthly normal	7.9	6.4	6.7	3.9	0.5	0.0	0.0	0.0	0.5	1.8	5.2	9.9	42.8
Standard deviation	0.9	0.8	1.0	0.7	0.4	0.0	0.0	0.0	0.3	0.5	0.7	1.0	0.5
Average monthly	11.5	8.7	6.8	4.3	0.7	0.1	0.0	0.0	0.2	2.1	5.8	8.7	48.8
Standard deviation	2.4	1.0	0.9	0.7	0.4	0.0	0.0	0.0	0.2	0.6	0.8	1.0	0.7
High monthly total	115.5	38.5	28.0	20.0	18.4	2.0	0.0[†]	0.0[†]	6.0	24.0	23.2	30.0	115.5
Year of occurrence	1956	1936	1967	1967	1950	1943	1995	1995	1984	1919	1945	1921	1956
Low monthly total	0.0[†]	0.0[†]	0.0[†]	0.0[†]	0.0[†]	0.0[†]	0.0[†]	0.0[†]	0.0[†]	0.0[†]	0.0[†]	0.0[†]	0.0[†]
Year of occurrence	1984	1991	1992	1992	1995	1995	1995	1995	1995	1995	1981	1986	1986
Record high daily	106.0	15.0	14.0	9.0[†]	12.0	2.0	0.0[†]	0.0[†]	6.0	15.0	9.0	13.0	106.0
Day of occurrence	2	14	14	15	3	4	31	31	24	25	2	10	2
Year of occurrence	1956	1995	1967	1967	1950	1943	1995	1995	1984	1919	1994	1921	1956
Days w/snow >= .1	4.7	4.1	3.4	1.9	0.4	0.0	0.0	0.0	0.1	0.8	2.7	4.1	22.0
Days w/snow >= 5	0.4	0.3	0.2	0.2	0.0	0.0	0.0	0.0	0.0	0.1	0.2	0.3	1.8
Days w/snow >= 10	0.0	0.1	0.0	0.0	0.0	0.0	0.0	0.0	0.0	0.0	0.0	0.1	0.2

Degree Days

	Jan	Feb	Mar	Apr	May	Jun	Jul	Aug	Sep	Oct	Nov	Dec	Annual
Heating normal	1331	1164	1063	730	469	223	45	79	306	633	953	1247	8248
Heating average	1357	1189	1077	724	456	227	51	79	301	628	967	1245	8306
Cooling normal	0	0	0	0	0	10	56	32	2	0	0	0	102
Cooling average	0	0	0	0	0	11	57	33	2	0	0	0	105
Growing 40 normal	11	21	67	204	380	518	683	641	473	298	86	16	3404
Growing 40 average	10	16	65	211	396	522	679	651	489	302	86	18	3450
Growing 50 normal	0	1	14	88	226	358	519	477	316	159	20	0	2184
Growing 50 average	0	0	12	93	238	366	520	490	330	160	20	1	2236

[†] Also occurred on earlier date(s).

Location: Logan Radio KVNU   County: Cache   Latitude: 41.750   Longitude: -111.833
Elevation: 4500 feet   Period of Record: 1956-1995

LOGAN RADIO KVNU
Monthly Data Summary

Maximum Temperature in °F

	Jan	Feb	Mar	Apr	May	Jun	Jul	Aug	Sep	Oct	Nov	Dec	Annual
Monthly normal	30.8	37.1	47.5	58.7	69.1	79.4	89.3	87.6	76.6	63.8	46.3	33.6	60.0
Standard deviation	11.2	11.0	10.3	10.5	10.3	9.5	5.2	6.6	9.8	10.7	10.2	10.7	9.7
Average monthly	30.8	37.6	48.2	58.8	69.4	79.5	89.0	87.6	76.9	63.8	45.9	34.2	60.1
Standard deviation	10.9	10.9	10.2	10.3	10.3	9.4	5.8	6.5	9.6	10.6	10.4	10.5	9.6
High monthly average	40.1	50.5	57.7	67.3	78.7	86.4	95.0	92.3	83.6	72.0	53.0	43.5	95.0
Year of occurrence	1959	1963	1992	1992	1958	1961	1960	1981	1979	1988	1962	1958	1960
Low monthly average	21.8	24.1	35.3	49.7	62.5	72.6	77.8	80.7	67.7	54.3	36.2	22.2	21.8
Year of occurrence	1979	1985	1985	1975	1995	1993	1993	1968	1965	1984	1985	1985	1979
Record high daily	60	67	74	84†	92†	99	104	102	99	86†	71†	67	104
Day of occurrence	21	5	29	22	11	21	21	5	11	3	8	2	21
Year of occurrence	1967	1963	1986	1994	1960	1961	1960	1979	1958	1992	1980	1995	1960
Record low daily	-4	-5	19	31	37	49	57	59	42†	29†	10	-14	-14
Day of occurrence	10	1	9	2	11	3	2	22	19	29	27	24	24
Year of occurrence	1987	1985	1969	1975	1983	1980	1992	1968	1978	1971	1992	1990	1990
Days w/max >= 100	0.0	0.0	0.0	0.0	0.0	0.0	0.2	0.1	0.0	0.0	0.0	0.0	0.4
Days w/max >= 90	0.0	0.0	0.0	0.0	0.1	3.9	16.0	13.8	1.6	0.0	0.0	0.0	36.0
Days w/max <= 32	15.8	8.3	1.9	0.0	0.0	0.0	0.0	0.0	0.0	0.0	0.1	2.6	12.9	42.1

Minimum Temperature in °F

	Jan	Feb	Mar	Apr	May	Jun	Jul	Aug	Sep	Oct	Nov	Dec	Annual
Monthly normal	11.3	16.1	24.8	32.8	40.8	47.7	54.4	52.5	43.2	33.1	24.9	14.8	33.0
Standard deviation	13.8	13.0	9.2	6.4	6.8	6.3	5.3	6.4	7.0	6.7	7.7	11.3	8.3
Average monthly	11.4	16.8	25.5	33.0	41.0	47.7	53.9	52.4	43.1	33.0	24.1	14.8	33.1
Standard deviation	13.6	12.7	8.9	6.3	6.7	6.2	5.4	6.4	6.9	6.5	8.5	11.2	8.3
High monthly average	23.8	28.6	32.7	38.7	47.4	51.9	57.4	61.1	49.1	39.6	29.4	24.4	61.1
Year of occurrence	1983	1963	1986	1965	1963	1986	1984	1982	1990	1963	1970	1977	1982
Low monthly average	-1.3	0.3	12.2	28.4	34.9	43.1	46.6	45.1	38.5	27.9	15.2	3.5	-1.3
Year of occurrence	1979	1985	1985	1967	1975	1980	1993	1980	1970	1970	1993	1990	1979
Record high daily	41†	43	50	57	63	67	73	70†	65	58	49	42	73
Day of occurrence	24	24	11	17	27	17	30	9	2	5	14	22	30
Year of occurrence	1970	1986	1995	1985	1969	1974	1968	1983	1983	1963	1981	1964	1968
Record low daily	-25	-29	-12	10	20	29	39	34†	22†	6	-10†	-30	-30
Day of occurrence	7	2	5	28	24	16	2	31	25	30	27	23	23
Year of occurrence	1973	1985	1966	1967	1960	1981	1968	1965	1970	1971	1992	1990	1990
Days w/min <= 32	29.7	26.3	25.5	14.7	3.1	0.2	0.0	0.0	1.9	14.2	25.4	29.6	174.0
Days w/min <= 0	7.1	3.7	0.6	0.0	0.0	0.0	0.0	0.0	0.0	0.0	0.4	3.4	15.4
Days w/min <= -20	0.3	0.3	0.0	0.0	0.0	0.0	0.0	0.0	0.0	0.0	0.0	0.2	0.8

Mean Temperature in °F

	Jan	Feb	Mar	Apr	May	Jun	Jul	Aug	Sep	Oct	Nov	Dec	Annual
Monthly normal	21.1	26.6	36.1	45.7	55.0	63.6	71.9	70.0	59.9	48.5	35.6	24.2	46.5
Standard deviation	12.0	11.5	9.0	7.5	7.8	7.2	4.3	5.4	7.4	7.6	8.0	10.4	8.2
Average monthly	21.1	27.3	36.8	45.9	55.2	63.6	71.5	70.0	60.0	48.4	35.0	24.5	46.6
Standard deviation	11.7	11.3	8.8	7.4	7.7	7.1	4.7	5.5	7.2	7.5	8.5	10.2	8.1
High monthly average	31.1	39.6	44.8	52.2	62.4	68.9	75.2	75.4	65.7	55.0	40.9	33.5	75.4
Year of occurrence	1983	1963	1986	1992	1958	1977	1960	1982	1990	1963	1995	1958	1982
Low monthly average	10.3	12.2	23.8	39.1	48.7	58.3	62.2	65.8	53.5	42.5	27.6	14.0	10.3
Year of occurrence	1979	1985	1985	1975	1975	1975	1993	1980	1965	1984	1985	1990	1979

† Also occurred on earlier date(s).

LOGAN RADIO KVNU
Monthly Data Summary

Precipitation in Inches

	Jan	Feb	Mar	Apr	May	Jun	Jul	Aug	Sep	Oct	Nov	Dec	Annual
Monthly normal	1.01	1.24	1.59	1.80	1.73	1.48	0.74	0.93	1.59	1.63	1.45	1.27	16.47
Standard deviation	0.09	0.12	0.13	0.14	0.14	0.17	0.09	0.14	0.19	0.17	0.14	0.11	0.14
Average monthly	1.08	1.20	1.73	1.74	1.77	1.39	0.73	0.88	1.43	1.59	1.45	1.25	16.25
Standard deviation	0.09	0.11	0.14	0.14	0.14	0.16	0.09	0.13	0.17	0.17	0.14	0.11	0.13
High monthly total	3.45	3.60	3.74	5.16	4.34	4.46	2.20	4.76	5.38	4.09	5.40	4.71	5.40
Year of occurrence	1980	1986	1995	1986	1987	1964	1993	1977	1973	1981	1965	1983	1965
Low monthly total	0.11	0.11	0.03	0.19	0.01	0.06	0.00†	0.00	0.00	0.00†	0.03†	0.02	0.00†
Year of occurrence	1961	1964	1965	1977	1969	1977	1988	1985	1974	1988	1976	1986	1988
Record high daily	1.05	1.51	1.39	1.10	1.10	2.20	1.18	2.48	2.15	1.75	1.49	1.12	2.48
Day of occurrence	14	18	23	2	19	3	14	19	27	7	14	25	19
Year of occurrence	1980	1986	1994	1986	1957	1980	1962	1977	1982	1961	1958	1959	1977
Days w/pcp >= .01	8.8	8.4	9.1	9.7	9.4	6.3	4.2	4.9	6.2	6.2	8.4	8.6	92.3
Days w/pcp >= .10	3.7	3.9	5.1	5.4	5.1	3.6	2.1	2.5	3.5	3.8	4.4	4.1	48.2
Days w/pcp >= .50	0.2	0.4	0.8	0.7	0.7	0.7	0.3	0.5	0.8	1.0	0.6	0.4	7.2

Snow and Sleet in Inches

	Jan	Feb	Mar	Apr	May	Jun	Jul	Aug	Sep	Oct	Nov	Dec	Annual
Monthly normal	6.0	5.4	3.3	0.5	0.0	0.0	0.0	0.0	0.0	0.4	2.2	6.3	24.0
Standard deviation	0.8	1.0	0.6	0.2	0.0	0.0	0.0	0.0	0.0	0.2	0.5	0.8	0.3
Average monthly	7.3	4.8	3.2	0.8	0.0	0.0	0.0	0.0	0.0	0.4	2.4	6.3	25.3
Standard deviation	0.8	0.9	0.6	0.3	0.0	0.0	0.0	0.0	0.0	0.2	0.5	0.8	0.3
High monthly total	15.5	30.3	17.0	6.0	0.0†	0.0†	0.0†	0.0†	0.3	4.0	11.5	22.5	30.3
Year of occurrence	1960	1969	1976	1993	1995	1995	1995	1995	1978	1984	1975	1992	1969
Low monthly total	0.0†	0.0†	0.0†	0.0†	0.0†	0.0†	0.0†	0.0†	0.0†	0.0†	0.0†	0.0†	0.0†
Year of occurrence	1980	1986	1983	1995	1995	1995	1995	1995	1995	1993	1989	1995	1995
Record high daily	6.0†	8.0†	9.0†	6.0	0.0†	0.0†	0.0†	0.0†	0.3	4.0	6.0	8.0	9.0
Day of occurrence	6	2	23	13	31	30	31	31	18	27	23	23	23
Year of occurrence	1989	1989	1994	1993	1995	1995	1995	1995	1978	1984	1992	1987	1994
Days w/snow >= .1	4.0	2.1	1.5	0.5	0.0	0.0	0.0	0.0	0.0	0.3	1.3	3.1	10.8
Days w/snow >= 5	0.2	0.3	0.1	0.0	0.0	0.0	0.0	0.0	0.0	0.0	0.2	0.3	1.0
Days w/snow >= 10	0.0	0.0	0.0	0.0	0.0	0.0	0.0	0.0	0.0	0.0	0.0	0.0	0.0

Degree Days

	Jan	Feb	Mar	Apr	May	Jun	Jul	Aug	Sep	Oct	Nov	Dec	Annual
Heating normal	1348	1077	882	562	314	108	4	21	174	506	868	1249	7118
Heating average	1343	1057	863	556	308	105	8	22	172	508	885	1238	7070
Cooling normal	0	0	0	0	6	66	213	173	24	0	0	0	485
Cooling average	0	0	0	0	7	65	205	175	24	0	0	0	478
Growing 40 normal	15	40	136	279	477	624	779	747	556	368	118	25	4171
Growing 40 average	15	43	144	281	478	627	771	751	557	367	114	26	4180
Growing 50 normal	1	7	46	144	299	442	608	578	395	222	37	3	2786
Growing 50 average	0	7	50	145	300	444	599	581	399	221	36	3	2789

† Also occurred on earlier date(s).

Location: Manti   County: Sanpete   Latitude: 39.250   Longitude: -111.633
Elevation: 5740 feet   Period of Record: 1928-1996

MANTI
Monthly Data Summary

Maximum Temperature in °F

	Jan	Feb	Mar	Apr	May	Jun	Jul	Aug	Sep	Oct	Nov	Dec	Annual
Monthly normal	36.9	42.4	50.6	59.8	69.4	79.8	86.7	84.4	75.6	64.6	49.6	38.3	61.5
Standard deviation	9.3	9.2	9.8	9.9	9.5	8.2	4.7	5.3	8.3	10.1	10.5	9.8	8.7
Average monthly	36.8	41.8	50.8	60.6	69.8	79.7	86.6	84.6	76.6	65.0	49.4	39.1	61.7
Standard deviation	8.9	8.9	9.3	9.9	9.3	8.2	4.9	5.2	7.8	9.6	10.6	9.3	8.5
High monthly average	45.7	51.7	61.2	69.1	76.7	86.1	91.6	89.9	82.6	74.0	61.1	50.9	91.6
Year of occurrence	1981	1963	1934	1934	1969	1961	1960	1958	1979	1950	1949	1980	1960
Low monthly average	23.7	31.8	40.6	51.8	61.7	72.9	81.8	78.5	68.9	55.5	39.8	31.1	23.7
Year of occurrence	1937	1933	1952	1975	1995	1995	1993	1968	1965	1969	1994	1990	1937
Record high daily	63†	69	78	83†	90	99	103	99†	97	87	90	66	103
Day of occurrence	7	25	26	19	23	23	26	7	3	20	25	1	26
Year of occurrence	1969	1986	1956	1980	1967	1954	1960	1960	1950	1950	1934	1995	1960
Record low daily	0	4	24	10	38	52	61	52	0	24	17†	-1†	-1
Day of occurrence	22	6	4	15	5	24	5	11	25	29	24	23	23
Year of occurrence	1937	1989	1989	1935	1975	1969	1982	1943	1933	1971	1931	1990	1990
Days w/max >= 100	0.0	0.0	0.0	0.0	0.0	0.0	0.0	0.0	0.0	0.0	0.0	0.0	0.0
Days w/max >= 90	0.0	0.0	0.0	0.0	0.0	2.3	9.1	5.4	0.5	0.0	0.0	0.0	17.3
Days w/max <= 32	9.0	4.2	0.5	0.0	0.0	0.0	0.0	0.0	0.0	0.1	2.1	6.9	23.0

Minimum Temperature in °F

	Jan	Feb	Mar	Apr	May	Jun	Jul	Aug	Sep	Oct	Nov	Dec	Annual
Monthly normal	13.9	19.0	25.1	31.9	39.5	47.4	54.7	52.7	44.2	34.6	25.0	16.2	33.7
Standard deviation	10.8	9.7	7.9	7.1	6.6	6.6	4.6	5.2	7.1	6.7	8.4	10.1	7.6
Average monthly	14.2	18.7	25.3	32.3	39.4	46.8	53.9	52.6	44.3	34.6	24.0	16.9	33.6
Standard deviation	10.7	10.3	7.7	7.1	6.5	6.5	4.7	5.0	6.9	6.6	8.3	9.8	7.5
High monthly average	23.9	28.4	32.1	37.9	45.1	52.9	56.7	56.3	50.1	40.3	30.4	25.0	56.7
Year of occurrence	1956	1934	1978	1992	1934	1988	1990	1994	1990	1963	1965	1946	1990
Low monthly average	-1.3	4.5	16.0	26.3	34.3	41.2	48.8	47.1	39.5	30.6	16.7	8.0	-1.3
Year of occurrence	1937	1933	1964	1975	1975	1945	1944	1950	1945	1970	1956	1990	1937
Record high daily	40	46†	50	59	61	68†	73	70	64†	58	51	51	73
Day of occurrence	28	19	31	21	28	29	7	8	3	1	6	24	7
Year of occurrence	1951	1986	1956	1960	1974	1970	1990	1995	1994	1946	1966	1955	1990
Record low daily	-27	-26	-5	10†	19	28	37	34†	17	8	-8	-24	-27
Day of occurrence	22	10	8	2	5	18	1	31	18	30	24	23	22
Year of occurrence	1937	1933	1964	1975	1975	1939	1968	1943	1965	1971	1931	1990	1937
Days w/min <= 32	30.2	26.8	26.1	16.1	5.0	0.4	0.0	0.0	1.5	11.3	25.8	29.8	173.2
Days w/min <= 0	3.5	1.6	0.1	0.0	0.0	0.0	0.0	0.0	0.0	0.0	0.2	1.8	7.2
Days w/min <= -20	0.1	0.0	0.0	0.0	0.0	0.0	0.0	0.0	0.0	0.0	0.0	0.0	0.2

Mean Temperature in °F

	Jan	Feb	Mar	Apr	May	Jun	Jul	Aug	Sep	Oct	Nov	Dec	Annual
Monthly normal	25.4	30.7	37.9	45.9	54.4	63.6	70.7	68.6	59.9	49.6	37.3	27.2	47.6
Standard deviation	9.5	8.8	7.8	7.5	7.3	6.6	3.5	4.3	6.7	7.4	8.6	9.3	7.3
Average monthly	25.5	30.3	38.1	46.4	54.6	63.2	70.2	68.6	60.5	49.8	36.7	28.0	47.7
Standard deviation	9.2	9.0	7.6	7.5	7.1	6.5	3.7	3.9	6.3	7.0	8.6	8.9	7.1
High monthly average	34.4	39.1	46.5	52.9	60.9	68.7	73.3†	72.1	64.4	55.5	44.4	37.4	73.3
Year of occurrence	1956	1995	1934	1992	1934	1961	1960	1994	1990	1963	1949	1980	1960
Low monthly average	11.2	18.1	29.1	38.8	48.7	57.2	66.2	63.9	54.3	43.1	29.9	19.6	11.2
Year of occurrence	1937	1933	1964	1975	1953	1945	1993	1968	1965	1969	1994	1990	1937

† Also occurred on earlier date(s).

MANTI
Monthly Data Summary

Precipitation in Inches

	Jan	Feb	Mar	Apr	May	Jun	Jul	Aug	Sep	Oct	Nov	Dec	Annual
Monthly normal	0.98	1.02	1.53	1.41	1.28	0.81	0.82	0.98	1.40	1.29	1.14	1.06	13.74
Standard deviation	0.09	0.10	0.12	0.11	0.12	0.11	0.08	0.10	0.15	0.13	0.12	0.10	0.11
Average monthly	1.01	1.11	1.43	1.30	1.27	0.80	0.77	0.90	1.01	1.20	1.00	1.01	12.82
Standard deviation	0.10	0.10	0.12	0.11	0.12	0.11	0.08	0.09	0.12	0.12	0.10	0.10	0.11
High monthly total	2.71	3.85	4.00	3.20	4.36	2.97	3.50	2.49	6.01	4.08	3.39	2.84	6.01
Year of occurrence	1969	1980	1961	1968	1995	1947	1936	1945	1982	1946	1983	1983	1982
Low monthly total	0.04	0.09	0.07	0.11	0.00	0.00†	0.00†	0.06	0.00†	0.00	0.02†	0.03	0.00†
Year of occurrence	1931	1946	1972	1977	1948	1978	1958	1940	1957	1952	1956	1930	1952
Record high daily	1.02	1.20	1.03	0.90	1.52	1.35	1.20	1.28	1.23	1.05	1.07	1.67	1.67
Day of occurrence	14	24	29	18	30	7	10	22	17	2	2	6	6
Year of occurrence	1953	1935	1993	1973	1937	1984	1953	1946	1965	1946	1978	1966	1966
Days w/pcp >= .01	7.4	7.9	8.8	8.6	7.4	4.5	5.9	6.8	5.4	6.1	6.3	7.0	82.1
Days w/pcp >= .10	3.2	3.8	4.6	4.3	3.8	2.1	2.6	2.9	2.7	3.4	3.1	3.3	39.9
Days w/pcp >= .50	0.3	0.3	0.5	0.5	0.5	0.4	0.2	0.3	0.6	0.6	0.4	0.3	4.8

Snow and Sleet in Inches

	Jan	Feb	Mar	Apr	May	Jun	Jul	Aug	Sep	Oct	Nov	Dec	Annual
Monthly normal	11.4	9.5	11.4	5.2	1.8	0.0	0.0	0.0	0.4	1.8	7.9	11.7	61.0
Standard deviation	1.1	1.0	1.0	0.7	0.5	0.0	0.0	0.0	0.3	0.4	1.1	1.1	0.6
Average monthly	11.7	10.2	9.4	4.1	1.4	0.0	0.0	0.0	0.2	1.4	6.7	9.7	54.8
Standard deviation	1.1	1.1	1.0	0.6	0.4	0.0	0.0	0.0	0.2	0.4	0.9	1.0	0.6
High monthly total	31.2	32.3	35.7	22.0	11.0	0.5	0.0†	0.0†	10.0	16.5	25.0	27.5	35.7
Year of occurrence	1982	1960	1961	1995	1964	1990	1995	1995	1965	1971	1951	1992	1961
Low monthly total	0.6	0.0†	0.0†	0.0†	0.0†	0.0†	0.0†	0.0†	0.0†	0.0†	0.0†	0.0	0.0†
Year of occurrence	1931	1991	1972	1994	1995	1995	1995	1995	1995	1995	1976	1986	1986
Record high daily	10.0†	15.0	10.0	8.0	10.0	0.5	0.0†	0.0†	8.0	7.0	12.0	10.0	15.0
Day of occurrence	18	24	15	2	19	1	31	31	17	20	19	20	24
Year of occurrence	1983	1935	1945	1957	1941	1990	1995	1995	1965	1949	1977	1984	1935
Days w/snow >= .1	6.1	5.3	4.6	2.1	0.5	0.0	0.0	0.0	0.1	0.7	3.1	4.8	27.4
Days w/snow >= 5	0.4	0.4	0.4	0.1	0.1	0.0	0.0	0.0	0.0	0.1	0.3	0.5	2.3
Days w/snow >= 10	0.0	0.1	0.0	0.0	0.0	0.0	0.0	0.0	0.0	0.0	0.0	0.0	0.2

Degree Days

	Jan	Feb	Mar	Apr	May	Jun	Jul	Aug	Sep	Oct	Nov	Dec	Annual
Heating normal	1226	969	841	573	329	101	3	18	171	477	832	1170	6715
Heating average	1218	981	834	556	323	105	5	13	156	470	848	1147	6662
Cooling normal	0	0	0	0	2	60	179	129	20	0	0	0	391
Cooling average	0	0	0	0	2	52	167	125	20	0	0	0	366
Growing 40 normal	34	68	174	304	480	639	798	765	580	389	161	46	4444
Growing 40 average	32	63	176	315	483	628	783	763	589	397	160	49	4443
Growing 50 normal	3	15	66	161	305	458	611	571	394	235	62	7	2892
Growing 50 average	3	11	65	171	309	453	599	570	408	240	60	7	2901

† Also occurred on earlier date(s).

Location: Milford   County: Beaver   Latitude: 38.400   Longitude: -113.017

Elevation: 5010 feet   Period of Record: 1906-1995

MILFORD
Monthly Data Summary

Maximum Temperature in °F

	Jan	Feb	Mar	Apr	May	Jun	Jul	Aug	Sep	Oct	Nov	Dec	Annual
Monthly normal	38.5	45.4	53.3	62.5	73.1	85.0	92.4	89.8	79.9	67.1	51.6	40.2	64.9
Standard deviation	10.6	10.8	11.1	10.8	10.2	8.7	5.2	5.9	9.2	10.9	11.4	11.2	9.7
Average monthly	38.4	45.1	53.9	63.6	73.4	84.3	92.0	89.6	80.6	67.4	52.1	40.7	65.1
Standard deviation	10.6	10.5	10.7	10.9	9.8	8.8	5.6	5.6	8.6	10.4	11.2	10.8	9.5
High monthly average	56.6	55.1	70.5	87.3	87.9	91.1	96.2	94.5†	89.5	76.5	66.2	52.7	96.2
Year of occurrence	1908	1915	1908	1908	1908	1974	1960	1969	1911	1952	1995	1917	1960
Low monthly average	18.6	28.3	38.2	50.3	64.1	71.6	79.2	83.2	71.4	58.1	42.8	28.2	18.6
Year of occurrence	1949	1949	1924	1922	1935	1913	1924	1921	1909	1946	1938	1909	1949
Record high daily	80	80	90	102†	102	105	104†	103†	99†	90	78	68	105
Day of occurrence	9	28	12	26	21	26	6	13	2	3	6	8	26
Year of occurrence	1908	1908	1908	1908	1908	1970	1985	1943	1948	1963	1931	1915	1970
Record low daily	-5	4	20	30	33	49	62	65	42	25	12	0†	-5
Day of occurrence	9	6	1	9	20	1	5	30	17	29	19	23	9
Year of occurrence	1937	1989	1922	1922	1975	1955	1982	1932	1965	1971	1906	1990	1937
Days w/max >= 100	0.0	0.0	0.0	0.1	0.0	0.3	1.7	0.5	0.0	0.0	0.0	0.0	2.6
Days w/max >= 90	0.0	0.0	0.0	0.2	0.6	9.2	23.0	17.1	3.9	0.0	0.0	0.0	53.8
Days w/max <= 32	8.3	3.3	0.6	0.0	0.0	0.0	0.0	0.0	0.0	0.1	1.6	6.8	20.9

Minimum Temperature in °F

	Jan	Feb	Mar	Apr	May	Jun	Jul	Aug	Sep	Oct	Nov	Dec	Annual
Monthly normal	12.5	18.5	24.2	30.4	38.2	46.6	55.3	54.1	43.8	32.5	22.9	14.0	32.7
Standard deviation	12.7	10.9	8.5	6.9	6.7	6.8	5.8	6.3	7.9	7.6	9.3	12.1	8.5
Average monthly	12.9	19.3	25.2	31.5	39.1	46.7	55.6	54.0	43.6	32.4	21.9	14.6	33.1
Standard deviation	13.0	11.0	7.9	7.2	6.9	6.7	5.9	6.3	8.1	7.8	9.1	12.1	8.5
High monthly average	27.5	28.2	36.3	38.5	46.2	52.2	62.2	59.6	50.4	42.4	28.3	24.3	62.2
Year of occurrence	1915	1941	1910	1910	1910	1940	1912	1969	1939	1921	1965	1906	1912
Low monthly average	-5.2	1.0	16.0	25.0	31.5	39.2	49.5	40.6	30.9	20.2	6.1	-2.9	-5.2
Year of occurrence	1937	1949	1976	1975	1913	1915	1911	1911	1911	1911	1911	1911	1937
Record high daily	43	48†	51	56	65	74	78	78†	64	58	45†	47	78†
Day of occurrence	30	26	29	24	19	22	27	19	20	2	1	3	19
Year of occurrence	1911	1915	1934	1910	1924	1932	1915	1907	1914	1929	1987	1915	1907
Record low daily	-34	-29	-14	5	17	20	33	30†	19	-2	-13	-35	-35
Day of occurrence	9	7	4	9	6	12	4	27	21	30	18	23	23
Year of occurrence	1937	1989	1966	1922	1975	1915	1921	1992	1924	1971	1958	1990	1990
Days w/min <= 32	29.9	25.9	26.0	16.7	5.5	0.5	0.0	0.0	3.0	15.8	26.6	29.5	181.4
Days w/min <= 0	5.6	2.0	0.2	0.0	0.0	0.0	0.0	0.0	0.0	0.0	0.4	3.9	12.2
Days w/min <= -20	0.4	0.1	0.0	0.0	0.0	0.0	0.0	0.0	0.0	0.0	0.0	0.3	0.8

Mean Temperature in °F

	Jan	Feb	Mar	Apr	May	Jun	Jul	Aug	Sep	Oct	Nov	Dec	Annual
Monthly normal	25.5	32.0	38.7	46.4	55.7	65.8	73.8	71.9	61.9	49.8	37.3	27.1	48.8
Standard deviation	10.8	9.8	8.6	7.6	7.3	6.8	4.1	4.8	7.4	7.8	9.0	10.6	7.9
Average monthly	25.7	32.2	39.5	47.6	56.3	65.5	73.8	71.8	62.1	49.9	37.0	27.7	49.1
Standard deviation	10.8	9.7	8.1	7.8	7.2	6.8	4.3	4.6	7.0	7.4	8.7	10.4	7.7
High monthly average	37.6	40.6	50.3	57.5	63.1	71.3	77.1	77.0	67.1	56.3	44.6	36.5	77.1
Year of occurrence	1953	1915	1910	1908	1940	1940	1909	1969	1943	1963	1995	1917	1909
Low monthly average	6.8	14.7	30.3	38.5	49.9	56.3	67.2	67.4	54.8	43.5	27.8	15.8	6.8
Year of occurrence	1949	1949	1924	1922	1975	1913	1924	1911	1909	1919	1911	1972	1949

† Also occurred on earlier date(s).

MILFORD

Monthly Data Summary

Precipitation in Inches

	Jan	Feb	Mar	Apr	May	Jun	Jul	Aug	Sep	Oct	Nov	Dec	Annual
Monthly normal	0.63	0.71	1.17	1.03	0.75	0.50	0.78	0.94	0.98	0.84	0.78	0.70	9.81
Standard deviation	0.06	0.07	0.09	0.10	0.09	0.08	0.10	0.11	0.14	0.10	0.09	0.08	0.09
Average monthly	0.63	0.72	1.09	0.81	0.74	0.44	0.73	0.87	0.67	0.82	0.64	0.70	8.84
Standard deviation	0.07	0.08	0.10	0.09	0.09	0.08	0.11	0.11	0.11	0.11	0.08	0.08	0.09
High monthly total	1.86	2.05	2.85	2.28	2.26	2.43	2.85	3.75	3.64	3.75	2.21	2.45	3.75
Year of occurrence	1980	1909	1992	1973	1981	1967	1936	1984	1982	1941	1978	1966	1941
Low monthly total	0.05	0.01	0.00†	0.02	0.00†	0.00†	0.00†	0.03†	0.00†	0.00†	0.00	0.00	0.00†
Year of occurrence	1972	1972	1972	1955	1963	1979	1948	1957	1979	1952	1932	1989	1989
Record high daily	0.87	1.60	1.14	1.00†	1.35	1.29	1.80	1.42	1.42	1.47	1.00	1.01	1.80
Day of occurrence	19	21	17	2	16	21	3	19	5	28	14	14	3
Year of occurrence	1954	1909	1933	1986	1981	1947	1934	1984	1981	1946	1909	1915	1934
Days w/pcp >= .01	6.2	6.3	7.7	5.7	5.1	3.0	4.6	5.4	3.7	4.4	4.5	5.3	62.2
Days w/pcp >= .10	2.0	2.4	3.7	2.6	2.3	1.4	1.8	2.2	1.8	2.4	2.0	2.3	27.1
Days w/pcp >= .50	0.1	0.1	0.4	0.2	0.3	0.2	0.4	0.5	0.3	0.5	0.2	0.2	3.5

Snow and Sleet in Inches

	Jan	Feb	Mar	Apr	May	Jun	Jul	Aug	Sep	Oct	Nov	Dec	Annual
Monthly normal	7.5	7.1	10.5	6.5	1.8	0.0	0.0	0.0	0.4	1.6	5.0	7.2	47.6
Standard deviation	0.8	0.9	1.0	0.8	0.4	0.0	0.0	0.0	0.2	0.4	0.8	0.8	0.5
Average monthly	7.7	6.4	7.6	3.6	2.6	0.0	0.0	0.0	0.2	1.1	4.1	6.4	39.7
Standard deviation	0.9	0.9	0.9	0.6	2.3	0.0	0.0	0.0	0.1	0.3	0.7	0.8	0.6
High monthly total	29.8	24.5	29.4	24.4	107.2	0.0†	0.0†	0.0†	8.4	17.4	20.1	30.6	107.2
Year of occurrence	1949	1990	1985	1973	1933	1993	1993	1992	1965	1971	1946	1972	1933
Low monthly total	0.0†	0.0†	0.0†	0.0†	0.0†	0.0†	0.0†	0.0†	0.0†	0.0†	0.0†	0.0†	0.0†
Year of occurrence	1940	1947	1992	1993	1992	1993	1993	1992	1992	1992	1995	1995	1995
Record high daily	35.0	20.0†	30.0	40.0	101.5	0.0†	0.0†	8.7	6.1	8.7	35.0	25.0†	101.5
Day of occurrence	27	19	23	17	2	30	31	9	17	4	13	25	2
Year of occurrence	1916	1918	1916	1920	1933	1993	1993	1921	1965	1921	1917	1916	1933
Days w/snow >= .1	5.0	4.2	4.6	2.3	0.8	0.0	0.0	0.0	0.1	0.8	2.6	4.0	24.9
Days w/snow >= 5	0.3	0.2	0.2	0.1	0.0	0.0	0.0	0.0	0.0	0.0	0.2	0.3	1.4
Days w/snow >= 10	0.0	0.0	0.0	0.0	0.0	0.0	0.0	0.0	0.0	0.0	0.0	0.0	0.1

Degree Days

	Jan	Feb	Mar	Apr	May	Jun	Jul	Aug	Sep	Oct	Nov	Dec	Annual
Heating normal	1224	932	814	557	293	72	1	7	138	472	831	1176	6522
Heating average	1219	927	789	523	277	73	2	6	129	468	837	1156	6411
Cooling normal	0	0	0	0	4	95	275	222	45	0	0	0	643
Cooling average	0	0	0	0	6	89	274	216	43	0	0	0	631
Growing 40 normal	54	106	215	337	506	646	809	790	600	420	190	70	4749
Growing 40 average	52	102	222	354	519	644	814	789	605	426	196	73	4802
Growing 50 normal	10	34	98	198	357	500	642	622	448	272	84	15	3286
Growing 50 average	9	30	102	213	363	495	644	621	458	275	87	16	3318

† Also occurred on earlier date(s).

Location: Moab   County: Grand   Latitude: 38.583   Longitude: -109.550
Elevation: 4020 feet   Period of Record: 1889-1996

MOAB
Monthly Data Summary

Maximum Temperature in °F

	Jan	Feb	Mar	Apr	May	Jun	Jul	Aug	Sep	Oct	Nov	Dec	Annual
Monthly normal	42.0	51.8	61.9	72.1	82.3	93.1	99.0	96.4	87.5	74.4	58.1	45.0	72.0
Standard deviation	9.8	9.4	9.5	9.2	8.6	7.5	4.6	5.4	7.7	9.2	8.9	8.3	8.2
Average monthly	41.9	50.7	61.7	72.1	81.9	92.3	97.8	95.0	86.5	73.2	56.9	44.2	71.2
Standard deviation	8.7	9.5	9.2	9.4	8.7	7.6	5.2	5.7	7.8	9.1	8.9	8.3	8.2
High monthly average	54.0	63.6	71.6	83.4	90.3	99.6	103.7	·100.8	95.3	83.8	64.0	54.5	103.7
Year of occurrence	1981	1954	1934	1992	1890	1994	1951	1994	1956	1952	1995	1980	1951
Low monthly average	26.3	36.8	52.3	63.8	69.9	85.3	87.8	84.3	77.0	59.8	48.7	29.7	26.3
Year of occurrence	1973	1939	1897	1920	1917	1907	1897	1893	1897	1897	1938	1909	1973
Record high daily	67†	78	88	96†	102†	113	114	110	108†	95†	82	69†	114
Day of occurrence	31	24	25	30	31	17	7	9	13	5	7	5	7
Year of occurrence	1986	1904	1896	1992	1910	1936	1989	1990	1990	1993	1898	1995	1989
Record low daily	10	16	30	42	49	55	70	71	48	41	20	19†	10
Day of occurrence	13	7	1	2	10	9	11	30	18	29	27	28	13
Year of occurrence	1963	1933	1937	1917	1905	1941	1895	1957	1965	1991	1919	1909	1963
Days w/max >= 100	0.0	0.0	0.0	0.0	0.1	4.6	12.4	6.9	0.6	0.0	0.0	0.0	24.8
Days w/max >= 90	0.0	0.0	0.0	0.3	6.1	20.7	29.1	26.0	11.2	0.6	0.0	0.0	95.1
Days w/max <= 32	4.2	0.9	0.0	0.0	0.0	0.0	0.0	0.0	0.0	0.0	0.1	2.5	7.8

Minimum Temperature in °F

	Jan	Feb	Mar	Apr	May	Jun	Jul	Aug	Sep	Oct	Nov	Dec	Annual
Monthly normal	18.0	25.5	34.2	41.9	49.9	57.5	64.1	62.4	52.9	40.7	30.4	21.3	41.6
Standard deviation	10.4	9.2	8.0	8.0	7.2	6.7	5.8	6.6	7.9	7.8	7.8	8.2	7.8
Average monthly	17.6	24.4	32.6	40.7	48.4	55.8	62.5	60.6	51.3	39.3	28.1	20.0	40.1
Standard deviation	10.2	9.3	8.3	8.1	7.5	7.7	6.2	6.4	8.2	8.2	8.1	8.8	8.1
High monthly average	29.4	32.3	41.0	50.3	56.4	63.7	68.5	69.5	59.9	48.0	36.8	28.7	69.5
Year of occurrence	1980	1986	1992	1992	1992	1931	1954	1992	1992	1992	1965	1922	1992
Low monthly average	1.6	8.3	25.3	34.7	42.0	47.4†	54.5	51.2	43.3	32.0	18.8	9.3	1.6
Year of occurrence	1925	1933	1917	1920	1909	1920	1902	1972	1912	1890	1929	1909	1925
Record high daily	55	61	64†	68	74	83†	86	84	77	68†	60†	56	86
Day of occurrence	31	25	17	25	12	20	11	21	12	3	5	24	11
Year of occurrence	1911	1904	1994	1943	1962	1919	1919	1992	1992	1967	1924	1955	1919
Record low daily	-24	-13	8	15	27	36†	43†	40†	28	15	2	-18	-24
Day of occurrence	22	13	17	8	1	1	9	27	27	26	24	25	22
Year of occurrence	1930	1905	1917	1928	1909	1923	1928	1931	1934	1932	1931	1924	1930
Days w/min <= 32	29.0	23.5	16.6	4.4	0.2	0.0	0.0	0.0	0.2	6.3	22.3	28.5	131.2
Days w/min <= 0	1.6	0.5	0.0	0.0	0.0	0.0	0.0	0.0	0.0	0.0	0.0	0.5	2.6
Days w/min <= -20	0.0	0.0	0.0	0.0	0.0	0.0	0.0	0.0	0.0	0.0	0.0	0.0	0.0

Mean Temperature in °F

	Jan	Feb	Mar	Apr	May	Jun	Jul	Aug	Sep	Oct	Nov	Dec	Annual
Monthly normal	30.0	38.6	48.0	57.0	66.1	75.3	81.6	79.4	70.2	57.6	44.2	33.1	56.8
Standard deviation	9.3	8.4	7.5	7.4	6.8	6.1	3.7	4.7	6.5	7.1	7.2	7.3	6.8
Average monthly	29.8	37.5	47.2	56.4	65.1	74.0	80.1	77.8	68.9	56.3	42.5	32.1	55.7
Standard deviation	8.7	8.5	7.5	7.5	6.9	6.4	4.3	4.7	6.6	7.2	7.3	7.6	6.9
High monthly average	38.6	46.1	55.2	66.8	72.1	79.9	84.8	84.9	76.7	65.2	49.5	41.3	84.9
Year of occurrence	1981	1986	1994	1992	1992	1988	1954	1992	1992	1992	1965	1980	1992
Low monthly average	14.4	23.0	40.6	49.2	57.9	68.0	73.9	71.8	62.0	50.7	35.3	19.5	14.4
Year of occurrence	1973	1933	1952	1920	1917	1915	1897	1893	1912	1908	1938	1909	1973

† Also occurred on earlier date(s).

MOAB
Monthly Data Summary

Precipitation in Inches

	Jan	Feb	Mar	Apr	May	Jun	Jul	Aug	Sep	Oct	Nov	Dec	Annual
Monthly normal	0.56	0.43	0.85	0.98	0.72	0.48	0.83	0.86	0.75	1.16	0.74	0.65	9.00
Standard deviation	0.06	0.05	0.09	0.13	0.09	0.09	0.13	0.11	0.11	0.14	0.09	0.08	0.10
Average monthly	0.66	0.60	0.83	0.81	0.73	0.42	0.76	0.83	0.85	1.02	0.70	0.77	8.99
Standard deviation	0.08	0.07	0.09	0.10	0.10	0.08	0.12	0.10	0.13	0.13	0.09	0.11	0.10
High monthly total	3.52	2.50	3.19	2.78	2.62	2.35	6.63	2.62	5.97	4.40	2.40	5.75	6.63
Year of occurrence	1916	1927	1975	1917	1995	1927	1918	1947	1896	1941	1983	1915	1918
Low monthly total	0.00†	0.00†	0.00†	0.00†	0.00†	0.00†	0.00†	0.00†	0.00†	0.00†	0.00†	0.00†	0.00†
Year of occurrence	1992	1972	1972	1982	1974	1991	1954	1985	1956	1954	1932	1995	1995
Record high daily	1.26	1.20	1.08	2.10	1.85	1.51	2.77	1.50	3.99	1.95	1.20	3.30	3.99
Day of occurrence	21	28	26	9	27	24	23	28	23	5	22	31	23
Year of occurrence	1917	1927	1910	1978	1926	1969	1983	1939	1896	1911	1902	1915	1896
Days w/pcp >= .01	4.7	4.4	5.7	4.9	4.5	2.8	4.5	5.3	4.3	4.5	3.8	4.4	53.7
Days w/pcp >= .10	2.2	2.2	2.8	2.6	2.1	1.2	2.0	2.4	2.2	2.7	2.1	2.2	26.9
Days w/pcp >= .50	0.2	0.1	0.3	0.3	0.4	0.2	0.3	0.3	0.4	0.6	0.3	0.3	3.8

Snow and Sleet in Inches

	Jan	Feb	Mar	Apr	May	Jun	Jul	Aug	Sep	Oct	Nov	Dec	Annual
Monthly normal	3.8	0.6	0.3	0.0	0.0	0.0	0.0	0.0	0.0	0.0	0.0	1.4	6.1
Standard deviation	0.7	0.2	0.2	0.0	0.0	0.0	0.0	0.0	0.0	0.0	0.0	0.4	0.1
Average monthly	4.1	1.6	0.9	0.2	0.0	0.0	0.0	0.0	0.0	0.0	0.6	2.8	10.2
Standard deviation	0.7	0.4	0.3	0.2	0.0	0.0	0.0	0.0	0.0	0.0	0.3	0.8	0.2
High monthly total	28.0	15.0	9.0	11.0	1.5	0.0†	0.0†	0.0†	0.0†	2.0	11.0	46.0	46.0
Year of occurrence	1917	1905	1948	1921	1899	1995	1995	1995	1995	1908	1893	1915	1915
Low monthly total	0.0†	0.0†	0.0†	0.0†	0.0†	0.0†	0.0†	0.0†	0.0†	0.0†	0.0†	0.0†	0.0†
Year of occurrence	1994	1995	1995	1995	1995	1995	1995	1995	1995	1995	1995	1995	1995
Record high daily	12.0†	8.0	8.0	7.0	1.5	0.0†	0.0†	0.0†	0.0†	2.0	8.0†	33.0	33.0
Day of occurrence	21	9	4	24	2	30	31	31	30	21	17	31	31
Year of occurrence	1917	1905	1948	1921	1899	1995	1995	1995	1995	1908	1955	1915	1915
Days w/snow >= .1	1.9	0.9	0.4	0.0	0.0	0.0	0.0	0.0	0.0	0.0	0.3	1.3	4.5
Days w/snow >= 5	0.2	0.0	0.0	0.0	0.0	0.0	0.0	0.0	0.0	0.0	0.0	0.1	0.4
Days w/snow >= 10	0.0	0.0	0.0	0.0	0.0	0.0	0.0	0.0	0.0	0.0	0.0	0.0	0.0

Degree Days

	Jan	Feb	Mar	Apr	May	Jun	Jul	Aug	Sep	Oct	Nov	Dec	Annual
Heating normal	1084	744	526	255	71	4	0	0	27	244	622	987	4569
Heating average	1089	775	552	270	84	9	0	0	35	281	674	1017	4792
Cooling normal	0	0	0	15	105	312	514	447	182	14	0	0	1593
Cooling average	0	0	0	12	88	280	469	398	152	11	0	0	1413
Growing 40 normal	79	178	355	519	704	816	947	921	741	548	280	102	6197
Growing 40 average	70	163	351	508	680	789	921	892	718	529	261	92	5980
Growing 50 normal	16	66	194	342	517	644	777	750	577	385	135	19	4427
Growing 50 average	11	59	191	339	505	623	750	720	559	365	121	17	4266

† Also occurred on earlier date(s).

Location: Monticello County: San Juan   Latitude: 37.867   Longitude: -109.300
Elevation: 6820 feet   Period of Record: 1948-1995

MONTICELLO
Monthly Data Summary

Maximum Temperature in °F

	Jan	Feb	Mar	Apr	May	Jun	Jul	Aug	Sep	Oct	Nov	Dec	Annual
Monthly normal	35.1	40.0	47.6	57.9	67.7	78.7	84.3	81.3	73.4	61.8	47.1	37.2	59.3
Standard deviation	8.3	8.4	9.4	8.9	8.0	7.1	4.4	5.0	6.9	9.1	9.5	8.7	7.8
Average monthly	35.4	40.0	47.6	58.1	67.4	78.5	83.9	81.3	74.0	62.4	47.3	37.9	59.5
Standard deviation	8.0	8.2	8.9	8.8	7.9	6.9	4.5	5.0	6.8	9.2	9.4	8.3	7.7
High monthly average	45.6	50.1	56.8	64.6	74.7	84.4	86.9	84.8	79.8	71.3	57.5	47.1	86.9
Year of occurrence	1981	1954	1972	1954	1984	1990	1978	1969	1956	1950	1949	1980	1978
Low monthly average	26.0	33.3	38.5	50.4	58.8	72.9	79.9	73.6	66.9	52.3	39.6	28.8	26.0
Year of occurrence	1979	1949	1952	1970	1957	1949	1992	1968	1986	1969	1972	1978	1979
Record high daily	56†	72	69†	78	88†	97	96	101	91	83	69†	58†	101
Day of occurrence	22	25	10	29	31	28	6	8	2	1	5	16	8
Year of occurrence	1981	1986	1989	1992	1984	1950	1989	1969	1948	1956	1975	1980	1969
Record low daily	5†	1	19	32†	40	54	63	60	43	26	20†	4†	1
Day of occurrence	6	6	28	4	9	8	31	23	30	30	28	23	6
Year of occurrence	1971	1989	1975	1983	1979	1979	1953	1992	1959	1972	1976	1990	1989
Days w/max >= 100	0.0	0.0	0.0	0.0	0.0	0.0	0.0	0.0	0.0	0.0	0.0	0.0	0.0
Days w/max >= 90	0.0	0.0	0.0	0.0	0.0	1.2	2.8	0.7	0.1	0.0	0.0	0.0	4.8
Days w/max <= 32	11.2	4.8	1.3	0.1	0.0	0.0	0.0	0.0	0.0	0.1	2.0	7.9	28.2

Minimum Temperature in °F

	Jan	Feb	Mar	Apr	May	Jun	Jul	Aug	Sep	Oct	Nov	Dec	Annual
Monthly normal	12.7	17.1	23.3	29.7	37.5	45.3	52.6	50.9	42.9	33.3	23.4	14.9	32.0
Standard deviation	10.1	9.7	7.6	6.9	6.5	6.8	4.8	5.5	6.6	7.0	8.3	9.5	7.4
Average monthly	13.7	17.6	23.6	30.3	37.7	45.5	52.5	51.2	43.7	33.9	23.1	15.7	32.4
Standard deviation	9.9	9.7	7.5	6.9	6.4	6.6	4.7	5.2	6.5	7.0	8.3	9.3	7.3
High monthly average	23.6	27.0	28.6	35.2	42.4	49.8	58.1	56.6	49.3	42.2	29.3	23.6	58.1
Year of occurrence	1956	1995	1989	1992	1958	1994	1971	1969	1948	1950	1962	1950	1971
Low monthly average	6.2	8.2	17.7	24.8	34.3	40.3	48.9	45.6	38.5	27.7	15.3	6.8	6.2
Year of occurrence	1979	1949	1969	1975	1975	1967	1993	1968	1968	1976	1979	1978	1979
Record high daily	38	39	46	50†	54†	66†	68†	65†	61	52†	46	39	68
Day of occurrence	24	19	23	21	21	29	21	9	1	12	14	6	21
Year of occurrence	1970	1986	1990	1989	1984	1994	1964	1971	1990	1971	1965	1966	1964
Record low daily	-18	-19	-1	5	15	27†	33	34†	24†	5	-8	-22	-22
Day of occurrence	30	7	6	2	7	2	6	25	30	30	27	22	22
Year of occurrence	1979	1989	1973	1975	1968	1990	1982	1968	1985	1971	1952	1990	1990
Days w/min <= 32	30.5	27.5	27.9	18.9	6.8	0.6	0.0	0.0	1.4	12.9	26.2	30.4	187.6
Days w/min <= 0	3.0	1.4	0.0	0.0	0.0	0.0	0.0	0.0	0.0	0.0	0.2	1.6	6.3
Days w/min <= -20	0.0	0.0	0.0	0.0	0.0	0.0	0.0	0.0	0.0	0.0	0.0	0.0	0.0

Mean Temperature in °F

	Jan	Feb	Mar	Apr	May	Jun	Jul	Aug	Sep	Oct	Nov	Dec	Annual
Monthly normal	23.9	28.6	35.4	43.8	52.6	62.0	68.4	66.1	58.2	47.6	35.2	26.1	45.7
Standard deviation	8.3	8.2	7.7	7.2	6.6	6.3	3.5	4.2	5.8	7.0	8.0	8.1	6.7
Average monthly	24.5	28.8	35.6	44.2	52.6	62.0	68.2	66.2	58.9	48.2	35.2	26.8	45.9
Standard deviation	8.1	8.1	7.4	7.2	6.5	6.1	3.4	4.1	5.8	7.2	7.9	7.9	6.7
High monthly average	33.0	37.7	42.4	49.9	57.7	67.0	71.9	70.7	63.5	56.7	41.4	35.0	71.9
Year of occurrence	1956	1995	1972	1992	1984	1990	1971	1969	1956	1950	1965	1950	1971
Low monthly average	16.3	20.7	28.3	38.5	47.2	57.9	64.7	59.6	53.2	42.0	27.9	17.7	16.3
Year of occurrence	1979	1949	1952	1970	1957	1949	1992	1968	1961	1984	1979	1978	1979

† Also occurred on earlier date(s).

MONTICELLO
Monthly Data Summary

Precipitation in Inches

	Jan	Feb	Mar	Apr	May	Jun	Jul	Aug	Sep	Oct	Nov	Dec	Annual
Monthly normal	1.41	1.00	1.18	0.85	0.92	0.57	1.57	1.90	1.58	1.62	1.37	1.49	15.47
Standard deviation	0.17	0.14	0.12	0.10	0.10	0.08	0.15	0.20	0.18	0.17	0.17	0.17	0.14
Average monthly	1.45	1.09	1.07	0.88	0.99	0.55	1.52	1.90	1.38	1.65	1.19	1.35	15.02
Standard deviation	0.17	0.14	0.11	0.10	0.11	0.09	0.16	0.19	0.16	0.18	0.15	0.16	0.14
High monthly total	6.25	4.03	3.09	2.65	3.49	2.26	4.60	4.26	4.82	7.64	4.32	4.79	7.64
Year of occurrence	1980	1993	1983	1957	1993	1973	1953	1982	1962	1972	1978	1978	1972
Low monthly total	0.01	0.00	0.02	0.00	0.03	0.00†	0.03	0.20	0.00†	0.00†	0.00	0.00†	0.00†
Year of occurrence	1972	1972	1972	1969	1984	1980	1993	1978	1957	1964	1989	1989	1989
Record high daily	1.72	1.89	0.95†	1.12	1.36	1.59	2.09	3.38	1.93	2.02	1.78	2.40	3.38
Day of occurrence	17	8	3	2	15	17	31	1	27	19	6	18	1
Year of occurrence	1979	1994	1989	1986	1993	1995	1956	1968	1962	1949	1987	1978	1968
Days w/pcp >= .01	6.2	5.9	6.8	5.4	6.1	3.0	7.7	8.7	6.3	5.4	5.0	5.6	73.3
Days w/pcp >= .10	3.6	2.9	3.1	2.7	2.9	1.5	3.9	4.9	3.3	3.8	2.7	3.2	39.3
Days w/pcp >= .50	0.9	0.5	0.4	0.4	0.4	0.3	0.8	1.0	0.7	1.1	0.7	0.9	8.2

Snow and Sleet in Inches

	Jan	Feb	Mar	Apr	May	Jun	Jul	Aug	Sep	Oct	Nov	Dec	Annual
Monthly normal	16.2	10.9	9.9	2.4	0.5	0.0	0.0	0.0	0.0	0.7	6.9	14.3	61.8
Standard deviation	1.9	1.5	1.1	0.6	0.2	0.0	0.0	0.0	0.0	0.2	1.1	1.5	0.7
Average monthly	16.6	11.2	8.3	2.5	0.5	0.0	0.0	0.0	0.0	0.8	5.9	12.4	58.2
Standard deviation	1.9	1.4	1.0	0.6	0.2	0.0	0.0	0.0	0.0	0.2	0.9	1.4	0.6
High monthly total	62.0	36.0	33.9	15.0†	8.0	0.0†	0.0†	0.0†	0.0†	9.0	22.0	47.5	62.0
Year of occurrence	1949	1979	1970	1995	1979	1995	1995	1995	1995	1991	1983	1967	1949
Low monthly total	0.0†	0.0†	0.0†	0.0†	0.0†	0.0†	0.0†	0.0†	0.0†	0.0†	0.0†	0.0†	0.0†
Year of occurrence	1972	1972	1994	1992	1994	1995	1995	1995	1995	1993	1989	1989	1989
Record high daily	24.0	17.0	12.0	12.0	5.0	0.0†	0.0†	0.0†	0.0†	5.0	12.0	13.0	24.0
Day of occurrence	4	24	31	5	5	30	31	31	30	30	25	19	4
Year of occurrence	1973	1987	1970	1983	1993	1995	1995	1995	1995	1991	1983	1967	1973
Days w/snow >= .1	4.7	3.9	3.4	1.1	0.3	0.0	0.0	0.0	0.0	0.5	2.2	4.1	20.3
Days w/snow >= 5	1.2	0.6	0.4	0.1	0.0	0.0	0.0	0.0	0.0	0.0	0.3	0.9	3.7
Days w/snow >= 10	0.4	0.1	0.0	0.0	0.0	0.0	0.0	0.0	0.0	0.0	0.1	0.2	0.9

Degree Days

	Jan	Feb	Mar	Apr	May	Jun	Jul	Aug	Sep	Oct	Nov	Dec	Annual
Heating normal	1266	1026	913	630	383	128	9	37	211	536	885	1197	7227
Heating average	1246	1021	908	619	385	124	11	34	193	517	885	1175	7125
Cooling normal	0	0	0	0	0	38	115	70	7	0	0	0	231
Cooling average	0	0	0	0	0	36	111	72	10	0	0	0	230
Growing 40 normal	21	46	132	271	448	613	765	729	547	345	125	34	4082
Growing 40 average	21	45	131	274	445	615	763	735	562	356	128	36	4117
Growing 50 normal	0	6	43	135	276	439	569	519	355	192	38	2	2579
Growing 50 average	1	6	39	136	271	437	564	521	367	200	38	2	2587

† Also occurred on earlier date(s).

Location: Nephi   County: Juab   Latitude: 39.700   Longitude: -111.833
Elevation: 5130 feet   Period of Record: 1889-1996

NEPHI
Monthly Data Summary

Maximum Temperature in °F

	Jan	Feb	Mar	Apr	May	Jun	Jul	Aug	Sep	Oct	Nov	Dec	Annual
Monthly normal	39.1	44.8	52.9	62.4	72.8	84.4	92.7	90.5	80.5	67.9	52.1	40.6	65.1
Standard deviation	9.1	9.7	10.6	11.5	10.6	9.5	5.2	5.9	9.3	11.3	11.2	9.9	9.5
Average monthly	39.6	45.1	53.0	63.0	73.1	83.9	92.9	90.8	81.7	68.8	52.3	41.9	65.5
Standard deviation	9.4	9.9	10.3	11.2	10.5	9.5	5.4	5.8	9.1	11.5	11.3	9.6	9.5
High monthly average	51.0	57.2	63.2	74.6	79.2†	91.9	99.0	95.5	88.8	82.5	65.4	50.6	99.0
Year of occurrence	1953	1995	1986	1987	1969	1986	1889	1958	1952	1952	1949	1958	1889
Low monthly average	29.6	34.3	42.3	51.2	65.1	75.9	87.6†	82.3	71.5	58.0	43.4	31.5	29.6
Year of occurrence	1984	1891	1964	1975	1953	1967	1993	1968	1965	1969	1947	1985	1984
Record high daily	68	74	80†	91	96†	110	106†	109	106	93	79	70	110
Day of occurrence	13	26	30	25	23	26	8	8	4	13	3	1	26
Year of occurrence	1953	1986	1986	1987	1984	1970	1989	1958	1950	1989	1953	1995	1970
Record low daily	5	6	24	33	39	51†	70†	61	43	25	20	4	4
Day of occurrence	7	7	2	1	6	11	4	18	18	30	28	23	23
Year of occurrence	1971	1989	1971	1975	1975	1970	1993	1968	1965	1971	1976	1990	1990
Days w/max >= 100	0.0	0.0	0.0	0.0	0.0	0.5	2.9	1.4	0.1	0.0	0.0	0.0	4.9
Days w/max >= 90	0.0	0.0	0.0	0.0	0.8	9.8	24.3	19.7	5.5	0.2	0.0	0.0	61.2
Days w/max <= 32	6.8	2.6	0.6	0.0	0.0	0.0	0.0	0.0	0.0	0.0	0.8	4.9	16.0

Minimum Temperature in °F

	Jan	Feb	Mar	Apr	May	Jun	Jul	Aug	Sep	Oct	Nov	Dec	Annual
Monthly normal	16.0	21.2	27.3	33.7	41.6	49.6	57.7	55.7	46.5	35.9	27.0	18.1	35.9
Standard deviation	11.1	10.0	7.8	7.1	7.2	7.1	5.3	5.9	7.6	7.2	8.4	10.2	7.9
Average monthly	16.2	21.1	27.3	34.2	41.9	49.1	57.4	55.4	46.3	36.1	26.1	19.1	35.9
Standard deviation	11.2	10.2	7.9	7.3	7.0	7.0	5.6	7.7	8.6	7.4	8.6	9.9	8.2
High monthly average	27.6	30.8	33.9	39.8	46.7	54.2	61.9	60.8	51.9	43.1	34.0	31.0	61.9
Year of occurrence	1953	1992	1992	1943	1969	1988	1954	1963	1990	1963	1965	1889	1954
Low monthly average	0.3	11.8	19.4	29.2	36.8	42.8	50.5	29.4	32.7	28.0	16.1	8.9	0.3
Year of occurrence	1949	1955	1964	1975	1975	1890	1891	1914	1914	1890	1890	1990	1949
Record high daily	42	45	56	59	62†	73	76†	71†	67	57†	51	46	76
Day of occurrence	21	20	28	23	28	27	25	8	2	3	12	24	25
Year of occurrence	1969	1992	1963	1956	1989	1970	1963	1985	1945	1967	1973	1955	1963
Record low daily	-23	-20†	-10	11	20	28	37†	0†	0†	12	-4	-21	-23
Day of occurrence	8	8	1	9	9	14	12	14	30	31	16	23	8
Year of occurrence	1890	1989	1890	1890	1990	1976	1891	1914	1914	1972	1955	1990	1890
Days w/min <= 32	29.4	25.3	23.0	13.2	3.2	0.2	0.0	0.2	1.5	10.1	23.4	28.8	159.5
Days w/min <= 0	3.1	1.0	0.1	0.0	0.0	0.0	0.0	0.2	0.2	0.0	0.1	1.1	5.9
Days w/min <= -20	0.0	0.1	0.0	0.0	0.0	0.0	0.0	0.0	0.0	0.0	0.0	0.0	0.1

Mean Temperature in °F

	Jan	Feb	Mar	Apr	May	Jun	Jul	Aug	Sep	Oct	Nov	Dec	Annual
Monthly normal	27.5	33.0	40.1	48.1	57.2	67.0	75.2	73.1	63.5	51.9	39.5	29.3	50.5
Standard deviation	9.4	9.1	8.5	8.4	8.2	7.6	4.3	5.1	7.8	8.4	8.9	9.2	7.9
Average monthly	27.9	33.1	40.2	48.6	57.5	66.5	75.2	73.2	64.0	52.5	39.2	30.5	50.7
Standard deviation	9.6	9.3	8.3	8.4	8.1	7.5	4.6	5.6	7.9	8.5	9.0	8.8	8.0
High monthly average	39.3	41.1	48.1	56.4	63.0	72.5	78.8	77.6	69.6	60.5†	47.2	37.4	78.8
Year of occurrence	1953	1992	1986	1943	1969	1986	1954	1952	1952	1952	1949	1958	1954
Low monthly average	15.2	23.9	30.8	40.2	51.3	59.7	69.1	59.9	55.9	44.6	32.1	22.8†	15.2
Year of occurrence	1949	1891	1964	1975	1975	1891	1891	1914	1914	1890	1994	1990	1949

† Also occurred on earlier date(s).

NEPHI
Monthly Data Summary

Precipitation in Inches

	Jan	Feb	Mar	Apr	May	Jun	Jul	Aug	Sep	Oct	Nov	Dec	Annual
Monthly normal	1.14	1.19	1.71	1.51	1.39	0.82	0.86	1.01	1.19	1.26	1.39	1.33	14.79
Standard deviation	0.11	0.12	0.13	0.13	0.12	0.11	0.10	0.11	0.14	0.14	0.13	0.12	0.12
Average monthly	1.22	1.24	1.65	1.48	1.49	0.83	0.76	1.00	0.97	1.26	1.21	1.33	14.43
Standard deviation	0.11	0.11	0.13	0.13	0.14	0.11	0.10	0.11	0.12	0.14	0.12	0.12	0.12
High monthly total	3.35	3.55	4.29	3.76	4.46	3.36	3.72	3.10	6.02	4.94	3.60	4.80	6.02
Year of occurrence	1969	1962	1906	1906	1908	1943	1985	1983	1982	1946	1978	1951	1982
Low monthly total	0.00	0.22	0.03	0.14	0.12	0.00†	0.00†	0.00†	0.00†	0.00†	0.00†	0.11	0.00†
Year of occurrence	1961	1967	1956	1954	1969	1979	1975	1985	1974	1958	1904	1976	1904
Record high daily	1.02	1.20	1.53	1.40	1.75	1.82	1.85	1.40	1.50	1.75	0.97	1.45	1.85
Day of occurrence	26	2	21	2	6	1	21	18	18	20	2	30	21
Year of occurrence	1969	1905	1944	1986	1889	1943	1943	1889	1978	1979	1978	1951	1943
Days w/pcp >= .01	7.1	7.9	9.3	8.0	7.4	4.5	5.0	6.0	4.6	5.5	6.7	7.5	79.8
Days w/pcp >= .10	4.1	4.2	5.1	4.6	4.3	2.5	2.2	2.8	2.6	3.4	3.6	4.3	44.1
Days w/pcp >= .50	0.4	0.4	0.7	0.7	0.7	0.3	0.2	0.4	0.5	0.7	0.6	0.5	6.1

Snow and Sleet in Inches

	Jan	Feb	Mar	Apr	May	Jun	Jul	Aug	Sep	Oct	Nov	Dec	Annual
Monthly normal	10.5	7.3	8.1	3.0	1.2	0.0	0.0	0.0	0.0	1.0	6.6	10.5	48.1
Standard deviation	1.2	0.9	1.1	0.6	0.5	0.0	0.0	0.0	0.0	0.3	0.8	1.1	0.5
Average monthly	10.7	6.8	7.0	2.6	0.8	0.0	0.0	0.0	0.0	0.7	5.3	11.7	45.7
Standard deviation	1.1	0.9	1.0	0.6	0.4	0.0	0.0	0.0	0.0	0.3	0.8	1.6	0.6
High monthly total	41.0	31.0	30.5	16.0	16.1	1.0	0.0†	0.0†	0.0†	7.2	26.0	69.5	69.5
Year of occurrence	1993	1990	1944	1906	1975	1990	1995	1995	1995	1991	1983	1889	1889
Low monthly total	0.0†	0.0†	0.0†	0.0†	0.0†	0.0†	0.0†	0.0†	0.0†	0.0†	0.0†	0.0†	0.0†
Year of occurrence	1964	1991	1994	1994	1995	1995	1995	1995	1995	1995	1995	1976	1976
Record high daily	11.0	9.0	19.0	12.0	13.1	1.0	0.0†	0.0†	0.0†	5.0	11.0	40.0	40.0
Day of occurrence	23	18	21	1	20	1	31	31	30	28	28	30	30
Year of occurrence	1978	1990	1944	1906	1975	1990	1995	1995	1995	1991	1960	1889	1889
Days w/snow >= .1	4.5	3.2	2.7	1.2	0.2	0.0	0.0	0.0	0.0	0.4	2.2	3.9	17.1
Days w/snow >= 5	0.5	0.3	0.4	0.2	0.1	0.0	0.0	0.0	0.0	0.0	0.3	0.6	2.3
Days w/snow >= 10	0.0	0.0	0.1	0.0	0.0	0.0	0.0	0.0	0.0	0.0	0.0	0.1	0.3

Degree Days

	Jan	Feb	Mar	Apr	May	Jun	Jul	Aug	Sep	Oct	Nov	Dec	Annual
Heating normal	1160	902	771	508	259	68	1	7	112	407	764	1105	6071
Heating average	1147	901	769	493	251	72	2	11	106	392	774	1068	5990
Cooling normal	0	0	0	0	16	127	317	258	68	2	0	0	791
Cooling average	0	0	0	1	18	117	318	264	76	3	0	0	799
Growing 40 normal	49	94	210	343	532	680	847	814	630	440	194	65	4902
Growing 40 average	54	98	210	354	537	672	843	816	637	449	197	75	4949
Growing 50 normal	6	25	92	199	358	509	674	643	463	285	88	12	3359
Growing 50 average	9	27	91	206	362	502	671	647	478	298	90	16	3403

† Also occurred on earlier date(s).

Location: Ogden Pioneer P H County: Weber Latitude: 41.250   Longitude: -111.950
Elevation: 4350 feet   Period of Record: 1902-1996

OGDEN PIONEER P H
Monthly Data Summary

Maximum Temperature in °F

	Jan	Feb	Mar	Apr	May	Jun	Jul	Aug	Sep	Oct	Nov	Dec	Annual
Monthly normal	36.4	43.1	51.5	61.0	71.2	81.9	91.0	88.6	77.9	65.4	49.5	37.9	62.9
Standard deviation	8.9	9.3	9.6	10.4	10.5	9.6	5.4	6.5	9.7	10.3	9.7	9.1	9.1
Average monthly	36.6	42.5	51.3	61.8	71.5	81.7	90.8	88.6	78.4	65.6	49.7	38.8	63.1
Standard deviation	8.6	9.0	9.4	10.2	10.1	9.3	5.7	6.1	9.3	10.1	9.9	8.9	8.9
High monthly average	48.2	52.5	62.3	71.9	82.9	89.3	95.5	93.7	86.1	75.6	59.8	50.1	95.5
Year of occurrence	1953	1995	1934	1934	1934	1918	1935	1940	1938	1933	1921	1933	1935
Low monthly average	24.6	27.0	42.1	52.0	64.4	72.3	82.6	81.5	67.4	51.5	39.8	26.9	24.6
Year of occurrence	1949	1903	1919	1920	1953	1907	1993	1968	1912	1919	1918	1909	1949
Record high daily	65	68	78	85†	93	102†	105	102†	97†	89	76†	66	105
Day of occurrence	23	25	28	22	20	19	13	5	7	2	7	1	13
Year of occurrence	1970	1986	1943	1994	1954	1940	1939	1994	1955	1935	1931	1995	1939
Record low daily	6	8	22	32	41	47	62	48	40	30†	14	1	1
Day of occurrence	23	10	2	5	5	1	3	30	25	29	16	23	23
Year of occurrence	1937	1933	1917	1921	1978	1908	1902	1932	1908	1971	1955	1990	1990
Days w/max >= 100	0.0	0.0	0.0	0.0	0.0	0.2	0.9	0.3	0.0	0.0	0.0	0.0	1.4
Days w/max >= 90	0.0	0.0	0.0	0.0	0.4	6.3	19.8	15.5	2.9	0.0	0.0	0.0	45.3
Days w/max <= 32	9.6	3.6	0.4	0.0	0.0	0.0	0.0	0.0	0.0	0.0	1.2	7.3	22.3

Minimum Temperature in °F

	Jan	Feb	Mar	Apr	May	Jun	Jul	Aug	Sep	Oct	Nov	Dec	Annual
Monthly normal	19.0	23.7	30.8	38.1	46.6	55.3	62.8	60.7	51.0	40.4	30.2	21.3	40.0
Standard deviation	9.9	9.3	7.8	7.5	7.8	7.3	5.1	5.7	7.5	7.2	7.1	8.6	7.6
Average monthly	18.5	23.2	30.0	37.8	45.6	53.1	60.8	59.2	49.7	39.4	28.8	21.3	39.0
Standard deviation	10.2	9.6	8.0	7.7	7.8	7.6	6.1	6.5	8.0	7.4	7.8	9.2	8.0
High monthly average	31.1	34.0	39.8	46.8	53.3	61.4	67.7	66.5	60.4	49.0	35.7	29.8	67.7
Year of occurrence	1953	1907	1986	1992	1912	1986	1989	1994	1990	1988	1995	1917	1989
Low monthly average	1.8	6.6	20.0	31.8	37.9	45.7	51.4	49.1	40.7	31.5	18.7	9.3	1.8
Year of occurrence	1949	1933	1917	1937	1933	1930	1911	1912	1912	1913	1930	1930	1949
Record high daily	47	51	60	70	68†	78	79	78	77	66	55	53	79
Day of occurrence	20	11	29	21	21	30	25	3	6	7	3	10	25
Year of occurrence	1969	1962	1943	1989	1993	1953	1943	1934	1945	1943	1942	1929	1943
Record low daily	-23	-23	3	6	21	29	36	33	20	11	-12	-20	-23†
Day of occurrence	21	7	8	2	29	3	1	31	25	28	16	12	7
Year of occurrence	1937	1933	1964	1936	1981	1929	1911	1932	1926	1970	1955	1932	1933
Days w/min <= 32	28.7	23.9	19.3	8.0	1.5	0.0	0.0	0.0	0.5	5.7	20.5	28.1	137.4
Days w/min <= 0	1.4	0.6	0.0	0.0	0.0	0.0	0.0	0.0	0.0	0.0	0.1	0.7	2.8
Days w/min <= -20	0.0	0.0	0.0	0.0	0.0	0.0	0.0	0.0	0.0	0.0	0.0	0.0	0.0

Mean Temperature in °F

	Jan	Feb	Mar	Apr	May	Jun	Jul	Aug	Sep	Oct	Nov	Dec	Annual
Monthly normal	27.7	33.4	41.1	49.6	58.9	68.6	76.9	74.7	64.4	52.9	39.8	29.6	51.5
Standard deviation	9.0	8.9	8.2	8.5	8.7	8.1	4.7	5.6	8.1	8.3	7.9	8.5	7.9
Average monthly	27.6	32.9	40.7	49.9	58.6	67.4	75.8	73.9	64.0	52.5	39.2	30.0	51.0
Standard deviation	8.8	8.8	8.1	8.3	8.3	7.7	5.1	5.4	7.8	8.0	8.1	8.5	7.7
High monthly average	39.6	42.8	49.9	58.8	66.0	74.7	80.7	79.3	72.6	61.6	46.8	38.0	80.7
Year of occurrence	1953	1995	1986	1992	1958	1988	1989	1994	1990	1988	1921	1939	1989
Low monthly average	13.2	18.5	31.3	43.2	51.5	60.6	67.6	68.1	54.1	41.8	32.1	19.7	13.2
Year of occurrence	1949	1903	1917	1920	1933	1908	1913	1968	1912	1919	1938	1930	1949

† Also occurred on earlier date(s).

OGDEN PIONEER P H
Monthly Data Summary

Precipitation in Inches

	Jan	Feb	Mar	Apr	May	Jun	Jul	Aug	Sep	Oct	Nov	Dec	Annual
Monthly normal	1.99	1.92	2.32	2.63	2.51	1.56	0.83	1.01	1.73	1.93	2.06	2.13	22.62
Standard deviation	0.15	0.19	0.19	0.21	0.22	0.19	0.13	0.15	0.20	0.20	0.18	0.17	0.18
Average monthly	2.11	1.92	2.19	2.28	2.28	1.32	0.67	0.95	1.34	1.83	1.81	1.92	20.62
Standard deviation	0.17	0.17	0.18	0.20	0.20	0.17	0.12	0.14	0.18	0.20	0.17	0.16	0.17
High monthly total	5.26	4.96	6.54	6.40	6.49	4.80	2.90	5.02	7.37	5.82	5.21	8.90	8.90
Year of occurrence	1914	1976	1904	1986	1977	1945	1912	1930	1982	1981	1988	1983	1983
Low monthly total	0.00†	0.18	0.03	0.10	0.00	0.00†	0.00†	0.00†	0.00†	0.00†	0.00	0.00	0.00†
Year of occurrence	1961	1988	1956	1918	1940	1994	1994	1967	1974	1978	1904	1986	1986
Record high daily	1.65	2.61	2.06	2.18	2.29	2.09	2.11	2.76	3.19	2.30	2.00	1.39	3.19
Day of occurrence	14	9	31	22	21	14	19	4	8	7	27	1	8
Year of occurrence	1953	1976	1936	1988	1981	1973	1912	1951	1991	1993	1989	1983	1991
Days w/pcp >= .01	9.4	8.4	9.1	8.3	8.2	4.9	3.2	4.3	4.8	5.9	7.1	8.7	82.9
Days w/pcp >= .10	5.9	5.2	5.6	5.4	5.1	2.9	1.5	2.2	2.8	3.9	4.5	5.5	51.0
Days w/pcp >= .50	1.3	1.1	1.3	1.4	1.5	0.9	0.4	0.6	0.9	1.2	1.1	1.0	12.7

Snow and Sleet in Inches

	Jan	Feb	Mar	Apr	May	Jun	Jul	Aug	Sep	Oct	Nov	Dec	Annual
Monthly normal	9.5	7.8	4.8	0.6	0.1	0.0	0.0	0.0	0.0	0.3	3.5	10.2	36.8
Standard deviation	1.1	1.0	0.8	0.2	0.1	0.0	0.0	0.0	0.0	0.2	0.7	1.2	0.4
Average monthly	13.4	9.0	5.7	0.9	0.1	0.0	0.0	0.0	0.0	0.4	3.1	10.7	43.3
Standard deviation	1.3	1.1	1.0	0.3	0.1	0.0	0.0	0.0	0.0	0.2	0.6	1.2	0.5
High monthly total	52.0	38.5	25.0	8.3	4.1	0.0†	0.0†	0.0†	0.0†	14.5	26.0	42.5	52.0
Year of occurrence	1949	1919	1938	1920	1964	1995	1995	1995	1995	1919	1985	1971	1949
Low monthly total	0.0†	0.0†	0.0†	0.0†	0.0†	0.0†	0.0†	0.0†	0.0†	0.0†	0.0†	0.0†	0.0†
Year of occurrence	1990	1991	1995	1995	1995	1995	1995	1995	1995	1995	1995	1994	1994
Record high daily	14.0	15.5	15.0	6.5	4.0	0.0†	0.0†	0.0†	0.0†	6.0†	10.0	13.0†	15.5
Day of occurrence	15	8	31	2	2	30	31	31	30	24	12	3	8
Year of occurrence	1916	1909	1936	1906	1964	1995	1995	1995	1995	1919	1978	1971	1909
Days w/snow >= .1	5.3	3.8	2.0	0.4	0.1	0.0	0.0	0.0	0.0	0.1	1.3	4.2	16.6
Days w/snow >= 5	0.8	0.4	0.4	0.0	0.0	0.0	0.0	0.0	0.0	0.0	0.2	0.6	2.2
Days w/snow >= 10	0.1	0.1	0.1	0.0	0.0	0.0	0.0	0.0	0.0	0.0	0.0	0.1	0.2

Degree Days

	Jan	Feb	Mar	Apr	May	Jun	Jul	Aug	Sep	Oct	Nov	Dec	Annual
Heating normal	1157	891	739	465	225	58	1	8	105	378	753	1096	5882
Heating average	1155	901	750	453	228	63	3	8	108	386	767	1084	5911
Cooling normal	0	0	0	4	36	165	368	308	88	3	0	0	975
Cooling average	0	0	0	2	31	136	334	283	79	3	0	0	870
Growing 40 normal	31	77	189	344	570	751	923	890	671	437	158	41	5087
Growing 40 average	30	69	186	354	563	719	887	865	658	429	161	44	4971
Growing 50 normal	3	18	71	180	355	542	744	702	461	249	57	5	3390
Growing 50 average	2	13	69	189	355	519	709	681	460	249	58	6	3317

† Also occurred on earlier date(s).

Location: Orem Treatment Plant   County: Utah   Latitude: 40.283   Longitude: -111.733
Elevation: 4510 feet   Period of Record: 1982-1995

OREM TREATMENT PLANT
Monthly Data Summary

Maximum Temperature in °F

	Jan	Feb	Mar	Apr	May	Jun	Jul	Aug	Sep	Oct	Nov	Dec	Annual
Monthly normal													
Standard deviation													
Average monthly	33.4	40.2	53.0	63.7	71.9	82.8	89.1	88.9	78.0	65.0	48.2	36.5	62.6
Standard deviation	8.9	10.7	9.4	10.0	9.8	8.2	5.4	5.2	8.7	9.2	9.9	9.3	8.7
High monthly average	41.4	49.2	59.8	71.5	77.8	87.7	93.0	96.3	82.9	71.5	56.4	45.7	96.3
Year of occurrence	1983	1992	1986	1992	1992	1988	1989	1995	1990	1988	1995	1995	1995
Low monthly average	26.4	29.5	46.3	55.4	65.6	77.7	87.0	85.8	72.1	57.9	40.4	30.3	26.4
Year of occurrence	1984	1989	1984	1983	1983	1984	1992	1987	1986	1984	1992	1985	1984
Record high daily	55	66†	84	85†	89	98†	101	104	97	84	73	64	104
Day of occurrence	12	29	29	29	30	30	26	6	1	5	1	1	6
Year of occurrence	1990	1992	1986	1992	1984	1990	1992	1995	1995	1985	1988	1995	1995
Record low daily	6	0†	28	37	44	55	67	69	45	36	23	4†	0
Day of occurrence	19	7	4	11	11	1	10	25	29	31	25	23	7
Year of occurrence	1984	1989	1989	1991	1983	1990	1983	1987	1982	1991	1992	1990	1989
Days w/max >= 100	0.0	0.0	0.0	0.0	0.0	0.0	0.2	0.8	0.0	0.0	0.0	0.0	1.0
Days w/max >= 90	0.0	0.0	0.0	0.0	0.0	5.6	16.1	14.2	1.8	0.0	0.0	0.0	37.2
Days w/max <= 32	14.8	5.5	0.1	0.0	0.0	0.0	0.0	0.0	0.0	0.0	1.5	9.6	33.6

Minimum Temperature in °F

	Jan	Feb	Mar	Apr	May	Jun	Jul	Aug	Sep	Oct	Nov	Dec	Annual
Monthly normal													
Standard deviation													
Average monthly	15.4	21.3	32.1	39.2	46.4	54.9	61.0	59.7	50.7	39.1	29.9	21.5	39.3
Standard deviation	11.0	11.3	6.5	6.9	7.5	6.0	5.0	5.1	7.4	5.8	7.5	9.2	7.4
High monthly average	25.5	30.4	37.8	45.0	52.2	58.4	65.1	63.9	56.9	41.8	35.6	32.2	65.1
Year of occurrence	1983	1986	1992	1992	1992	1986	1984	1995	1995	1988	1995	1995	1984
Low monthly average	6.0	11.6	26.8	35.1	42.7	52.8	57.5	55.2	46.4	36.0	24.6	12.0	6.0
Year of occurrence	1989	1989	1984	1984	1983	1991	1987	1987	1988	1982	1992	1990	1989
Record high daily	37†	43†	46	58†	66	74	76	78	76	73	49	46	78
Day of occurrence	13	24	25	30	22	29	6	29	7	1	30	12	29
Year of occurrence	1990	1986	1985	1992	1984	1984	1984	1982	1982	1993	1995	1995	1982
Record low daily	-19†	-27	11	24	28	38†	42	43	32	22	7	-14	-27
Day of occurrence	19	7	4	9	7	2	19	25	29	31	29	23	7
Year of occurrence	1984	1989	1985	1988	1984	1990	1987	1989	1985	1991	1992	1990	1989
Days w/min <= 32	29.9	24.0	15.6	6.2	0.8	0.0	0.0	0.0	0.1	4.8	19.3	27.7	135.3
Days w/min <= 0	2.6	1.4	0.0	0.0	0.0	0.0	0.0	0.0	0.0	0.0	0.0	0.8	4.9
Days w/min <= -20	0.0	0.3	0.0	0.0	0.0	0.0	0.0	0.0	0.0	0.0	0.0	0.0	0.3

Mean Temperature in °F

	Jan	Feb	Mar	Apr	May	Jun	Jul	Aug	Sep	Oct	Nov	Dec	Annual
Monthly normal													
Standard deviation													
Average monthly	24.4	30.8	42.5	51.5	59.2	68.8	75.1	74.3	64.4	52.1	39.0	29.0	50.9
Standard deviation	9.4	10.5	7.2	7.7	8.0	6.4	4.3	4.4	7.3	6.8	8.0	8.7	7.4
High monthly average	33.4	39.8	48.1	58.2	65.0	72.4	77.4	80.1	69.8	56.7	46.0	39.0	80.1
Year of occurrence	1983	1992	1986	1992	1992	1986	1989	1995	1995	1988	1995	1995	1995
Low monthly average	16.9	20.5	36.6	45.3	54.1	66.5	72.4	70.5	59.3	47.0	32.5	21.5	16.9
Year of occurrence	1989	1989	1984	1983	1983	1983	1987	1987	1986	1982	1992	1990	1989

† Also occurred on earlier date(s).

Data copyright (c) 1995 Utah Climate Center - Phone (801) 797-2190, Fax (801) 797-2117
Use of data is encouraged, but must credit the Utah Climate Center

OREM TREATMENT PLANT
Monthly Data Summary

Precipitation in Inches

	Jan	Feb	Mar	Apr	May	Jun	Jul	Aug	Sep	Oct	Nov	Dec	Annual
Monthly normal													
Standard deviation													
Average monthly	0.86	1.19	1.18	1.18	1.58	0.85	0.72	0.95	1.43	1.45	1.15	0.88	13.41
Standard deviation	0.09	0.12	0.10	0.13	0.15	0.11	0.08	0.10	0.16	0.15	0.12	0.09	0.12
High monthly total	1.84	2.79	2.54	2.83	4.81	2.43	1.20	·2.28	5.75	2.97	2.24	3.35	5.75
Year of occurrence	1993	1986	1993	1994	1995	1984	1985	1983	1982	1994	1983	1983	1982
Low monthly total	0.25	0.00	0.35	0.05	0.33	0.00	0.09	0.08	0.20	0.45	0.34	0.08	0.00†
Year of occurrence	1989	1988	1988	1987	1984	1994	1991	1985	1987	1995	1993	1989	1994
Record high daily	1.01	0.95	0.95	1.30	1.31†	0.89	0.80	0.67	1.27	1.16	0.85	0.69	1.31
Day of occurrence	10	27	9	26	2	6	21	16	7	19	20	25	2
Year of occurrence	1993	1983	1986	1989	1995	1984	1987	1990	1991	1990	1983	1983	1995
Days w/pcp >= .01	6.7	7.0	8.2	7.2	8.5	4.2	5.0	6.0	6.2	6.1	6.9	5.9	78.2
Days w/pcp >= .10	2.8	3.5	4.1	3.2	4.6	2.4	2.5	2.7	3.4	3.8	3.1	3.2	39.5
Days w/pcp >= .50	0.2	0.6	0.4	0.7	0.6	0.6	0.3	0.4	0.9	1.0	0.7	0.3	6.8

Snow and Sleet in Inches

	Jan	Feb	Mar	Apr	May	Jun	Jul	Aug	Sep	Oct	Nov	Dec	Annual
Monthly normal													
Standard deviation													
Average monthly	9.6	6.7	1.7	1.1	0.2	0.0	0.0	0.0	0.0	0.6	2.7	7.0	29.5
Standard deviation	1.1	1.0	0.5	0.3	0.1	0.0	0.0	0.0	0.0	0.3	0.5	0.8	0.4
High monthly total	32.1	19.5	8.0	5.5	2.0	0.0†	0.0†	0.0†	0.0†	6.0	16.3	16.0	32.1
Year of occurrence	1993	1989	1983	1984	1983	1995	1995	1995	1995	1995	1994	1988	1993
Low monthly total	0.5	0.0†	0.0†	0.0†	0.0†	0.0†	0.0†	0.0†	0.0†	0.0†	0.0†	0.0	0.0†
Year of occurrence	1983	1988	1994	1994	1995	1995	1995	1995	1995	1994	1995	1987	1987
Record high daily	12.0	10.0	7.5	3.0	2.0	0.0†	0.0†	0.0†	0.0†	6.0	7.0	6.0†	12.0
Day of occurrence	10	3	25	13	11	30	31	31	30	22	18	2	10
Year of occurrence	1993	1989	1983	1991	1983	1995	1995	1995	1995	1995	1994	1991	1993
Days w/snow >= .1	4.5	3.3	1.0	0.8	0.2	0.0	0.0	0.0	0.0	0.2	1.5	3.2	15.3
Days w/snow >= 5	0.3	0.4	0.1	0.0	0.0	0.0	0.0	0.0	0.0	0.1	0.1	0.2	1.2
Days w/snow >= 10	0.2	0.1	0.0	0.0	0.0	0.0	0.0	0.0	0.0	0.0	0.0	0.0	0.2

Degree Days

	Jan	Feb	Mar	Apr	May	Jun	Jul	Aug	Sep	Oct	Nov	Dec	Annual
Heating normal													
Heating average	1257	967	696	408	210	36	2	2	96	401	779	1113	5973
Cooling normal													
Cooling average	0	0	0	1	29	151	314	292	77	0	0	0	867
Growing 40 normal													
Growing 40 average	19	59	209	387	581	756	897	878	675	413	143	33	5055
Growing 50 normal													
Growing 50 average	0	12	83	214	365	549	714	696	461	239	49	4	3392

† Also occurred on earlier date(s).

Location: Panguitch   County: Garfield   Latitude: 37.817   Longitude: -112.433
Elevation: 6610 feet   Period of Record: 1904-1996

PANGUITCH
Monthly Data Summary

Maximum Temperature in °F

	Jan	Feb	Mar	Apr	May	Jun	Jul	Aug	Sep	Oct	Nov	Dec	Annual
Monthly normal	40.1	44.5	50.8	60.0	69.5	79.9	85.3	82.5	75.9	66.1	51.7	41.8	62.3
Standard deviation	9.2	9.4	9.9	9.7	9.1	7.4	5.0	5.4	7.1	9.3	10.7	10.0	8.5
Average monthly	39.2	43.1	50.2	60.0	69.0	78.8	84.0	81.6	75.6	65.2	51.2	41.1	61.6
Standard deviation	9.0	9.2	9.4	9.7	8.8	7.7	5.8	5.6	7.1	9.3	10.5	9.6	8.5
High monthly average	49.5	53.5	62.5	69.2	75.9	87.3	90.3	88.2	81.6	74.6	63.7	53.0	90.3
Year of occurrence	1981	1995	1934	1989	1984	1994	1994	1994	1979	1952	1949	1958	1994
Low monthly average	23.2	30.7	41.1	50.6	61.9	67.5	75.5	73.5	64.3	53.9	38.2	30.0	23.2
Year of occurrence	1937	1933	1952	1975	1915	1925	1925	1925	1925	1912	1925	1913	1937
Record high daily	63	69	75	82†	89†	98	100	98	94	85†	77	63†	100
Day of occurrence	12	26	31	29	7	25	6	5	1	1	6	10	6
Year of occurrence	1990	1986	1966	1992	1962	1994	1989	1994	1995	1980	1934	1987	1989
Record low daily	3	10	19	0	36	0	60†	61	46	0	17	2	0†
Day of occurrence	9	6	1	1	8	1	12	29	18	1	23	13	1
Year of occurrence	1937	1989	1971	1928	1930	1915	1936	1951	1965	1917	1931	1932	1917
Days w/max >= 100	0.0	0.0	0.0	0.0	0.0	0.0	0.0	0.0	0.0	0.0	0.0	0.0	0.0
Days w/max >= 90	0.0	0.0	0.0	0.0	0.0	1.6	5.1	2.2	0.3	0.0	0.0	0.0	9.4
Days w/max <= 32	6.7	3.5	0.9	0.1	0.0	0.0	0.0	0.0	0.0	0.1	1.4	5.7	18.4

Minimum Temperature in °F

	Jan	Feb	Mar	Apr	May	Jun	Jul	Aug	Sep	Oct	Nov	Dec	Annual
Monthly normal	7.8	13.5	19.2	24.6	31.7	38.5	46.2	44.7	36.2	26.3	17.9	9.5	26.4
Standard deviation	11.8	10.9	8.3	7.0	6.4	6.0	6.0	6.1	7.4	7.6	9.3	11.3	8.2
Average monthly	6.8	12.5	19.1	24.6	31.2	37.9	45.3	43.9	35.2	25.6	16.5	9.2	25.6
Standard deviation	12.2	11.7	8.1	6.9	6.3	6.3	6.0	6.1	7.3	7.4	9.1	11.4	8.2
High monthly average	17.7	23.0	26.3	30.8	36.2	47.7	52.1	49.4	41.2	34.0	24.4	17.6	52.1
Year of occurrence	1956	1930	1978	1946	1994	1922	1917	1955	1963	1972	1963	1977	1917
Low monthly average	-10.0	-7.8	12.5	19.3	26.6	31.3	39.4	34.7	28.4	20.0	9.3	-2.0	-10.0
Year of occurrence	1924	1933	1964	1922	1933	1923	1944	1949	1912	1923	1929	1932	1924
Record high daily	38	38†	47	55	58†	67	68	62	64	52	43	37	68
Day of occurrence	7	19	31	17	28	22	13	5	9	29	8	24	13
Year of occurrence	1962	1986	1946	1946	1986	1912	1923	1957	1927	1940	1931	1955	1923
Record low daily	-38	-31†	-11	-2	10†	0	29†	25	14	-10	-20	-39	-39
Day of occurrence	9	7	2	7	9	1	8	27	22	30	17	27	27
Year of occurrence	1937	1989	1939	1921	1930	1915	1948	1992	1912	1971	1964	1916	1916
Days w/min <= 32	30.6	27.8	29.9	26.3	18.1	5.5	0.3	1.0	11.1	25.5	28.6	30.2	234.6
Days w/min <= 0	9.0	4.4	0.6	0.0	0.0	0.0	0.0	0.0	0.0	0.0	1.2	6.5	21.8
Days w/min <= -20	0.7	0.3	0.0	0.0	0.0	0.0	0.0	0.0	0.0	0.0	0.0	0.2	1.2

Mean Temperature in °F

	Jan	Feb	Mar	Apr	May	Jun	Jul	Aug	Sep	Oct	Nov	Dec	Annual
Monthly normal	24.0	29.0	35.0	42.3	50.6	59.2	65.7	63.6	56.1	46.2	34.8	25.6	44.3
Standard deviation	9.3	8.9	7.7	6.9	6.6	5.7	3.8	4.2	5.8	6.7	8.4	9.3	6.9
Average monthly	23.1	27.8	34.6	42.3	50.1	58.3	64.6	62.8	55.4	45.4	33.8	25.1	43.6
Standard deviation	9.4	9.1	7.2	6.8	6.3	5.8	4.1	4.1	5.5	6.3	7.9	9.1	6.8
High monthly average	32.5	36.5	42.1	48.8	55.6	65.7	69.4	68.6	60.1	50.6	39.2	33.2	69.4
Year of occurrence	1956	1995	1989	1989	1984	1994	1917	1994	1960	1963	1962	1980	1917
Low monthly average	6.9	11.4	28.0	35.3	44.4	51.2	59.0	57.9	48.8	38.2	27.2	14.4	6.9
Year of occurrence	1937	1933	1948	1922	1933	1923	1924	1925	1912	1923	1925	1932	1937

† Also occurred on earlier date(s).

PANGUITCH
Monthly Data Summary

Precipitation in Inches

	Jan	Feb	Mar	Apr	May	Jun	Jul	Aug	Sep	Oct	Nov	Dec	Annual
Monthly normal	0.48	0.61	0.79	0.67	0.82	0.63	1.50	1.78	1.05	0.71	0.78	0.51	10.32
Standard deviation	0.06	0.09	0.08	0.08	0.09	0.08	0.14	0.16	0.13	0.09	0.10	0.06	0.10
Average monthly	0.56	0.59	0.83	0.66	0.64	0.50	1.41	1.64	0.92	0.87	0.70	0.54	9.86
Standard deviation	0.07	0.09	0.10	0.08	0.08	0.08	0.14	0.16	0.12	0.13	0.17	0.07	0.11
High monthly total	2.45	2.46	2.93	2.39	2.33	2.23	3.97	5.17	5.14	4.37	8.60	1.98	8.60
Year of occurrence	1993	1993	1906	1988	1992	1972	1929	1987	1967	1912	1905	1949	1905
Low monthly total	0.00	0.00†	0.00†	0.00†	0.00†	0.00†	0.07	0.00	0.00†	0.00†	0.00†	0.00†	0.00†
Year of occurrence	1932	1964	1915	1938	1974	1987	1949	1985	1993	1995	1948	1989	1989
Record high daily	1.27	2.30	1.90	1.20	1.03	1.00	1.85	2.00	1.44†	2.47	7.00	1.05	7.00
Day of occurrence	28	1	4	7	30	8	14	29	15	27	30	20	30
Year of occurrence	1915	1923	1938	1906	1937	1909	1964	1904	1978	1912	1905	1949	1905
Days w/pcp >= .01	4.4	4.4	5.7	4.9	4.9	3.3	7.2	8.5	4.4	3.8	3.4	3.8	59.4
Days w/pcp >= .10	1.9	2.0	2.8	2.3	2.1	1.6	3.9	4.5	2.4	2.2	1.9	1.8	29.8
Days w/pcp >= .50	0.1	0.1	0.3	0.2	0.1	0.2	0.7	0.8	0.5	0.5	0.3	0.2	4.2

Snow and Sleet in Inches

	Jan	Feb	Mar	Apr	May	Jun	Jul	Aug	Sep	Oct	Nov	Dec	Annual
Monthly normal	4.0	4.1	4.5	0.6	0.4	0.0	0.0	0.0	0.0	0.1	2.2	3.0	19.0
Standard deviation	0.7	0.9	0.8	0.2	0.3	0.0	0.0	0.0	0.0	0.1	0.7	0.6	0.3
Average monthly	6.1	4.7	4.3	1.1	0.3	0.0	0.0	0.0	0.0	0.9	2.8	4.6	24.9
Standard deviation	0.9	0.7	0.7	0.3	0.2	0.0	0.0	0.0	0.0	0.4	0.7	0.8	0.4
High monthly total	32.0	23.5	24.0	9.0	8.0	1.0	0.0†	0.0†	0.0†	24.0	15.0	21.0	32.0
Year of occurrence	1949	1909	1961	1945	1979	1925	1995	1995	1995	1908	1906	1967	1949
Low monthly total	0.0†	0.0†	0.0†	0.0†	0.0†	0.0†	0.0†	0.0†	0.0†	0.0†	0.0†	0.0†	0.0†
Year of occurrence	1988	1995	1995	1995	1995	1995	1995	1995	1995	1995	1995	1994	1994
Record high daily	12.0	12.0	10.0	6.0	8.0	1.0	0.0†	0.0†	0.0†	12.0	10.0	11.0	12.0†
Day of occurrence	30	7	18	10	8	5	31	31	30	17	16	12	17
Year of occurrence	1993	1965	1961	1945	1979	1925	1995	1995	1995	1908	1964	1940	1908
Days w/snow >= .1	2.9	2.6	2.2	0.7	0.2	0.0	0.0	0.0	0.0	0.2	1.1	2.1	11.0
Days w/snow >= 5	0.2	0.1	0.1	0.0	0.0	0.0	0.0	0.0	0.0	0.1	0.2	0.2	1.0
Days w/snow >= 10	0.0	0.0	0.0	0.0	0.0	0.0	0.0	0.0	0.0	0.0	0.0	0.0	0.1

Degree Days

	Jan	Feb	Mar	Apr	May	Jun	Jul	Aug	Sep	Oct	Nov	Dec	Annual
Heating normal	1271	1016	929	680	445	186	35	76	271	582	906	1220	7622
Heating average	1290	1042	936	674	452	207	55	92	286	605	926	1224	7793
Cooling normal	0	0	0	0	0	12	58	33	2	0	0	0	107
Cooling average	0	0	0	0	0	8	42	23	1	0	0	0	77
Growing 40 normal	58	90	179	301	451	553	673	651	528	403	187	77	4157
Growing 40 average	49	75	167	298	437	538	648	632	512	389	179	67	3996
Growing 50 normal	8	21	69	165	304	439	536	500	388	255	80	14	2784
Growing 50 average	7	16	60	163	291	421	512	483	377	241	73	12	2661

† Also occurred on earlier date(s).

Location: Park City Radio   County: Summit   Latitude: 40.650   Longitude: -111.500
Elevation: 7140 feet   Period of Record: 1889-1991

PARK CITY RADIO
Monthly Data Summary

Maximum Temperature in °F

	Jan	Feb	Mar	Apr	May	Jun	Jul	Aug	Sep	Oct	Nov	Dec	Annual
Monthly normal	35.0	36.3	44.3	54.7	63.5	75.1	81.7	79.9	69.6	59.6	41.4	32.0	56.1
Standard deviation	9.1	9.6	9.1	10.1	10.5	8.5	5.9	4.8	10.1	9.1	10.5	10.3	9.0
Average monthly	32.3	35.7	41.4	52.8	63.3	74.4	81.9	79.3	70.2	58.2	43.5	34.3	55.6
Standard deviation	8.6	9.3	9.2	10.9	10.3	9.5	6.9	5.8	8.9	10.3	10.7	9.2	9.1
High monthly average	41.4	57.0	61.0	68.1	74.4	83.2	88.7	84.5	77.0	72.1	58.9	43.0	88.7
Year of occurrence	1911	1913	1910	1910	1913	1903	1901	1940	1948	1901	1912	1939	1901
Low monthly average	19.3	18.9	30.5	40.7	47.0	64.8	71.5	72.6	61.6	45.7	33.1	23.9	18.9
Year of occurrence	1937	1920	1924	1896	1896	1932	1897	1904	1889	1923	1922	1990	1920
Record high daily	56	64	71†	86	91	101	100†	95	91	82	77	62	101
Day of occurrence	13	2	21	26	13	28	24	13	4	2	8	5	28
Year of occurrence	1953	1913	1910	1910	1903	1903	1931	1940	1903	1901	1899	1939	1903
Record low daily	-2†	-6	10	23†	33	41	0	53	35	25†	9	-8	-8
Day of occurrence	21	9	1	1	12	6	31	19	24	30	22	21	21
Year of occurrence	1937	1933	1922	1936	1896	1932	1914	1889	1934	1919	1931	1990	1990
Days w/max >= 100	0.0	0.0	0.0	0.0	0.0	0.0	0.0	0.0	0.0	0.0	0.0	0.0	0.1
Days w/max >= 90	0.0	0.0	0.0	0.0	0.0	0.8	3.1	0.8	0.0	0.0	0.0	0.0	4.7
Days w/max <= 32	14.7	9.0	5.1	0.9	0.0	0.0	0.0	0.0	0.0	0.3	5.0	12.7	48.1

Minimum Temperature in °F

	Jan	Feb	Mar	Apr	May	Jun	Jul	Aug	Sep	Oct	Nov	Dec	Annual
Monthly normal	15.2	16.4	23.7	30.4	37.2	45.7	51.8	51.4	42.0	33.1	21.9	13.5	31.9
Standard deviation	9.4	10.3	7.5	8.7	7.0	7.3	4.8	4.6	8.3	6.5	9.2	10.7	7.9
Average monthly	11.9	15.0	20.0	28.0	36.1	43.6	50.0	48.7	41.0	31.8	21.5	14.8	30.2
Standard deviation	10.5	10.6	9.4	8.5	7.6	7.8	7.4	6.2	7.9	7.3	9.5	10.4	8.6
High monthly average	21.6	27.8	29.4	35.4	46.8	53.0	59.6	53.1	52.6	38.7	29.5	25.0	59.6
Year of occurrence	1986	1991	1986	1987	1913	1924	1916	1982	1916	1988	1908	1917	1916
Low monthly average	-5.8	2.6	-1.5	14.1	25.8	35.9	31.8	30.0	28.7	19.3	9.9	0.3	-5.8
Year of occurrence	1917	1933	1917	1917	1917	1907	1913	1913	1912	1912	1916	1916	1917
Record high daily	54	40†	46	54†	57†	73	76	71	76	56	44	40	76†
Day of occurrence	20	28	18	22	17	26	12	3	4	12	7	29	4
Year of occurrence	1920	1908	1921	1989	1927	1924	1903	1916	1924	1908	1917	1896	1924
Record low daily	-28	-28	-23	-4	0	11	0	26†	8	-5	-11†	-30	-30
Day of occurrence	16	10	2	1	17	11	31	17	26	24	22	20	20
Year of occurrence	1917	1933	1917	1917	1982	1917	1914	1913	1908	1908	1985	1990	1990
Days w/min <= 32	30.0	27.1	28.7	21.1	9.7	2.2	0.7	0.7	4.6	15.5	26.3	30.0	197.8
Days w/min <= 0	4.1	2.7	1.1	0.1	0.0	0.0	0.0	0.0	0.0	0.0	0.9	2.7	11.6
Days w/min <= -20	0.2	0.2	0.0	0.0	0.0	0.0	0.0	0.0	0.0	0.0	0.0	0.2	0.7

Mean Temperature in °F

	Jan	Feb	Mar	Apr	May	Jun	Jul	Aug	Sep	Oct	Nov	Dec	Annual
Monthly normal	25.1	26.3	34.0	42.5	50.4	60.4	66.8	65.7	55.8	46.4	31.6	22.7	44.0
Standard deviation	8.6	9.4	7.6	8.8	8.1	7.3	4.4	4.0	8.6	6.9	9.2	10.0	7.7
Average monthly	22.1	25.5	30.7	40.4	49.8	59.0	65.9	64.0	55.7	45.1	32.6	24.6	43.0
Standard deviation	8.7	8.9	8.4	8.7	8.1	7.7	6.1	4.8	7.3	7.6	8.9	9.1	7.9
High monthly average	30.9	36.7	42.4	48.5	60.6	65.7	71.3	68.1	62.3	52.9	39.3	33.0	71.3
Year of occurrence	1986	1991	1910	1987	1913	1988	1931	1937	1990	1901	1899	1896	1931
Low monthly average	9.3	14.8	16.1	30.0	38.2	51.0	53.7	52.6	50.7	35.9	24.8	13.7	9.3
Year of occurrence	1937	1933	1917	1917	1896	1907	1913	1913	1929	1919	1938	1916	1937

† Also occurred on earlier date(s).

PARK CITY RADIO
Monthly Data Summary

Precipitation in Inches

	Jan	Feb	Mar	Apr	May	Jun	Jul	Aug	Sep	Oct	Nov	Dec	Annual
Monthly normal	2.00	1.40	1.49	1.40	1.55	1.11	2.30	1.62	2.39	1.35	1.95	2.13	20.68
Standard deviation	0.14	0.13	0.11	0.12	0.15	0.13	0.24	0.17	0.23	0.15	0.19	0.18	0.16
Average monthly	2.37	2.10	2.39	1.58	1.20	0.79	1.31	1.46	1.21	1.41	1.58	2.07	19.48
Standard deviation	0.23	0.20	0.19	0.15	0.13	0.11	0.17	0.18	0.16	0.16	0.16	0.21	0.17
High monthly total	10.51	7.12	9.14	4.89	3.80	3.15	7.06	7.45	7.29	4.17	4.40	6.70	10.51
Year of occurrence	1907	1891	1912	1929	1949	1984	1913	1922	1982	1910	1922	1922	1907
Low monthly total	0.00†	0.00	0.00†	0.00†	0.00†	0.00†	0.00†	0.00†	0.00	0.00†	0.00†	0.00†	0.00†
Year of occurrence	1917	1919	1990	1920	1990	1991	1917	1990	1890	1988	1990	1990	1990
Record high daily	2.63	3.60	1.54	2.00	1.42	1.77	2.22	2.55†	2.10	2.00	1.90	3.00	3.60
Day of occurrence	17	25	3	19	10	16	18	19	26	19	16	31	25
Year of occurrence	1906	1891	1938	1896	1985	1929	1913	1922	1982	1910	1930	1889	1891
Days w/pcp >= .01	7.9	8.1	8.8	6.9	5.8	3.8	4.8	5.2	5.0	5.2	5.8	6.9	75.2
Days w/pcp >= .10	5.5	5.5	6.3	4.6	3.2	2.2	3.1	3.3	3.0	3.7	4.2	4.7	50.1
Days w/pcp >= .50	1.5	1.2	1.5	0.8	0.7	0.4	0.8	1.0	0.7	0.9	1.1	1.4	12.0

Snow and Sleet in Inches

	Jan	Feb	Mar	Apr	May	Jun	Jul	Aug	Sep	Oct	Nov	Dec	Annual
Monthly normal	24.0	25.8	17.5	10.2	3.5	0.4	0.0	0.0	1.7	0.8	28.0	26.8	138.9
Standard deviation	1.9	2.3	1.4	1.3	0.6	0.2	0.0	0.0	0.5	0.3	2.8	2.0	1.1
Average monthly	22.0	21.8	20.7	11.2	3.1	0.3	0.0	0.0	1.1	3.9	15.4	20.8	120.3
Standard deviation	2.0	2.2	1.8	1.4	0.6	0.2	0.0	0.0	0.4	0.8	1.8	2.0	1.1
High monthly total	75.0	76.0	57.0	48.5	20.5	6.6	0.0†	0.0†	10.3	42.0	70.1	70.3	76.0
Year of occurrence	1923	1936	1924	1929	1907	1914	1990	1990	1900	1949	1983	1983	1936
Low monthly total	0.0†	0.0†	0.0†	0.0†	0.0†	0.0†	0.0†	0.0†	0.0†	0.0†	0.0†	0.0†	0.0†
Year of occurrence	1917	1991	1991	1990	1991	1991	1990	1990	1990	1989	1939	1919	1919
Record high daily	26.0	36.0	15.0	20.0	9.0	5.5	0.0†	0.0†	8.0	12.0†	22.0	24.0	36.0
Day of occurrence	17	25	23	19	24	6	31	31	30	19	16	30	25
Year of occurrence	1906	1891	1924	1896	1907	1914	1990	1990	1926	1949	1930	1891	1891
Days w/snow >= .1	6.7	6.5	6.7	4.1	1.3	0.2	0.0	0.0	0.4	1.4	4.3	6.3	38.6
Days w/snow >= 5	1.5	1.5	1.3	0.6	0.2	0.0	0.0	0.0	0.1	0.2	1.3	1.5	8.3
Days w/snow >= 10	0.3	0.3	0.3	0.1	0.0	0.0	0.0	0.0	0.0	0.1	0.2	0.4	1.8

Degree Days

	Jan	Feb	Mar	Apr	May	Jun	Jul	Aug	Sep	Oct	Nov	Dec	Annual
Heating normal	1230	1088	960	673	448	160	31	37	279	551	995	1294	7752
Heating average	1291	1098	1057	733	469	197	57	72	280	604	948	1236	8047
Cooling normal	0	0	0	0	0	27	85	58	11	0	0	0	182
Cooling average	0	0	0	0	0	22	84	42	5	0	0	0	155
Growing 40 normal	24	28	94	235	383	585	717	730	486	293	77	14	3671
Growing 40 average	10	24	67	203	379	541	704	672	488	286	94	21	3493
Growing 50 normal	1	2	25	104	217	389	509	495	301	153	18	0	2219
Growing 50 average	0	2	14	90	216	366	511	461	308	148	26	1	2149

† Also occurred on earlier date(s).

Location: Price Game Farm   County: Carbon   Latitude: 39.617   Longitude: -110.833
Elevation: 5580 feet   Period of Record: 1888-1968

PRICE GAME FARM
Monitorly Data Summary

Maximum Temperature in °F

	Jan	Feb	Mar	Apr	May	Jun	Jul	Aug	Sep	Oct	Nov	Dec	Annual
Monthly normal													
Standard deviation													
Average monthly	36.6	42.9	52.2	63.4	73.2	83.6	90.2	87.7	79.9	67.9	51.5	39.8	64.1
Standard deviation	8.3	9.0	9.2	9.6	9.3	8.0	5.1	5.5	7.6	9.0	9.3	8.3	8.2
High monthly average	47.7	56.0	64.5	74.8	82.3	91.5	95.6	92.8	84.7	76.0	60.0	50.0	95.6
Year of occurrence	1961	1934	1934	1934	1934	1934	1940	1934	1956	1926	1949	1958	1934
Low monthly average	21.3	30.3	41.0	54.7	63.0	76.3	85.7	81.8	70.8	57.2	41.6	30.6	21.3
Year of occurrence	1937	1955	1952	1922	1917	1967	1918	1968	1961	1919	1922	1951	1937
Record high daily	62	68†	79	86†	94	101†	108	110	96†	87†	78	65	110
Day of occurrence	24	22	14	25	4	23	14	3	3	6	3	7	3
Year of occurrence	1917	1958	1934	1946	1962	1954	1925	1918	1950	1963	1920	1920	1918
Record low daily	8	10†	0	35	38	54	64	67†	50†	37†	22	10	0
Day of occurrence	12	10	31	17	11	7	12	30	18	29	27	27	31
Year of occurrence	1963	1933	1935	1922	1918	1941	1936	1932	1965	1961	1919	1924	1935
Days w/max >= 100	0.0	0.0	0.0	0.0	0.0	0.2	0.9	0.3	0.0	0.0	0.0	0.0	1.5
Days w/max >= 90	0.0	0.0	0.0	0.0	0.4	7.3	17.8	11.7	2.2	0.0	0.0	0.0	40.5
Days w/max <= 32	9.2	3.5	0.3	0.0	0.0	0.0	0.0	0.0	0.0	0.0	0.5	6.2	20.3

Minimum Temperature in °F

	Jan	Feb	Mar	Apr	May	Jun	Jul	Aug	Sep	Oct	Nov	Dec	Annual
Monthly normal													
Standard deviation													
Average monthly	9.1	17.1	25.2	32.9	41.4	49.2	56.1	54.0	45.3	35.0	22.9	13.7	33.5
Standard deviation	10.9	10.8	7.0	7.7	6.8	6.6	5.3	5.4	7.0	7.0	7.5	10.0	7.7
High monthly average	22.2	26.3	30.5	40.9	48.3	56.9	61.9	59.6	52.5	41.5	29.6	24.4	61.9
Year of occurrence	1965	1954	1949	1946	1947	1918	1917	1945	1947	1940	1954	1946	1917
Low monthly average	-9.0	-2.8	16.0	18.0	36.0	40.4	50.3	47.5	37.0	29.5	15.3	-2.2	-9.0
Year of occurrence	1937	1933	1964	1924	1968	1924	1958	1924	1924	1919	1938	1924	1937
Record high daily	47	42	53	56	76	75	72	94	63†	63	50	40	94
Day of occurrence	20	18	31	23	19	20	3	4	2	15	6	1	4
Year of occurrence	1911	1948	1935	1949	1919	1919	1934	1918	1955	1943	1944	1929	1918
Record low daily	-29	-23†	-7	8	19	27	31	32†	21	9	-3	-31	-31
Day of occurrence	23	10	7	3	7	8	3	29	20	31	24	26	26
Year of occurrence	1937	1933	1964	1945	1968	1966	1921	1964	1924	1935	1931	1924	1924
Days w/min <= 32	30.1	27.0	26.1	14.3	3.0	0.2	0.0	0.0	1.1	10.8	26.7	30.0	170.0
Days w/min <= 0	6.3	2.7	0.1	0.0	0.0	0.0	0.0	0.0	0.0	0.0	0.1	3.3	12.8
Days w/min <= -20	0.3	0.1	0.0	0.0	0.0	0.0	0.0	0.0	0.0	0.0	0.0	0.1	0.5

Mean Temperature in °F

	Jan	Feb	Mar	Apr	May	Jun	Jul	Aug	Sep	Oct	Nov	Dec	Annual
Monthly normal													
Standard deviation													
Average monthly	22.8	30.0	38.6	48.2	57.3	66.4	73.2	70.9	62.6	51.4	37.1	26.7	48.8
Standard deviation	8.7	9.0	7.1	7.5	7.1	6.4	4.1	4.3	6.1	6.8	7.1	7.9	6.9
High monthly average	33.1	40.9	46.6	56.1	64.8	72.7	77.2	74.7	67.7	56.4	43.5	34.1	77.2
Year of occurrence	1956	1934	1934	1946	1934	1940	1917	1934	1956	1950	1949	1950	1917
Low monthly average	6.0	14.3	30.4	40.9	51.5	61.0	69.5	66.6	54.8	43.3	29.8	17.8	6.0
Year of occurrence	1937	1933	1964	1920	1917	1967	1915	1916	1965	1919	1938	1967	1937

† Also occurred on earlier date(s).

PRICE GAME FARM
Monthly Data Summary

Precipitation in Inches

	Jan	Feb	Mar	Apr	May	Jun	Jul	Aug	Sep	Oct	Nov	Dec	Annual
Monthly normal													
Standard deviation													
Average monthly	0.67	0.70	0.70	0.64	0.64	0.72	1.03	1.32	1.15	0.86	0.53	0.90	9.87
Standard deviation	0.08	0.10	0.09	0.08	0.09	0.12	0.13	0.14	0.15	0.12	0.09	0.11	0.11
High monthly total	1.91	2.44	2.58	2.22	1.91	3.69	5.50	.4.32	5.91	3.24	2.84	2.86	5.91
Year of occurrence	1914	1919	1912	1941	1921	1927	1888	1921	1927	1941	1957	1966	1927
Low monthly total	0.00†	0.00†	0.00†	0.00†	0.00†	0.00†	0.05	0.00†	0.00	0.00†	0.00†	0.00†	0.00†
Year of occurrence	1966	1967	1956	1966	1927	1956	1963	1962	1934	1952	1956	1960	1960
Record high daily	0.85	1.97	0.98	0.80	1.45	2.85	2.30	2.00†	2.00	1.75	1.97	1.16	2.85
Day of occurrence	18	7	23	8	30	28	30	23	12	9	3	6	28
Year of occurrence	1921	1919	1929	1935	1937	1927	1888	1921	1927	1960	1957	1966	1927
Days w/pcp >= .01	4.4	4.3	4.0	4.1	3.8	3.6	5.1	6.7	5.0	3.5	2.6	4.5	52.2
Days w/pcp >= .10	2.2	2.3	2.2	2.2	2.1	1.8	2.8	3.6	2.7	2.2	1.5	2.8	28.8
Days w/pcp >= .50	0.2	0.2	0.3	0.2	0.3	0.3	0.5	0.7	0.6	0.5	0.3	0.4	4.5

Snow and Sleet in Inches

	Jan	Feb	Mar	Apr	May	Jun	Jul	Aug	Sep	Oct	Nov	Dec	Annual
Monthly normal													
Standard deviation													
Average monthly	8.0	5.6	2.6	0.1	0.3	0.0	0.0	0.0	0.0	0.2	1.6	7.2	25.8
Standard deviation	1.0	1.0	0.5	0.1	0.3	0.0	0.0	0.0	0.1	0.1	0.4	1.0	0.4
High monthly total	23.0	27.0	26.0	2.0†	13.0	0.0†	0.0†	0.0†	2.5	8.0	12.5	42.0	42.0
Year of occurrence	1930	1939	1952	1944	1922	1967	1968	1968	1965	1920	1951	1951	1951
Low monthly total	0.0†	0.0†	0.0†	0.0†	0.0†	0.0†	0.0†	0.0†	0.0†	0.0†	0.0†	0.0†	0.0†
Year of occurrence	1966	1967	1968	1966	1968	1967	1968	1968	1967	1967	1966	1963	1963
Record high daily	18.0	18.0	6.0	2.0	13.0	0.0†	0.0†	0.0†	2.5	3.5†	8.0	13.0	18.0†
Day of occurrence	18	12	18	21	10	30	31	31	17	20	24	30	12
Year of occurrence	1916	1915	1963	1944	1922	1967	1968	1968	1965	1949	1951	1951	1915
Days w/snow >= .1	3.7	2.5	1.4	0.2	0.1	0.0	0.0	0.0	0.0	0.1	0.8	2.9	11.6
Days w/snow >= 5	0.4	0.3	0.0	0.0	0.0	0.0	0.0	0.0	0.0	0.0	0.1	0.4	1.2
Days w/snow >= 10	0.0	0.0	0.0	0.0	0.0	0.0	0.0	0.0	0.0	0.0	0.0	0.1	0.1

Degree Days

	Jan	Feb	Mar	Apr	May	Jun	Jul	Aug	Sep	Oct	Nov	Dec	Annual
Heating normal													
Heating average	1271	975	798	496	242	58	1	7	108	409	822	1167	6358
Cooling normal													
Cooling average	0	0	0	0	10	97	248	184	38	0	0	0	579
Growing 40 normal													
Growing 40 average	27	71	188	354	529	661	798	771	603	426	176	49	4659
Growing 50 normal													
Growing 50 average	2	15	74	206	357	494	628	596	441	272	68	5	3164

† Also occurred on earlier date(s).

Location: Price Warehouses   County: Carbon   Latitude: 39.617   Longitude: -110.800
Elevation: 5700 feet   Period of Record: 1968-1995

PRICE WAREHOUSES
Monthly Data Summary

Maximum Temperature in °F

	Jan	Feb	Mar	Apr	May	Jun	Jul	Aug	Sep	Oct	Nov	Dec	Annual
Monthly normal													
Standard deviation													
Average monthly	36.9	42.7	52.7	63.1	72.5	83.8	90.0	88.4	79.5	65.1	49.5	39.9	63.7
Standard deviation	8.2	8.7	8.6	9.2	8.7	8.4	5.1	5.6	7.6	10.2	8.8	7.8	8.1
High monthly average	47.8	50.7	63.0	71.5	79.7	91.3	93.4	91.6	88.1	72.6	55.4	50.6	93.4
Year of occurrence	1981	1977	1972	1992	1974	1974	1988	1971	1974	1988	1976	1980	1988
Low monthly average	27.3	34.8	45.5	55.0	66.5	75.4	86.1	84.5	73.4	57.2	43.3	30.4	27.3
Year of occurrence	1979	1979	1969	1983	1980	1975	1983	1979	1985	1984	1985	1978	1979
Record high daily	62	68†	75	84†	91	101	107	100†	95†	86	69†	59†	107
Day of occurrence	31	23	26	30	28	27	26	9	15	5	4	25	26
Year of occurrence	1971	1995	1971	1992	1983	1994	1978	1990	1990	1979	1988	1980	1978
Record low daily	11†	13	28	37†	46	52	71	68	47	31	26	9	9
Day of occurrence	7	1	2	28	8	20	27	15	29	30	25	24	24
Year of occurrence	1971	1985	1971	1994	1986	1975	1983	1979	1982	1991	1993	1990	1990
Days w/max >= 100	0.0	0.0	0.0	0.0	0.0	0.0	0.3	0.1	0.0	0.0	0.0	0.0	0.4
Days w/max >= 90	0.0	0.0	0.0	0.0	0.1	7.8	18.4	14.2	1.9	0.0	0.0	0.0	42.8
Days w/max <= 32	8.8	2.1	0.1	0.0	0.0	0.0	0.0	0.0	0.0	0.1	0.6	5.5	18.4

Minimum Temperature in °F

	Jan	Feb	Mar	Apr	May	Jun	Jul	Aug	Sep	Oct	Nov	Dec	Annual
Monthly normal													
Standard deviation													
Average monthly	13.4	19.7	27.7	34.5	42.9	51.7	58.3	57.0	48.2	37.6	25.9	16.4	36.1
Standard deviation	9.2	8.9	6.7	7.3	6.6	7.3	5.4	5.2	6.9	7.6	7.5	8.2	7.2
High monthly average	22.8	28.9	34.2	43.1	47.8	57.1	62.7	60.4	53.5	42.7	30.7	24.2	62.7
Year of occurrence	1981	1986	1986	1992	1992	1974	1974	1994	1979	1972	1976	1977	1974
Low monthly average	4.4	9.8	20.5	28.4†	37.6	44.4	54.0	53.8	42.1	31.4	19.8	8.9	4.4
Year of occurrence	1973	1974	1969	1974	1975	1975	1993	1990	1986	1986	1993	1972	1973
Record high daily	34	46	48	55†	61	74	74	74†	67	57	50	41	74†
Day of occurrence	14	24	17	28	9	29	17	10	5	6	1	3	10
Year of occurrence	1980	1986	1972	1992	1989	1974	1978	1969	1974	1979	1987	1977	1969
Record low daily	-15	-10	4	8	21	28	38†	34†	24†	4	4	-14	-15
Day of occurrence	7	1	2	8	10	14	6	19	30	30	26	24	7
Year of occurrence	1971	1985	1971	1980	1986	1976	1982	1980	1986	1971	1993	1990	1971
Days w/min <= 32	30.7	26.5	23.5	11.3	2.1	0.1	0.0	0.0	0.7	7.8	23.9	30.0	163.1
Days w/min <= 0	2.9	0.8	0.0	0.0	0.0	0.0	0.0	0.0	0.0	0.0	0.0	1.1	5.2
Days w/min <= -20	0.0	0.0	0.0	0.0	0.0	0.0	0.0	0.0	0.0	0.0	0.0	0.0	0.0

Mean Temperature in °F

	Jan	Feb	Mar	Apr	May	Jun	Jul	Aug	Sep	Oct	Nov	Dec	Annual
Monthly normal													
Standard deviation													
Average monthly	25.1	31.2	40.1	48.8	57.7	67.8	74.2	72.7	63.8	51.2	37.7	28.2	49.9
Standard deviation	8.0	8.1	6.8	7.6	7.0	7.3	4.5	4.8	6.6	8.2	7.5	7.2	7.0
High monthly average	35.3	39.3	47.6	57.3	62.3	74.2	78.0	75.9	69.4	57.4	44.5	37.2	78.0
Year of occurrence	1981	1986	1986	1992	1992	1974	1974	1994	1979	1988	1976	1980	1974
Low monthly average	16.6	22.3	33.0	43.0	53.5	60.4	70.9	70.0	58.9	45.2	32.8	19.8	16.6
Year of occurrence	1979	1979	1969	1970	1975	1975	1993	1979	1985	1969	1993	1978	1979

† Also occurred on earlier date(s).

PRICE WAREHOUSES
Monthly Data Summary

Precipitation in Inches

	Jan	Feb	Mar	Apr	May	Jun	Jul	Aug	Sep	Oct	Nov	Dec	Annual
Monthly normal													
Standard deviation													
Average monthly	0.80	0.79	0.81	0.50	0.73	0.55	0.93	0.98	1.01	1.23	0.61	0.56	9.49
Standard deviation	0.09	0.12	0.10	0.08	0.09	0.09	0.11	0.11	0.14	0.16	0.09	0.08	0.11
High monthly total	2.57	3.81	2.38	1.95	2.34	2.41	3.14	2.00	3.06	4.34	3.47	1.51	4.34
Year of occurrence	1980	1980	1979	1988	1992	1969	1985	1995	1982	1972	1978	1971	1972
Low monthly total	0.00†	0.00†	0.00†	0.00†	0.00†	0.00†	0.01	0.04	0.00†	0.00	0.00†	0.00†	0.00†
Year of occurrence	1994	1988	1977	1984	1994	1979	1993	1985	1979	1975	1976	1986	1986
Record high daily	0.76	1.60	1.50	1.15	0.92	1.27	0.93	2.16	1.70	1.66	1.20	0.88	2.16
Day of occurrence	4	18	9	18	21	10	15	21	24	15	21	7	21
Year of occurrence	1982	1980	1987	1988	1987	1970	1973	1989	1986	1980	1983	1987	1989
Days w/pcp >= .01	4.2	3.7	4.5	3.2	4.4	3.3	5.5	5.8	4.9	4.4	3.3	3.8	51.3
Days w/pcp >= .10	2.7	2.2	2.5	1.3	2.2	1.5	2.5	3.0	2.6	2.7	1.8	1.8	27.0
Days w/pcp >= .50	0.3	0.4	0.3	0.2	0.3	0.3	0.6	0.5	0.5	0.8	0.4	0.2	4.9

Snow and Sleet in Inches

	Jan	Feb	Mar	Apr	May	Jun	Jul	Aug	Sep	Oct	Nov	Dec	Annual
Monthly normal													
Standard deviation													
Average monthly	8.7	4.8	1.2	0.3	0.0	0.0	0.0	0.0	0.0	0.3	2.4	6.0	23.7
Standard deviation	1.1	0.7	0.3	0.2	0.0	0.0	0.0	0.0	0.0	0.1	0.5	0.9	0.3
High monthly total	30.7	19.7	8.6	6.0	1.0	0.0†	0.0†	0.0†	0.0†	3.5	7.8	20.5	30.7
Year of occurrence	1978	1978	1975	1973	1979	1995	1995	1995	1995	1971	1994	1984	1978
Low monthly total	0.0†	0.0†	0.0†	0.0†	0.0†	0.0†	0.0†	0.0†	0.0†	0.0†	0.0†	0.0†	0.0†
Year of occurrence	1994	1995	1995	1995	1995	1995	1995	1995	1995	1994	1990	1989	1989
Record high daily	13.0	8.4	4.0	4.0	1.0	0.0†	0.0†	0.0†	0.0†	2.0	6.5	13.0	13.0†
Day of occurrence	19	10	24	1	7	30	31	31	30	29	25	20	20
Year of occurrence	1988	1978	1983	1973	1979	1995	1995	1995	1995	1971	1983	1984	1984
Days w/snow >= .1	3.9	2.5	0.9	0.2	0.0	0.0	0.0	0.0	0.0	0.3	1.2	2.7	11.3
Days w/snow >= 5	0.4	0.2	0.0	0.0	0.0	0.0	0.0	0.0	0.0	0.0	0.1	0.2	0.9
Days w/snow >= 10	0.0	0.0	0.0	0.0	0.0	0.0	0.0	0.0	0.0	0.0	0.0	0.0	0.1

Degree Days

	Jan	Feb	Mar	Apr	May	Jun	Jul	Aug	Sep	Oct	Nov	Dec	Annual
Heating normal													
Heating average	1227	936	749	479	236	55	2	4	94	417	809	1119	6132
Cooling normal													
Cooling average	0	0	0	0	13	139	285	241	59	2	0	0	742
Growing 40 normal													
Growing 40 average	29	68	193	353	540	708	855	828	641	397	151	47	4814
Growing 50 normal													
Growing 50 average	3	15	72	199	349	528	676	644	451	232	49	3	3229

† Also occurred on earlier date(s).

Location: Provo BYU County: Utah Latitude: 40.250   Longitude: -111.650
Elevation: 4570 feet   Period of Record: 1980-1996

PROVO BYU
Monthly Data Summary

Maximum Temperature in °F

	Jan	Feb	Mar	Apr	May	Jun	Jul	Aug	Sep	Oct	Nov	Dec	Annual
Monthly normal													
Standard deviation													
Average monthly	38.3	45.4	56.0	65.6	74.5	85.6	92.6	92.0	81.8	67.5	51.1	40.2	65.9
Standard deviation	9.1	11.4	9.5	10.4	10.4	9.3	6.0	5.3	9.3	10.6	10.8	9.9	9.3
High monthly average	46.6	57.7	63.2	74.6	80.6	92.4	97.6	95.6	86.8	74.5	60.9	46.5	97.6
Year of occurrence	1994	1995	1986	1992	1992	1994	1994	1994	1990	1988	1995	1995	1994
Low monthly average	27.6	34.6	50.0	56.0	67.9	80.7	89.6	88.5	74.0	58.9	45.4	31.9	27.6
Year of occurrence	1984	1989	1984	1983	1983	1984	1987	1987	1986	1984	1992	1985	1984
Record high daily	63	73	80	89	95	104†	104†	107	98†	90	74†	72	107
Day of occurrence	27	25	28	29	30	25	29	4	3	1	1	1	4
Year of occurrence	1987	1986	1986	1992	1984	1994	1995	1994	1995	1992	1988	1995	1994
Record low daily	11	6	29	39	44†	58†	70	69	43	36	25	5	5
Day of occurrence	19	6	3	11	16	8	3	11	29	29	25	23	23
Year of occurrence	1984	1989	1985	1991	1983	1995	1995	1981	1982	1991	1993	1990	1990
Days w/max >= 100	0.0	0.0	0.0	0.0	0.0	1.4	3.3	1.9	0.0	0.0	0.0	0.0	6.5
Days w/max >= 90	0.0	0.0	0.0	0.0	0.7	11.3	23.1	22.7	6.1	0.1	0.0	0.0	63.9
Days w/max <= 32	8.2	3.1	0.1	0.0	0.0	0.0	0.0	0.0	0.0	0.0	1.3	5.6	18.8

Minimum Temperature in °F

	Jan	Feb	Mar	Apr	May	Jun	Jul	Aug	Sep	Oct	Nov	Dec	Annual
Monthly normal													
Standard deviation													
Average monthly	19.7	23.5	32.7	39.0	45.7	53.3	59.4	58.5	49.7	38.7	29.7	22.4	39.3
Standard deviation	9.8	10.4	6.9	7.2	7.0	6.4	5.3	4.9	7.1	6.5	7.9	9.0	7.4
High monthly average	26.5	30.6	36.5	43.2	49.7	57.7	62.1	61.5	54.9	44.0	33.2	27.9	62.1
Year of occurrence	1981	1986	1986	1992	1987	1986	1988	1994	1990	1988	1995	1995	1988
Low monthly average	12.2	12.8	26.9	34.1†	41.5	50.1	55.0	55.5	45.5	34.5	23.6	13.6	12.2
Year of occurrence	1984	1985	1984	1984	1983	1995	1993	1985	1985	1984	1993	1990	1984
Record high daily	40†	49	54	62	62†	76	77	72	67	56	51	46	77
Day of occurrence	10	18	21	22	23	27	1	22	3	12	17	4	1
Year of occurrence	1996	1986	1995	1994	1989	1981	1990	1992	1994	1995	1986	1980	1990
Record low daily	-16	-20	8	19	29†	35	43	40	28	19	3	-16	-20
Day of occurrence	19	6	4	7	7	2	6	25	29	31	26	23	6
Year of occurrence	1984	1989	1985	1983	1984	1990	1982	1989	1985	1991	1993	1990	1989
Days w/min <= 32	28.9	22.9	15.3	5.6	0.5	0.0	0.0	0.0	0.3	5.4	19.4	27.5	129.3
Days w/min <= 0	1.1	0.8	0.0	0.0	0.0	0.0	0.0	0.0	0.0	0.0	0.0	0.6	2.5
Days w/min <= -20	0.0	0.1	0.0	0.0	0.0	0.0	0.0	0.0	0.0	0.0	0.0	0.0	0.1

Mean Temperature in °F

	Jan	Feb	Mar	Apr	May	Jun	Jul	Aug	Sep	Oct	Nov	Dec	Annual
Monthly normal													
Standard deviation													
Average monthly	29.0	34.5	44.3	52.3	60.1	69.5	76.0	75.2	65.7	53.1	40.4	31.3	52.6
Standard deviation	8.8	10.3	7.3	8.0	8.0	7.2	4.7	4.1	7.3	7.7	8.5	8.8	7.6
High monthly average	35.7	43.8	49.8	58.9	64.9	74.3	79.4	78.6	70.9	59.3	47.0	37.2	79.4
Year of occurrence	1994	1995	1986	1992	1992	1994	1989	1994	1990	1988	1995	1995	1989
Low monthly average	19.9	24.8	38.4	45.2	54.7	65.8	72.6	72.2	60.7	46.7	35.5	24.1	19.9
Year of occurrence	1984	1985	1984	1983	1983	1995	1993	1987	1986	1984	1992	1990	1984

† Also occurred on earlier date(s).

PROVO BYU
Monthly Data Summary

Precipitation in Inches

	Jan	Feb	Mar	Apr	May	Jun	Jul	Aug	Sep	Oct	Nov	Dec	Annual
Monthly normal													
Standard deviation													
Average monthly	1.77	1.93	2.33	1.72	2.31	1.22	1.10	1.35	1.76	2.21	1.97	1.81	21.49
Standard deviation	0.14	0.16	0.17	0.14	0.19	0.14	0.12	0.13	0.18	0.19	0.16	0.14	0.16
High monthly total	4.60	3.93	3.61	4.10	5.11	4.01	2.80	4.38	6.53	5.05	4.31	6.00	6.53
Year of occurrence	1993	1983	1981	1986	1995	1984	1984	1983	1982	1981	1983	1983	1982
Low monthly total	0.81	0.21	0.84	0.39	0.72	0.08	0.09	0.07	0.10	0.60	0.68	0.15	0.07
Year of occurrence	1989	1988	1988	1992	1989	1994	1994	1985	1987	1995	1993	1989	1985
Record high daily	0.97	1.14	1.66	1.28	1.62	1.22	1.10	1.13	1.34	1.27	1.04	0.83	1.66
Day of occurrence	8	27	9	2	10	5	9	17	28	27	20	8	9
Year of occurrence	1993	1983	1986	1986	1985	1984	1984	1983	1982	1991	1983	1985	1986
Days w/pcp >= .01	10.1	10.2	11.8	9.5	10.3	6.1	7.3	7.8	8.1	7.6	10.3	9.8	110.6
Days w/pcp >= .10	5.6	5.3	6.9	5.3	5.7	3.1	3.2	3.7	3.9	4.9	5.4	5.2	59.2
Days w/pcp >= .50	1.0	1.1	1.2	0.6	1.3	0.8	0.6	0.7	1.3	1.7	1.1	0.8	12.5

Snow and Sleet in Inches

	Jan	Feb	Mar	Apr	May	Jun	Jul	Aug	Sep	Oct	Nov	Dec	Annual
Monthly normal													
Standard deviation													
Average monthly	15.6	13.1	6.9	3.4	0.5	0.0	0.0	0.0	0.0	0.9	9.6	14.2	64.2
Standard deviation	1.3	1.4	0.8	0.6	0.3	0.0	0.0	0.0	0.0	0.2	1.1	1.3	0.6
High monthly total	39.0	36.0	20.2	22.5	6.0	0.0†	0.0†	0.0†	0.0†	4.5	26.5	39.5	39.5
Year of occurrence	1993	1989	1983	1984	1983	1995	1995	1995	1995	1995	1983	1983	1983
Low monthly total	3.5	0.0	0.0†	0.0†	0.0†	0.0†	0.0†	0.0†	0.0†	0.0†	0.0†	0.0	0.0†
Year of occurrence	1986	1988	1993	1988	1995	1995	1995	1995	1995	1994	1987	1986	1986
Record high daily	9.0	13.0	10.0	8.0	5.5	0.0†	0.0†	0.0†	0.0†	4.5	9.5	8.5	13.0
Day of occurrence	10	3	25	27	11	30	31	31	30	22	20	9	3
Year of occurrence	1993	1989	1983	1984	1983	1995	1995	1995	1995	1995	1983	1985	1989
Days w/snow >= .1	6.8	5.4	3.9	1.7	0.2	0.0	0.0	0.0	0.0	0.8	4.4	6.0	30.1
Days w/snow >= 5	0.8	0.8	0.1	0.1	0.1	0.0	0.0	0.0	0.0	0.0	0.4	0.9	3.4
Days w/snow >= 10	0.0	0.1	0.1	0.0	0.0	0.0	0.0	0.0	0.0	0.0	0.0	0.0	0.2

Degree Days

	Jan	Feb	Mar	Apr	May	Jun	Jul	Aug	Sep	Oct	Nov	Dec	Annual
Heating normal													
Heating average	1116	861	640	385	191	41	2	1	76	370	738	1043	5469
Cooling normal													
Cooling average	0	0	0	4	39	174	343	319	99	1	0	0	981
Growing 40 normal													
Growing 40 average	45	108	257	411	588	735	872	859	675	445	184	62	5246
Growing 50 normal													
Growing 50 average	6	37	117	241	393	551	695	684	493	278	76	13	3589

† Also occurred on earlier date(s).

Location: Randolph   County: Rich   Latitude: 41.667   Longitude: -111.183
Elevation: 6270 feet   Period of Record: 1892-1993

RANDOLPH
Monthly Data Summary

Maximum Temperature in °F

	Jan	Feb	Mar	Apr	May	Jun	Jul	Aug	Sep	Oct	Nov	Dec	Annual
Monthly normal	26.8	31.0	41.7	55.9	64.4	74.9	81.1	80.8	70.7	59.5	41.0	26.3	54.5
Standard deviation	10.8	11.3	8.6	10.9	10.3	8.8	5.8	4.4	9.8	9.6	11.0	11.8	9.4
Average monthly	26.1	30.9	40.6	54.7	64.0	74.5	80.5	80.3	70.2	58.9	40.2	26.5	53.9
Standard deviation	10.7	11.2	9.6	10.6	10.2	8.5	6.7	5.4	8.9	10.1	11.2	11.7	9.6
High monthly average	33.1	38.9	48.2	63.6	70.1	81.3	85.8	83.8	76.3	68.0	45.6†	37.0	85.8
Year of occurrence	1983	1987	1992	1987	1894	1988	1989	1894	1990	1988	1989	1986	1989
Low monthly average	17.9	22.2	32.7	46.0	58.0	69.6	70.4	72.5	63.7	51.0	32.4	17.7	17.7
Year of occurrence	1992	1894	1893	1983	1983	1983	1993	1993	1986	1984	1992	1985	1985
Record high daily	53	55	69	77	85	91†	97	96	89†	77†	66	62	97
Day of occurrence	26	24	29	21	28	25	19	3	14	1	4	4	19
Year of occurrence	1987	1986	1986	1989	1894	1988	1893	1893	1990	1992	1985	1893	1893
Record low daily	-5	-9	11	29	35	47	55	63†	41	18	11†	-16	-16
Day of occurrence	19	6	3	4	11	3	23	25	24	30	27	22	22
Year of occurrence	1984	1989	1893	1983	1983	1993	1993	1992	1984	1991	1992	1990	1990
Days w/max >= 100	0.0	0.0	0.0	0.0	0.0	0.0	0.0	0.0	0.0	0.0	0.0	0.0	0.0
Days w/max >= 90	0.0	0.0	0.0	0.0	0.0	0.4	1.6	0.9	0.0	0.0	0.0	0.0	3.4
Days w/max <= 32	21.1	13.5	4.8	0.2	0.0	0.0	0.0	0.0	0.0	0.3	7.5	20.7	63.8

Minimum Temperature in °F

	Jan	Feb	Mar	Apr	May	Jun	Jul	Aug	Sep	Oct	Nov	Dec	Annual
Monthly normal	0.8	4.6	16.5	24.9	30.7	38.6	43.7	40.4	33.0	23.3	15.3	1.1	22.7
Standard deviation	14.7	15.7	10.0	7.1	6.7	6.1	6.4	6.7	7.8	7.5	11.2	13.6	9.5
Average monthly	0.6	4.9	15.1	24.4	30.9	38.0	42.4	40.3	31.9	22.9	14.7	1.3	22.3
Standard deviation	14.2	15.0	11.4	6.8	6.4	6.1	6.8	7.0	7.8	7.6	11.7	13.8	9.6
High monthly average	9.7	16.8	22.5	28.8	34.6	41.2	46.3	45.5	37.6	26.4	18.2	13.2	46.3
Year of occurrence	1990	1986	1989	1989	1987	1988	1985	1983	1990	1983	1988	1893	1985
Low monthly average	-7.4	-6.1	7.2	20.8	27.8	35.0	33.1	35.2	26.4	19.1	8.4	-7.3	-7.4
Year of occurrence	1985	1985	1893	1984	1983	1893	1993	1993	1993	1991	1992	1990	1985
Record high daily	32	36	36†	44	50	57	62†	58	52	47	41	33	62
Day of occurrence	31	24	31	16	21	26	8	21	16	17	2	10	8
Year of occurrence	1986	1986	1986	1985	1993	1988	1991	1894	1990	1988	1987	1893	1991
Record low daily	-40	-43	-21	6	10	-24	26	17	8	-1	-21†	-41	-43
Day of occurrence	18	1	1	6	13	24	7	26	30	31	27	23	1
Year of occurrence	1984	1985	1993	1983	1983	1993	1993	1992	1985	1991	1992	1990	1985
Days w/min <= 32	30.8	27.7	28.9	25.6	18.6	5.6	1.8	3.7	15.1	27.4	27.6	30.1	239.8
Days w/min <= 0	16.4	10.2	3.7	0.0	0.0	0.0	0.0	0.0	0.0	0.1	3.9	15.2	46.2
Days w/min <= -20	2.4	1.5	0.2	0.0	0.0	0.0	0.0	0.0	0.0	0.0	0.2	2.0	5.9

Mean Temperature in °F

	Jan	Feb	Mar	Apr	May	Jun	Jul	Aug	Sep	Oct	Nov	Dec	Annual
Monthly normal	13.7	17.8	29.2	40.4	47.6	56.7	62.3	60.6	51.8	41.4	28.2	13.7	38.6
Standard deviation	12.2	13.0	8.2	7.5	7.1	6.3	4.5	4.1	6.9	6.5	9.8	12.0	8.2
Average monthly	13.4	17.9	27.9	39.5	47.4	56.2	61.4	60.3	51.1	40.9	27.5	13.9	38.1
Standard deviation	11.9	12.4	9.5	7.3	6.9	6.0	5.3	4.8	6.5	6.9	10.2	12.1	8.3
High monthly average	21.2	26.4	35.3	44.2	51.3	61.3	65.2	64.1	56.9	46.8	30.7	24.4	65.2
Year of occurrence	1990	1987	1989	1987	1894	1988	1988	1894	1990	1988	1989	1893	1988
Low monthly average	5.6	10.1	20.0	33.7	42.9	53.1	51.7	53.8	47.2	35.7	20.4	5.9	5.6
Year of occurrence	1992	1985	1893	1983	1983	1984	1993	1993	1993	1984	1992	1990	1992

† Also occurred on earlier date(s).

RANDOLPH
Monthly Data Summary

Precipitation in Inches

	Jan	Feb	Mar	Apr	May	Jun	Jul	Aug	Sep	Oct	Nov	Dec	Annual
Monthly normal	0.28	0.68	0.72	0.99	1.44	0.67	0.87	0.97	1.86	0.79	0.97	0.53	10.77
Standard deviation	0.03	0.11	0.07	0.08	0.13	0.07	0.10	0.11	0.17	0.09	0.08	0.05	0.09
Average monthly	0.26	0.63	0.74	0.95	1.41	0.75	0.94	0.99	1.61	0.94	1.06	0.51	10.80
Standard deviation	0.03	0.10	0.08	0.08	0.13	0.09	0.11	0.11	0.15	0.11	0.10	0.05	0.09
High monthly total	0.53	3.06	1.85	2.26	3.79	2.48	1.80	2.63	4.55	1.90	1.72	1.50	4.55
Year of occurrence	1992	1986	1894	1986	1987	1991	1984	1983	1982	1991	1991	1983	1982
Low monthly total	0.05	0.00	0.08	0.10	0.00	0.00	0.06	0.06	0.22	0.00	0.20	0.06	0.00†
Year of occurrence	1894	1991	1992	1987	1893	1893	1988	1985	1993	1893	1989	1991	1893
Record high daily	0.48	1.04	0.75	0.55†	1.07	0.86	1.26	0.92	1.18	0.97	0.85	0.42	1.26
Day of occurrence	7	18	16	21	21	2	21	8	26	30	9	9	21
Year of occurrence	1992	1986	1987	1991	1987	1991	1984	1982	1982	1992	1991	1985	1984
Days w/pcp >= .01	4.7	5.1	8.1	8.3	8.1	4.8	5.5	6.4	6.9	5.8	9.5	5.2	79.8
Days w/pcp >= .10	0.5	2.2	2.4	3.7	4.0	2.7	2.9	3.0	4.3	2.8	3.7	1.8	35.2
Days w/pcp >= .50	0.0	0.3	0.2	0.2	0.5	0.2	0.3	0.4	0.9	0.6	0.4	0.0	4.2

Snow and Sleet in Inches

	Jan	Feb	Mar	Apr	May	Jun	Jul	Aug	Sep	Oct	Nov	Dec	Annual
Monthly normal	6.4	6.9	5.4	2.2	1.9	0.3	0.0	0.0	1.6	1.3	6.3	6.1	38.3
Standard deviation	0.6	0.9	0.9	0.6	0.7	0.2	0.0	0.0	0.6	0.3	1.0	0.8	0.5
Average monthly	5.4	5.4	3.8	3.3	2.3	0.2	0.0	0.0	1.0	0.9	6.5	6.5	35.2
Standard deviation	0.7	0.8	0.7	0.6	0.7	0.1	0.0	0.0	0.5	0.3	1.0	0.9	0.5
High monthly total	12.0	17.0	11.0	7.5†	12.0	2.5	0.0†	0.0†	8.0	7.8	11.5	14.3	17.0
Year of occurrence	1988	1989	1987	1894	1892	1990	1993	1993	1986	1984	1987	1992	1989
Low monthly total	0.0	0.0†	0.0†	0.0†	0.0†	0.0†	0.0†	0.0†	0.0†	0.0†	0.0	0.5	0.0†
Year of occurrence	1894	1991	1993	1992	1993	1993	1993	1993	1993	1993	1989	1986	1989
Record high daily	8.0	6.0	6.0†	6.0	10.0	2.5	0.0†	0.0†	8.0	4.0	7.0†	6.0†	10.0
Day of occurrence	7	2	15	25	11	1	31	31	26	21	25	30	11
Year of occurrence	1992	1989	1988	1983	1983	1990	1993	1993	1986	1984	1987	1992	1983
Days w/snow >= .1	3.7	2.3	1.7	1.6	0.6	0.1	0.0	0.0	0.1	0.6	2.4	2.7	13.6
Days w/snow >= 5	0.1	0.2	0.3	0.2	0.1	0.0	0.0	0.0	0.1	0.0	0.5	0.4	1.8
Days w/snow >= 10	0.0	0.0	0.0	0.0	0.1	0.0	0.0	0.0	0.0	0.0	0.0	0.0	0.1

Degree Days

	Jan	Feb	Mar	Apr	May	Jun	Jul	Aug	Sep	Oct	Nov	Dec	Annual
Heating normal	1568	1334	996	680	536	248	96	139	376	716	1035	1519	9247
Heating average	1520	1332	1080	724	542	257	123	151	406	733	1054	1530	9459
Cooling normal	0	0	0	0	0	6	20	8	0	0	0	0	36
Cooling average	0	0	0	0	0	4	18	9	0	0	0	0	33
Growing 40 normal	6	10	57	228	377	501	604	596	430	301	71	5	3190
Growing 40 average	5	10	57	215	371	486	585	594	433	294	66	9	3131
Growing 50 normal	0	0	15	114	229	360	463	466	295	163	20	0	2129
Growing 50 average	0	0	12	102	224	350	449	462	293	157	16	1	2071

† Also occurred on earlier date(s).

Location: Richfield Radio KSVC   County: Sevier   Latitude: 38.767   Longitude: -112.083
Elevation: 5300 feet   Period of Record: 1893-1996

RICHFIELD RADIO KSVC
Monthly Data Summary

Maximum Temperature in °F

	Jan	Feb	Mar	Apr	May	Jun	Jul	Aug	Sep	Oct	Nov	Dec	Annual
Monthly normal	40.6	46.8	54.7	63.4	72.7	82.9	89.5	87.3	79.5	68.3	53.2	42.4	65.1
Standard deviation	10.4	10.2	10.1	9.6	9.1	7.9	4.6	5.1	7.7	9.7	10.9	10.7	8.8
Average monthly	41.3	46.7	55.5	64.4	73.4	83.3	90.0	88.0	80.2	68.6	54.5	43.5	65.8
Standard deviation	10.7	10.1	9.7	9.7	9.3	8.1	5.4	5.3	7.6	9.4	10.7	10.2	8.9
High monthly average	52.2	58.3	69.0	75.0	81.8	91.6	96.4	95.5	87.7	76.2	67.5	54.7	96.4
Year of occurrence	1935	1924	1900	1943	1940	1900	1901	1940	1943	1952	1921	1917	1901
Low monthly average	0.0	30.8	44.5	54.6	52.2	75.8	81.2	79.9	69.7	59.8	43.2	28.3	0.0
Year of occurrence	1993	1903	1952	1900	1898	1967	1918	1899	1900	1984	1994	1909	1993
Record high daily	71	72	81	90	103	100†	104†	103	98†	90	82	73	104
Day of occurrence	12	28	19	26	31	26	14	14	6	4	10	13	14
Year of occurrence	1927	1972	1907	1910	1910	1970	1939	1940	1944	1922	1906	1921	1939
Record low daily	0†	3	19	35	41	52	66	65	40	27	20†	-3	-3
Day of occurrence	31	6	2	1	7	6	11	22	18	29	29	23	23
Year of occurrence	1993	1989	1908	1975	1965	1914	1936	1911	1965	1971	1896	1990	1990
Days w/max >= 100	0.0	0.0	0.0	0.0	0.0	0.0	0.9	0.2	0.0	0.0	0.0	0.0	1.2
Days w/max >= 90	0.0	0.0	0.0	0.0	0.5	7.2	18.0	12.9	2.5	0.0	0.0	0.0	41.1
Days w/max <= 32	5.7	2.4	0.3	0.0	0.0	0.0	0.0	0.0	0.0	0.0	1.0	4.4	13.7

Minimum Temperature in °F

	Jan	Feb	Mar	Apr	May	Jun	Jul	Aug	Sep	Oct	Nov	Dec	Annual
Monthly normal	13.3	18.6	24.5	30.3	37.7	45.1	52.5	50.6	41.4	31.1	22.6	15.0	31.9
Standard deviation	12.1	10.5	8.3	7.5	6.6	6.8	5.8	6.2	8.1	7.7	8.7	10.9	8.3
Average monthly	13.9	18.7	24.9	30.8	37.9	44.8	51.9	50.4	40.8	31.0	21.8	15.4	31.9
Standard deviation	11.2	10.4	8.1	7.3	6.5	6.8	6.0	6.0	7.7	7.1	8.2	10.3	8.0
High monthly average	24.7	28.1	35.2	36.2†	44.5	51.6	61.7	56.4	46.9	37.9	29.0	24.2	61.7
Year of occurrence	1911	1907	1928	1992	1934	1938	1899	1926	1983	1918	1927	1917	1899
Low monthly average	-1.7	0.9	13.4	22.5	28.7	33.3	40.4	41.4	27.3	19.0	11.1	5.2	-1.7
Year of occurrence	1937	1903	1901	1908	1908	1908	1897	1900	1898	1898	1898	1990	1937
Record high daily	45	54	53†	59	64	74	79	78	67	58	50†	49	79
Day of occurrence	30	29	31	22	24	7	3	26	7	11	3	10	3
Year of occurrence	1911	1972	1944	1965	1984	1938	1913	1926	1989	1975	1988	1939	1913
Record low daily	-28†	-33†	-12	5	18	20	30	22	12	0	-12	-32	-33
Day of occurrence	22	7	1	2	1	3	19	31	29	30	17	23	7
Year of occurrence	1937	1989	1962	1908	1950	1897	1897	1908	1898	1971	1964	1990	1989
Days w/min <= 32	29.9	26.5	25.9	17.9	6.2	0.8	0.1	0.1	4.3	18.9	27.3	29.8	187.2
Days w/min <= 0	3.9	1.6	0.2	0.0	0.0	0.0	0.0	0.0	0.0	0.0	0.2	2.2	8.1
Days w/min <= -20	0.2	0.1	0.0	0.0	0.0	0.0	0.0	0.0	0.0	0.0	0.0	0.1	0.4

Mean Temperature in °F

	Jan	Feb	Mar	Apr	May	Jun	Jul	Aug	Sep	Oct	Nov	Dec	Annual
Monthly normal	27.0	32.7	39.6	46.9	55.2	64.0	71.0	68.9	60.4	49.7	37.9	28.7	48.5
Standard deviation	10.2	9.2	7.7	7.0	6.6	6.3	3.6	4.2	6.6	7.1	8.2	9.7	7.2
Average monthly	27.6	32.7	40.2	47.6	55.6	64.1	71.0	69.2	60.5	49.8	38.2	29.5	48.8
Standard deviation	9.8	9.1	7.4	7.1	6.8	6.3	4.1	4.2	6.2	6.7	7.9	9.0	7.1
High monthly average	36.4	43.2	48.6	55.3	62.9	69.9	75.6	73.5	64.8	54.9	45.1	39.4	75.6
Year of occurrence	1956	1907	1934	1943	1934	1922	1934	1926	1983	1933	1900	1917	1934
Low monthly average	0.0	15.8	32.0	39.8	41.2	58.5	64.4	61.3	48.6	41.8	30.5	17.4	0.0
Year of occurrence	1993	1903	1897	1900	1898	1908	1897	1899	1900	1898	1938	1909	1993

† Also occurred on earlier date(s).

RICHFIELD RADIO KSVC
Monthly Data Summary

Precipitation in Inches

	Jan	Feb	Mar	Apr	May	Jun	Jul	Aug	Sep	Oct	Nov	Dec	Annual
Monthly normal	0.56	0.58	0.73	0.75	0.84	0.58	0.79	0.70	0.93	0.84	0.68	0.59	8.57
Standard deviation	0.06	0.07	0.07	0.09	0.09	0.09	0.10	0.08	0.12	0.10	0.09	0.07	0.09
Average monthly	0.53	0.61	0.80	0.69	0.88	0.52	0.77	0.77	0.71	0.74	0.57	0.53	8.12
Standard deviation	0.06	0.07	0.09	0.08	0.10	0.09	0.10	0.09	0.10	0.09	0.08	0.07	0.08
High monthly total	1.79	2.23	2.31	2.38	2.85	2.72	3.28	2.20	2.92[†]	3.16	2.09	2.62	3.28
Year of occurrence	1974	1962	1945	1935	1995	1984	1936	1953	1980	1981	1985	1966	1936
Low monthly total	0.00[†]	0.01	0.00	0.00	0.00[†]	0.00[†]	0.00[†]	0.00[†]	0.00[†]	0.00[†]	0.00[†]	0.00[†]	0.00[†]
Year of occurrence	1993	1970	1900	1911	1948	1990	1988	1976	1957	1973	1956	1986	1986
Record high daily	1.05	1.20	2.00	1.17	1.28	1.40	1.62	1.80	1.17	1.14	1.18	1.19	2.00
Day of occurrence	17	23	24	4	31	7	27	1	23	19	2	6	24
Year of occurrence	1921	1912	1899	1935	1991	1908	1929	1953	1967	1990	1978	1966	1899
Days w/pcp >= .01	5.1	5.5	6.6	5.7	6.0	3.7	5.6	6.5	4.4	4.3	4.6	4.8	63.0
Days w/pcp >= .10	1.7	2.1	2.6	2.1	2.8	1.4	2.5	2.3	2.0	2.2	1.8	1.9	25.5
Days w/pcp >= .50	0.1	0.1	0.2	0.2	0.3	0.2	0.2	0.3	0.4	0.3	0.2	0.1	2.6

Snow and Sleet in Inches

	Jan	Feb	Mar	Apr	May	Jun	Jul	Aug	Sep	Oct	Nov	Dec	Annual
Monthly normal	3.3	4.4	2.7	1.1	0.5	0.0	0.0	0.0	0.2	0.6	2.1	4.2	19.1
Standard deviation	0.6	0.8	0.6	0.4	0.4	0.0	0.0	0.0	0.2	0.3	0.5	0.6	0.4
Average monthly	4.3	4.4	3.0	1.0	0.3	0.0	0.0	0.0	0.1	0.5	2.0	3.5	19.1
Standard deviation	0.7	0.8	0.7	0.4	0.2	0.0	0.0	0.0	0.1	0.2	0.5	0.6	0.4
High monthly total	20.5	20.5	22.6	30.0	10.0	0.0[†]	0.0[†]	0.0[†]	7.0	10.0	13.0	15.0	30.0
Year of occurrence	1944	1948	1945	1912	1975	1995	1995	1995	1965	1971	1964	1921	1912
Low monthly total	0.0[†]	0.0[†]	0.0[†]	0.0[†]	0.0[†]	0.0[†]	0.0[†]	0.0[†]	0.0[†]	0.0[†]	0.0[†]	0.0[†]	0.0[†]
Year of occurrence	1995	1994	1994	1995	1995	1995	1995	1995	1995	1995	1992	1992	1992
Record high daily	8.0	12.0	16.0	10.0	10.0	0.0[†]	0.0[†]	0.0[†]	5.0	6.0[†]	10.0	11.0	16.0
Day of occurrence	4	23	15	10	20	30	31	31	17	28	13	31	15
Year of occurrence	1989	1912	1945	1912	1975	1995	1995	1995	1965	1971	1964	1921	1945
Days w/snow >= .1	2.4	1.8	1.2	0.4	0.1	0.0	0.0	0.0	0.0	0.2	1.1	1.8	7.5
Days w/snow >= 5	0.2	0.2	0.1	0.1	0.0	0.0	0.0	0.0	0.0	0.0	0.1	0.1	0.7
Days w/snow >= 10	0.0	0.0	0.0	0.0	0.0	0.0	0.0	0.0	0.0	0.0	0.0	0.0	0.1

Degree Days

	Jan	Feb	Mar	Apr	May	Jun	Jul	Aug	Sep	Oct	Nov	Dec	Annual
Heating normal	1178	910	788	544	306	91	2	15	160	474	813	1125	6410
Heating average	1157	911	768	521	295	88	5	13	155	470	804	1099	6292
Cooling normal	0	0	0	0	2	62	188	136	23	0	0	0	413
Cooling average	0	0	0	0	5	60	190	143	19	0	0	0	419
Growing 40 normal	70	119	233	355	506	625	767	737	584	439	210	86	4736
Growing 40 average	74	117	246	367	511	620	758	735	579	439	227	94	4771
Growing 50 normal	13	37	107	208	353	483	606	577	443	289	94	21	3238
Growing 50 average	14	36	114	221	362	484	599	577	449	291	106	24	3283

[†] Also occurred on earlier date(s).

Location: Roosevelt Radio County: Uintah   Latitude: 40.283   Longitude:-109.967
Elevation: 5010 feet   Period of Record: 1939-1995

ROOSEVELT RADIO
Monthly Data Summary

Maximum Temperature in °F

	Jan	Feb	Mar	Apr	May	Jun	Jul	Aug	Sep	Oct	Nov	Dec	Annual
Monthly normal	29.2	37.6	51.9	64.0	74.3	84.2	90.9	88.6	78.9	65.9	48.1	32.9	62.2
Standard deviation	11.8	11.8	10.3	10.2	9.5	9.0	5.3	6.0	8.9	9.8	10.7	11.5	9.6
Average monthly	29.3	37.3	51.8	64.2	74.4	83.9	90.9	88.6	79.5	65.9	47.6	34.2	62.3
Standard deviation	11.4	11.9	10.2	9.9	9.1	9.2	6.1	6.0	8.5	9.8	10.2	10.7	9.4
High monthly average	46.4	52.6	63.4	73.2	82.1	92.1	95.8	94.5	86.8	74.4	58.9	46.9	95.8
Year of occurrence	1981	1954	1972	1992	1969	1977	1989	1958	1956	1988	1949	1958	1989
Low monthly average	14.1	22.5	36.0	56.9	66.8	75.3	83.7	81.3	70.1	57.2	36.4	17.5	14.1
Year of occurrence	1979	1973	1952	1983	1995	1947	1947	1968	1961	1969	1971	1978	1979
Record high daily	60†	68	76†	88†	94†	102	105†	105	98	87	70†	63	105†
Day of occurrence	26	28	31	30	23	25	3	12	1	1	3	5	12
Year of occurrence	1975	1972	1966	1992	1984	1988	1985	1958	1950	1957	1978	1958	1958
Record low daily	-9	-6	18	35†	44†	0	0†	62	36	27†	11	-10	-10
Day of occurrence	3	6	1	7	16	30	10	29	17	29	22	22	22
Year of occurrence	1952	1989	1962	1973	1983	1946	1947	1957	1965	1991	1964	1990	1990
Days w/max >= 100	0.0	0.0	0.0	0.0	0.0	0.2	0.8	0.6	0.0	0.0	0.0	0.0	1.6
Days w/max >= 90	0.0	0.0	0.0	0.0	0.7	9.1	20.5	14.8	3.1	0.0	0.0	0.0	48.8
Days w/max <= 32	18.2	9.9	1.1	0.0	0.0	0.0	0.0	0.0	0.0	0.1	2.4	12.5	45.2

Minimum Temperature in °F

	Jan	Feb	Mar	Apr	May	Jun	Jul	Aug	Sep	Oct	Nov	Dec	Annual
Monthly normal	3.3	9.9	22.9	31.6	40.5	48.4	55.1	53.0	43.3	32.6	21.0	7.9	30.8
Standard deviation	12.3	12.0	7.8	6.7	6.3	6.0	5.0	5.7	7.3	6.9	8.3	11.3	8.0
Average monthly	4.0	10.1	22.6	31.7	40.2	47.4	53.9	52.1	42.7	32.6	20.5	9.7	30.6
Standard deviation	12.2	12.0	7.7	6.8	6.4	6.0	5.7	5.7	7.2	6.6	8.1	10.8	7.9
High monthly average	17.4	22.1	28.8	36.8	44.8	52.7	58.1	58.0	49.0	39.6	28.0	20.7	58.1
Year of occurrence	1956	1963	1983	1943	1969	1977	1976	1969	1981	1963	1965	1950	1976
Low monthly average	-10.1	-4.6	15.1	26.4†	33.5	42.9	45.6	46.9	36.3	26.8	12.8	-5.6	-10.1
Year of occurrence	1949	1949	1952	1970	1946	1946	1993	1944	1988	1970	1964	1978	1949
Record high daily	39	36	44	51	58†	70†	70†	69†	62	55	47	40†	70†
Day of occurrence	25	14	11	29	31	26	23	22	10	3	1	9	23
Year of occurrence	1975	1954	1995	1943	1984	1981	1982	1969	1988	1967	1987	1958	1982
Record low daily	-32†	-47	-10	8†	0	0	0†	32†	21†	2	-6†	-40†	-47
Day of occurrence	4	6	1	5	18	30	10	27	19	30	27	23	6
Year of occurrence	1952	1989	1962	1994	1946	1946	1947	1992	1988	1971	1993	1990	1989
Days w/min <= 32	31.0	28.1	28.6	15.9	3.8	0.1	0.0	0.0	2.5	15.9	27.9	30.8	188.1
Days w/min <= 0	11.6	6.3	0.3	0.0	0.0	0.0	0.0	0.0	0.0	0.0	0.3	5.7	24.8
Days w/min <= -20	1.0	0.2	0.0	0.0	0.0	0.0	0.0	0.0	0.0	0.0	0.0	0.2	1.4

Mean Temperature in °F

	Jan	Feb	Mar	Apr	May	Jun	Jul	Aug	Sep	Oct	Nov	Dec	Annual
Monthly normal	16.3	23.7	37.4	47.8	57.4	66.3	73.0	70.8	61.1	49.3	34.6	20.4	46.5
Standard deviation	11.4	11.3	8.1	7.2	6.7	6.4	3.4	4.4	6.8	7.1	8.6	10.7	7.7
Average monthly	16.6	23.7	37.2	48.0	57.3	65.6	72.4	70.4	61.1	49.2	34.0	21.9	46.5
Standard deviation	11.2	11.4	8.0	7.1	6.6	6.5	4.6	4.4	6.5	6.9	8.2	9.9	7.6
High monthly average	31.0	37.2	44.8	54.2	63.5	72.4	75.5	74.6	65.3	55.6	42.0	33.4	75.5
Year of occurrence	1981	1954	1972	1943	1969	1977	1960	1983	1960	1963	1965	1980	1960
Low monthly average	2.8	9.5	25.5	42.1	51.8	59.6	65.9	65.8	54.3	43.3	25.6	5.9	2.8
Year of occurrence	1949	1949	1952	1970	1953	1947	1947	1968	1965	1970	1964	1978	1949

† Also occurred on earlier date(s).

ROOSEVELT RADIO
Monthly Data Summary

Precipitation in Inches

	Jan	Feb	Mar	Apr	May	Jun	Jul	Aug	Sep	Oct	Nov	Dec	Annual
Monthly normal	0.55	0.44	0.56	0.55	0.78	0.66	0.49	0.57	0.63	0.88	0.47	0.52	7.11
Standard deviation	0.08	0.06	0.06	0.07	0.09	0.10	0.06	0.07	0.07	0.11	0.06	0.06	0.07
Average monthly	0.54	0.44	0.55	0.60	0.73	0.65	0.46	0.71	0.68	0.99	0.46	0.53	7.36
Standard deviation	0.07	0.07	0.07	0.07	0.09	0.09	0.06	0.09	0.08	0.12	0.06	0.07	0.08
High monthly total	1.87	1.64	1.70	2.15	2.89	3.84	2.15	2.91	3.86	3.54	2.23	2.62	3.86
Year of occurrence	1988	1944	1979	1968	1995	1965	1987	1955	1954	1941	1957	1951	1954
Low monthly total	0.00†	0.00†	0.00	0.00	0.00†	0.00†	0.01	0.00	0.00†	0.00†	0.00†	0.00†	0.00†
Year of occurrence	1966	1974	1947	1992	1974	1987	1978	1985	1979	1964	1976	1989	1989
Record high daily	1.48	1.10	1.14	0.85	0.82	1.45	0.94	1.88	0.84	1.12	0.97	1.32	1.88
Day of occurrence	18	21	11	27	20	16	29	25	26	3	3	30	25
Year of occurrence	1988	1944	1940	1994	1975	1969	1987	1955	1954	1994	1957	1951	1955
Days w/pcp >= .01	5.1	4.4	5.2	4.7	5.4	4.2	4.4	5.8	5.0	5.0	4.0	4.7	57.9
Days w/pcp >= .10	1.9	1.5	1.8	2.1	2.2	1.8	1.6	2.3	2.1	2.7	1.5	1.7	23.3
Days w/pcp >= .50	0.1	0.1	0.1	0.1	0.3	0.2	0.1	0.2	0.3	0.5	0.1	0.1	2.3

Snow and Sleet in Inches

	Jan	Feb	Mar	Apr	May	Jun	Jul	Aug	Sep	Oct	Nov	Dec	Annual
Monthly normal	7.2	4.4	2.2	0.5	0.0	0.0	0.0	0.0	0.0	0.1	2.6	3.7	20.7
Standard deviation	0.9	0.8	0.6	0.2	0.0	0.0	0.0	0.0	0.0	0.1	0.6	0.5	0.3
Average monthly	6.8	4.0	2.2	0.5	0.0	0.0	0.0	0.0	0.0	0.1	1.8	5.1	20.5
Standard deviation	0.8	0.7	0.5	0.2	0.0	0.0	0.0	0.0	0.0	0.1	0.4	0.8	0.3
High monthly total	22.0	19.0	14.0	4.0	0.0†	0.0†	0.0†	0.0†	0.0†	2.0†	18.0	28.0	28.0
Year of occurrence	1950	1989	1975	1979	1995	1995	1995	1995	1995	1991	1978	1949	1949
Low monthly total	0.0†	0.0†	0.0†	0.0†	0.0†	0.0†	0.0†	0.0†	0.0†	0.0†	0.0†	0.0†	0.0†
Year of occurrence	1994	1994	1995	1995	1995	1995	1995	1995	1995	1994	1995	1995	1995
Record high daily	11.0	9.0	8.0†	4.0	0.0†	0.0†	0.0†	0.0†	0.0†	2.0†	6.0†	12.0	12.0
Day of occurrence	3	5	2	10	31	30	31	31	30	28	20	19	19
Year of occurrence	1950	1976	1976	1979	1995	1995	1995	1995	1995	1991	1983	1949	1949
Days w/snow >= .1	3.9	2.2	1.0	0.2	0.0	0.0	0.0	0.0	0.0	0.1	0.9	2.7	10.2
Days w/snow >= 5	0.3	0.2	0.1	0.0	0.0	0.0	0.0	0.0	0.0	0.0	0.1	0.2	0.9
Days w/snow >= 10	0.0	0.0	0.0	0.0	0.0	0.0	0.0	0.0	0.0	0.0	0.0	0.0	0.1

Degree Days

	Jan	Feb	Mar	Apr	May	Jun	Jul	Aug	Sep	Oct	Nov	Dec	Annual
Heating normal	1511	1165	855	516	242	61	1	8	147	487	913	1383	7294
Heating average	1495	1165	858	510	245	67	4	8	145	489	926	1329	7248
Cooling normal	0	0	0	0	8	100	250	187	30	0	0	0	577
Cooling average	0	0	0	0	7	86	233	173	29	0	0	0	531
Growing 40 normal	16	50	194	359	535	665	807	769	588	405	146	26	4565
Growing 40 average	15	50	192	363	535	649	785	753	586	402	134	27	4496
Growing 50 normal	1	10	80	215	376	496	633	597	431	252	51	2	3150
Growing 50 average	1	10	78	218	377	489	617	586	438	250	44	2	3115

† Also occurred on earlier date(s).

Location: Salt Lake City NWSFO County: Salt Lake   Latitude: 40.783   Longitude: -111.950
Elevation: 4220 feet   Period of Record: 1928-1996

SALT LAKE CITY NWSFO
Monthly Data Summary

Maximum Temperature in °F

	Jan	Feb	Mar	Apr	May	Jun	Jul	Aug	Sep	Oct	Nov	Dec	Annual
Monthly normal	36.4	43.6	52.3	61.3	71.9	83.4	92.8	90.0	79.0	65.8	50.5	37.8	63.7
Standard deviation	9.0	9.8	9.8	10.3	10.4	9.9	5.7	6.5	9.8	10.1	9.7	9.1	9.2
Average monthly	36.4	42.9	51.8	61.8	72.0	82.5	92.4	90.0	79.4	65.9	49.6	38.9	63.6
Standard deviation	9.2	9.8	9.7	10.3	10.5	10.0	6.1	6.3	9.5	10.1	10.0	9.0	9.2
High monthly average	48.1	54.1	62.0	70.7	82.4	92.2	98.2	95.7	87.5	74.3	58.0	48.1	98.2
Year of occurrence	1953	1995	1934	1934	1934	1961	1960	1967	1979	1988	1995	1939	1960
Low monthly average	21.7	29.1	40.5	53.4	63.7	73.0	83.6	82.3	70.8	56.4	41.0	28.1	21.7
Year of occurrence	1949	1933	1952	1975	1933	1945	1993	1968	1965	1946	1994	1930	1949
Record high daily	62	69	78†	86	93†	104†	107	106	100	89	75	69	107
Day of occurrence	26	28	26	29	30	29	26	4	8	3	12	1	26
Year of occurrence	1982	1972	1960	1992	1984	1979	1960	1994	1979	1963	1967	1995	1960
Record low daily	4	6	26	35†	39	49	62†	60	43†	30	15	2	2
Day of occurrence	12	7	4	3	2	11	23	22	17	29	15	22	22
Year of occurrence	1963	1933	1966	1955	1964	1947	1993	1968	1965	1971	1955	1990	1990
Days w/max >= 100	0.0	0.0	0.0	0.0	0.0	0.6	3.2	0.9	0.0	0.0	0.0	0.0	4.9
Days w/max >= 90	0.0	0.0	0.0	0.0	0.6	8.3	22.5	18.8	4.1	0.0	0.0	0.0	55.1
Days w/max <= 32	10.5	4.1	0.6	0.0	0.0	0.0	0.0	0.0	0.0	0.0	1.1	7.6	24.4

Minimum Temperature in °F

	Jan	Feb	Mar	Apr	May	Jun	Jul	Aug	Sep	Oct	Nov	Dec	Annual
Monthly normal	19.3	24.6	31.4	37.9	45.6	54.5	62.8	60.9	50.8	40.0	30.6	21.6	40.0
Standard deviation	11.2	9.6	7.6	6.8	7.1	7.4	5.8	6.2	8.0	7.1	7.4	9.7	7.8
Average monthly	18.8	24.2	31.0	38.0	45.6	53.5	62.0	60.5	50.5	39.9	29.0	21.9	39.6
Standard deviation	11.2	10.0	7.3	6.9	7.2	7.2	5.9	6.2	7.9	7.1	8.2	9.9	7.9
High monthly average	30.9	33.6	38.9	44.0	52.5	61.3	67.2	66.2	58.8	45.6	35.9	30.8	67.2
Year of occurrence	1953	1986	1992	1992	1992	1988	1985	1994	1990	1988	1953	1950	1985
Low monthly average	1.4	3.4	22.2	32.5	40.6	47.5	56.1	53.2	43.8	33.9	19.3	6.5	1.4
Year of occurrence	1949	1933	1964	1970	1930	1945	1993	1928	1964	1932	1930	1932	1949
Record high daily	47	51	56	64	67†	75†	79	76	73	66†	54	52	79
Day of occurrence	13	18	29	21	27	30	10	7	5	1	4	23	10
Year of occurrence	1980	1986	1943	1989	1985	1990	1956	1995	1978	1953	1977	1955	1956
Record low daily	-22	-30	2	14	25	35†	40†	37†	27	16	-14	-21	-30
Day of occurrence	25	9	4	2	6	7	1	31	18	30	16	13	9
Year of occurrence	1949	1933	1966	1936	1965	1962	1968	1965	1965	1971	1955	1932	1933
Days w/min <= 32	28.0	22.8	17.8	6.7	0.8	0.0	0.0	0.0	0.3	4.7	20.2	27.3	130.1
Days w/min <= 0	2.0	0.7	0.0	0.0	0.0	0.0	0.0	0.0	0.0	0.0	0.0	0.9	3.7
Days w/min <= -20	0.0	0.0	0.0	0.0	0.0	0.0	0.0	0.0	0.0	0.0	0.0	0.0	0.1

Mean Temperature in °F

	Jan	Feb	Mar	Apr	May	Jun	Jul	Aug	Sep	Oct	Nov	Dec	Annual
Monthly normal	27.9	34.1	41.8	49.6	58.8	69.0	77.8	75.5	64.9	52.9	40.6	29.7	51.9
Standard deviation	9.6	9.3	8.1	7.9	8.1	8.1	4.8	5.6	8.3	7.9	8.0	8.9	7.9
Average monthly	27.6	33.6	41.4	49.9	58.8	68.0	77.2	75.3	65.0	52.9	39.3	30.4	51.6
Standard deviation	9.7	9.4	7.9	8.0	8.2	8.0	5.1	5.4	8.0	7.8	8.4	8.9	7.9
High monthly average	39.5	42.3	49.2	57.1	66.7	75.7	81.2	80.8	72.0	60.0	46.1†	37.9	81.2
Year of occurrence	1953	1995	1992	1992	1934	1988	1960	1994	1990	1988	1995	1977	1960
Low monthly average	11.5	16.3	32.0	44.1	52.2	60.2	69.9	69.3	57.5	46.6	32.3	18.0	11.5
Year of occurrence	1949	1933	1964	1970	1933	1945	1993	1968	1965	1946	1938	1932	1949

† Also occurred on earlier date(s).

SALT LAKE CITY NWSFO
Monthly Data Summary

Precipitation in Inches

	Jan	Feb	Mar	Apr	May	Jun	Jul	Aug	Sep	Oct	Nov	Dec	Annual
Monthly normal	1.11	1.24	1.91	2.12	1.80	0.93	0.81	0.86	1.28	1.44	1.29	1.40	16.20
Standard deviation	0.09	0.11	0.14	0.18	0.16	0.11	0.13	0.11	0.18	0.14	0.11	0.12	0.13
Average monthly	1.29	1.22	1.70	1.96	1.66	0.92	0.67	0.86	0.94	1.33	1.31	1.26	15.12
Standard deviation	0.11	0.11	0.13	0.17	0.15	0.12	0.11	0.12	0.14	0.14	0.12	0.11	0.13
High monthly total	3.23	3.22	3.97	4.90	4.76	2.93	2.57	3.66	7.04	3.91	2.96	4.37	7.04
Year of occurrence	1993	1936	1983	1944	1977	1947	1982	1968	1982	1981	1994	1983	1982
Low monthly total	0.09	0.12	0.10	0.45	0.00	0.00	0.00†	0.00	0.00†	0.00†	0.01	0.08	0.00†
Year of occurrence	1961	1946	1956	1981	1934	1994	1963	1944	1951	1978	1939	1976	1978
Record high daily	1.36	0.90†	1.56	1.62	1.55	1.75	2.28	1.96	2.27	1.53	1.13	1.21	2.28
Day of occurrence	14	25	13	25	16	21	13	26	26	7	16	28	13
Year of occurrence	1953	1969	1944	1976	1942	1948	1962	1932	1982	1993	1954	1972	1962
Days w/pcp >= .01	10.0	8.9	9.9	9.5	8.3	5.4	4.4	5.6	5.2	6.3	7.9	9.0	91.4
Days w/pcp >= .10	4.0	4.0	5.3	5.2	4.4	2.5	1.7	2.2	2.2	3.6	3.9	4.0	43.4
Days w/pcp >= .50	0.4	0.3	0.7	1.0	0.9	0.4	0.4	0.4	0.6	0.7	0.5	0.4	6.7

Snow and Sleet in Inches

	Jan	Feb	Mar	Apr	May	Jun	Jul	Aug	Sep	Oct	Nov	Dec	Annual
Monthly normal	12.4	10.1	11.7	6.8	1.1	0.0	0.0	0.0	0.2	2.1	6.5	13.7	64.7
Standard deviation	1.1	1.1	1.3	1.0	0.4	0.0	0.0	0.0	0.2	0.7	0.8	1.2	0.6
Average monthly	14.4	9.9	9.2	5.6	0.7	0.0	0.1	0.0	0.1	1.5	7.0	12.8	61.5
Standard deviation	1.2	1.1	1.1	0.9	0.3	0.0	0.1	0.0	0.1	0.5	0.9	1.2	0.6
High monthly total	50.3	36.5	41.9	26.4	7.5	0.0†	7.1	0.0†	4.0	20.4	33.3	36.1	50.3
Year of occurrence	1993	1989	1977	1974	1975	1995	1931	1995	1971	1984	1994	1948	1993
Low monthly total	0.1	0.0	0.0†	0.0†	0.0†	0.0†	0.0†	0.0†	0.0†	0.0†	0.0†	0.9	0.0†
Year of occurrence	1961	1953	1993	1989	1995	1995	1995	1995	1995	1994	1976	1962	1976
Record high daily	13.4	10.9	11.5	11.8	5.3	0.0†	4.7	0.0†	4.0	13.8	11.0	12.6	13.8
Day of occurrence	25	1	22	10	5	30	30	31	30	18	17	28	18
Year of occurrence	1996	1989	1964	1974	1965	1995	1931	1995	1971	1984	1930	1972	1984
Days w/snow >= .1	9.2	6.1	4.9	2.8	0.4	0.0	0.1	0.0	0.1	0.6	3.9	8.0	36.6
Days w/snow >= 5	0.6	0.4	0.4	0.3	0.0	0.0	0.0	0.0	0.0	0.1	0.3	0.4	2.5
Days w/snow >= 10	0.0	0.0	0.1	0.0	0.0	0.0	0.0	0.0	0.0	0.0	0.0	0.0	0.2

Degree Days

	Jan	Feb	Mar	Apr	May	Jun	Jul	Aug	Sep	Oct	Nov	Dec	Annual
Heating normal	1150	873	718	464	224	52	0	7	102	380	732	1093	5800
Heating average	1158	888	730	456	223	60	1	5	97	379	771	1070	5844
Cooling normal	0	0	0	2	31	171	398	331	98	4	0	0	1039
Cooling average	0	0	0	2	31	150	379	323	96	4	0	0	990
Growing 40 normal	33	86	202	344	563	747	926	894	674	437	171	41	5123
Growing 40 average	33	79	195	352	564	727	913	888	673	437	161	48	5076
Growing 50 normal	4	22	79	182	357	546	749	711	474	253	65	6	3454
Growing 50 average	4	19	76	188	358	525	735	706	478	255	59	8	3415

† Also occurred on earlier date(s).

Location: Snowville   County: Box Elder   Latitude: 41.967   Longitude:-112.717
Elevation: 4560 feet   Period of Record: 1948-1991

SNOWVILLE
Monthly Data Summary

Maximum Temperature in °F

	Jan	Feb	Mar	Apr	May	Jun	Jul	Aug	Sep	Oct	Nov	Dec	Annual
Monthly normal	33.3	40.0	48.6	59.5	69.7	80.8	90.5	88.5	77.7	65.2	47.6	36.1	61.4
Standard deviation	7.6	9.2	9.3	9.8	10.2	9.6	6.3	6.7	9.9	10.5	9.9	8.9	9.0
Average monthly	33.3	39.5	47.7	59.1	69.1	80.1	90.3	88.3	78.1	65.0	47.8	36.1	61.2
Standard deviation	7.8	9.2	9.2	9.9	10.3	9.7	6.1	6.3	9.8	10.5	10.0	8.5	9.0
High monthly average	43.3	49.1	59.4	67.1	76.3	88.6	94.9	95.9	85.9	71.8	55.8	43.5	95.9
Year of occurrence	1953	1963	1986	1977	1958	1974	1985	1981	1990	1988	1954	1976	1981
Low monthly average	25.1	28.6	37.5	48.2	62.0	73.0	84.4	84.5	69.6	55.2	41.2	27.1	25.1
Year of occurrence	1989	1989	1952	1975	1991	1967	1987	1987	1965	1949	1957	1985	1989
Record high daily	56	65†	75†	87	91	101	105†	106	100	89	72†	57†	106
Day of occurrence	13	26	31	27	29	24	8	9	1	8	4	11	9
Year of occurrence	1959	1986	1986	1987	1983	1988	1985	1990	1967	1980	1985	1981	1990
Record low daily	5	3	22†	33†	36	44	65†	60	41	29	21†	-6	-6
Day of occurrence	30	6	28	27	5	1	23	20	17	21	29	22	22
Year of occurrence	1951	1989	1975	1955	1975	1955	1973	1980	1965	1984	1979	1990	1990
Days w/max >= 100	0.0	0.0	0.0	0.0	0.0	0.1	0.9	0.6	0.0	0.0	0.0	0.0	1.6
Days w/max >= 90	0.0	0.0	0.0	0.0	0.1	4.8	19.2	14.5	2.8	0.0	0.0	0.0	41.2
Days w/max <= 32	13.7	5.7	1.7	0.0	0.0	0.0	0.0	0.0	0.0	0.1	1.6	9.3	32.2

Minimum Temperature in °F

	Jan	Feb	Mar	Apr	May	Jun	Jul	Aug	Sep	Oct	Nov	Dec	Annual
Monthly normal	9.6	15.0	21.8	28.3	35.8	43.1	50.5	48.7	39.0	28.7	21.0	11.4	29.4
Standard deviation	12.5	11.7	8.8	7.2	6.4	6.6	6.3	6.7	7.7	6.8	8.9	11.3	8.4
Average monthly	9.4	14.7	21.6	28.3	35.8	43.0	50.5	48.6	39.0	28.7	20.7	12.0	29.4
Standard deviation	12.5	12.0	8.8	6.9	6.4	6.7	6.6	6.7	7.6	6.7	9.1	11.1	8.4
High monthly average	24.5	23.9	29.4	33.1	40.7	49.6	61.3	58.3	49.6	33.9	29.4	24.2	61.3
Year of occurrence	1953	1958	1983	1989	1987	1991	1991	1991	1990	1988	1966	1950	1991
Low monthly average	-0.6	0.5	9.9	16.8	31.9	38.2	45.9	41.0	32.1	21.4	13.0	-1.2	-1.2
Year of occurrence	1955	1985	1968	1968	1950	1950	1962	1962	1965	1966	1979	1990	1990
Record high daily	40	39	44	51	55	67	73	73	69	49†	44†	36†	73†
Day of occurrence	29	19	17	24	30	25	17	25	1	1	1	22	25
Year of occurrence	1965	1986	1950	1974	1983	1988	1991	1991	1967	1983	1987	1964	1991
Record low daily	-25	-27	-11	-3	11	22	35†	23	15	7	-22	-27	-27†
Day of occurrence	12	1	7	9	6	30	8	31	18	15	15	23	23
Year of occurrence	1963	1951	1964	1968	1965	1968	1981	1965	1965	1966	1955	1990	1990
Days w/min <= 32	30.2	27.5	28.8	21.9	9.1	1.7	0.0	0.2	5.9	22.2	27.2	30.5	204.7
Days w/min <= 0	7.9	4.3	0.8	0.0	0.0	0.0	0.0	0.0	0.0	0.0	0.7	4.8	18.6
Days w/min <= -20	0.2	0.1	0.0	0.0	0.0	0.0	0.0	0.0	0.0	0.0	0.0	0.2	0.6

Mean Temperature in °F

	Jan	Feb	Mar	Apr	May	Jun	Jul	Aug	Sep	Oct	Nov	Dec	Annual
Monthly normal	21.4	27.6	35.2	43.9	52.7	62.0	70.5	68.6	58.4	47.0	34.3	23.7	45.4
Standard deviation	9.1	9.6	7.8	7.2	7.3	7.2	4.9	5.5	7.7	7.3	8.1	9.1	7.6
Average monthly	21.4	27.1	34.7	43.7	52.5	61.5	70.4	68.4	58.5	46.8	34.2	24.1	45.3
Standard deviation	9.2	9.7	7.8	7.1	7.4	7.2	5.1	5.3	7.6	7.4	8.2	8.8	7.6
High monthly average	33.9	36.3	43.5	49.4	57.4	67.8	75.9	73.4	67.7	52.8	40.3	31.8	75.9
Year of occurrence	1953	1963	1986	1990	1958	1977	1991	1991	1990	1988	1953	1981	1991
Low monthly average	13.5	15.7	25.8	36.9	47.1	56.5	67.4	64.4	50.8	41.4	27.7	13.9	13.5
Year of occurrence	1955	1985	1952	1968	1975	1951	1962	1962	1965	1949	1985	1990	1955

† Also occurred on earlier date(s).

SNOWVILLE
Monthly Data Summary

Precipitation in Inches

	Jan	Feb	Mar	Apr	May	Jun	Jul	Aug	Sep	Oct	Nov	Dec	Annual
Monthly normal	1.05	0.84	1.08	1.20	1.74	1.18	0.86	0.74	0.91	0.93	1.23	1.06	12.82
Standard deviation	0.11	0.09	0.10	0.11	0.15	0.13	0.13	0.10	0.11	0.11	0.11	0.10	0.11
Average monthly	1.07	0.80	0.99	1.17	1.72	1.10	0.71	0.73	0.82	0.84	1.09	1.04	12.10
Standard deviation	0.10	0.09	0.10	0.11	0.15	0.12	0.12	0.11	0.10	0.10	0.11	0.10	0.11
High monthly total	2.83	2.20	3.07	3.91	4.44	4.18	3.41	2.57	3.62	2.30	4.03	3.34	4.44
Year of occurrence	1980	1980	1982	1971	1980	1967	1983	1979	1982	1981	1965	1983	1980
Low monthly total	0.22	0.03	0.04	0.04	0.12	0.06	0.00†	0.00†	0.00†	0.00†	0.00†	0.00†	0.00†
Year of occurrence	1985	1989	1969	1969	1972	1951	1988	1975	1974	1978	1976	1976	1976
Record high daily	1.10	1.20	1.14	1.15	1.40	1.43	2.10	1.65	1.02	0.96	1.10	1.10	2.10
Day of occurrence	31	15	31	26	4	25	10	15	27	26	26	25	10
Year of occurrence	1963	1984	1958	1971	1982	1965	1983	1979	1982	1991	1961	1959	1983
Days w/pcp >= .01	6.5	5.8	6.9	6.9	8.4	5.5	3.2	3.7	4.1	4.2	6.2	6.5	69.0
Days w/pcp >= .10	3.6	2.9	3.4	3.9	5.0	3.4	1.8	1.9	2.6	2.4	3.7	3.7	38.9
Days w/pcp >= .50	0.4	0.1	0.3	0.4	0.8	0.5	0.3	0.4	0.4	0.4	0.6	0.2	4.9

Snow and Sleet in Inches

	Jan	Feb	Mar	Apr	May	Jun	Jul	Aug	Sep	Oct	Nov	Dec	Annual
Monthly normal	6.6	5.0	3.1	1.1	0.1	0.0	0.0	0.0	0.0	0.1	4.7	4.3	24.9
Standard deviation	1.0	0.8	0.6	0.3	0.1	0.0	0.0	0.0	0.0	0.1	1.0	0.7	0.4
Average monthly	6.5	3.5	2.2	0.7	0.1	0.0	0.0	0.0	0.0	0.1	3.0	4.1	20.1
Standard deviation	1.0	0.7	0.5	0.3	0.1	0.0	0.0	0.0	0.0	0.1	0.8	0.7	0.3
High monthly total	26.0	19.0	14.0	14.9	2.4	0.0†	0.0†	0.0†	0.0†	2.0	25.0	20.0	26.0
Year of occurrence	1949	1976	1964	1967	1964	1991	1991	1991	1991	1974	1978	1949	1949
Low monthly total	0.0†	0.0†	0.0†	0.0†	0.0†	0.0†	0.0†	0.0†	0.0†	0.0†	0.0†	0.0†	0.0†
Year of occurrence	1990	1991	1991	1991	1991	1991	1991	1991	1991	1991	1990	1990	1990
Record high daily	12.0	8.0	8.0	4.1	2.0	0.0†	0.0†	0.0†	0.0†	2.0	14.0	10.0	14.0
Day of occurrence	22	10	13	1	2	30	31	31	30	21	13	18	13
Year of occurrence	1949	1976	1973	1967	1964	1991	1991	1991	1991	1974	1978	1984	1978
Days w/snow >= .1	2.1	1.5	0.9	0.3	0.1	0.0	0.0	0.0	0.0	0.1	1.1	1.9	6.6
Days w/snow >= 5	0.5	0.2	0.1	0.0	0.0	0.0	0.0	0.0	0.0	0.0	0.2	0.2	0.9
Days w/snow >= 10	0.0	0.0	0.0	0.0	0.0	0.0	0.0	0.0	0.0	0.0	0.0	0.0	0.1

Degree Days

	Jan	Feb	Mar	Apr	May	Jun	Jul	Aug	Sep	Oct	Nov	Dec	Annual
Heating normal	1330	1052	915	625	381	137	10	27	218	556	921	1278	7457
Heating average	1337	1065	934	630	388	146	13	27	214	561	917	1267	7504
Cooling normal	0	0	0	0	2	46	180	137	19	0	0	0	386
Cooling average	0	0	0	0	2	43	179	133	20	0	0	0	378
Growing 40 normal	9	49	145	288	453	583	731	703	537	385	131	25	4045
Growing 40 average	10	46	133	283	445	579	733	704	540	382	133	24	4017
Growing 50 normal	0	8	47	152	305	445	582	556	408	243	44	1	2795
Growing 50 average	0	7	41	148	296	439	584	559	413	239	46	1	2778

† Also occurred on earlier date(s).

Location: Spanish Fork Pwr House   County: Utah   Latitude: 40.083   Longitude: -111.600
Elevation: 4720 feet   Period of Record: 1928-1995

SPANISH FORK PWR HOUSE
Monthly Data Summary

Maximum Temperature in °F

	Jan	Feb	Mar	Apr	May	Jun	Jul	Aug	Sep	Oct	Nov	Dec	Annual
Monthly normal	36.2	43.2	52.8	62.7	73.6	84.5	92.7	89.8	79.7	66.5	50.0	37.8	64.1
Standard deviation	9.3	10.0	10.2	10.7	10.3	9.3	4.8	5.7	8.8	10.4	10.4	9.7	9.1
Average monthly	37.2	43.6	53.2	63.9	73.9	84.9	93.1	90.5	81.2	67.3	50.2	39.7	64.9
Standard deviation	9.2	9.6	9.8	10.7	10.3	9.3	5.4	5.7	8.6	10.3	10.7	9.4	9.1
High monthly average	49.3	55.4	65.8	75.1	85.8	93.3	98.9	94.5	88.2	76.4	60.5	49.7	98.9
Year of occurrence	1953	1995	1934	1934	1934	1933	1931	1937	1943	1933	1949	1939	1931
Low monthly average	22.8	32.5	42.3	53.8	66.1	77.2	87.7	83.3	72.4	58.0	41.5	27.6	22.8
Year of occurrence	1937	1933	1952	1975	1953	1945	1993	1968	1965	1969	1992	1930	1937
Record high daily	63	72†	80†	87†	97†	104	108†	104†	98†	89	76†	65†	108
Day of occurrence	12	25	28	16	31	21	26	13	7	1	9	1	26
Year of occurrence	1953	1986	1986	1936	1994	1936	1931	1940	1966	1957	1953	1995	1931
Record low daily	0	2	26	33†	41	49	68	64	44	27	17	-1	-1
Day of occurrence	22	6	1	11	5	9	12	30	17	29	16	23	23
Year of occurrence	1937	1989	1971	1991	1975	1941	1992	1932	1965	1971	1955	1990	1990
Days w/max >= 100	0.0	0.0	0.0	0.0	0.0	0.5	2.8	0.9	0.0	0.0	0.0	0.0	4.1
Days w/max >= 90	0.0	0.0	0.0	0.0	1.1	10.8	24.4	19.3	4.3	0.0	0.0	0.0	59.6
Days w/max <= 32	9.3	3.5	0.3	0.0	0.0	0.0	0.0	0.0	0.0	0.0	1.4	6.6	21.4

Minimum Temperature in °F

	Jan	Feb	Mar	Apr	May	Jun	Jul	Aug	Sep	Oct	Nov	Dec	Annual
Monthly normal	18.8	23.7	30.0	36.7	44.8	52.2	59.7	57.6	49.2	39.9	30.4	21.2	38.7
Standard deviation	10.2	9.8	7.8	7.0	7.1	6.6	4.7	5.3	7.2	7.1	8.0	9.4	7.5
Average monthly	19.2	23.6	29.9	37.0	44.7	51.9	59.3	58.0	49.5	40.2	29.4	22.0	38.7
Standard deviation	10.2	9.7	7.7	7.1	6.9	6.6	4.9	5.1	7.0	6.9	8.3	9.2	7.5
High monthly average	28.8	33.9	36.9	43.2	51.0	57.5	64.2	62.2	56.0	46.4	36.3	28.7	64.2
Year of occurrence	1953	1934	1934	1992	1934	1931	1931	1994	1990	1963	1965	1933	1931
Low monthly average	3.5	11.2	21.6	30.4	39.5	45.0	55.1	52.3	43.6	34.2	22.6	10.5	3.5
Year of occurrence	1949	1933	1964	1945	1975	1945	1993	1950	1945	1956	1930	1949
Record high daily	44	50	52†	60†	75	75	77	74†	70	69	53	48	77
Day of occurrence	13	18	8	18	21	20	13	8	2	5	7	4	13
Year of occurrence	1980	1986	1986	1987	1966	1931	1931	1994	1939	1929	1980	1980	1931
Record low daily	-16†	-20	1	14	25	29	41	38	26	13	-6	-14	-20
Day of occurrence	26	7	11	3	6	14	6	30	18	30	16	23	7
Year of occurrence	1949	1989	1948	1945	1965	1976	1982	1964	1965	1971	1955	1990	1989
Days w/min <= 32	28.5	23.4	19.2	8.0	1.3	0.0	0.0	0.0	0.3	4.4	18.6	27.7	133.2
Days w/min <= 0	1.4	0.5	0.0	0.0	0.0	0.0	0.0	0.0	0.0	0.0	0.0	0.6	2.7
Days w/min <= -20	0.0	0.0	0.0	0.0	0.0	0.0	0.0	0.0	0.0	0.0	0.0	0.0	0.0

Mean Temperature in °F

	Jan	Feb	Mar	Apr	May	Jun	Jul	Aug	Sep	Oct	Nov	Dec	Annual
Monthly normal	27.5	33.5	41.4	49.7	59.2	68.4	76.2	73.7	64.4	53.2	40.2	29.5	51.4
Standard deviation	9.3	9.4	8.3	8.2	8.1	7.3	3.9	4.8	7.3	8.2	8.6	9.2	7.7
Average monthly	28.2	33.6	41.6	50.5	59.3	68.4	76.2	74.2	65.4	53.8	39.8	30.9	51.8
Standard deviation	9.3	9.1	8.0	8.2	8.0	7.3	4.2	4.5	7.1	7.9	8.9	8.8	7.6
High monthly average	39.0	43.8	51.3	58.9	68.4	74.7	81.5	77.8	70.2	60.1	46.4	38.9	81.5
Year of occurrence	1953	1934	1934	1934	1934	1933	1931	1937	1933	1933	1965	1939	1931
Low monthly average	14.2	21.9	32.3	43.1	53.3	61.1	71.4	68.8	58.5	47.1†	32.7	19.1	14.2
Year of occurrence	1949	1933	1964	1975	1953	1945	1993	1968	1961	1984	1938	1930	1949

† Also occurred on earlier date(s).

SPANISH FORK PWR HOUSE
Monthly Data Summary

Precipitation in Inches

	Jan	Feb	Mar	Apr	May	Jun	Jul	Aug	Sep	Oct	Nov	Dec	Annual
Monthly normal	1.57	1.74	2.29	2.12	1.94	1.23	0.92	1.21	1.59	1.96	2.04	2.04	20.67
Standard deviation	0.13	0.17	0.17	0.17	0.20	0.15	0.14	0.14	0.18	0.20	0.18	0.16	0.17
Average monthly	1.69	1.71	2.12	2.02	1.80	1.07	0.82	1.04	1.18	1.76	1.87	1.79	18.87
Standard deviation	0.14	0.15	0.17	0.17	0.18	0.14	0.11	0.13	0.15	0.18	0.18	0.15	0.15
High monthly total	4.21	4.54	4.28	4.92	6.10	3.72	3.15	4.77	8.08	6.76	4.62	6.10	8.08
Year of occurrence	1980	1983	1978	1944	1995	1964	1974	1983	1982	1981	1994	1983	1982
Low monthly total	0.00	0.30	0.13	0.04	0.01	0.00†	0.00†	0.00†	0.00†	0.00	0.03	0.18	0.00†
Year of occurrence	1961	1988	1956	1949	1940	1994	1958	1962	1951	1952	1959	1976	1952
Record high daily	1.32	1.49	1.71	1.49	2.86	1.55	2.87	1.67	1.88	2.54	1.64	1.78	2.87
Day of occurrence	25	28	9	2	20	25	16	24	6	20	15	29	16
Year of occurrence	1954	1983	1986	1986	1975	1985	1974	1987	1963	1979	1958	1951	1974
Days w/pcp >= .01	9.3	8.7	9.2	8.6	7.3	4.8	4.9	5.7	5.1	6.2	7.8	9.0	87.7
Days w/pcp >= .10	5.0	4.8	5.8	5.6	4.6	2.6	2.4	2.7	3.0	4.1	4.5	5.1	51.0
Days w/pcp >= .50	0.8	0.8	1.4	1.3	1.1	0.6	0.3	0.6	0.7	1.1	1.2	0.9	10.7

Snow and Sleet in Inches

	Jan	Feb	Mar	Apr	May	Jun	Jul	Aug	Sep	Oct	Nov	Dec	Annual
Monthly normal	13.3	10.7	9.2	2.8	0.2	0.0	0.0	0.0	0.0	0.7	5.4	12.0	54.2
Standard deviation	1.4	1.3	1.2	0.7	0.2	0.0	0.0	0.0	0.0	0.3	1.2	1.3	0.6
Average monthly	13.6	8.8	7.4	2.2	0.3	0.0	0.0	0.0	0.0	0.4	6.0	10.1	48.8
Standard deviation	1.4	1.1	1.1	0.6	0.2	0.0	0.0	0.0	0.0	0.2	1.1	1.2	0.6
High monthly total	48.5	36.2	24.0	25.5	6.0†	0.0†	0.0†	0.0†	0.0†	10.0	40.5	45.5	48.5
Year of occurrence	1993	1989	1945	1929	1975	1995	1995	1995	1995	1984	1994	1983	1993
Low monthly total	0.0†	0.0†	0.0†	0.0†	0.0†	0.0†	0.0†	0.0†	0.0†	0.0†	0.0†	0.0†	0.0†
Year of occurrence	1961	1967	1993	1992	1995	1995	1995	1995	1995	1993	1987	1986	1986
Record high daily	13.0	12.0†	16.0	13.0	6.0†	0.0†	0.0†	0.0†	0.0†	8.0	23.0	13.0	23.0
Day of occurrence	24	13	14	6	15	30	31	31	30	28	29	8	29
Year of occurrence	1950	1990	1944	1929	1955	1995	1995	1995	1995	1961	1975	1985	1975
Days w/snow >= .1	5.4	3.9	2.4	0.7	0.1	0.0	0.0	0.0	0.0	0.2	2.0	4.0	16.9
Days w/snow >= 5	0.8	0.4	0.5	0.2	0.0	0.0	0.0	0.0	0.0	0.0	0.3	0.6	2.6
Days w/snow >= 10	0.1	0.1	0.1	0.0	0.0	0.0	0.0	0.0	0.0	0.0	0.1	0.1	0.4

Degree Days

	Jan	Feb	Mar	Apr	May	Jun	Jul	Aug	Sep	Oct	Nov	Dec	Annual
Heating normal	1156	888	731	458	208	51	0	5	93	366	743	1097	5802
Heating average	1136	884	724	436	204	50	0	3	78	350	752	1056	5680
Cooling normal	0	0	0	1	29	151	344	273	76	2	0	0	879
Cooling average	0	0	0	1	29	152	347	288	89	3	0	0	912
Growing 40 normal	32	81	208	356	570	715	871	841	658	444	169	44	4993
Growing 40 average	36	83	214	376	572	712	869	848	672	456	171	55	5071
Growing 50 normal	3	21	86	201	376	529	698	662	467	263	65	6	3381
Growing 50 average	4	20	90	217	379	530	695	670	487	276	68	9	3450

† Also occurred on earlier date(s).

Location: St. George   County: Washington   Latitude: 37.100   Longitude: -113.583

Elevation: 940 feet   Period of Record: 1862-1996

ST GEORGE
Monthly Data Summary

Maximum Temperature in °F

	Jan	Feb	Mar	Apr	May	Jun	Jul	Aug	Sep	Oct	Nov	Dec	Annual
Monthly normal	53.6	61.0	67.4	76.4	86.4	96.7	102.2	99.7	92.5	80.5	64.4	54.1	77.9
Standard deviation	7.6	8.6	8.9	9.0	8.5	7.1	4.6	5.3	6.9	8.6	8.7	7.2	7.6
Average monthly	53.3	59.8	67.4	76.6	85.7	96.0	101.5	99.3	92.6	80.1	64.6	53.9	77.6
Standard deviation	7.9	8.7	8.9	9.2	8.6	7.3	5.1	5.3	6.8	8.7	8.4	7.3	7.7
High monthly average	63.3	70.9	79.2	85.0	94.1	104.4	106.8	106.3	97.8	88.0	71.6	62.2	106.8
Year of occurrence	1986	1995	1934	1989	1984	1994	1994	1969	1995	1964	1995	1980	1994
Low monthly average	33.0	47.5	57.1	67.2	76.1	90.5	92.4	92.9	85.0	71.0†	58.2	40.4	33.0
Year of occurrence	1937	1903	1964	1975	1917	1965	1912	1941	1900	1946	1972	1909	1937
Record high daily	72†	84†	89†	100	108	115†	117	113	109†	99†	88	75†	117
Day of occurrence	24	27	27	25	31	26	5	5	3	1	2	23	5
Year of occurrence	1948	1986	1986	1946	1910	1970	1985	1895	1995	1980	1945	1955	1985
Record low daily	17	27	42†	45	51	65†	79†	73	58	40	32	26†	17
Day of occurrence	22	6	5	10	1	6	25	28	29	29	24	13	22
Year of occurrence	1937	1989	1948	1893	1915	1934	1941	1896	1905	1971	1991	1932	1937
Days w/max >= 100	0.0	0.0	0.0	0.0	0.8	10.2	21.7	16.1	4.5	0.0	0.0	0.0	53.8
Days w/max >= 90	0.0	0.0	0.0	1.7	11.5	24.7	30.3	29.6	21.6	4.3	0.0	0.0	124.9
Days w/max <= 32	0.4	0.1	0.0	0.0	0.0	0.0	0.0	0.0	0.0	0.0	0.0	0.2	0.7

Minimum Temperature in °F

	Jan	Feb	Mar	Apr	May	Jun	Jul	Aug	Sep	Oct	Nov	Dec	Annual
Monthly normal	26.7	32.0	37.6	44.2	53.0	61.7	68.9	66.8	57.5	45.6	34.6	27.4	46.3
Standard deviation	7.9	7.4	6.8	6.9	7.0	6.2	5.5	5.8	7.2	7.0	6.9	6.9	6.8
Average monthly	25.3	30.1	35.8	42.6	50.5	58.5	66.0	64.6	54.8	42.9	31.5	25.5	44.0
Standard deviation	8.0	7.9	7.3	7.1	7.1	7.0	6.4	6.4	7.9	7.7	7.4	7.8	7.3
High monthly average	35.6	39.9	43.5	50.7†	59.5	68.9	74.0	73.4	63.5	51.8	38.6†	33.2	74.0
Year of occurrence	1995	1957	1992	1992	1984	1994	1994	1994	1983	1992	1983	1984	1994
Low monthly average	10.8	15.9	23.2	31.1	39.7	48.3	54.1	52.5	42.6	33.5	20.0	12.0	10.8
Year of occurrence	1937	1903	1897	1896	1899	1894	1902	1899	1900	1898	1896	1895	1937
Record high daily	50	52†	59†	69	75	82†	89	84	78	70	54	56	89
Day of occurrence	21	27	21	13	24	27	15	20	2	6	15	24	15
Year of occurrence	1969	1989	1995	1987	1984	1981	1970	1992	1981	1977	1963	1955	1970
Record low daily	-11†	1†	12†	18†	20	35†	41†	43†	25	20†	4	-4†	-11
Day of occurrence	26	7	1	8	3	1	3	1	21	30	29	27	26
Year of occurrence	1937	1899	1903	1901	1899	1908	1902	1903	1895	1971	1896	1909	1937
Days w/min <= 32	25.6	17.7	10.0	2.3	0.2	0.0	0.0	0.0	0.1	2.8	17.0	26.0	102.4
Days w/min <= 0	0.1	0.0	0.0	0.0	0.0	0.0	0.0	0.0	0.0	0.0	0.0	0.0	0.1
Days w/min <= -20	0.0	0.0	0.0	0.0	0.0	0.0	0.0	0.0	0.0	0.0	0.0	0.0	0.0

Mean Temperature in °F

	Jan	Feb	Mar	Apr	May	Jun	Jul	Aug	Sep	Oct	Nov	Dec	Annual
Monthly normal	40.2	46.5	52.5	60.3	69.7	79.2	85.5	83.2	75.0	63.0	49.5	40.8	62.1
Standard deviation	6.5	6.9	6.8	7.1	7.1	6.1	4.0	4.7	6.2	6.9	6.8	6.0	6.3
Average monthly	39.3	44.9	51.6	59.6	68.1	77.3	83.8	82.0	73.7	61.5	48.1	39.7	60.8
Standard deviation	6.6	7.0	6.7	7.0	6.9	6.2	4.6	4.7	6.2	6.9	6.6	6.2	6.3
High monthly average	47.4	54.5	59.7	67.8	76.8	86.7	90.4	89.4	80.0	69.2	54.8	46.0	90.4
Year of occurrence	1986	1995	1994	1989	1984	1994	1994	1994	1995	1988	1995	1995	1994
Low monthly average	21.9	31.7	40.9	51.2	60.0	70.2	76.1	72.8	63.8	54.8	40.8	29.0	21.9
Year of occurrence	1937	1903	1897	1900	1899	1894	1902	1899	1900	1899	1896	1909	1937

† Also occurred on earlier date(s).

ST GEORGE
Monthly Data Summary

Precipitation in Inches

	Jan	Feb	Mar	Apr	May	Jun	Jul	Aug	Sep	Oct	Nov	Dec	Annual
Monthly normal	1.04	0.84	1.10	0.53	0.39	0.17	0.60	0.77	0.54	0.51	0.84	0.71	8.05
Standard deviation	0.12	0.11	0.11	0.07	0.07	0.04	0.09	0.10	0.09	0.07	0.11	0.08	0.09
Average monthly	1.06	0.98	0.97	0.51	0.40	0.19	0.68	0.77	0.59	0.67	0.62	0.80	8.22
Standard deviation	0.12	0.11	0.11	0.07	0.07	0.05	0.10	0.11	0.10	0.10	0.09	0.09	0.09
High monthly total	4.74	3.61	4.38	2.86	1.97	1.75	3.00	3.01	4.16	5.42	2.55	3.17	5.42
Year of occurrence	1993	1932	1978	1988	1977	1932	1909	1925	1939	1912	1931	1921	1912
Low monthly total	0.00†	0.00†	0.00†	0.00†	0.00†	0.00†	0.00†	0.00†	0.00†	0.00†	0.00†	0.00†	0.00†
Year of occurrence	1976	1974	1972	1992	1974	1992	1993	1985	1993	1995	1992	1989	1989
Record high daily	1.50	1.10	1.33	1.10	1.52	1.16	1.82	2.40	1.63	1.80	1.00	1.01	2.40
Day of occurrence	26	14	6	29	11	4	25	31	19	26	21	25	31
Year of occurrence	1865	1980	1995	1917	1958	1925	1902	1909	1972	1912	1967	1942	1909
Days w/pcp >= .01	5.0	5.1	5.2	3.5	2.7	1.3	3.5	4.1	2.7	3.1	3.0	4.4	43.6
Days w/pcp >= .10	3.1	3.0	3.0	1.7	1.2	0.6	1.9	2.1	1.6	1.8	1.8	2.5	24.4
Days w/pcp >= .50	0.6	0.4	0.4	0.2	0.2	0.1	0.3	0.4	0.4	0.4	0.3	0.3	3.9

Snow and Sleet in Inches

	Jan	Feb	Mar	Apr	May	Jun	Jul	Aug	Sep	Oct	Nov	Dec	Annual
Monthly normal	1.1	0.3	0.0	0.0	0.0	0.0	0.0	0.0	0.0	0.0	0.1	0.8	2.4
Standard deviation	0.5	0.1	0.0	0.0	0.0	0.0	0.0	0.0	0.0	0.0	0.1	0.3	0.1
Average monthly	1.4	0.7	0.2	0.0	0.0	0.0	0.0	0.0	0.0	0.0	0.3	0.9	3.4
Standard deviation	0.4	0.3	0.1	0.0	0.0	0.0	0.0	0.0	0.0	0.0	0.2	0.3	0.1
High monthly total	17.0	9.0	4.5†	0.2	0.0†	0.0†	0.0†	0.0†	0.0†	1.3	16.0	10.0	17.0
Year of occurrence	1898	1939	1923	1927	1995	1995	1995	1995	1995	1971	1919	1865	1898
Low monthly total	0.0†	0.0†	0.0†	0.0†	0.0†	0.0†	0.0†	0.0†	0.0†	0.0†	0.0†	0.0†	0.0†
Year of occurrence	1995	1995	1995	1995	1995	1995	1995	1995	1995	1995	1995	1995	1995
Record high daily	10.0	6.0	3.0	0.2	0.0†	0.0†	0.0†	0.0†	0.0†	1.0	8.0†	7.0	10.0
Day of occurrence	5	4	20	11	31	30	31	31	30	29	27	11	5
Year of occurrence	1974	1939	1894	1927	1995	1995	1995	1995	1995	1971	1919	1945	1974
Days w/snow >= .1	0.6	0.4	0.1	0.0	0.0	0.0	0.0	0.0	0.0	0.0	0.1	0.5	1.6
Days w/snow >= 5	0.1	0.0	0.0	0.0	0.0	0.0	0.0	0.0	0.0	0.0	0.0	0.0	0.2
Days w/snow >= 10	0.0	0.0	0.0	0.0	0.0	0.0	0.0	0.0	0.0	0.0	0.0	0.0	0.0

Degree Days

	Jan	Feb	Mar	Apr	May	Jun	Jul	Aug	Sep	Oct	Nov	Dec	Annual
Heating normal	769	521	388	171	38	0	0	0	6	115	463	751	3227
Heating average	795	566	417	186	48	2	0	0	9	149	507	783	3466
Cooling normal	0	0	1	31	184	426	635	565	307	55	0	0	2206
Cooling average	0	0	0	24	145	371	582	526	271	41	0	0	1963
Growing 40 normal	216	304	441	576	764	880	1017	987	815	640	378	223	7247
Growing 40 average	211	285	435	562	725	832	975	954	776	612	375	220	6966
Growing 50 normal	81	162	272	402	580	712	848	817	649	472	220	85	5304
Growing 50 average	79	147	271	399	552	667	805	784	620	462	222	83	5097

† Also occurred on earlier date(s).

Location: Tooele   County: Tooele   Latitude: 40.533   Longitude: -112.300
Elevation: 5070 feet   Period of Record: 1897-1996

TOOELE
Monthly Data Summary

Maximum Temperature in °F

	Jan	Feb	Mar	Apr	May	Jun	Jul	Aug	Sep	Oct	Nov	Dec	Annual
Monthly normal	37.5	43.2	50.7	59.8	69.7	80.1	88.5	86.1	75.9	63.3	48.7	38.3	61.8
Standard deviation	9.3	9.2	9.7	10.5	10.1	9.4	5.4	5.9	9.1	10.0	9.5	9.3	8.9
Average monthly	37.9	42.5	50.7	60.3	69.6	79.8	88.4	86.6	76.8	63.4	49.0	39.1	62.0
Standard deviation	9.0	9.1	9.5	10.3	10.0	9.2	5.9	5.8	8.8	9.7	9.6	8.9	8.8
High monthly average	49.5	54.6	60.9	70.9	81.1	89.2	94.8	·93.2	84.7	75.2	59.2	49.9	94.8
Year of occurrence	1953	1995	1934	1987	1934	1988	1988	1940	1990	1988	1995	1917	1988
Low monthly average	24.3	30.9	41.2	50.5†	62.6†	71.2	81.5	78.0	67.3	54.6	41.4	28.4	24.3
Year of occurrence	1949	1911	1952	1975	1933	1908	1913	1968	1965	1897	1957	1930	1949
Record high daily	63†	70	76†	87	94	101	105	102†	98	87	75	70	105
Day of occurrence	9	28	30	22	15	24	21	4	12	1	7	1	21
Year of occurrence	1990	1972	1986	1914	1927	1988	1931	1994	1990	1992	1931	1995	1931
Record low daily	4	5	22	28	37	47	60	58	38	32	18	4	4†
Day of occurrence	12	9	1	13	7	1	1	22	17	30	16	22	22
Year of occurrence	1963	1933	1971	1911	1965	1955	1992	1968	1965	1972	1955	1990	1990
Days w/max >= 100	0.0	0.0	0.0	0.0	0.0	0.0	0.5	0.1	0.0	0.0	0.0	0.0	0.6
Days w/max >= 90	0.0	0.0	0.0	0.0	0.1	4.3	14.7	10.1	1.3	0.0	0.0	0.0	30.8
Days w/max <= 32	8.6	3.8	0.6	0.0	0.0	0.0	0.0	0.0	0.0	0.0	1.2	7.3	21.8

Minimum Temperature in °F

	Jan	Feb	Mar	Apr	May	Jun	Jul	Aug	Sep	Oct	Nov	Dec	Annual
Monthly normal	19.5	24.2	30.3	37.3	46.2	55.2	63.1	60.8	50.8	39.9	29.6	21.0	39.8
Standard deviation	9.8	9.0	7.7	8.1	8.7	8.2	5.8	6.1	8.3	7.9	7.6	9.0	8.0
Average monthly	19.3	23.6	30.0	37.6	45.7	54.3	62.3	60.6	51.3	40.0	29.2	21.4	39.6
Standard deviation	9.9	9.1	7.9	8.3	8.5	8.5	6.4	6.3	8.5	7.8	8.1	9.1	8.2
High monthly average	31.1	33.1	38.6	46.6	54.2	61.8	68.1	65.8	59.6	47.2	40.2	31.9	68.1
Year of occurrence	1953	1934	1934	1934	1934	1922	1940	1967	1922	1963	1926	1917	1940
Low monthly average	4.1	8.8	20.7	31.0	38.0	43.8	52.8	53.2	42.1	34.1	18.5	9.3	4.1
Year of occurrence	1937	1903	1917	1922	1995	1995	1995	1995	1912	1970	1992	1990	1937
Record high daily	51	52	59	67	77	88	87	81†	79	71	59†	54	88
Day of occurrence	30	14	29	1	24	27	29	3	10	1	14	9	27
Year of occurrence	1911	1921	1943	1932	1922	1922	1921	1934	1923	1953	1953	1929	1922
Record low daily	-15	-16	3†	14	21	27	35	31	28†	11	-7	-16	-16†
Day of occurrence	22	10	2	1	6	6	3	30	25	29	16	23	23
Year of occurrence	1937	1933	1971	1920	1965	1995	1902	1923	1970	1971	1955	1990	1990
Days w/min <= 32	28.4	24.1	19.7	8.5	1.5	0.1	0.0	0.0	0.3	5.3	20.2	27.9	137.0
Days w/min <= 0	1.1	0.4	0.0	0.0	0.0	0.0	0.0	0.0	0.0	0.0	0.0	0.4	2.0
Days w/min <= -20	0.0	0.0	0.0	0.0	0.0	0.0	0.0	0.0	0.0	0.0	0.0	0.0	0.0

Mean Temperature in °F

	Jan	Feb	Mar	Apr	May	Jun	Jul	Aug	Sep	Oct	Nov	Dec	Annual
Monthly normal	28.5	33.7	40.5	48.6	57.9	67.6	75.8	73.5	63.4	51.6	39.2	29.6	50.8
Standard deviation	9.1	8.7	8.2	8.9	8.9	8.4	5.1	5.5	8.2	8.4	8.1	8.8	8.0
Average monthly	28.6	33.0	40.3	49.0	57.7	67.0	75.4	73.6	64.0	51.7	39.1	30.2	50.8
Standard deviation	9.0	8.6	8.1	8.8	8.7	8.4	5.6	5.4	8.0	8.1	8.4	8.6	8.0
High monthly average	40.3	41.9	49.7	58.5	67.7	75.0	81.1	77.8	71.2	60.2	48.7	40.9	81.1
Year of occurrence	1953	1907	1934	1934	1934	1988	1988	1940	1922	1988	1926	1917	1988
Low monthly average	14.6	20.2	32.2	41.1	51.6	58.4	68.5	66.9	55.3	44.9	30.6	20.0	14.6
Year of occurrence	1949	1903	1917	1975	1995	1908	1993	1968	1912	1919	1994	1930	1949

† Also occurred on earlier date(s).

TOOELE

Monthly Data Summary

Precipitation in Inches

	Jan	Feb	Mar	Apr	May	Jun	Jul	Aug	Sep	Oct	Nov	Dec	Annual
Monthly normal	1.08	1.33	2.33	2.49	1.91	1.12	0.92	0.94	1.42	1.81	1.69	1.48	18.50
Standard deviation	0.11	0.13	0.18	0.21	0.18	0.12	0.11	0.11	0.18	0.19	0.17	0.13	0.15
Average monthly	1.27	1.44	2.07	2.18	1.89	0.97	0.79	0.90	1.04	1.59	1.63	1.36	17.12
Standard deviation	0.13	0.14	0.17	0.20	0.19	0.12	0.10	0.11	0.15	0.18	0.17	0.13	0.15
High monthly total	4.74	3.13	4.89	5.99	5.94	3.65	3.47	· 4.06	8.06	5.29	4.91	3.62	8.06
Year of occurrence	1916	1936	1938	1986	1898	1947	1984	1983	1982	1981	1983	1983	1982
Low monthly total	0.00	0.00	0.08	0.21	0.05†	0.00†	0.00†	0.00†	0.00†	0.00†	0.00†	0.01	0.00†
Year of occurrence	1961	1928	1934	1934	1969	1961	1978	1985	1952	1978	1959	1900	1959
Record high daily	1.82	1.40	1.74	2.60	2.17	1.30	1.62	1.40	2.09	2.01	2.65	1.56	2.65
Day of occurrence	5	12	24	2	3	10	6	4	26	23	15	29	15
Year of occurrence	1904	1915	1916	1986	1901	1947	1937	1954	1982	1923	1958	1972	1958
Days w/pcp >= .01	6.8	7.0	8.6	8.2	7.6	4.9	4.7	5.5	4.6	5.5	6.1	6.9	76.5
Days w/pcp >= .10	3.8	4.1	5.5	5.2	4.4	2.7	2.2	2.5	2.5	3.7	4.0	4.0	44.9
Days w/pcp >= .50	0.5	0.8	1.3	1.3	1.2	0.6	0.4	0.4	0.6	1.1	1.0	0.7	9.8

Snow and Sleet in Inches

	Jan	Feb	Mar	Apr	May	Jun	Jul	Aug	Sep	Oct	Nov	Dec	Annual
Monthly normal	12.7	14.1	16.0	8.1	1.8	0.0	0.0	0.0	0.1	3.8	10.2	16.8	83.6
Standard deviation	1.3	1.6	1.6	1.1	0.6	0.0	0.0	0.0	0.1	1.0	1.3	1.6	0.8
Average monthly	11.7	11.2	12.0	5.2	1.3	0.0	0.0	0.0	0.1	2.2	8.5	12.6	64.8
Standard deviation	1.3	1.4	2.3	0.9	0.5	0.0	0.0	0.0	0.1	0.7	1.3	1.5	0.8
High monthly total	46.0	56.5	108.0	27.0	15.0	0.5	0.0†	0.0†	3.0	36.0	33.0	59.0	108.0
Year of occurrence	1993	1955	1949	1984	1975	1995	1995	1995	1971	1971	1983	1972	1949
Low monthly total	0.0†	0.0†	0.0†	0.0†	0.0†	0.0†	0.0†	0.0†	0.0†	0.0†	0.0†	0.0†	0.0†
Year of occurrence	1961	1991	1993	1992	1994	1994	1995	1995	1995	1995	1959	1914	1914
Record high daily	18.2	16.0†	100.0	13.0	13.0	0.5	0.0†	0.0†	3.0	20.0	18.0	22.0	100.0
Day of occurrence	5	26	27	17	1	6	31	31	30	28	15	29	27
Year of occurrence	1904	1962	1949	1920	1988	1995	1995	1995	1971	1971	1958	1972	1949
Days w/snow >= .1	4.1	3.6	3.1	1.5	0.4	0.0	0.0	0.0	0.0	0.6	2.5	4.1	19.9
Days w/snow >= 5	0.7	0.8	0.8	0.4	0.1	0.0	0.0	0.0	0.0	0.2	0.6	0.8	4.5
Days w/snow >= 10	0.1	0.1	0.2	0.0	0.0	0.0	0.0	0.0	0.0	0.0	0.1	0.2	0.8

Degree Days

	Jan	Feb	Mar	Apr	May	Jun	Jul	Aug	Sep	Oct	Nov	Dec	Annual
Heating normal	1131	884	760	495	251	70	2	8	122	418	775	1096	6019
Heating average	1126	902	764	484	256	75	4	7	111	416	777	1078	6004
Cooling normal	0	0	0	3	32	149	336	270	74	3	0	0	871
Cooling average	0	0	0	3	29	136	326	273	81	3	0	0	854
Growing 40 normal	40	78	180	328	555	743	929	890	662	406	148	45	5009
Growing 40 average	40	71	180	337	548	731	916	888	675	408	153	49	5002
Growing 50 normal	6	17	66	168	337	527	743	693	440	222	50	7	3280
Growing 50 average	5	13	66	173	332	518	729	693	457	222	51	8	3272

† Also occurred on earlier date(s).

Location: Tremonton County: Box Elder   Latitude: 41.717   Longitude: -112.167

Elevation: 4310 feet   Period of Record: 1979-1996

TREMONTON
Monthly Data Summary

Maximum Temperature in °F

	Jan	Feb	Mar	Apr	May	Jun	Jul	Aug	Sep	Oct	Nov	Dec	Annual
Monthly normal													
Standard deviation													
Average monthly	32.4	39.0	50.8	61.2	69.2	79.7	87.7	87.7	77.1	63.3	45.9	34.7	60.7
Standard deviation	8.5	10.8	8.6	10.1	10.7	9.3	6.8	6.0	9.5	10.0	9.9	9.4	9.1
High monthly average	42.2	49.1	57.8	68.2	76.9	85.9	92.3	92.2	84.1	72.7	53.1	41.6	92.3
Year of occurrence	1994	1995	1986	1992	1992	1986	1994	1981	1990	1988	1995	1995	1994
Low monthly average	25.0	29.0	41.8	53.1	63.2	73.2	79.2	83.5	69.9	56.0	37.8	26.5	25.0
Year of occurrence	1989	1989	1985	1983	1995	1993	1993	1993	1986	1984	1994	1985	1989
Record high daily	53	65	72†	84†	93	100	101	101†	94†	92	70	63	101†
Day of occurrence	24	26	30	28	29	25	27	6	2	3	2	2	6
Year of occurrence	1994	1986	1986	1987	1983	1988	1994	1994	1995	1992	1980	1995	1994
Record low daily	2	4	28	36	39	49	58	60	46†	35	19†	-7	-7
Day of occurrence	19	6	4	4	12	8	2	25	25	30	26	23	23
Year of occurrence	1984	1982	1989	1983	1983	1993	1992	1989	1984	1991	1992	1990	1990
Days w/max >= 100	0.0	0.0	0.0	0.0	0.0	0.1	0.2	0.3	0.0	0.0	0.0	0.0	0.6
Days w/max >= 90	0.0	0.0	0.0	0.0	0.1	4.2	14.6	13.3	2.2	0.1	0.0	0.0	34.6
Days w/max <= 32	14.6	7.2	0.6	0.0	0.0	0.0	0.0	0.0	0.0	0.0	2.3	10.9	37.4

Minimum Temperature in °F

	Jan	Feb	Mar	Apr	May	Jun	Jul	Aug	Sep	Oct	Nov	Dec	Annual
Monthly normal													
Standard deviation													
Average monthly	16.7	20.9	31.0	37.2	45.1	52.9	59.5	58.6	49.0	37.3	27.0	18.2	37.8
Standard deviation	10.5	11.2	6.3	6.9	6.9	6.6	5.6	5.4	7.2	6.4	7.9	9.3	7.5
High monthly average	25.6	29.4	35.9	41.8	49.0	57.4	63.0	61.2	56.5	41.9	31.1	25.5	63.0
Year of occurrence	1994	1986	1986	1992	1992	1988	1988	1994	1990	1988	1995	1995	1988
Low monthly average	6.6	7.7	24.4	32.5	42.1	49.1	52.1	55.4	45.2	32.8	20.7	7.8	6.6
Year of occurrence	1989	1985	1985	1982	1991	1993	1993	1985	1985	1995	1993	1990	1989
Record high daily	36†	41	47	58†	62	71	72	72†	66	52	48	41	72†
Day of occurrence	11	19	11	22	29	25	13	3	4	7	2	12	3
Year of occurrence	1995	1986	1995	1994	1983	1988	1990	1992	1990	1980	1987	1995	1992
Record low daily	-16	-15	11†	21	29	33	43	38	31†	19	2	-19	-19
Day of occurrence	18	6	2	5	3	6	5	27	19	31	30	30	30
Year of occurrence	1984	1982	1993	1982	1988	1995	1986	1992	1988	1991	1979	1990	1990
Days w/min <= 32	29.6	24.3	18.4	8.0	0.9	0.0	0.0	0.0	0.4	7.1	22.6	29.6	146.2
Days w/min <= 0	2.1	1.4	0.0	0.0	0.0	0.0	0.0	0.0	0.0	0.0	0.0	1.0	4.8
Days w/min <= -20	0.0	0.0	0.0	0.0	0.0	0.0	0.0	0.0	0.0	0.0	0.0	0.0	0.0

Mean Temperature in °F

	Jan	Feb	Mar	Apr	May	Jun	Jul	Aug	Sep	Oct	Nov	Dec	Annual
Monthly normal													
Standard deviation													
Average monthly	24.6	29.9	40.9	49.2	57.2	66.3	73.6	73.2	63.1	50.3	36.4	26.5	49.3
Standard deviation	9.0	10.6	7.0	8.0	8.3	7.6	5.6	5.1	7.7	7.5	8.3	8.9	7.8
High monthly average	33.9	38.7	46.9	55.0	63.0	71.5	77.5	76.3	70.3	57.3	42.1	33.6	77.5
Year of occurrence	1994	1995	1986	1992	1992	1986	1988	1981	1990	1988	1995	1995	1988
Low monthly average	15.8	18.4	33.1	43.5	53.0	61.1	65.7	69.6	58.2	45.4	30.3	17.4	15.8
Year of occurrence	1989	1985	1985	1983	1991	1993	1993	1993	1986	1984	1994	1990	1989

† Also occurred on earlier date(s).

TREMONTON
Monthly Data Summary

Precipitation in Inches

	Jan	Feb	Mar	Apr	May	Jun	Jul	Aug	Sep	Oct	Nov	Dec	Annual
Monthly normal													
Standard deviation													
Average monthly	1.40	1.43	1.85	1.49	2.50	1.10	1.31	0.69	1.56	1.55	1.48	1.34	17.70
Standard deviation	0.12	0.13	0.15	0.12	0.20	0.14	0.18	0.10	0.18	0.16	0.12	0.12	0.15
High monthly total	3.78	3.49	4.52	4.31	5.97	2.71	4.18	·2.89	5.13	4.62	3.24	5.70	5.97
Year of occurrence	1980	1986	1982	1986	1987	1980	1985	1983	1986	1981	1985	1983	1987
Low monthly total	0.46	0.07	0.91	0.20	0.44	0.16	0.01	0.00	0.23	0.00	0.07	0.09	0.00†
Year of occurrence	1985	1988	1984	1987	1994	1986	1988	1985	1981	1988	1993	1986	1988
Record high daily	1.10	1.43	1.21	0.96	1.73	1.72	2.86	1.24	1.82	1.40	1.10	1.18	2.86
Day of occurrence	14	18	15	2	27	3	24	19	25	11	9	1	24
Year of occurrence	1980	1986	1982	1986	1987	1980	1985	1983	1986	1981	1984	1982	1985
Days w/pcp >= .01	8.7	8.5	10.1	9.1	10.8	5.0	5.2	4.1	6.4	6.8	9.4	8.5	94.1
Days w/pcp >= .10	4.5	4.3	5.4	4.8	6.1	2.9	3.1	1.9	3.6	3.6	4.6	4.2	49.8
Days w/pcp >= .50	0.6	0.7	0.9	0.4	1.4	0.7	0.6	0.3	0.8	1.0	0.6	0.5	8.7

Snow and Sleet in Inches

	Jan	Feb	Mar	Apr	May	Jun	Jul	Aug	Sep	Oct	Nov	Dec	Annual
Monthly normal													
Standard deviation													
Average monthly	10.5	6.9	2.6	0.8	0.1	0.0	0.0	0.0	0.1	0.4	5.6	10.0	37.1
Standard deviation	0.9	0.8	0.4	0.2	0.1	0.0	0.0	0.0	0.1	0.1	0.6	1.0	0.3
High monthly total	26.3	17.0	7.6	3.3	1.8	0.5	0.0†	0.0†	2.0	2.8	24.2	46.2	46.2
Year of occurrence	1993	1984	1982	1982	1991	1995	1995	1995	1986	1984	1985	1983	1983
Low monthly total	3.2	0.0†	0.0†	0.0†	0.0†	0.0†	0.0†	0.0†	0.0†	0.0†	0.0†	0.6	0.0†
Year of occurrence	1994	1981	1993	1995	1995	1994	1995	1995	1995	1994	1995	1986	1995
Record high daily	5.8	6.0	3.4	2.2	1.8	0.5	0.0†	0.0†	2.0	1.5	4.5	9.5	9.5
Day of occurrence	1	13	16	19	3	6	31	31	26	17	18	1	1
Year of occurrence	1989	1986	1988	1987	1991	1995	1995	1995	1986	1984	1994	1983	1983
Days w/snow >= .1	7.1	4.3	2.4	0.8	0.1	0.1	0.0	0.0	0.1	0.5	4.0	5.5	25.4
Days w/snow >= 5	0.4	0.2	0.0	0.0	0.0	0.0	0.0	0.0	0.0	0.0	0.0	0.2	0.8
Days w/snow >= 10	0.0	0.0	0.0	0.0	0.0	0.0	0.0	0.0	0.0	0.0	0.0	0.0	0.0

Degree Days

	Jan	Feb	Mar	Apr	May	Jun	Jul	Aug	Sep	Oct	Nov	Dec	Annual
Heating normal													
Heating average	1243	990	748	475	264	75	9	8	120	457	857	1193	6444
Cooling normal													
Cooling average	0	0	0	1	21	113	276	261	62	0	0	0	737
Growing 40 normal													
Growing 40 average	11	52	175	339	525	708	868	858	641	379	115	22	4700
Growing 50 normal													
Growing 50 average	0	10	60	178	314	494	676	670	436	213	33	2	3092

† Also occurred on earlier date(s).

Location: Trenton   County: Cache   Latitude: 41.917   Longitude: -111.933
Elevation: 4470 feet   Period of Record: 1948-1996

TRENTON
Monthly Data Summary

Maximum Temperature in °F

	Jan	Feb	Mar	Apr	May	Jun	Jul	Aug	Sep	Oct	Nov	Dec	Annual
Monthly normal	30.1	37.4	49.3	61.3	68.1	79.7	86.9	85.7	76.0	63.9	45.9	34.0	59.9
Standard deviation	10.6	11.1	8.9	10.7	10.6	8.8	5.7	6.2	9.8	9.7	10.6	10.2	9.4
Average monthly	30.9	37.6	49.5	60.9	68.6	79.4	86.9	86.6	76.8	63.8	45.1	34.1	60.0
Standard deviation	10.3	10.8	8.9	10.5	10.8	9.1	6.6	6.5	9.6	9.5	10.8	9.9	9.4
High monthly average	39.9	46.2	57.4	70.1	76.8	85.1	92.7	92.7	83.1	73.3	52.2	40.9	92.7
Year of occurrence	1994	1995	1986	1987	1992	1988	1994	1994	1979	1988	1976	1976	1994
Low monthly average	21.8	27.5	40.6	52.5	62.5	72.8	77.3	81.8	69.2	55.1	36.2	24.4	21.8
Year of occurrence	1979	1989	1985	1983	1995	1993	1993	1993	1986	1984	1994	1985	1979
Record high daily	52†	63	73†	85†	89	100	102	102†	96†	87	70	62	102†
Day of occurrence	10	25	29	27	28	24	27	5	10	1	7	2	5
Year of occurrence	1990	1986	1986	1987	1983	1988	1994	1994	1948	1992	1980	1995	1994
Record low daily	-1	-3	26	32	41†	49	56	60	46†	35	16†	0	-3
Day of occurrence	3	7	4	7	6	8	2	19	27	20	27	23	7
Year of occurrence	1988	1989	1989	1982	1993	1993	1992	1980	1986	1984	1992	1983	1989
Days w/max >= 100	0.0	0.0	0.0	0.0	0.0	0.1	0.2	0.1	0.0	0.0	0.0	0.0	0.3
Days w/max >= 90	0.0	0.0	0.0	0.0	0.0	2.9	12.3	11.3	1.8	0.0	0.0	0.0	29.9
Days w/max <= 32	14.9	7.9	0.6	0.1	0.0	0.0	0.0	0.0	0.0	0.0	3.9	12.8	41.1

Minimum Temperature in °F

	Jan	Feb	Mar	Apr	May	Jun	Jul	Aug	Sep	Oct	Nov	Dec	Annual
Monthly normal	9.9	15.0	25.6	31.4	37.6	44.4	49.9	48.0	39.7	30.3	22.4	13.5	30.6
Standard deviation	15.6	14.8	8.1	7.1	6.3	6.2	6.2	6.4	7.3	6.7	9.5	12.0	8.8
Average monthly	10.9	14.8	25.4	31.3	38.1	44.2	48.8	47.6	39.5	30.0	21.1	13.4	30.4
Standard deviation	15.1	14.2	8.2	6.6	6.0	5.9	6.1	6.4	7.5	6.6	10.4	12.0	8.7
High monthly average	23.9	26.8	31.6	35.4	42.1	48.7	52.9	53.9	49.1	34.4	26.6	24.1	53.9
Year of occurrence	1978	1986	1986	1989	1987	1988	1985	1983	1948	1988	1983	1977	1983
Low monthly average	-1.4	2.0	13.7	26.7	34.8	40.4	40.7	42.9	33.9	24.3	11.9	4.1	-1.4
Year of occurrence	1979	1985	1985	1982	1978	1978	1993	1993	1993	1995	1993	1992	1979
Record high daily	35†	42	46	52	57	64	70	63†	64	50	48	38†	70
Day of occurrence	10	24	31	17	9	30	4	8	3	2	2	4	4
Year of occurrence	1996	1986	1978	1985	1985	1979	1988	1983	1987	1976	1987	1977	1988
Record low daily	-32†	-35	-8	16†	22	28	34	28†	19	12	-17	-24†	-35
Day of occurrence	31	6	1	10	7	21	13	27	29	31	29	31	6
Year of occurrence	1985	1982	1993	1988	1984	1989	1993	1992	1985	1993	1979	1978	1982
Days w/min <= 32	30.2	26.7	26.4	17.9	6.1	0.7	0.0	0.5	5.3	20.6	26.6	29.9	194.0
Days w/min <= 0	7.8	4.3	0.7	0.0	0.0	0.0	0.0	0.0	0.0	0.0	1.2	4.1	18.6
Days w/min <= -20	1.1	0.6	0.0	0.0	0.0	0.0	0.0	0.0	0.0	0.0	0.0	0.4	2.1

Mean Temperature in °F

	Jan	Feb	Mar	Apr	May	Jun	Jul	Aug	Sep	Oct	Nov	Dec	Annual
Monthly normal	20.0	26.2	37.5	46.3	52.9	62.1	68.4	66.8	57.9	47.1	34.2	23.8	45.3
Standard deviation	12.7	12.5	7.4	7.5	7.2	6.4	4.3	4.5	6.8	6.4	8.9	10.4	7.9
Average monthly	20.9	26.2	37.4	46.1	53.3	61.8	67.9	67.1	58.2	46.9	33.1	23.8	45.2
Standard deviation	12.2	11.9	7.5	7.3	7.3	6.5	4.9	5.0	6.9	6.3	9.5	10.2	8.0
High monthly average	30.6	35.5	44.5	50.9	58.9	66.9	71.9	71.1	65.3	53.8	38.2	32.3	71.9
Year of occurrence	1978	1986	1986	1987	1992	1988	1988	1948	1948	1988	1995	1977	1988
Low monthly average	10.2	14.9	27.2	40.7	50.0	57.1	59.0	62.4	54.0	43.0	26.2	15.0	10.2
Year of occurrence	1979	1985	1985	1982	1978	1993	1993	1993	1986	1984	1994	1985	1979

† Also occurred on earlier date(s).

TRENTON
Monthly Data Summary

Precipitation in Inches

	Jan	Feb	Mar	Apr	May	Jun	Jul	Aug	Sep	Oct	Nov	Dec	Annual
Monthly normal	1.34	1.64	1.97	1.89	2.63	1.11	0.94	0.98	1.63	1.56	1.68	1.41	18.78
Standard deviation	0.12	0.17	0.14	0.17	0.19	0.14	0.12	0.16	0.20	0.17	0.14	0.13	0.15
Average monthly	1.38	1.63	2.07	1.88	2.53	1.10	0.92	0.82	1.39	1.54	1.54	1.44	18.24
Standard deviation	0.12	0.17	0.16	0.17	0.18	0.13	0.12	0.14	0.18	0.17	0.13	0.14	0.15
High monthly total	4.23	5.67	4.99	4.94	5.37	3.15	2.35	3.84	4.04	4.62	3.62	4.63	5.67
Year of occurrence	1980	1986	1982	1986	1980	1980	1983	1977	1982	1981	1983	1983	1986
Low monthly total	0.29	0.04	0.55	0.31	1.01	0.01	0.00	0.01	0.00	0.00†	0.00	0.04	0.00†
Year of occurrence	1984	1988	1987	1985	1979	1978	1988	1985	1987	1988	1976	1976	1976
Record high daily	1.11	1.68	1.11†	1.62	1.22	1.28	0.94	2.40	2.38	1.50	1.11	1.64	2.40
Day of occurrence	12	17	23	2	16	3	31	18	26	2	19	31	18
Year of occurrence	1980	1986	1994	1986	1980	1980	1976	1977	1982	1983	1982	1948	1977
Days w/pcp >= .01	10.1	9.3	10.8	9.7	12.6	6.2	4.8	4.9	5.9	6.5	8.8	9.1	101.9
Days w/pcp >= .10	4.8	4.4	6.1	5.1	6.6	2.7	2.4	1.9	3.5	3.4	4.7	4.5	51.6
Days w/pcp >= .50	0.4	0.8	0.9	0.9	1.4	0.6	0.5	0.3	0.7	0.8	0.5	0.5	8.6

Snow and Sleet in Inches

	Jan	Feb	Mar	Apr	May	Jun	Jul	Aug	Sep	Oct	Nov	Dec	Annual
Monthly normal	11.8	9.6	7.3	2.7	0.5	0.0	0.0	0.0	0.0	1.0	9.1	13.0	55.0
Standard deviation	1.0	1.1	0.8	0.5	0.1	0.0	0.0	0.0	0.0	0.4	0.9	1.3	0.5
Average monthly	12.2	10.4	6.8	2.6	0.4	0.0	0.0	0.0	0.0	0.9	8.4	12.5	54.2
Standard deviation	1.0	1.1	0.8	0.5	0.1	0.0	0.0	0.0	0.0	0.3	0.9	1.2	0.5
High monthly total	39.0	25.8	26.3	11.0	2.1	0.0†	0.0†	0.0†	0.5	7.2	26.7	48.0	48.0
Year of occurrence	1993	1985	1985	1993	1979	1995	1995	1995	1978	1984	1985	1983	1983
Low monthly total	1.8	0.7	0.0†	0.0†	0.0†	0.0†	0.0†	0.0†	0.0†	0.0†	0.0†	0.0	0.0†
Year of occurrence	1991	1981	1991	1995	1995	1995	1995	1995	1995	1993	1993	1986	1986
Record high daily	7.0	9.0	8.0	6.0	1.5	0.0†	0.0†	0.0†	0.5	6.0	7.0	12.0	12.0
Day of occurrence	1	1	3	13	11	30	31	31	18	17	30	25	25
Year of occurrence	1982	1989	1985	1993	1983	1995	1995	1995	1978	1984	1982	1988	1988
Days w/snow >= .1	6.9	5.4	4.0	1.3	0.4	0.0	0.0	0.0	0.1	0.5	4.3	6.8	29.7
Days w/snow >= 5	0.4	0.3	0.2	0.2	0.0	0.0	0.0	0.0	0.0	0.1	0.2	0.5	1.9
Days w/snow >= 10	0.0	0.0	0.0	0.0	0.0	0.0	0.0	0.0	0.0	0.0	0.0	0.1	0.1

Degree Days

	Jan	Feb	Mar	Apr	May	Jun	Jul	Aug	Sep	Oct	Nov	Dec	Annual
Heating normal	1393	1095	853	558	376	123	16	33	222	554	925	1278	7432
Heating average	1357	1092	854	566	362	130	27	35	218	561	956	1277	7440
Cooling normal	0	0	0	0	1	35	122	90	8	0	0	0	257
Cooling average	0	0	0	0	1	34	116	101	13	0	0	0	265
Growing 40 normal	10	41	152	321	442	595	723	696	531	371	118	25	4030
Growing 40 average	10	41	155	314	449	588	704	692	538	369	112	24	4001
Growing 50 normal	0	6	51	180	283	444	568	544	390	222	37	2	2732
Growing 50 average	0	6	52	174	291	436	554	546	399	220	34	2	2718

† Also occurred on earlier date(s).

Location: Vernal Arpt County: Uintah   Latitude: 40.450   Longitude: -109.517
Elevation: 5260 feet   Period of Record: 1894-1996

VERNAL ARPT
Monthly Data Summary

Maximum Temperature in °F

	Jan	Feb	Mar	Apr	May	Jun	Jul	Aug	Sep	Oct	Nov	Dec	Annual
Monthly normal	28.1	36.4	49.8	62.3	72.8	83.2	90.0	87.6	77.1	63.2	45.8	31.2	60.6
Standard deviation	10.9	11.3	10.5	9.7	9.1	8.5	4.8	5.6	8.7	9.6	9.8	10.6	9.1
Average monthly	29.2	36.8	49.6	62.2	72.3	82.5	88.9	86.7	77.4	63.9	46.9	32.4	60.7
Standard deviation	10.4	10.5	9.9	9.9	9.3	8.5	5.6	5.5	8.2	9.6	9.8	10.3	9.0
High monthly average	43.6	51.1	62.8	71.7	86.5	94.4	94.8	92.6	84.2	72.7	60.0	46.4	94.8
Year of occurrence	1981	1954	1934	1934	1913	1913	1901	1971	1979	1950	1937	1917	1901
Low monthly average	11.4	21.7	39.6	54.8	62.9	62.3	75.4	80.1	68.5	52.6	36.3	15.5	11.4
Year of occurrence	1937	1973	1909	1922	1917	1927	1927	1899	1965	1908	1971	1909	1937
Record high daily	57	64†	79	91	106	106	103†	100†	97	89	72†	65	106†
Day of occurrence	7	26	19	30	28	21	14	5	1	7	10	1	21
Year of occurrence	1956	1986	1907	1947	1913	1919	1939	1994	1954	1979	1937	1995	1919
Record low daily	-8	-9	16	29	40†	50†	59†	64†	33	27†	8	-10	-10
Day of occurrence	4	4	1	2	6	11	7	27	17	30	13	22	22
Year of occurrence	1952	1923	1962	1945	1950	1947	1927	1977	1965	1991	1916	1990	1990
Days w/max >= 100	0.0	0.0	0.0	0.0	0.0	0.1	0.3	0.0	0.0	0.0	0.0	0.0	0.5
Days w/max >= 90	0.0	0.0	0.0	0.0	0.3	6.3	15.6	10.1	1.1	0.0	0.0	0.0	34.0
Days w/max <= 32	18.8	9.3	1.3	0.0	0.0	0.0	0.0	0.0	0.0	0.1	2.4	14.7	46.3

Minimum Temperature in °F

	Jan	Feb	Mar	Apr	May	Jun	Jul	Aug	Sep	Oct	Nov	Dec	Annual
Monthly normal	4.9	11.2	22.6	30.9	39.1	47.2	53.4	51.0	42.0	31.6	20.9	8.9	30.3
Standard deviation	11.3	11.3	8.1	7.2	6.4	5.9	4.9	5.7	7.1	6.9	7.9	10.5	7.8
Average monthly	4.1	10.1	22.1	30.9	38.7	46.2	51.9	50.3	41.3	30.8	20.1	8.6	29.6
Standard deviation	12.0	12.3	8.7	7.9	7.1	7.5	6.3	6.7	7.7	7.2	8.3	11.0	8.6
High monthly average	18.7	24.0	40.5	47.7	52.5	68.4	72.5	69.7	58.3	48.4	36.3	27.5	72.5
Year of occurrence	1956	1995	1918	1916	1918	1918	1917	1918	1917	1917	1917	1917	1917
Low monthly average	-19.6	-8.7	10.1	22.3	31.1	36.4	44.4	40.9	32.7	25.1	9.4	-10.6	-19.6
Year of occurrence	1937	1933	1952	1945	1950	1916	1946	1928	1945	1916	1930	1919	1937
Record high daily	35	94	55	65	70†	85	80	80	74	60†	52	38	94
Day of occurrence	31	15	25	26	15	26	30	3	3	7	1	5	15
Year of occurrence	1911	1995	1918	1916	1936	1918	1918	1918	1917	1917	1914	1914	1995
Record low daily	-38†	-38	-16	0	12	24	25	32†	17	6	-16	-32	-38†
Day of occurrence	3	7	1	16	9	2	3	27	25	30	21	14	7
Year of occurrence	1952	1989	1922	1922	1948	1916	1921	1992	1926	1971	1953	1932	1989
Days w/min <= 32	30.7	27.8	28.2	17.8	5.8	0.7	0.0	0.0	3.7	18.6	28.1	30.8	192.5
Days w/min <= 0	11.6	6.2	0.5	0.0	0.0	0.0	0.0	0.0	0.0	0.0	0.5	6.9	26.0
Days w/min <= -20	0.9	0.3	0.0	0.0	0.0	0.0	0.0	0.0	0.0	0.0	0.0	0.3	1.5

Mean Temperature in °F

	Jan	Feb	Mar	Apr	May	Jun	Jul	Aug	Sep	Oct	Nov	Dec	Annual
Monthly normal	16.5	23.8	36.2	46.6	56.0	65.2	71.7	69.3	59.6	47.4	33.4	20.1	45.5
Standard deviation	10.5	10.8	8.4	7.2	6.7	6.3	3.5	4.5	6.8	7.1	8.0	10.0	7.5
Average monthly	16.7	23.5	35.8	46.5	55.5	64.4	70.4	68.5	59.4	47.3	33.5	20.6	45.2
Standard deviation	10.5	10.6	8.2	7.6	7.0	6.8	4.5	4.6	6.5	7.0	8.1	9.9	7.6
High monthly average	29.8	36.2	48.7	56.4	63.6	77.2	80.0	77.1	66.6	56.5	46.6	37.0	80.0
Year of occurrence	1981	1934	1918	1916	1936	1918	1917	1918	1917	1917	1914	1917	1917
Low monthly average	-4.1	9.5	25.1	38.8	48.9	51.5	61.2	62.1	52.0	41.3	26.3	3.8	-4.1
Year of occurrence	1937	1933	1952	1945	1953	1927	1927	1916	1912	1905	1964	1919	1937

† Also occurred on earlier date(s).

VERNAL ARPT
Monthly Data Summary

Precipitation in Inches

	Jan	Feb	Mar	Apr	May	Jun	Jul	Aug	Sep	Oct	Nov	Dec	Annual
Monthly normal	0.39	0.41	0.65	0.81	0.88	0.79	0.50	0.58	0.87	1.06	0.60	0.61	8.16
Standard deviation	0.05	0.06	0.08	0.10	0.10	0.11	0.06	0.07	0.10	0.13	0.08	0.08	0.09
Average monthly	0.53	0.49	0.70	0.82	0.85	0.64	0.56	0.71	0.89	1.01	0.60	0.61	8.41
Standard deviation	0.07	0.07	0.09	0.10	0.10	0.10	0.08	0.09	0.11	0.13	0.09	0.08	0.09
High monthly total	2.83	2.20	2.53	2.65	2.81	2.92	2.01	2.43	2.99	4.36	2.77	2.71	4.36
Year of occurrence	1916	1937	1938	1935	1995	1947	1987	1925	1939	1981	1906	1936	1981
Low monthly total	0.00†	0.00†	0.00†	0.00†	0.00†	0.00†	0.00†	0.00†	0.00†	0.00†	0.00†	0.00†	0.00†
Year of occurrence	1972	1972	1971	1943	1974	1980	1978	1974	1979	1988	1979	1993	1993
Record high daily	0.76	1.20	1.24	1.00	1.07	1.36	0.90	1.15	1.32	1.60	1.60	1.19	1.60†
Day of occurrence	16	6	29	10	2	1	14	22	30	11	26	19	26
Year of occurrence	1956	1905	1979	1905	1995	1943	1922	1947	1905	1981	1919	1949	1919
Days w/pcp >= .01	3.6	3.4	4.0	4.5	5.0	3.5	3.6	4.3	4.2	3.8	3.0	3.5	46.5
Days w/pcp >= .10	1.9	1.8	2.3	2.4	2.6	1.8	1.8	2.2	2.5	2.7	1.8	2.1	26.0
Days w/pcp >= .50	0.1	0.1	0.3	0.5	0.4	0.3	0.2	0.3	0.5	0.7	0.3	0.2	3.8

Snow and Sleet in Inches

	Jan	Feb	Mar	Apr	May	Jun	Jul	Aug	Sep	Oct	Nov	Dec	Annual
Monthly normal	2.5	2.4	0.7	0.0	0.0	0.0	0.0	0.0	0.0	0.2	0.4	2.9	9.1
Standard deviation	0.4	0.5	0.3	0.0	0.0	0.0	0.0	0.0	0.0	0.1	0.2	0.7	0.2
Average monthly	5.0	3.6	2.6	0.5	0.1	0.0	0.0	0.0	0.0	0.6	1.4	4.9	18.7
Standard deviation	0.7	0.6	0.5	0.2	0.1	0.0	0.0	0.0	0.0	0.3	0.5	0.9	0.3
High monthly total	28.3	14.3	9.2	5.0†	3.6	0.0†	0.0†	0.0†	0.5	16.0	14.0	37.0	37.0
Year of occurrence	1916	1913	1952	1936	1905	1995	1995	1995	1912	1908	1930	1949	1949
Low monthly total	0.0†	0.0†	0.0†	0.0†	0.0†	0.0†	0.0†	0.0†	0.0†	0.0†	0.0†	0.0†	0.0†
Year of occurrence	1995	1991	1995	1995	1995	1995	1995	1995	1995	1995	1995	1995	1995
Record high daily	10.0	12.0	9.0	5.0	2.0	0.0†	0.0†	0.0†	0.5	10.0	12.0†	24.0	24.0
Day of occurrence	25	6	22	1	26	30	31	31	14	16	17	19	19
Year of occurrence	1944	1905	1929	1936	1929	1995	1995	1995	1912	1908	1930	1949	1949
Days w/snow >= .1	2.5	1.9	1.5	0.3	0.0	0.0	0.0	0.0	0.0	0.2	0.7	2.2	9.9
Days w/snow >= 5	0.2	0.2	0.1	0.0	0.0	0.0	0.0	0.0	0.0	0.0	0.1	0.2	0.8
Days w/snow >= 10	0.0	0.0	0.0	0.0	0.0	0.0	0.0	0.0	0.0	0.0	0.0	0.1	0.1

Degree Days

	Jan	Feb	Mar	Apr	May	Jun	Jul	Aug	Sep	Oct	Nov	Dec	Annual
Heating normal	1496	1161	889	550	282	74	2	14	180	542	944	1393	7533
Heating average	1485	1164	902	550	297	90	8	17	183	544	938	1373	7557
Cooling normal	0	0	0	0	4	80	209	145	18	0	0	0	458
Cooling average	0	0	0	0	5	71	172	124	16	0	0	0	391
Growing 40 normal	9	39	166	337	511	643	776	728	563	364	114	14	4268
Growing 40 average	9	37	161	336	508	630	743	724	563	370	125	18	4230
Growing 50 normal	0	7	63	192	352	481	607	565	405	212	32	0	2920
Growing 50 average	0	5	58	191	347	480	583	564	412	220	37	1	2905

† Also occurred on earlier date(s).

Location: Wendover WSO Airport County: Tooele Latitude: 40.733 Longitude: -114.033
Elevation: 4240 feet   Period of Record: 1911-1995

WENDOVER WSO AIRPORT
Monthly Data Summary

Maximum Temperature in °F

	Jan	Feb	Mar	Apr	May	Jun	Jul	Aug	Sep	Oct	Nov	Dec	Annual
Monthly normal	34.9	42.7	51.9	61.3	71.5	82.1	91.7	88.5	77.3	62.5	47.0	35.4	62.2
Standard deviation	9.6	9.6	8.6	9.7	10.0	10.0	5.8	6.8	9.3	9.1	8.1	9.3	8.8
Average monthly	35.7	43.3	52.8	62.8	72.8	82.9	92.4	89.7	78.9	63.9	47.8	37.0	63.3
Standard deviation	9.8	9.4	8.8	9.6	9.9	9.9	6.0	6.3	8.9	8.8	8.5	9.6	8.8
High monthly average	47.2	58.0	63.6	73.8	84.6	94.0	98.8	95.7	86.1	70.3	55.5	54.7	98.8
Year of occurrence	1953	1912	1934	1934	1919	1924	1919	1915	1943	1933	1949	1917	1919
Low monthly average	19.9	28.6	44.6	52.9	63.7	73.4	81.8	81.1	70.6	55.4	38.9	23.1	19.9
Year of occurrence	1937	1984	1952	1975	1995	1963	1993	1968	1965	1969	1994	1927	1937
Record high daily	64	70	81	92	103	105†	112	112	100	88	78	65	112†
Day of occurrence	7	17	31	23	28	7	13	11	2	1	7	15	11
Year of occurrence	1969	1912	1917	1919	1919	1985	1939	1915	1956	1924	1980	1946	1915
Record low daily	0†	12†	27	37†	44	48	60	63	48†	0	17	0†	0†
Day of occurrence	9	8	27	2	11	1	1	24	30	13	16	23	23
Year of occurrence	1925	1989	1975	1945	1942	1955	1992	1989	1971	1918	1955	1990	1990
Days w/max >= 100	0.0	0.0	0.0	0.0	0.0	0.8	2.5	0.8	0.0	0.0	0.0	0.0	4.1
Days w/max >= 90	0.0	0.0	0.0	0.0	1.0	8.2	22.7	18.2	3.2	0.0	0.0	0.0	53.5
Days w/max <= 32	11.1	3.5	0.2	0.0	0.0	0.0	0.0	0.0	0.0	0.0	0.9	8.8	24.7

Minimum Temperature in °F

	Jan	Feb	Mar	Apr	May	Jun	Jul	Aug	Sep	Oct	Nov	Dec	Annual
Monthly normal	18.7	24.7	32.4	40.0	50.0	59.6	67.9	64.7	53.9	41.5	30.0	20.1	42.0
Standard deviation	8.9	8.4	6.7	7.0	7.5	7.5	5.1	5.8	7.4	7.0	6.9	8.5	7.2
Average monthly	18.4	24.5	31.9	40.2	49.9	58.8	67.1	64.4	53.4	41.4	29.0	20.5	41.6
Standard deviation	9.1	8.3	6.9	7.1	7.4	8.0	5.7	6.0	7.5	6.9	7.4	8.3	7.4
High monthly average	29.5	33.5	40.1	46.7†	56.2	75.0	79.6	73.5	60.4	48.3	35.5	29.5	79.6
Year of occurrence	1953	1986	1986	1992	1969	1911	1911	1944	1990	1914	1927	1950	1911
Low monthly average	1.0	12.7	20.7	34.0	43.2†	51.6	55.3	55.6	44.9	31.4	21.2	7.1	1.0
Year of occurrence	1937	1984	1917	1918	1942	1915	1912	1913	1912	1913	1938	1913	1937
Record high daily	51	54†	57	62	71	89	88	89	76	65†	54†	51	89†
Day of occurrence	7	18	24	29	15	21	12	18	2	31	3	23	18
Year of occurrence	1962	1986	1938	1987	1987	1911	1911	1911	1933	1914	1988	1955	1911
Record low daily	-16	-12	8	18	27	0	43	0	0	18	6†	-18	-18
Day of occurrence	18	1	2	1	7	6	3	18	1	30	27	23	23
Year of occurrence	1984	1937	1917	1913	1981	1926	1921	1919	1915	1917	1993	1990	1990
Days w/min <= 32	29.3	23.8	16.6	4.2	0.2	0.0	0.0	0.0	0.1	2.9	20.4	29.1	127.0
Days w/min <= 0	1.1	0.3	0.0	0.0	0.0	0.0	0.0	0.0	0.0	0.0	0.0	0.5	1.9
Days w/min <= -20	0.0	0.0	0.0	0.0	0.0	0.0	0.0	0.0	0.0	0.0	0.0	0.0	0.0

Mean Temperature in °F

	Jan	Feb	Mar	Apr	May	Jun	Jul	Aug	Sep	Oct	Nov	Dec	Annual
Monthly normal	26.8	33.7	42.2	50.7	60.8	70.8	79.8	76.6	65.6	52.0	38.5	27.7	52.1
Standard deviation	8.7	8.5	7.0	7.8	8.3	8.3	4.8	5.7	7.8	7.5	7.0	8.4	7.5
Average monthly	27.0	33.9	42.3	51.5	61.3	70.8	79.7	77.1	66.2	52.7	38.3	28.7	52.5
Standard deviation	8.9	8.3	7.1	7.7	8.1	8.3	5.1	5.4	7.5	7.2	7.4	8.3	7.4
High monthly average	38.4	44.3	49.9	60.0	69.6	83.6	87.7	83.7	72.1	58.5	45.1	41.0	87.7
Year of occurrence	1953	1912	1986	1934	1934	1911	1911	1911	1943	1988	1927	1917	1911
Low monthly average	10.5	20.6	36.0	43.8	54.1	63.4	71.3	70.1	59.5	46.2	30.5	17.0	10.5
Year of occurrence	1937	1984	1942	1975	1942	1963	1993	1968	1965	1969	1993	1990	1937

† Also occurred on earlier date(s).

WENDOVER WSO AIRPORT
Monthly Data Summary

Precipitation in Inches

	Jan	Feb	Mar	Apr	May	Jun	Jul	Aug	Sep	Oct	Nov	Dec	Annual
Monthly normal	0.22	0.32	0.42	0.56	0.90	0.65	0.29	0.45	0.38	0.54	0.39	0.28	5.39
Standard deviation	0.03	0.04	0.06	0.07	0.12	0.09	0.05	0.07	0.07	0.08	0.06	0.04	0.06
Average monthly	0.26	0.31	0.38	0.51	0.74	0.55	0.28	0.33	0.36	0.47	0.30	0.29	4.79
Standard deviation	0.04	0.05	0.05	0.07	0.10	0.08	0.05	0.06	0.07	0.07	0.05	0.05	0.06
High monthly total	1.42	1.29	1.34	2.01	4.19	3.01	1.35	2.56	3.37	2.41	1.83	2.72	4.19
Year of occurrence	1949	1962	1978	1940	1987	1964	1938	1941	1982	1972	1957	1921	1987
Low monthly total	0.00†	0.00†	0.00†	0.00†	0.00†	0.00†	0.00†	0.00†	0.00†	0.00†	0.00†	0.00†	0.00†
Year of occurrence	1961	1988	1923	1992	1948	1994	1979	1995	1992	1988	1962	1994	1994
Record high daily	0.52	0.65	0.72	0.91	1.95	0.91	1.00	1.27	1.55	1.15	1.19	0.90	1.95
Day of occurrence	24	20	11	1	19	4	21	12	26	13	6	21	19
Year of occurrence	1954	1914	1973	1940	1987	1945	1987	1941	1982	1987	1970	1921	1987
Days w/pcp >= .01	3.4	3.7	4.0	4.6	4.9	3.9	2.7	2.9	2.6	3.2	3.2	3.3	42.7
Days w/pcp >= .10	1.0	1.1	1.3	1.6	2.2	1.6	0.9	1.0	1.1	1.5	0.9	1.0	15.3
Days w/pcp >= .50	0.0	0.1	0.1	0.1	0.3	0.2	0.1	0.1	0.1	0.1	0.1	0.1	1.5

Snow and Sleet in Inches

	Jan	Feb	Mar	Apr	May	Jun	Jul	Aug	Sep	Oct	Nov	Dec	Annual
Monthly normal	1.4	1.4	0.9	0.3	0.0	0.0	0.0	0.0	0.0	0.2	0.5	1.4	6.1
Standard deviation	0.3	0.3	0.3	0.1	0.0	0.0	0.0	0.0	0.0	0.1	0.2	0.2	0.1
Average monthly	1.7	1.6	0.7	0.2	0.1	0.0	0.0	0.0	0.0	0.1	0.3	1.5	6.2
Standard deviation	0.3	0.4	0.2	0.1	0.1	0.0	0.0	0.0	0.0	0.1	0.2	0.4	0.1
High monthly total	14.6	9.0	8.5	4.0	4.1	0.0†	0.0†	0.0†	0.0†	2.0	6.7	15.2	15.2
Year of occurrence	1949	1936	1967	1921	1922	1995	1995	1995	1995	1961	1961	1921	1921
Low monthly total	0.0†	0.0†	0.0†	0.0†	0.0†	0.0†	0.0†	0.0†	0.0†	0.0†	0.0†	0.0†	0.0†
Year of occurrence	1995	1995	1995	1995	1995	1995	1995	1995	1995	1995	1995	1995	1995
Record high daily	100.0	7.0	5.4	3.1	3.1	0.0†	0.0†	0.0†	0.0†	1.8	4.2	8.0	100.0
Day of occurrence	23	2	13	21	19	30	31	31	30	17	15	20	23
Year of occurrence	1934	1936	1967	1968	1922	1995	1995	1995	1995	1938	1961	1921	1934
Days w/snow >= .1	1.8	1.5	0.6	0.3	0.1	0.0	0.0	0.0	0.0	0.1	0.3	1.4	5.6
Days w/snow >= 5	0.0	0.0	0.0	0.0	0.0	0.0	0.0	0.0	0.0	0.0	0.0	0.1	0.1
Days w/snow >= 10	0.0	0.0	0.0	0.0	0.0	0.0	0.0	0.0	0.0	0.0	0.0	0.0	0.0

Degree Days

	Jan	Feb	Mar	Apr	May	Jun	Jul	Aug	Sep	Oct	Nov	Dec	Annual
Heating normal	1173	882	704	432	181	41	0	4	85	400	790	1148	5844
Heating average	1169	869	700	406	166	39	1	2	75	381	794	1116	5724
Cooling normal	0	0	0	3	49	207	453	358	101	2	0	0	1178
Cooling average	0	0	0	3	53	211	455	373	108	3	0	0	1209
Growing 40 normal	29	74	194	356	618	793	992	936	697	396	120	27	5237
Growing 40 average	31	79	207	380	630	798	985	938	705	418	130	35	5341
Growing 50 normal	5	14	68	179	377	577	814	746	470	201	30	4	3491
Growing 50 average	4	16	79	200	393	587	809	755	489	223	36	5	3600

† Also occurred on earlier date(s).

Location: Zion National Park   County: Washington   Latitude: 37.217   Longitude: -112.983
Elevation: 4050 feet   Period of Record: 1928-1996

ZION NATIONAL PARK
Monthly Data Summary

Maximum Temperature in °F

	Jan	Feb	Mar	Apr	May	Jun	Jul	Aug	Sep	Oct	Nov	Dec	Annual
Monthly normal	51.9	57.4	62.8	71.9	82.4	93.5	99.1	96.2	88.9	77.6	62.2	52.6	74.7
Standard deviation	8.2	9.1	9.5	9.8	9.0	7.4	4.9	5.5	6.9	9.4	9.5	8.5	8.1
Average monthly	51.4	56.7	63.4	72.8	82.6	93.5	99.4	96.7	90.1	77.9	62.6	53.0	75.0
Standard deviation	8.4	9.2	9.2	9.6	8.9	7.6	5.6	6.1	7.0	9.4	9.4	8.1	8.2
High monthly average	62.0	67.5	74.5	82.8	90.5	100.0	103.7	100.8	96.1	88.5	72.4	61.8	103.7
Year of occurrence	1986	1995	1972	1989	1947	1994	1989	1969	1953	1952	1949	1980	1989
Low monthly average	35.1	45.2	54.3	62.2	72.7	86.7	94.2	90.3	83.1	68.1	53.9	45.6	35.1
Year of occurrence	1937	1939	1973	1941	1933	1965	1932	1968	1961	1984	1957	1967	1937
Record high daily	73	81	86	94	102†	114	115	112	110	98	85	75	115
Day of occurrence	20	26	24	24	31	22	1	16	1	4	6	5	1
Year of occurrence	1971	1986	1956	1946	1950	1954	1950	1939	1950	1978	1934	1939	1950
Record low daily	16	27	35	43†	48	64†	5	0	58	39	31†	25	0
Day of occurrence	21	9	2	16	8	6	5	26	25	29	23	22	26
Year of occurrence	1937	1933	1951	1976	1930	1993	1942	1944	1986	1971	1931	1990	1944
Days w/max >= 100	0.0	0.0	0.0	0.0	0.2	6.1	16.9	10.4	2.1	0.0	0.0	0.0	35.8
Days w/max >= 90	0.0	0.0	0.0	0.5	7.3	22.1	29.6	27.8	17.1	2.8	0.0	0.0	107.0
Days w/max <= 32	0.4	0.2	0.0	0.0	0.0	0.0	0.0	0.0	0.0	0.0	0.0	0.3	0.9

Minimum Temperature in °F

	Jan	Feb	Mar	Apr	May	Jun	Jul	Aug	Sep	Oct	Nov	Dec	Annual
Monthly normal	28.5	32.7	36.7	43.0	51.8	61.4	68.6	66.9	59.5	49.2	37.5	29.5	47.1
Standard deviation	8.9	8.7	8.1	7.9	7.8	6.9	4.5	4.8	6.7	8.5	8.8	8.9	7.5
Average monthly	28.6	32.6	36.8	43.6	52.0	61.2	68.5	67.0	60.3	49.3	36.9	30.1	47.2
Standard deviation	8.6	8.4	7.6	7.7	7.6	6.8	4.7	4.6	6.2	8.2	8.8	8.5	7.3
High monthly average	37.3	40.3	45.6	50.4	58.9	68.2	72.9	72.4	65.2	56.3	44.3	38.8	72.9
Year of occurrence	1986	1995	1934	1934	1934	1936	1931	1939	1960	1988	1949	1950	1931
Low monthly average	14.4	21.0	28.3	36.6	46.4	55.0	63.6	63.4	53.2	40.3	28.1	20.8	14.4
Year of occurrence	1937	1933	1948	1975	1991	1995	1948	1951	1965	1984	1992	1930	1937
Record high daily	48†	51†	57	62	74	79†	87	78†	79	73	65	52	87
Day of occurrence	20	27	27	28	11	27	13	6	12	7	4	1	13
Year of occurrence	1971	1988	1928	1987	1941	1981	1941	1978	1941	1930	1944	1950	1941
Record low daily	-15	0	12	21	22	36	50	50	33	17	6	-5	-15
Day of occurrence	21	6	2	26	1	4	6	29	20	30	28	23	21
Year of occurrence	1937	1989	1971	1984	1967	1973	1952	1942	1965	1971	1976	1990	1937
Days w/min <= 32	20.2	12.9	9.2	2.9	0.3	0.0	0.0	0.0	0.0	1.0	9.7	18.2	75.6
Days w/min <= 0	0.1	0.0	0.0	0.0	0.0	0.0	0.0	0.0	0.0	0.0	0.0	0.0	0.2
Days w/min <= -20	0.0	0.0	0.0	0.0	0.0	0.0	0.0	0.0	0.0	0.0	0.0	0.0	0.0

Mean Temperature in °F

	Jan	Feb	Mar	Apr	May	Jun	Jul	Aug	Sep	Oct	Nov	Dec	Annual
Monthly normal	40.2	45.0	49.7	57.5	67.1	77.5	83.9	81.5	74.2	63.3	49.8	41.1	60.9
Standard deviation	7.6	8.1	8.2	8.3	8.0	6.8	4.2	4.7	6.4	8.4	8.4	8.0	7.3
Average monthly	40.0	44.7	50.1	58.2	67.3	77.4	84.0	81.9	75.2	63.6	49.8	41.5	61.1
Standard deviation	7.6	8.0	7.7	8.1	7.8	6.8	4.4	4.7	6.0	8.2	8.4	7.5	7.1
High monthly average	49.7	53.9	60.1	65.5	73.7	82.9	87.8	86.5	79.7	70.6	58.4	49.9	87.8
Year of occurrence	1986	1995	1934	1989	1934	1940	1960	1939	1979	1988	1949	1950	1960
Low monthly average	24.7	34.1	42.5	49.5	60.0	71.2	80.8†	76.9	68.3	54.2	43.2	34.3	24.7
Year of occurrence	1937	1933	1952	1975	1933	1965	1993	1968	1965	1984	1994	1932	1937

† Also occurred on earlier date(s).

ZION NATIONAL PARK
Monthly Data Summary

Precipitation in Inches

	Jan	Feb	Mar	Apr	May	Jun	Jul	Aug	Sep	Oct	Nov	Dec	Annual
Monthly normal	1.59	1.60	2.05	1.15	0.84	0.48	1.25	1.79	1.00	0.92	1.46	1.28	15.42
Standard deviation	0.17	0.18	0.18	0.13	0.10	0.10	0.17	0.18	0.15	0.12	0.16	0.15	0.15
Average monthly	1.66	1.75	1.98	1.13	0.83	0.49	0.98	1.49	1.03	0.99	1.23	1.39	14.93
Standard deviation	0.16	0.18	0.18	0.13	0.11	0.11	0.14	0.16	0.15	0.12	0.15	0.15	0.15
High monthly total	7.53	6.65	7.07	4.67	3.00	4.00	4.93	4.83†	6.70	3.30	4.02	4.27	7.53
Year of occurrence	1993	1980	1978	1988	1977	1972	1975	1963	1939	1941	1931	1966	1993
Low monthly total	0.00	0.00†	0.00†	0.00†	0.00†	0.00†	0.00	0.13	0.00†	0.00†	0.00†	0.00†	0.00†
Year of occurrence	1972	1972	1972	1989	1972	1980	1993	1985	1979	1995	1992	1989	1989
Record high daily	1.63	1.77	2.77	1.73	1.80	2.15	2.76	2.04	2.02	1.48	1.55	2.02	2.77
Day of occurrence	25	14	3	21	16	7	29	27	10	31	6	6	3
Year of occurrence	1969	1980	1938	1988	1944	1949	1975	1932	1984	1992	1987	1966	1938
Days w/pcp >= .01	6.4	6.2	7.4	5.2	4.4	2.2	5.0	6.6	4.2	4.3	4.3	5.5	61.9
Days w/pcp >= .10	4.3	4.4	4.8	2.9	2.2	1.1	2.5	3.6	2.2	2.6	2.9	3.6	37.3
Days w/pcp >= .50	1.0	1.1	1.2	0.7	0.4	0.2	0.6	0.8	0.7	0.6	0.9	0.8	9.0

Snow and Sleet in Inches

	Jan	Feb	Mar	Apr	May	Jun	Jul	Aug	Sep	Oct	Nov	Dec	Annual
Monthly normal	3.3	1.9	0.9	0.2	0.0	0.0	0.0	0.0	0.0	0.1	1.0	2.5	9.8
Standard deviation	0.7	0.5	0.3	0.1	0.0	0.0	0.0	0.0	0.0	0.1	0.3	0.6	0.2
Average monthly	3.8	1.9	1.1	0.2	0.0	0.0	0.0	0.0	0.0	0.1	0.6	2.0	9.7
Standard deviation	0.8	0.5	0.4	0.1	0.0	0.0	0.0	0.0	0.0	0.1	0.2	0.5	0.2
High monthly total	27.1	18.0	14.5	4.0	0.0†	1.0	0.0†	0.0†	0.0†	3.0	6.0	21.0	27.1
Year of occurrence	1937	1949	1952	1975	1995	1949	1995	1995	1995	1971	1983	1967	1937
Low monthly total	0.0†	0.0†	0.0†	0.0†	0.0†	0.0†	0.0†	0.0†	0.0†	0.0†	0.0†	0.0†	0.0†
Year of occurrence	1995	1995	1994	1994	1995	1995	1995	1995	1995	1995	1995	1995	1995
Record high daily	12.5	8.0	7.0	4.0	0.0†	1.0	0.0†	0.0†	0.0†	3.0	4.5†	8.0	12.5
Day of occurrence	19	3	1	1	31	7	31	31	30	29	14	26	19
Year of occurrence	1955	1949	1952	1975	1995	1949	1995	1995	1995	1971	1978	1941	1955
Days w/snow >= .1	1.4	1.0	0.5	0.1	0.0	0.0	0.0	0.0	0.0	0.0	0.3	0.8	4.0
Days w/snow >= 5	0.2	0.0	0.0	0.0	0.0	0.0	0.0	0.0	0.0	0.0	0.0	0.2	0.5
Days w/snow >= 10	0.0	0.0	0.0	0.0	0.0	0.0	0.0	0.0	0.0	0.0	0.0	0.0	0.0

Degree Days

	Jan	Feb	Mar	Apr	May	Jun	Jul	Aug	Sep	Oct	Nov	Dec	Annual
Heating normal	769	563	474	245	74	3	0	0	11	127	455	740	3465
Heating average	772	571	463	226	69	5	0	0	6	122	458	726	3422
Cooling normal	0	0	1	19	141	378	584	512	286	76	0	0	2000
Cooling average	0	0	0	22	141	375	587	523	311	79	0	0	2042
Growing 40 normal	191	258	378	527	733	875	1015	990	842	671	367	205	7057
Growing 40 average	183	245	385	542	736	869	1011	990	852	675	370	209	7074
Growing 50 normal	66	120	204	337	539	704	845	817	664	459	192	76	5030
Growing 50 average	63	112	213	350	541	698	841	818	676	465	197	77	5056

† Also occurred on earlier date(s).

Location: Salt Lake City NWSFO　　　　　　　Period of Record: 1928-1996

Utah Climate Center

SALT LAKE CITY NWSFO
Daily Data Summary

January

| Day | Average temperature | | | | Extreme maximum | | | | Extreme minimum | | | | | Degree Days | | |
	Max	Min	Mean	High	Year	Low	Year	High	Year	Low	Year	HDD	CDD	GDD40	GDD50
1	34.8	17.3	26.1	58	1943	14	1979	42	1934	-4†	1974	38	0	0	0
2	34.5	17.3	25.9	50	1943	16	1942	37	1940	-6	1974	39	0	0	0
3	33.4	16.5	24.9	52	1934	14	1949	35	1996	-3	1932	40	0	0	0
4	34.5	17.3	25.9	53	1956	13	1960	37	1987	-13	1973	39	0	0	0
5	35.6	19.0	27.3	56	1980	15†	1973	40	1978	-6	1973	37	0	0	0
6	35.3	18.2	26.7	55	1948	10	1971	42	1965	-13	1942	38	0	0	0
7	35.4	16.9	26.2	58	1956	16	1937	36	1983	-11	1973	38	0	1	0
8	36.1	18.1	27.1	57†	1956	9	1937	39	1953	-11	1937	37	0	1	0
9	35.9	19.1	27.5	59	1953	7	1937	42	1995	-11	1937	37	0	1	0
10	36.3	20.2	28.3	57	1953	18	1937	43	1995	-8	1937	36	0	1	0
11	36.7	19.2	27.9	54	1953	10	1963	36†	1971	-9	1963	37	0	1	0
12	37.2	18.8	28.0	60	1953	4	1963	41	1969	-18	1963	36	0	1	0
13	36.8	19.8	28.3	57	1953	8	1963	47	1980	-15	1963	36	0	1	0
14	37.9	20.2	29.1	59†	1945	17	1964	39	1995	-10	1932	35	0	1	0
15	38.4	21.1	29.7	57	1996	20	1947	40	1954	-6	1964	35	0	1	0
16	37.5	20.4	28.9	56	1974	19	1984	38	1954	-5	1947	36	0	1	0
17	37.8	19.8	28.8	54†	1982	17	1949	40	1950	-9	1930	36	0	1	0
18	37.0	20.3	28.6	54	1994	15	1930	39	1950	-6†	1984	36	0	1	0
19	36.9	18.8	27.8	53	1971	9	1963	38	1969	-15	1963	37	0	0	0
20	35.7	18.4	27.1	58	1953	7	1937	46	1969	-8	1937	37	0	1	0
21	35.3	16.9	26.1	57	1943	6	1937	45	1943	-20	1937	38	0	1	0
22	36.2	17.4	26.8	56	1970	8	1937	43	1970	-14†	1937	38	0	1	0
23	36.8	18.5	27.6	60	1970	9	1937	41	1970	-14	1962	37	0	1	0
24	37.5	19.8	28.7	59	1970	14	1929	39	1970	-9	1929	36	0	1	0
25	37.4	19.5	28.4	59	1953	8	1949	39	1975	-22	1949	36	0	1	0
26	38.2	19.2	28.7	62	1982	18	1949	35	1971	-15	1949	36	0	1	0
27	37.9	19.9	28.9	54	1971	15	1949	39	1983	-6	1949	36	0	1	0
28	37.2	18.3	27.7	57	1938	18	1949	39	1981	-8	1949	37	0	1	0
29	35.7	17.9	26.8	54	1953	18	1949	36†	1958	-12	1949	38	0	0	0
30	36.9	18.9	27.9	61	1971	18	1949	40	1965	-6	1979	37	0	1	0
31	36.9	19.7	28.3	61	1971	17	1951	46	1963	-8	1979	36	0	1	0

| | Total precipitation | | | Percent of years with precipitation | | | | Total snowfall | | | Percent with snowfall | | | |
Day	Avg	High	Year	None	Trace	.01 or more	.10 or more	.50 or more	Avg	High	Year	None	.1 or more	2.0 or more	ETo
1	0.02	0.20	1940	48.5	26.5	25.0	8.8	0.0	0.2	2.3	1960	47.3	23.6	3.6	0.02
2	0.06	1.20	1932	47.1	23.5	29.4	14.7	2.9	0.6	9.0	1993	50.9	32.7	9.1	0.02
3	0.04	0.45	1940	50.0	19.1	30.9	14.7	0.0	0.4	5.0	1977	52.7	27.3	5.5	0.02
4	0.03	0.27	1978	47.1	19.1	33.8	11.8	0.0	0.4	3.3	1929	50.9	34.5	10.9	0.02
5	0.06	0.81	1987	36.8	23.5	39.7	16.2	2.9	0.5	6.1	1987	41.8	36.4	9.1	0.02
6	0.03	0.41	1944	47.1	27.9	25.0	10.3	0.0	0.4	7.6	1967	56.4	21.8	7.3	0.02
7	0.04	0.52	1993	54.4	19.1	26.5	11.8	1.5	0.6	7.7	1974	58.2	27.3	10.9	0.02
8	0.05	0.56	1975	47.1	22.1	30.9	13.2	1.5	0.7	6.4	1985	54.5	29.1	12.7	0.03
9	0.03	0.51	1993	48.5	26.5	25.0	8.8	1.5	0.5	8.4	1993	49.1	30.9	7.3	0.02
10	0.02	0.26	1968	48.5	17.6	33.8	10.3	0.0	0.3	4.0	1968	54.5	25.5	3.6	0.02
11	0.03	0.26	1965	39.7	22.1	38.2	10.3	0.0	0.5	7.5	1993	50.9	34.5	7.3	0.03
12	0.04	0.43	1932	47.1	22.1	30.9	11.8	0.0	0.5	5.7	1932	52.7	29.1	9.1	0.03
13	0.03	0.28†	1971	38.2	27.9	33.8	13.2	0.0	0.3	3.0†	1971	50.9	29.1	7.3	0.03
14	0.06	1.36	1953	48.5	19.1	32.4	11.8	2.9	0.3	8.5	1953	58.2	27.3	3.6	0.03
15	0.06	0.91	1995	41.2	23.5	35.3	19.1	2.9	0.4	4.9	1991	49.1	23.6	5.5	0.03
16	0.05	0.56	1956	41.2	22.1	36.8	17.6	1.5	0.4	6.9	1955	47.3	29.1	9.1	0.03
17	0.05	0.73	1996	48.5	19.1	32.4	10.3	2.9	0.4	10.0	1996	60.0	16.4	7.3	0.03
18	0.04	0.60	1953	41.2	23.5	35.3	13.2	1.5	0.4	5.0	1964	50.9	27.3	7.3	0.03
19	0.04	0.61	1973	42.6	25.0	32.4	14.7	1.5	0.6	7.5	1973	43.6	27.3	12.7	0.03
20	0.05	0.56	1962	44.1	25.0	30.9	17.6	2.9	0.7	9.7	1962	49.1	29.1	10.9	0.02
21	0.03	0.53	1953	50.0	19.1	30.9	8.8	1.5	0.4	4.5	1952	47.3	30.9	10.9	0.02
22	0.05	0.81	1951	48.5	17.6	33.8	13.2	2.9	0.5	5.4	1949	50.9	32.7	9.1	0.03
23	0.05	0.52	1967	42.6	17.6	39.7	16.2	2.9	0.6	5.5	1950	49.1	36.4	9.1	0.03
24	0.06	0.54	1934	42.6	20.6	36.8	16.2	1.5	0.6	6.4	1996	50.9	32.7	12.7	0.03
25	0.05	0.67	1996	44.1	25.0	30.9	16.2	1.5	0.7	13.4	1996	49.1	30.9	12.7	0.03
26	0.04	0.44	1969	48.5	25.0	26.5	10.3	0.0	0.4	4.7	1969	52.7	29.1	7.3	0.03
27	0.04	0.61	1956	42.6	26.5	30.9	13.2	1.5	0.5	5.1	1980	45.5	32.7	10.9	0.03
28	0.06	0.45	1965	42.6	17.6	39.7	19.1	0.0	0.6	5.8	1933	45.5	45.5	9.1	0.03
29	0.04	0.49	1980	52.9	17.6	29.4	11.8	0.0	0.3	9.9	1980	60.0	27.3	3.6	0.02
30	0.02	0.30	1996	54.4	14.7	30.9	7.4	0.0	0.2	4.2	1996	61.8	27.3	3.6	0.03
31	0.04	0.48	1939	39.7	26.5	33.8	11.8	0.0	0.5	5.5	1981	47.3	32.7	12.7	0.03

† Also occurred on earlier date(s).

February

Day	Average temperature				Extreme maximum				Extreme minimum				HDD	Degree Days		
	Max	Min	Mean	High	Year	Low	Year	High	Year	Low	Year		CDD	GDD40	GDD50
1	38.1	20.1	29.1	61	1995	17	1985	38†	1995	-9	1985	35	0	1	0
2	38.4	20.3	29.4	58	1995	20†	1956	38†	1978	-4†	1950	35	0	1	0
3	38.8	20.6	29.7	64	1953	22	1979	38†	1953	-12	1996	35	0	1	0
4	39.7	19.9	29.8	59†	1965	20	1982	35	1958	-2	1996	35	0	1	0
5	38.8	21.6	30.2	62	1963	18†	1989	43	1978	-8	1989	34	0	1	0
6	40.6	22.8	31.7	63	1934	17	1989	38	1934	-14	1989	33	0	1	0
7	41.0	22.9	31.9	60	1995	6	1933	41†	1994	-12	1933	33	0	2	0
8	40.9	22.4	31.6	60	1945	20	1989	39†	1957	-7†	1989	33	0	2	0
9	40.3	22.4	31.4	61	1951	8	1933	40	1938	-30	1933	33	0	1	0
10	41.2	23.1	32.2	68	1951	10	1933	48	1962	-26	1933	32	0	2	0
11	42.2	24.4	33.3	65	1961	19	1933	50	1961	-1	1929	31	0	2	0
12	42.4	23.7	33.1	61	1970	24	1949	40	1970	1	1949	31	0	2	0
13	42.8	23.3	33.0	61	1971	18	1949	40	1954	-9	1949	31	0	2	0
14	42.0	23.4	32.7	58†	1971	19	1949	38	1982	-13	1933	32	0	2	0
15	42.1	23.8	32.9	58	1947	26	1929	45	1986	-4	1933	32	0	2	0
16	43.2	25.4	34.3	62	1947	23	1956	43	1986	4†	1989	30	0	2	0
17	44.2	25.9	35.1	63	1930	26	1956	44	1986	-5	1933	29	0	3	0
18	44.2	25.4	34.8	66†	1958	22	1942	51	1986	0	1942	30	0	3	0
19	44.0	26.4	35.2	66	1958	23	1955	45	1958	4†	1956	29	0	3	0
20	44.4	25.8	35.1	65	1958	25	1955	43	1957	0	1955	29	0	3	0
21	44.8	26.1	35.5	66	1982	25	1955	38†	1996	6†	1984	29	0	3	0
22	46.4	26.9	36.6	65	1958	29†	1975	43	1982	6	1975	28	0	3	0
23	45.9	26.9	36.4	60	1986	29	1960	44	1986	6†	1960	28	0	3	0
24	46.6	26.8	36.7	68	1981	26	1960	46	1986	5	1960	28	0	4	1
25	46.3	26.7	36.5	68	1950	27	1964	45	1981	2	1933	28	0	3	1
26	46.4	26.5	36.5	67	1950	23	1962	40†	1976	3	1962	28	0	4	1
27	45.8	26.4	36.1	67	1980	14	1962	44	1940	-2	1962	28	0	3	1
28	47.9	27.2	37.5	69	1972	25†	1962	45	1940	1	1962	27	0	4	1
29	48.4	27.4	37.9	66	1992	24	1960	41	1980	-4	1960	27	0	4	1

	Total precipitation			Percent of years with precipitation					Total snowfall			Percent with snowfall			
Day	Avg	High	Year	None	Trace	.01 or more	.10 or more	.50 or more	Avg	High	Year	None	.1 or more	2.0 or more	ETo
1	0.03	0.43	1989	48.5	25.0	26.5	11.8	0.0	0.5	10.9	1989	54.5	20.0	7.3	0.04
2	0.05	0.89	1936	41.2	25.0	33.8	11.8	2.9	0.4	10.0	1989	47.3	34.5	5.5	0.04
3	0.02	0.40	1945	50.0	27.9	22.1	8.8	0.0	0.2	4.8	1989	58.2	20.0	5.5	0.04
4	0.03	0.44	1976	50.0	25.0	25.0	13.2	0.0	0.3	4.6	1976	63.6	18.2	9.1	0.04
5	0.03	0.47	1974	41.2	35.3	23.5	11.8	0.0	0.3	6.2	1974	56.4	18.2	3.6	0.04
6	0.06	0.81	1969	48.5	19.1	32.4	17.6	4.4	0.4	7.9	1969	60.0	23.6	5.5	0.04
7	0.03	0.32	1950	48.5	23.5	27.9	11.8	0.0	0.2	3.3	1990	58.2	21.8	7.3	0.04
8	0.06	0.65	1959	42.6	20.6	36.8	22.1	2.9	0.4	8.5	1959	61.8	18.2	5.5	0.04
9	0.03	0.41	1976	39.7	29.4	30.9	11.8	0.0	0.2	4.5	1965	61.8	20.0	1.8	0.04
10	0.04	0.36	1947	54.4	16.2	29.4	13.2	0.0	0.3	7.7	1984	67.3	20.0	3.6	0.04
11	0.03	0.44	1995	42.6	27.9	29.4	11.8	0.0	0.3	5.1	1995	60.0	18.2	3.6	0.04
12	0.07	0.64	1952	41.2	19.1	39.7	22.1	1.5	0.8	7.7	1952	50.9	30.9	16.4	0.04
13	0.07	0.60	1970	41.2	23.5	35.3	22.1	1.5	0.5	5.8	1968	52.7	27.3	10.9	0.04
14	0.06	0.54	1987	41.2	19.1	39.7	22.1	1.5	0.5	5.0	1995	50.9	25.5	9.1	0.04
15	0.04	0.55	1936	51.5	17.6	30.9	14.7	1.5	0.2	3.1	1978	61.8	18.2	3.6	0.04
16	0.05	0.44	1969	47.1	16.2	36.8	13.2	0.0	0.4	4.2	1992	60.0	27.3	9.1	0.04
17	0.04	0.49	1955	45.6	14.7	39.7	10.3	0.0	0.3	3.1	1955	56.4	25.5	9.1	0.04
18	0.06	0.78	1980	39.7	17.6	42.6	16.2	4.4	0.5	7.4	1961	50.9	34.5	5.5	0.05
19	0.03	0.38	1974	50.0	19.1	30.9	8.8	0.0	0.2	2.4	1989	63.6	14.5	1.8	0.04
20	0.06	0.90	1934	51.5	17.6	30.9	13.2	1.5	0.2	3.9	1985	63.6	16.4	3.6	0.05
21	0.04	0.45	1979	55.9	17.6	26.5	13.2	0.0	0.2	3.1	1975	70.9	16.4	7.3	0.05
22	0.05	0.50	1996	51.5	13.2	35.3	14.7	1.5	0.5	9.9	1994	69.1	27.3	7.3	0.05
23	0.05	0.72	1930	41.2	23.5	35.3	17.6	2.9	0.3	6.4	1956	60.0	21.8	7.3	0.05
24	0.03	0.55	1943	60.3	11.8	27.9	10.3	1.5	0.2	5.1	1972	76.4	18.2	3.6	0.05
25	0.05	0.90†	1969	50.0	23.5	26.5	14.7	2.9	0.6	8.3	1969	63.6	18.2	12.7	0.05
26	0.04	0.51	1981	51.5	19.1	29.4	17.6	1.5	0.4	6.0	1996	63.6	18.2	9.1	0.05
27	0.04	0.41	1947	52.9	16.2	30.9	16.2	0.0	0.3	6.0	1930	63.6	20.0	7.3	0.05
28	0.01	0.30	1930	61.8	14.7	23.5	4.4	0.0	0.2	3.0	1930	76.4	14.5	1.8	0.05
29	0.01	0.16	1940	52.9	23.5	23.5	5.9	0.0	0.0	0.0†	1996	76.9	0.0	0.0	0.05

† Also occurred on earlier date(s).

March

Day	Average temperature			Extreme maximum				Extreme minimum				HDD	Degree Days		
	Max	Min	Mean	High	Year	Low	Year	High	Year	Low	Year		CDD	GDD40	GDD50
1	48.6	29.7	39.2	67	1967	29	1971	47	1983	13	1960	25	0	4	1
2	46.9	28.8	37.9	64	1992	30	1953	48	1983	3	1971	27	0	4	1
3	46.0	27.2	36.6	67	1994	27†	1966	40	1980	5	1952	28	0	3	1
4	46.1	27.5	36.8	69	1987	26	1966	47	1991	2	1966	28	0	3	1
5	47.5	27.9	37.7	68	1972	31	1955	46	1987	5	1966	27	0	4	1
6	47.6	28.2	37.9	69	1972	31	1964	44	1987	10†	1966	27	0	4	1
7	49.7	29.8	39.8	66	1986	32	1964	43	1975	5	1964	25	0	5	1
8	52.1	30.7	41.4	68	1972	33	1964	46	1954	7	1964	23	0	6	2
9	53.1	31.1	42.1	76	1989	33	1964	46	1995	20†	1958	22	0	6	2
10	51.4	31.0	41.2	75	1989	29	1962	53	1989	13	1964	23	0	6	2
11	49.6	30.0	39.8	70	1989	29	1962	46	1983	14	1948	25	0	5	1
12	50.5	29.6	40.0	68	1972	30	1962	45	1967	12	1990	24	0	5	2
13	50.8	30.5	40.6	70	1934	29	1962	46	1983	9	1962	24	0	5	2
14	49.7	30.0	39.9	70	1935	31	1962	42†	1992	11†	1964	25	0	5	1
15	51.6	30.3	40.9	72†	1994	32	1943	46	1992	15	1962	24	0	6	2
16	53.4	31.4	42.4	69†	1974	36	1963	48	1994	10	1963	22	0	6	2
17	52.0	31.2	41.6	68†	1972	34	1951	48	1974	18	1942	23	0	6	2
18	52.1	32.1	42.1	72	1972	31	1965	44	1993	12	1965	22	0	6	2
19	53.5	31.6	42.6	71	1949	34	1943	48	1975	10	1965	22	0	7	2
20	53.3	31.5	42.4	71	1988	31	1955	46†	1990	17	1965	22	0	6	2
21	54.4	31.6	43.0	73	1972	33	1952	46	1988	14	1948	22	0	7	3
22	54.6	33.5	44.1	75	1972	32	1952	47	1978	17	1966	20	0	7	3
23	54.2	33.7	44.0	73	1961	31	1952	47	1967	19	1952	21	0	7	3
24	53.4	32.6	43.0	78	1956	38†	1980	48†	1986	18	1965	21	0	7	2
25	54.3	32.2	43.2	75	1956	36	1942	50	1993	14	1965	21	0	7	3
26	53.6	32.4	43.0	78	1960	32	1975	49	1993	19	1955	22	0	7	2
27	53.6	32.3	42.9	73†	1953	27	1975	51	1960	14	1931	22	0	7	3
28	55.1	33.0	44.0	77	1943	28	1975	51	1934	18†	1956	20	0	8	3
29	55.1	33.1	44.1	75	1968	35†	1977	56	1943	17	1975	20	0	7	3
30	55.6	33.5	44.6	73†	1978	39†	1967	50	1978	13	1977	20	0	8	3
31	57.2	34.4	45.8	75	1966	41†	1980	51	1956	19	1970	19	0	8	4

Day	Total precipitation			Percent of years with precipitation					Total snowfall			Percent with snowfall			ETo
	Avg	High	Year	None	Trace	.01 or more	.10 or more	.50 or more	Avg	High	Year	None	.1 or more	2.0 or more	
1	0.06	0.59	1977	50.7	20.9	28.4	17.9	1.5	0.6	7.3	1977	74.1	20.4	11.1	0.07
2	0.13	1.11	1941	38.8	7.5	53.7	34.3	10.4	1.0	10.1	1977	59.3	29.6	16.7	0.07
3	0.06	0.66	1938	41.8	19.4	38.8	19.4	1.5	0.3	4.2	1962	61.1	20.4	7.4	0.07
4	0.04	0.63	1938	50.7	22.4	26.9	13.4	1.5	0.1	2.3	1995	63.0	7.4	3.7	0.07
5	0.04	0.55	1978	41.8	19.4	38.8	16.4	1.5	0.2	2.4	1980	61.1	20.4	5.6	0.07
6	0.04	0.48	1930	49.3	28.4	22.4	16.4	0.0	0.3	4.0	1930	68.5	11.1	5.6	0.07
7	0.02	0.50	1960	61.2	17.9	20.9	4.5	1.5	0.1	1.6	1991	75.9	11.1	0.0	0.07
8	0.03	0.59	1986	70.1	7.5	22.4	11.9	1.5	0.1	2.6	1958	90.7	5.6	1.9	0.08
9	0.04	0.64	1987	56.7	20.9	22.4	13.4	1.5	0.2	4.2	1964	70.4	11.1	3.7	0.08
10	0.04	0.65	1962	59.7	14.9	25.4	13.4	1.5	0.3	7.4	1962	72.2	16.7	5.6	0.08
11	0.09	0.82	1990	52.2	7.5	40.3	28.4	4.5	0.7	11.0	1952	64.8	20.4	11.1	0.07
12	0.05	0.47	1944	52.2	22.4	25.4	16.4	0.0	0.1	1.8	1964	68.5	18.5	0.0	0.08
13	0.08	1.56	1944	38.8	19.4	41.8	17.9	3.0	0.3	8.2	1973	61.1	22.2	1.9	0.08
14	0.07	0.41†	1960	46.3	10.4	43.3	28.4	0.0	0.3	5.2	1960	66.7	20.4	3.7	0.07
15	0.05	0.92	1963	58.2	11.9	29.9	14.9	1.5	0.4	7.9	1963	70.4	16.7	5.6	0.08
16	0.03	0.53	1975	56.7	16.4	26.9	10.4	1.5	0.2	5.6	1958	83.3	5.6	3.7	0.08
17	0.07	0.61	1968	44.8	17.9	37.3	19.4	4.5	0.3	6.3	1968	59.3	25.9	5.6	0.08
18	0.04	0.43	1937	47.8	25.4	26.9	11.9	0.0	0.1	2.1	1968	72.2	13.0	1.9	0.08
19	0.06	0.68	1983	53.7	14.9	31.3	20.9	3.0	0.2	6.1	1983	77.8	11.1	3.7	0.08
20	0.04	0.69	1946	61.2	16.4	22.4	16.4	1.5	0.1	2.0	1952	77.8	7.4	1.9	0.08
21	0.05	0.71	1980	59.7	13.4	26.9	19.4	1.5	0.3	6.4	1980	68.5	18.5	7.4	0.09
22	0.07	0.83	1964	50.7	20.9	28.4	17.9	4.5	0.5	11.5	1964	74.1	13.0	7.4	0.08
23	0.06	0.88	1949	49.3	10.4	40.3	17.9	3.0	0.2	2.8	1975	70.4	20.4	3.7	0.08
24	0.08	0.66	1952	44.8	13.4	41.8	25.4	4.5	0.5	4.7	1952	70.4	18.5	13.0	0.08
25	0.06	0.68	1975	50.7	14.9	34.3	17.9	3.0	0.4	4.5	1975	59.3	24.1	9.3	0.08
26	0.03	0.55	1981	52.2	20.9	26.9	9.0	1.5	0.2	4.2	1981	66.7	18.5	1.9	0.08
27	0.05	0.81	1940	59.7	7.5	32.8	14.9	3.0	0.2	2.6	1981	72.2	14.8	1.9	0.08
28	0.04	0.51	1963	52.2	25.4	22.4	14.9	1.5	0.1	3.0	1987	74.1	11.1	1.9	0.09
29	0.06	0.73	1967	46.3	17.9	35.8	13.4	3.0	0.5	8.2	1967	64.8	16.7	7.4	0.09
30	0.06	0.72	1948	46.3	16.4	37.3	19.4	1.5	0.3	5.2	1980	72.2	16.7	7.4	0.09
31	0.06	0.78	1936	46.3	19.4	34.3	16.4	1.5	0.1	4.1	1958	74.1	7.4	1.9	0.09

† Also occurred on earlier date(s).

April

Day	Average temperature			High	Extreme maximum			Extreme minimum				HDD	Degree Days		
	Max	Min	Mean		Year	Low	Year	High	Year	Low	Year		CDD	GDD40	GDD50
1	57.2	35.2	46.2	74	1932	35	1936	50	1968	19	1936	18	0	8	4
2	56.2	34.1	45.2	77	1943	37	1945	46	1961	14	1936	19	0	8	3
3	57.5	34.8	46.2	76	1961	35	1955	48†	1985	18	1945	18	0	9	4
4	59.0	34.9	47.0	76	1959	39	1955	49	1992	20	1955	18	0	9	4
5	59.7	36.2	48.0	82	1959	38	1936	52†	1991	15	1955	17	0	10	5
6	59.8	36.2	48.0	81	1930	35	1929	53	1991	24†	1961	16	0	10	5
7	59.3	36.0	47.6	84	1930	37	1929	50	1930	21	1929	17	0	10	5
8	58.8	35.6	47.2	81	1977	41	1933	58	1930	25†	1973	17	0	9	4
9	58.7	36.0	47.3	82	1960	37†	1933	52	1966	22	1933	17	0	9	4
10	58.5	35.5	47.0	76	1971	37	1974	51†	1992	19	1933	17	0	9	4
11	60.6	36.6	48.6	80	1934	38	1991	52	1985	21	1929	16	0	10	5
12	61.8	37.1	49.5	81	1936	39	1945	62	1992	26	1953	15	0	11	6
13	63.1	37.8	50.4	80	1988	44	1968	52	1934	24	1945	14	0	12	6
14	62.7	38.2	50.5	81	1962	44	1945	54	1935	25	1933	14	0	12	6
15	64.3	38.6	51.5	85	1985	47†	1995	55	1979	25	1945	13	0	13	7
16	64.4	38.2	51.3	84	1936	43	1976	61	1985	28†	1970	13	0	13	7
17	64.9	39.5	52.2	85	1987	41	1963	59	1985	24	1960	12	0	13	7
18	62.6	39.9	51.2	84	1962	40	1972	59	1946	27	1941	13	0	12	6
19	61.6	38.8	50.2	85	1962	41	1933	58	1994	24	1982	15	0	11	6
20	63.0	38.3	50.6	85†	1989	40	1968	53†	1994	24	1982	14	0	12	6
21	64.7	40.4	52.6	85	1994	36	1963	64	1989	22	1982	12	0	13	7
22	64.9	40.5	52.7	83	1934	44	1963	55	1980	26	1963	12	0	13	7
23	63.8	39.9	51.9	85	1934	43	1960	56†	1974	27	1968	13	0	13	7
24	64.2	40.4	52.3	85	1977	44†	1964	58	1930	27	1950	12	0	13	7
25	63.1	39.9	51.5	84	1946	44†	1984	58	1959	26	1950	13	0	12	6
26	62.8	39.2	51.0	84	1992	41	1986	55†	1981	27	1975	14	0	12	6
27	62.8	39.9	51.4	85	1987	36	1970	57	1992	30†	1972	13	0	12	6
28	64.7	40.5	52.6	85	1987	42	1937	56	1987	28	1966	12	0	13	7
29	64.6	40.5	52.6	86	1992	44	1970	59	1987	29	1990	12	0	13	7
30	63.7	40.2	52.0	84	1959	40†	1967	56	1934	28†	1972	13	0	13	7

	Total precipitation					Percent of years with precipitation			Total snowfall			Percent with snowfall			
Day	Avg	High	Year	None	Trace	.01 or more	.10 or more	.50 or more	Avg	High	Year	None	.1 or more	2.0 or more	ETo
1	0.07	0.95	1984	49.3	14.9	35.8	20.9	3.0	0.4	6.0†	1984	72.2	14.8	7.4	0.11
2	0.11	1.57	1986	44.8	16.4	38.8	22.4	7.5	0.4	9.6	1955	72.2	16.7	7.4	0.11
3	0.04	0.73	1994	56.7	17.9	25.4	9.0	1.5	0.2	7.2	1983	77.8	9.3	3.7	0.12
4	0.03	0.67	1947	67.2	10.4	22.4	9.0	1.5	0.1	2.7	1982	83.3	11.1	1.9	0.12
5	0.05	0.76	1941	61.2	14.9	23.9	16.4	3.0	0.0	0.0†	1995	90.7	0.0	0.0	0.12
6	0.06	0.62	1929	53.7	16.4	29.9	22.4	1.5	0.2	3.1	1968	81.5	13.0	3.7	0.12
7	0.05	0.58	1946	52.2	16.4	31.3	9.0	3.0	0.0	0.5	1982	79.6	9.3	0.0	0.12
8	0.06	0.94	1949	58.2	13.4	28.4	16.4	3.0	0.0	0.9	1984	81.5	3.7	0.0	0.12
9	0.11	1.19	1974	55.2	7.5	37.3	26.9	4.5	0.4	9.0	1929	79.6	13.0	7.4	0.12
10	0.08	1.54	1974	52.2	14.9	32.8	20.9	3.0	0.4	11.8	1974	77.8	9.3	5.6	0.12
11	0.03	0.27	1970	59.7	9.0	31.3	10.4	0.0	0.1	2.3	1991	81.5	9.3	1.9	0.13
12	0.05	0.65	1944	61.2	16.4	22.4	14.9	3.0	0.2	3.8	1974	83.3	13.0	3.7	0.13
13	0.03	0.98	1972	64.2	13.4	22.4	7.5	1.5	0.2	7.9	1972	85.2	9.3	1.9	0.13
14	0.06	1.01	1952	58.2	11.9	29.9	17.9	1.5	0.1	3.0	1995	87.0	7.4	1.9	0.13
15	0.03	0.51	1969	67.2	13.4	19.4	11.9	1.5	0.0	2.2	1967	87.0	1.9	1.9	0.14
16	0.06	1.12	1941	62.7	16.4	20.9	13.4	4.5	0.0	1.4	1967	87.0	3.7	0.0	0.14
17	0.06	0.89	1953	53.7	14.9	31.3	14.9	3.0	0.0	1.3	1963	88.9	1.9	0.0	0.14
18	0.07	1.07	1959	49.3	13.4	37.3	14.9	4.5	0.2	6.5	1972	83.3	13.0	1.9	0.13
19	0.06	0.95	1984	55.2	6.0	38.8	17.9	3.0	0.1	2.1	1987	72.2	14.8	1.9	0.13
20	0.08	0.90	1932	56.7	13.4	29.9	20.9	7.5	0.2	5.4	1968	77.8	9.3	3.7	0.13
21	0.06	0.56	1962	56.7	7.5	35.8	16.4	3.0	0.2	4.5	1968	85.2	9.3	5.6	0.14
22	0.06	1.00	1957	46.3	19.4	34.3	17.9	1.5	0.1	1.8	1970	79.6	7.4	0.0	0.14
23	0.10	1.46	1958	52.2	17.9	29.9	17.9	4.5	0.3	10.1	1958	88.9	5.6	3.7	0.13
24	0.06	0.70	1945	53.7	16.4	29.9	19.4	6.0	0.1	1.6	1958	88.9	9.3	0.0	0.14
25	0.12	1.62	1976	35.8	19.4	44.8	25.4	7.5	0.4	8.5	1975	72.2	16.7	5.6	0.13
26	0.07	0.69	1962	47.8	14.9	37.3	17.9	3.0	0.4	8.1	1955	79.6	14.8	5.6	0.13
27	0.06	0.66	1970	43.3	19.4	37.3	16.4	3.0	0.3	6.3	1991	85.2	7.4	5.6	0.13
28	0.08	0.62†	1970	49.3	10.4	40.3	20.9	9.0	0.2	6.4	1970	83.3	7.4	1.9	0.14
29	0.09	0.91	1951	46.3	13.4	40.3	26.9	4.5	0.3	5.8	1967	79.6	9.3	5.6	0.14
30	0.07	0.50	1953	52.2	16.4	31.3	19.4	1.5	0.1	3.5	1970	88.9	9.3	1.9	0.13

† Also occurred on earlier date(s).

SALT LAKE CITY NWSFO
Daily Data Summary

May

| Day | Average temperature | | | Extreme maximum | | | | Extreme minimum | | | | HDD | Degree Days | | |
---	Max	Min	Mean	High	Year	Low	Year	High	Year	Low	Year		CDD	GDD40	GDD50
1	66.7	40.7	53.7	87	1981	45	1954	56	1943	27†	1967	11	0	14	8
2	67.1	41.6	54.3	91	1947	39	1964	60	1985	28	1967	11	0	14	8
3	68.9	43.2	56.0	91	1947	44	1950	64	1985	28†	1964	9	0	16	9
4	69.2	42.6	55.9	88	1947	49	1950	59	1962	31	1964	9	0	16	9
5	68.4	43.2	55.8	88†	1966	45	1978	59	1979	28	1961	9	0	15	9
6	68.8	43.8	56.3	91	1947	46	1965	57	1980	25	1965	9	0	16	9
7	69.0	44.1	56.6	89†	1947	45	1975	61	1947	27	1965	9	0	16	10
8	69.0	44.2	56.6	87†	1962	46	1930	59†	1989	30	1931	9	0	16	10
9	69.4	44.3	56.8	87	1954	46	1933	62	1962	28	1930	8	0	16	10
10	69.1	44.3	56.7	92	1961	47	1983	59	1954	31	1948	8	0	16	9
11	68.6	43.7	56.1	91	1960	44	1983	55†	1994	32†	1933	9	0	16	9
12	69.0	43.4	56.2	92	1960	45	1942	63	1960	32	1967	9	0	16	9
13	71.3	44.7	58.0	92	1959	50	1942	62	1993	30	1967	7	0	17	11
14	72.2	45.3	58.8	89	1936	53	1968	66	1984	33	1967	7	1	18	11
15	71.7	45.5	58.6	88	1934	50	1955	62	1987	32	1955	7	1	18	11
16	71.2	45.6	58.4	90	1948	48	1977	64	1987	30	1955	7	0	17	11
17	71.9	45.9	58.9	89	1948	48	1977	60	1948	33†	1971	6	0	18	11
18	73.1	46.1	59.6	92	1932	45	1977	62	1992	33†	1971	6	1	18	12
19	72.7	45.1	58.9	93	1958	53	1945	59†	1993	31	1960	6	0	18	11
20	72.9	46.4	59.6	92	1958	43	1975	63	1954	33	1959	6	1	18	12
21	74.3	46.5	60.4	86†	1979	51	1962	62	1958	35	1959	5	0	19	12
22	73.7	46.8	60.3	89†	1989	54†	1986	59	1963	33	1960	5	1	19	12
23	75.5	47.9	61.7	91†	1967	53	1995	62	1934	30	1966	4	1	20	13
24	75.5	48.0	61.7	90†	1988	56	1939	62†	1973	35	1930	4	1	20	13
25	76.0	47.8	61.9	92	1961	55	1980	63	1993	32	1975	4	1	20	13
26	76.5	49.4	63.0	92	1958	48	1929	66	1988	34†	1975	4	2	21	14
27	76.6	49.4	63.0	93	1951	57	1954	67†	1985	33	1929	4	2	21	14
28	76.4	49.1	62.7	92†	1961	55	1935	63†	1993	32	1954	4	1	21	14
29	76.6	49.4	63.0	91	1939	55	1964	62	1943	37	1946	3	1	21	14
30	75.6	48.9	62.3	93	1984	52†	1988	62	1984	34	1979	4	1	20	13
31	75.0	48.0	61.5	93	1956	54	1955	62	1993	36	1978	4	1	20	13

| Day | Total precipitation | | | Percent of years with precipitation | | | | Total snowfall | | | Percent with snowfall | | | ETo |
---	Avg	High	Year	None	Trace	.01 or more	.10 or more	.50 or more	Avg	High	Year	None	.1 or more	2.0 or more	
1	0.03	0.57	1987	58.8	11.8	29.4	11.8	1.5	0.0	0.9	1988	89.3	1.8	0.0	0.17
2	0.06	0.82	1938	63.2	13.2	23.5	13.2	4.4	0.1	4.9	1964	90.9	1.8	1.8	0.17
3	0.04	0.56	1991	55.9	22.1	22.1	10.3	4.4	0.0	2.2	1950	92.7	1.8	1.8	0.17
4	0.06	0.92	1993	60.3	11.8	27.9	16.2	2.9	0.1	4.0	1975	92.7	5.5	1.8	0.18
5	0.07	1.12	1965	54.4	17.6	27.9	13.2	2.9	0.2	5.3	1965	89.1	7.3	5.5	0.17
6	0.05	0.99	1993	44.1	22.1	33.8	14.7	2.9	0.0	1.1	1975	83.6	1.8	0.0	0.17
7	0.05	0.57	1933	54.4	13.2	32.4	16.2	1.5	0.0	0.0†	1995	92.7	0.0	0.0	0.17
8	0.06	1.03	1986	51.5	11.8	36.8	11.8	4.4	0.0	1.0†	1993	83.6	3.6	0.0	0.17
9	0.07	0.87	1992	58.8	16.2	25.0	17.6	4.4	0.0	0.0†	1995	92.7	0.0	0.0	0.17
10	0.07	1.03	1985	50.0	17.6	32.4	14.7	4.4	0.0	0.1	1953	96.4	1.8	0.0	0.17
11	0.06	1.20	1983	54.4	20.6	25.0	14.7	2.9	0.1	5.0	1983	92.7	3.6	1.8	0.17
12	0.07	0.69	1995	63.2	7.4	29.4	16.2	5.9	0.0	0.0†	1995	89.1	0.0	0.0	0.17
13	0.04	1.03	1957	61.8	17.6	20.6	8.8	1.5	0.0	0.0†	1995	98.2	0.0	0.0	0.18
14	0.05	0.69	1977	55.9	20.6	23.5	13.2	1.5	0.0	0.0†	1995	98.2	0.0	0.0	0.19
15	0.07	0.76	1981	52.9	14.7	32.4	23.5	2.9	0.1	2.9	1955	98.2	1.8	1.8	0.18
16	0.07	1.55	1942	52.9	14.7	32.4	14.7	2.9	0.0	0.0†	1995	96.4	0.0	0.0	0.18
17	0.06	0.86	1944	63.2	13.2	23.5	14.7	5.9	0.0	1.4	1971	94.5	3.6	0.0	0.18
18	0.04	1.00	1977	64.7	14.7	20.6	10.3	1.5	0.0	1.0	1960	94.5	3.6	0.0	0.19
19	0.06	1.08	1957	69.1	5.9	25.0	14.7	2.9	0.0	0.0†	1995	98.2	0.0	0.0	0.19
20	0.04	1.00	1949	55.9	19.1	25.0	14.7	1.5	0.0	0.0†	1995	94.5	0.0	0.0	0.19
21	0.07	0.89	1992	52.9	20.6	26.5	14.7	2.9	0.0	0.0†	1995	96.4	0.0	0.0	0.19
22	0.04	0.55	1976	55.9	19.1	25.0	13.2	1.5	0.0	0.0†	1995	96.4	0.0	0.0	0.19
23	0.03	0.53	1968	57.4	19.1	23.5	8.8	1.5	0.0	0.0†	1995	98.2	0.0	0.0	0.20
24	0.03	0.30	1980	55.9	16.2	27.9	16.2	0.0	0.0	0.0†	1995	96.4	0.0	0.0	0.20
25	0.04	1.27	1973	60.3	17.6	22.1	8.8	1.5	0.0	0.0†	1995	98.2	0.0	0.0	0.20
26	0.05	0.59	1977	55.9	20.6	23.5	13.2	2.9	0.0	0.0†	1995	98.2	0.0	0.0	0.20
27	0.04	0.60	1959	57.4	11.8	30.9	11.8	1.5	0.0	0.0†	1995	96.4	0.0	0.0	0.20
28	0.05	0.78	1935	58.8	19.1	22.1	10.3	2.9	0.0	0.0†	1995	98.2	0.0	0.0	0.20
29	0.06	0.66	1988	58.8	19.1	22.1	14.7	5.9	0.0	0.0†	1995	100.0	0.0	0.0	0.20
30	0.07	0.80	1937	52.9	20.6	26.5	16.2	4.4	0.0	0.0†	1995	100.0	0.0	0.0	0.20
31	0.06	0.56	1947	51.5	16.2	32.4	22.1	2.9	0.0	0.0†	1995	100.0	0.0	0.0	0.20

† Also occurred on earlier date(s).

SALT LAKE CITY NWSFO
Daily Data Summary

June

Day	Average temperature				Extreme maximum				Extreme minimum					Degree Days		
	Max	Min	Mean	High	Year	Low	Year	High	Year	Low	Year	HDD	CDD	GDD40	GDD50
1	75.2	48.4	61.8	92	1977	51	1955	60	1940	38	1969	4	1	20	13
2	76.4	48.5	62.4	89†	1992	52	1943	62	1986	35	1954	4	1	20	13
3	76.9	49.5	63.2	94	1994	56	1955	63	1968	35	1929	3	2	21	14
4	77.6	50.5	64.1	96	1988	52	1943	66†	1988	39	1962	3	2	22	14
5	78.2	50.1	64.1	93†	1988	60	1945	68	1987	35	1937	3	2	22	14
6	78.1	51.0	64.6	95	1959	52	1932	67	1950	37	1954	3	2	22	15
7	78.0	51.2	64.6	100	1985	52	1993	64	1985	35	1962	3	3	22	15
8	77.9	51.5	64.7	96	1961	56†	1995	64†	1985	39†	1979	3	3	22	15
9	79.2	51.4	65.3	101	1973	57	1941	64	1956	36	1950	2	3	22	15
10	79.3	51.9	65.6	95†	1961	59†	1970	65†	1973	40	1947	2	3	23	15
11	80.7	51.6	66.2	96	1961	49	1947	66	1992	40†	1947	2	3	23	16
12	82.4	52.7	67.6	98	1979	63	1928	68	1994	41	1970	1	4	23	17
13	82.0	53.6	67.8	98†	1979	62†	1981	70	1959	40†	1993	1	4	24	17
14	82.2	52.9	67.5	101	1974	60†	1945	69	1959	39	1981	2	4	23	17
15	82.2	53.2	67.7	102	1974	61	1957	71	1974	39	1945	1	4	24	17
16	82.3	53.5	67.9	100	1940	62	1957	72	1974	40†	1957	1	4	24	17
17	81.6	53.1	67.3	103	1940	50	1939	72	1933	37	1939	2	4	23	16
18	84.3	53.9	69.1	102	1940	54	1975	70	1986	37	1928	1	5	24	18
19	84.7	55.4	70.1	101	1940	62	1975	72	1994	40†	1973	1	6	25	19
20	85.5	54.4	70.0	101	1936	66	1975	73	1940	41	1929	0	5	25	19
21	85.1	55.4	70.2	104	1961	58	1948	68†	1994	38	1960	1	6	25	18
22	86.8	56.0	71.4	101†	1961	60	1948	74	1937	42	1960	0	7	26	19
23	87.2	57.3	72.2	100†	1990	67	1993	71	1990	44	1964	0	7	26	20
24	86.3	56.3	71.3	102	1988	64	1952	72	1959	43	1993	0	7	26	19
25	87.1	56.3	71.7	102	1994	62	1969	75	1988	40†	1953	0	7	26	20
26	86.9	56.5	71.7	103	1970	63	1942	75	1981	42	1978	0	7	26	20
27	87.7	57.5	72.6	102	1958	61	1942	75	1981	43	1942	0	8	26	20
28	88.8	56.8	72.8	102	1961	65	1959	74	1986	40	1945	0	8	26	20
29	87.7	57.9	72.8	104	1979	64	1959	72	1935	42	1968	0	8	27	20
30	87.7	56.7	72.2	103	1990	73†	1992	75	1990	40	1968	0	7	26	20

	Total precipitation			Percent of years with precipitation				Total snowfall			Percent with snowfall			
Day	Avg	High	Year	None	Trace	.01 or more	.10 or more	.50 or more	Avg	High	Year	None	.1 or more	2.0 or more	ETo
1	0.05	0.86	1943	44.1	20.6	35.3	13.2	1.5	0.0	0.0†	1995	96.4	0.0	0.0	0.21
2	0.05	0.82	1991	57.4	14.7	27.9	13.2	2.9	0.0	0.0†	1995	96.4	0.0	0.0	0.21
3	0.04	0.58	1944	51.5	23.5	25.0	11.8	1.5	0.0	0.0†	1995	100.0	0.0	0.0	0.21
4	0.05	0.54	1943	52.9	19.1	27.9	14.7	1.5	0.0	0.0†	1995	100.0	0.0	0.0	0.21
5	0.06	0.80	1954	57.4	19.1	23.5	11.8	5.9	0.0	0.0†	1995	96.4	0.0	0.0	0.22
6	0.04	0.43	1932	48.5	25.0	26.5	11.8	0.0	0.0	0.0†	1995	100.0	0.0	0.0	0.22
7	0.06	0.94	1964	57.4	13.2	29.4	20.6	1.5	0.0	0.0†	1995	94.5	0.0	0.0	0.21
8	0.04	0.94	1968	57.4	14.7	27.9	10.3	1.5	0.0	0.0†	1995	98.2	0.0	0.0	0.21
9	0.05	0.98	1970	55.9	13.2	30.9	16.2	1.5	0.0	0.0†	1995	98.2	0.0	0.0	0.22
10	0.04	0.78	1945	61.8	16.2	22.1	11.8	1.5	0.0	0.0†	1995	100.0	0.0	0.0	0.22
11	0.04	1.26	1947	70.6	16.2	13.2	7.4	1.5	0.0	0.0†	1995	100.0	0.0	0.0	0.23
12	0.02	0.71	1967	66.2	11.8	22.1	2.9	1.5	0.0	0.0†	1995	100.0	0.0	0.0	0.24
13	0.02	0.43	1976	69.1	14.7	16.2	8.8	0.0	0.0	0.0†	1995	98.2	0.0	0.0	0.23
14	0.02	0.31	1955	72.1	13.2	14.7	10.3	0.0	0.0	0.0†	1995	98.2	0.0	0.0	0.23
15	0.03	0.53	1956	69.1	14.7	16.2	8.8	1.5	0.0	0.0†	1995	100.0	0.0	0.0	0.23
16	0.02	0.43	1957	66.2	13.2	20.6	7.4	0.0	0.0	0.0†	1995	100.0	0.0	0.0	0.23
17	0.05	0.63	1939	63.2	19.1	17.6	11.8	4.4	0.0	0.0†	1995	98.2	0.0	0.0	0.23
18	0.01	0.32	1975	75.0	11.8	13.2	4.4	0.0	0.0	0.0†	1995	100.0	0.0	0.0	0.24
19	0.01	0.41	1975	73.5	14.7	11.8	2.9	0.0	0.0	0.0†	1995	100.0	0.0	0.0	0.24
20	0.01	0.40	1967	73.5	14.7	11.8	4.4	0.0	0.0	0.0†	1995	100.0	0.0	0.0	0.25
21	0.04	1.75	1948	70.6	16.2	13.2	7.4	1.5	0.0	0.0†	1995	100.0	0.0	0.0	0.25
22	0.01	0.25	1948	73.5	14.7	11.8	1.5	0.0	0.0	0.0†	1995	100.0	0.0	0.0	0.26
23	0.01	0.27	1967	72.1	19.1	8.8	2.9	0.0	0.0	0.0†	1995	100.0	0.0	0.0	0.25
24	0.07	1.08	1969	73.5	10.3	16.2	8.8	7.4	0.0	0.0†	1995	98.2	0.0	0.0	0.25
25	0.02	0.36	1969	73.5	16.2	10.3	5.9	0.0	0.0	0.0†	1995	100.0	0.0	0.0	0.26
26	0.03	0.42	1965	73.5	11.8	14.7	7.4	0.0	0.0	0.0†	1995	100.0	0.0	0.0	0.25
27	0.01	0.42	1959	72.1	17.6	10.3	2.9	0.0	0.0	0.0†	1995	100.0	0.0	0.0	0.26
28	0.01	0.39	1959	73.5	23.5	2.9	2.9	0.0	0.0	0.0†	1995	100.0	0.0	0.0	0.27
29	0.01	0.22	1971	72.1	19.1	8.8	1.5	0.0	0.0	0.0†	1995	98.2	0.0	0.0	0.26
30	0.00	0.11	1940	79.4	13.2	7.4	1.5	0.0	0.0	0.0†	1995	100.0	0.0	0.0	0.26

† Also occurred on earlier date(s).

SALT LAKE CITY NWSFO
Daily Data Summary

July

| Day | Average temperature | | | High | Extreme maximum | | | | Extreme minimum | | | HDD | Degree Days | | |
	Max	Min	Mean		Year	Low	Year	High	Year	Low	Year		CDD	GDD40	GDD50
1	89.4	57.7	73.5	101†	1990	62	1992	77	1990	40	1968	0	8	27	21
2	90.6	58.8	74.7	101	1990	73	1938	70†	1950	43	1968	0	9	27	22
3	89.9	58.7	74.3	101†	1985	70	1993	73	1988	49†	1974	0	9	27	21
4	90.1	59.0	74.6	102†	1989	72	1993	71	1988	47	1938	0	9	27	21
5	92.0	58.7	75.3	104	1973	65	1982	72†	1992	44	1932	0	10	27	21
6	91.0	60.8	75.9	102	1973	73	1994	74†	1981	44	1938	0	11	28	22
7	91.0	60.3	75.7	102	1976	76†	1955	73	1985	40	1928	0	10	28	22
8	92.2	60.8	76.5	101	1976	76	1937	74	1963	45	1955	0	11	28	23
9	92.9	62.3	77.6	102†	1994	78	1946	73	1989	48	1959	0	12	29	23
10	91.4	62.5	77.0	104	1973	71	1983	79	1956	50	1946	0	12	29	23
11	91.2	61.1	76.2	103	1976	72	1936	76	1981	48†	1983	0	11	29	23
12	91.8	60.8	76.3	103	1934	74	1992	74	1980	49†	1951	0	11	28	23
13	92.8	61.1	76.9	102†	1939	74	1962	69†	1982	47	1943	0	11	29	23
14	93.7	62.4	78.0	103	1939	78	1962	77	1931	49	1932	0	13	29	24
15	93.7	63.0	78.3	103	1960	75	1983	75†	1991	52	1962	0	13	29	24
16	93.3	62.8	78.1	103	1960	77	1993	75†	1991	52†	1956	0	13	29	24
17	93.0	62.3	77.6	103	1960	78	1986	73†	1991	53†	1943	0	12	29	23
18	93.4	62.9	78.2	104	1960	75	1987	73	1977	54	1939	0	13	29	24
19	92.8	63.1	78.0	104†	1960	70	1973	71†	1984	52	1928	0	12	29	24
20	92.7	63.0	77.8	105	1960	80†	1951	73	1960	50	1932	0	12	29	24
21	92.2	62.0	77.1	106	1931	80†	1993	75	1966	50†	1949	0	12	29	23
22	92.7	63.1	77.9	103	1931	74	1973	75	1982	47	1954	0	12	30	24
23	93.4	63.4	78.4	103	1931	62	1993	72†	1989	47	1954	0	13	30	24
24	93.2	64.0	78.6	105	1931	74	1993	77	1953	50	1954	0	13	30	24
25	93.5	64.4	79.0	103	1933	70	1941	77	1953	51	1964	0	13	30	25
26	93.6	63.7	78.6	107	1960	73	1993	74	1984	54†	1993	0	13	30	24
27	93.9	63.5	78.7	105	1994	81	1993	74	1960	48	1963	0	13	30	24
28	94.2	64.3	79.3	106	1934	71	1948	77	1931	51	1929	0	14	30	24
29	93.5	64.5	79.0	106	1995	77	1950	75†	1976	45	1948	0	14	30	25
30	92.7	63.6	78.2	103	1934	77†	1950	74	1935	48	1950	0	13	30	24
31	92.3	63.5	77.9	102†	1990	78	1975	77	1989	45	1950	0	12	30	24

| Day | Total precipitation | | | None | Trace | Percent of years with precipitation | | | Total snowfall | | | Percent with snowfall | | | ETo |
	Avg	High	Year			.01 or more	.10 or more	.50 or more	Avg	High	Year	None	.1 or more	2.0 or more	
1	0.02	0.85	1980	77.6	13.4	9.0	6.0	1.5	0.0	0.0†	1995	100.0	0.0	0.0	0.26
2	0.01	0.24	1949	74.6	16.4	9.0	3.0	0.0	0.0	0.0†	1995	100.0	0.0	0.0	0.26
3	0.00	0.09	1993	73.1	16.4	10.4	0.0	0.0	0.0	0.0†	1995	100.0	0.0	0.0	0.26
4	0.02	0.46	1961	68.7	20.9	10.4	4.5	0.0	0.0	0.0†	1995	100.0	0.0	0.0	0.26
5	0.01	0.41	1982	77.6	14.9	7.5	1.5	0.0	0.0	0.0†	1995	100.0	0.0	0.0	0.27
6	0.01	0.52	1937	73.5	16.2	10.3	4.4	1.5	0.0	0.0†	1995	100.0	0.0	0.0	0.26
7	0.01	0.25	1984	73.1	13.4	13.4	3.0	0.0	0.0	0.0†	1995	100.0	0.0	0.0	0.26
8	0.01	0.27	1980	76.5	7.4	16.2	8.8	0.0	0.0	0.0†	1995	100.0	0.0	0.0	0.27
9	0.02	0.52	1950	69.1	19.1	11.8	5.9	1.5	0.0	0.0†	1995	96.4	0.0	0.0	0.27
10	0.02	0.46	1936	70.6	13.2	16.2	5.9	0.0	0.0	0.0†	1995	100.0	0.0	0.0	0.26
11	0.01	0.29	1930	69.1	14.7	16.2	2.9	0.0	0.0	0.0†	1995	100.0	0.0	0.0	0.26
12	0.01	0.30	1989	73.1	11.9	14.9	3.0	0.0	0.0	0.0†	1995	100.0	0.0	0.0	0.27
13	0.04	2.28	1962	79.1	11.9	9.0	6.0	1.5	0.0	0.0†	1995	100.0	0.0	0.0	0.27
14	0.01	0.18	1959	71.6	17.9	10.4	4.5	0.0	0.0	0.0†	1995	100.0	0.0	0.0	0.27
15	0.01	0.21	1942	70.1	14.9	14.9	4.5	0.0	0.0	0.0†	1995	100.0	0.0	0.0	0.27
16	0.03	0.94	1967	66.2	19.1	14.7	5.9	2.9	0.0	0.0†	1995	100.0	0.0	0.0	0.27
17	0.02	0.69	1976	69.1	13.2	17.6	4.4	1.5	0.0	0.0†	1995	100.0	0.0	0.0	0.27
18	0.02	0.47	1965	69.1	17.6	13.2	4.4	0.0	0.0	0.0†	1995	100.0	0.0	0.0	0.27
19	0.03	0.90	1971	66.2	14.7	19.1	7.4	1.5	0.0	0.0†	1995	100.0	0.0	0.0	0.27
20	0.01	0.24	1954	68.7	17.9	13.4	4.5	0.0	0.0	0.0†	1995	100.0	0.0	0.0	0.27
21	0.04	0.59†	1987	65.7	16.4	17.9	10.4	4.5	0.0	0.0†	1995	100.0	0.0	0.0	0.26
22	0.02	0.31	1970	67.2	14.9	17.9	7.5	0.0	0.0	0.0†	1995	100.0	0.0	0.0	0.26
23	0.02	0.65	1993	64.2	17.9	17.9	3.0	1.5	0.0	0.0†	1995	100.0	0.0	0.0	0.27
24	0.04	0.75	1955	61.2	22.4	16.4	10.4	4.5	0.0	0.0†	1995	100.0	0.0	0.0	0.27
25	0.02	0.23	1965	59.7	20.9	19.4	7.5	0.0	0.0	0.0†	1995	98.2	0.0	0.0	0.27
26	0.03	0.53	1941	59.7	23.9	16.4	11.9	1.5	0.0	0.0†	1995	98.2	0.0	0.0	0.27
27	0.01	0.57	1951	70.1	19.4	10.4	1.5	1.5	0.0	0.0†	1995	98.2	0.0	0.0	0.27
28	0.04	1.25	1982	71.6	14.9	13.4	6.0	3.0	0.0	0.0†	1995	98.2	0.0	0.0	0.27
29	0.04	1.36	1969	64.2	16.4	19.4	7.5	3.0	0.0	2.1	1931	98.2	1.8	1.8	0.27
30	0.04	1.65	1945	55.2	23.9	20.9	9.0	1.5	0.1	4.7	1931	98.2	1.8	1.8	0.26
31	0.03	0.75	1952	57.4	25.0	17.6	10.3	2.9	0.0	0.3	1931	98.2	1.8	0.0	0.26

† Also occurred on earlier date(s).

SALT LAKE CITY NWSFO
Daily Data Summary

August

Day	Average temperature Max	Min	Mean	High	Extreme maximum Year	Low	Year	High	Extreme minimum Year	Low	Year	HDD	Degree Days CDD	GDD40	GDD50
1	92.0	63.5	77.8	102	1979	79	1965	74	1989	49	1932	0	12	30	24
2	92.0	61.8	76.9	103	1992	79	1928	72†	1981	45	1928	0	11	29	23
3	92.7	61.3	77.0	102†	1994	77	1951	73	1992	47	1928	0	12	29	23
4	92.0	62.3	77.1	106	1994	76	1951	70†	1994	48	1944	0	12	29	23
5	92.0	63.1	77.6	105	1994	78	1962	74	1994	50	1928	0	12	30	24
6	92.1	62.4	77.3	101	1995	74	1939	75	1975	48	1950	0	12	29	24
7	92.6	62.4	77.5	100†	1995	79	1939	76	1995	49	1928	0	12	29	24
8	92.2	62.1	77.1	103	1990	77	1995	73†	1992	49†	1976	0	12	29	23
9	92.1	61.6	76.9	103	1940	77†	1985	73	1990	51	1931	0	11	29	23
10	92.8	61.7	77.3	101†	1972	76	1947	72	1983	50	1939	0	12	29	23
11	91.6	62.2	76.9	102	1972	72	1985	74	1991	48†	1962	0	11	29	23
12	91.1	61.3	76.2	102	1940	74	1930	72	1980	49	1935	0	11	29	23
13	91.2	60.6	75.9	102	1937	74	1930	70†	1992	50†	1969	0	10	28	22
14	90.4	61.5	76.0	100†	1971	68	1978	72	1992	47	1938	0	11	29	23
15	90.5	61.5	76.0	101	1962	68	1968	72	1943	49†	1978	0	11	29	23
16	90.2	61.4	75.8	100	1994	72	1960	73	1995	48†	1976	0	10	29	23
17	90.3	61.4	75.8	100†	1967	69	1978	73	1986	48	1968	0	10	29	23
18	90.0	61.5	75.8	99	1932	70†	1968	72	1934	45†	1968	0	10	29	23
19	89.1	60.5	74.8	99	1961	66	1980	72	1932	47	1978	0	9	28	22
20	89.7	60.9	75.3	103	1960	71	1964	74	1961	40†	1964	0	10	28	23
21	88.9	60.3	74.6	102	1960	70†	1968	74	1960	43	1964	0	9	28	22
22	88.8	59.8	74.3	99	1991	60	1968	73	1937	45	1933	0	9	28	22
23	88.8	58.7	73.7	99	1967	70	1968	70†	1995	44†	1933	0	9	27	21
24	87.8	58.6	73.2	99†	1994	63	1989	70	1955	40	1928	0	8	27	21
25	88.2	57.8	73.0	100	1985	71	1933	70	1981	44†	1989	0	8	27	21
26	87.9	58.6	73.2	101	1985	70	1977	74	1981	42	1992	0	8	27	21
27	86.9	58.1	72.5	99	1937	69	1977	70	1985	42	1964	0	8	27	21
28	87.5	58.2	72.9	97†	1961	75	1977	70	1984	42	1964	0	8	27	21
29	87.0	57.4	72.2	99	1948	68	1964	68	1981	37	1964	0	7	27	20
30	86.8	56.7	71.8	100	1954	61	1932	68	1983	38	1964	0	7	26	20
31	85.7	56.2	71.0	98	1950	69	1932	67†	1983	37	1965	0	6	26	20

Day	Total precipitation Avg	High	Year	None	Percent of years with precipitation Trace	.01 or more	.10 or more	.50 or more	Total snowfall Avg	High	Year	Percent with snowfall None	.1 or more	2.0 or more	ETo
1	0.01	0.28	1960	66.2	16.2	17.6	2.9	0.0	0.0	0.0†	1995	100.0	0.0	0.0	0.23
2	0.05	1.72	1930	67.6	16.2	16.2	10.3	1.5	0.0	0.0†	1995	100.0	0.0	0.0	0.24
3	0.03	1.22	1945	66.2	22.1	11.8	7.4	1.5	0.0	0.0†	1995	100.0	0.0	0.0	0.24
4	0.06	1.62	1954	60.3	16.2	23.5	8.8	2.9	0.0	0.0†	1995	98.2	0.0	0.0	0.23
5	0.03	0.48	1977	61.8	19.1	19.1	7.4	0.0	0.0	0.0†	1995	100.0	0.0	0.0	0.23
6	0.02	0.40	1946	66.2	13.2	20.6	4.4	0.0	0.0	0.0†	1995	100.0	0.0	0.0	0.23
7	0.01	0.16	1979	72.1	17.6	10.3	4.4	0.0	0.0	0.0†	1995	100.0	0.0	0.0	0.24
8	0.03	0.94	1968	67.6	14.7	17.6	8.8	2.9	0.0	0.0†	1995	98.2	0.0	0.0	0.24
9	0.02	0.37	1930	67.6	14.7	17.6	8.8	0.0	0.0	0.0†	1995	100.0	0.0	0.0	0.24
10	0.02	0.69	1947	67.6	20.6	11.8	5.9	1.5	0.0	0.0†	1995	100.0	0.0	0.0	0.24
11	0.02	0.27	1993	52.9	29.4	17.6	7.4	0.0	0.0	0.0†	1995	98.2	0.0	0.0	0.23
12	0.02	0.50	1930	61.8	14.7	23.5	7.4	1.5	0.0	0.0†	1995	100.0	0.0	0.0	0.23
13	0.02	0.72	1978	72.1	11.8	16.2	4.4	1.5	0.0	0.0†	1995	100.0	0.0	0.0	0.23
14	0.03	0.85	1968	57.4	14.7	27.9	7.4	1.5	0.0	0.0†	1995	100.0	0.0	0.0	0.23
15	0.03	0.54	1961	55.9	17.6	26.5	11.8	1.5	0.0	0.0†	1995	98.2	0.0	0.0	0.23
16	0.03	0.38	1984	64.7	11.8	23.5	10.3	0.0	0.0	0.0†	1995	100.0	0.0	0.0	0.23
17	0.04	0.70	1983	57.4	22.1	20.6	7.4	1.5	0.0	0.0†	1995	100.0	0.0	0.0	0.23
18	0.04	0.90	1983	60.3	17.6	22.1	11.8	1.5	0.0	0.0†	1995	100.0	0.0	0.0	0.23
19	0.04	1.42	1945	51.5	25.0	23.5	8.8	2.9	0.0	0.0†	1995	100.0	0.0	0.0	0.22
20	0.03	0.97	1986	55.9	29.4	14.7	4.4	1.5	0.0	0.0†	1995	100.0	0.0	0.0	0.23
21	0.03	1.05	1965	60.3	22.1	17.6	10.3	1.5	0.0	0.0†	1995	100.0	0.0	0.0	0.22
22	0.04	1.04	1960	60.3	23.5	16.2	7.4	2.9	0.0	0.0†	1995	100.0	0.0	0.0	0.22
23	0.02	0.45	1976	76.5	10.3	13.2	7.4	0.0	0.0	0.0†	1995	100.0	0.0	0.0	0.23
24	0.02	0.30	1949	66.2	16.2	17.6	10.3	0.0	0.0	0.0†	1995	96.4	0.0	0.0	0.22
25	0.01	0.16	1984	69.1	11.8	19.1	1.5	0.0	0.0	0.0†	1995	100.0	0.0	0.0	0.22
26	0.05	1.96	1932	63.2	17.6	19.1	2.9	2.9	0.0	0.0†	1995	100.0	0.0	0.0	0.22
27	0.02	0.33	1970	69.1	13.2	17.6	7.4	0.0	0.0	0.0†	1995	100.0	0.0	0.0	0.22
28	0.02	0.51	1971	60.3	19.1	20.6	7.4	1.5	0.0	0.0†	1995	100.0	0.0	0.0	0.22
29	0.05	0.91	1957	70.6	8.8	20.6	8.8	4.4	0.0	0.0†	1995	100.0	0.0	0.0	0.22
30	0.01	0.15	1963	73.5	17.6	8.8	1.5	0.0	0.0	0.0†	1995	100.0	0.0	0.0	0.22
31	0.01	0.32	1963	75.0	14.7	10.3	5.9	0.0	0.0	0.0†	1995	98.2	0.0	0.0	0.21

† Also occurred on earlier date(s).

Utah's Weather and Climate

September

Day	Average temperature			High	Extreme maximum			High	Extreme minimum			HDD	Degree Days		
---	Max	Min	Mean	High	Year	Low	Year	High	Year	Low	Year	HDD	CDD	GDD40	GDD50
1	86.2	56.0	71.1	98	1995	57	1973	71	1929	43†	1965	0	6	26	19
2	85.4	56.3	70.8	98	1947	64†	1973	70	1990	41	1964	0	6	26	19
3	84.8	55.0	69.9	96	1950	65†	1971	67†	1990	39†	1964	0	5	25	19
4	85.5	54.4	69.9	98	1950	69	1929	71	1978	41	1964	0	5	25	19
5	85.9	55.4	70.6	96	1967	55	1970	73	1978	41	1956	0	6	25	19
6	84.9	56.5	70.7	97†	1979	56	1970	70	1933	44†	1943	0	6	26	19
7	84.3	55.6	70.0	99	1979	60†	1939	67†	1986	44	1948	1	6	25	18
8	82.5	55.3	68.9	100	1979	57	1973	71	1994	38	1962	1	5	25	18
9	82.2	53.0	67.6	95	1990	67	1928	72†	1994	34	1962	1	4	24	17
10	82.9	52.5	67.7	94	1958	64	1986	66	1972	38	1932	1	3	24	17
11	81.6	53.0	67.3	97	1990	59	1950	70	1959	38	1947	1	4	23	17
12	80.2	52.1	66.2	99	1990	63†	1988	69	1984	36	1928	2	3	23	16
13	80.0	50.3	65.1	93	1948	56	1988	66	1968	32	1928	2	2	22	16
14	79.0	50.5	64.7	96†	1990	61†	1982	63	1955	35	1928	3	2	22	15
15	79.4	50.0	64.7	93	1995	62	1933	72	1990	33	1936	2	2	22	15
16	80.4	49.6	65.0	94	1995	55	1965	64†	1990	33	1936	2	2	22	16
17	79.8	50.2	65.0	93	1937	43	1965	62†	1990	31	1965	2	2	22	16
18	77.3	49.0	63.1	94	1937	52	1978	64	1930	27	1965	4	2	21	14
19	77.5	48.5	63.0	97	1956	55	1978	65	1984	31	1964	4	2	21	14
20	75.1	47.5	61.3	91	1933	58†	1988	63	1929	30	1965	5	1	20	13
21	73.7	45.8	59.8	90	1944	52	1961	62	1930	35†	1968	6	0	18	12
22	75.3	46.5	60.9	91†	1966	57	1961	62	1934	32	1968	5	1	19	13
23	75.1	46.8	60.9	92	1992	55	1941	63	1992	31	1968	5	1	19	13
24	74.8	46.4	60.6	90	1992	43	1934	61†	1979	32	1961	5	1	19	13
25	75.2	46.9	61.0	90	1979	47	1934	64	1949	30	1970	5	1	19	13
26	76.0	47.3	61.6	89	1956	51	1934	64	1989	31	1970	4	1	20	13
27	75.3	46.1	60.7	91	1969	53	1982	59	1957	31	1934	5	1	19	13
28	75.1	46.4	60.8	91	1994	54†	1986	64	1981	31	1936	5	1	19	13
29	74.3	45.9	60.1	91†	1969	47	1982	62	1947	33†	1986	6	1	19	12
30	73.8	45.1	59.5	90	1957	49	1950	58	1938	30	1954	6	0	18	12

Day	Total precipitation			Percent of years with precipitation				Total snowfall			Percent with snowfall			ETo
---	Avg	High	Year	None	Trace	.01 or more	.10 or more	.50 or more	Avg	High	Year	None	.1 or more	2.0 or more	ETo
1	0.03	1.37	1973	70.6	14.7	14.7	4.4	1.5	0.0	0.0†	1995	100.0	0.0	0.0	0.18
2	0.02	0.24	1929	64.7	16.2	19.1	5.9	0.0	0.0	0.0†	1995	100.0	0.0	0.0	0.17
3	0.03	0.49	1929	72.1	13.2	14.7	7.4	0.0	0.0	0.0†	1995	100.0	0.0	0.0	0.17
4	0.02	0.44	1992	70.6	10.3	19.1	4.4	0.0	0.0	0.0†	1995	100.0	0.0	0.0	0.18
5	0.05	2.19	1970	70.6	13.2	16.2	7.4	2.9	0.0	0.0†	1995	100.0	0.0	0.0	0.18
6	0.04	0.81	1965	64.7	16.2	19.1	8.8	2.9	0.0	0.0†	1995	100.0	0.0	0.0	0.17
7	0.03	1.29	1991	63.2	22.1	14.7	5.9	1.5	0.0	0.0†	1995	100.0	0.0	0.0	0.17
8	0.03	0.81	1991	61.8	23.5	14.7	5.9	2.9	0.0	0.0†	1995	98.2	0.0	0.0	0.16
9	0.02	0.64	1986	73.5	14.7	11.8	7.4	1.5	0.0	0.0†	1995	100.0	0.0	0.0	0.16
10	0.03	1.15	1982	66.2	13.2	20.6	5.9	1.5	0.0	0.0†	1995	100.0	0.0	0.0	0.17
11	0.04	0.86	1985	63.2	17.6	19.1	8.8	2.9	0.0	0.0†	1995	98.2	0.0	0.0	0.16
12	0.01	0.17	1940	70.6	11.8	17.6	5.9	0.0	0.0	0.0†	1995	100.0	0.0	0.0	0.16
13	0.03	0.89	1982	76.5	7.4	16.2	2.9	2.9	0.0	0.0†	1995	100.0	0.0	0.0	0.16
14	0.02	0.66†	1977	73.5	10.3	16.2	2.9	2.9	0.0	0.0†	1995	100.0	0.0	0.0	0.15
15	0.01	0.23	1959	73.5	17.6	8.8	1.5	0.0	0.0	0.0†	1995	100.0	0.0	0.0	0.16
16	0.01	0.31	1965	83.8	5.9	10.3	2.9	0.0	0.0	0.0†	1995	100.0	0.0	0.0	0.16
17	0.04	1.38	1978	67.6	14.7	17.6	11.8	1.5	0.0	2.2	1965	98.2	1.8	1.8	0.16
18	0.06	0.82	1947	67.6	10.3	22.1	14.7	4.4	0.0	1.0	1978	98.2	1.8	0.0	0.15
19	0.03	0.56	1972	66.2	11.8	22.1	11.8	2.9	0.0	0.0†	1995	100.0	0.0	0.0	0.15
20	0.03	0.57	1984	63.2	8.8	27.9	8.8	2.9	0.0	0.0†	1995	100.0	0.0	0.0	0.14
21	0.01	0.22	1929	73.5	10.3	16.2	2.9	0.0	0.0	0.0†	1995	100.0	0.0	0.0	0.15
22	0.04	0.68	1977	73.5	10.3	16.2	10.3	2.9	0.0	0.0†	1995	100.0	0.0	0.0	0.15
23	0.04	1.09	1973	64.7	11.8	23.5	10.3	2.9	0.0	0.0†	1995	100.0	0.0	0.0	0.15
24	0.03	0.41	1930	66.2	13.2	20.6	10.3	0.0	0.0	0.0†	1995	98.2	0.0	0.0	0.14
25	0.05	0.95	1986	69.1	8.8	22.1	13.2	4.4	0.0	0.0†	1995	96.4	0.0	0.0	0.15
26	0.04	2.27	1982	76.5	11.8	11.8	4.4	1.5	0.0	0.0†	1995	100.0	0.0	0.0	0.15
27	0.03	0.84	1982	73.5	7.4	19.1	7.4	2.9	0.0	0.0†	1995	100.0	0.0	0.0	0.15
28	0.03	0.96	1982	72.1	13.2	14.7	5.9	1.5	0.0	0.0†	1995	100.0	0.0	0.0	0.15
29	0.04	1.01	1995	72.1	13.2	14.7	8.8	2.9	0.0	0.0†	1995	96.4	0.0	0.0	0.14
30	0.04	1.20	1971	69.1	8.8	22.1	10.3	1.5	0.1	4.0	1971	96.4	1.8	1.8	0.14

† Also occurred on earlier date(s).

October

Day	Average temperature Max	Min	Mean	High	Extreme maximum Year	Low	Year	Extreme minimum High	Year	Low	Year	HDD	Degree Days CDD	GDD40	GDD50
1	73.4	45.4	59.4	88†	1992	45	1971	66	1953	31	1950	6	0	18	12
2	73.3	45.5	59.4	88	1979	52†	1971	59	1929	31	1959	6	0	18	12
3	71.7	44.0	57.8	89	1963	53	1994	58	1948	33	1971	7	0	17	10
4	71.2	43.6	57.4	86	1963	53	1951	56	1963	33†	1973	7	0	17	10
5	71.4	43.4	57.4	87	1993	45	1941	62	1990	30	1932	8	0	17	11
6	71.2	43.4	57.3	86	1975	46	1946	61	1975	26	1955	8	0	17	10
7	70.4	43.1	56.7	88	1979	50	1949	58	1960	31	1955	8	0	16	10
8	69.2	42.3	55.8	85†	1979	45	1949	57	1954	29	1959	9	0	16	9
9	69.0	42.6	55.8	84	1963	41	1960	57	1983	29	1968	9	0	16	9
10	70.3	42.9	56.6	85	1955	49†	1949	63	1962	28	1932	8	0	16	10
11	69.6	43.1	56.4	84	1980	50†	1947	56†	1995	27	1946	8	0	16	9
12	67.6	42.7	55.2	83	1958	47	1969	58	1968	28	1986	9	0	15	8
13	67.7	41.7	54.7	85	1958	48	1966	63	1962	31	1986	10	0	15	9
14	66.7	40.2	53.5	81	1958	45	1969	56	1938	28†	1969	11	0	14	8
15	65.1	40.0	52.6	83	1958	43	1994	55	1946	26	1966	12	0	13	7
16	65.7	39.4	52.5	85	1991	42	1980	53	1972	27†	1970	12	0	13	8
17	65.7	39.5	52.6	83	1958	43	1938	54	1943	23	1964	12	0	13	8
18	64.9	38.7	51.8	84	1958	41†	1984	50	1958	23	1964	13	0	13	7
19	64.5	37.9	51.2	82	1958	43	1949	51†	1955	26	1976	13	0	12	7
20	64.6	38.5	51.5	81†	1950	41	1949	55	1961	24	1932	13	0	13	7
21	63.6	37.2	50.4	79	1967	42	1949	52	1989	27	1958	14	0	12	6
22	62.1	37.0	49.6	77	1973	45	1935	53†	1991	24	1966	15	0	11	6
23	62.6	36.9	49.7	77	1952	42	1975	51	1940	24	1935	15	0	11	6
24	62.1	37.2	49.6	78	1959	39	1956	53	1939	21	1935	15	0	11	6
25	63.0	36.7	49.9	78	1979	41	1954	54	1940	19	1932	15	0	12	6
26	63.4	37.2	50.3	80	1977	44	1970	53	1950	28†	1970	14	0	12	6
27	61.4	36.2	48.8	76	1977	43†	1991	52	1945	24	1970	16	0	11	5
28	60.0	36.1	48.0	79	1990	33	1971	50†	1992	23	1970	16	0	10	5
29	59.1	35.5	47.3	79†	1964	30	1971	60	1950	18	1971	17	0	10	5
30	57.7	34.6	46.2	77	1950	35	1971	66	1950	16	1971	18	0	9	4
31	56.2	33.2	44.7	73	1988	35	1971	53	1990	18	1935	20	0	8	3

Day	Total precipitation Avg	High	Year	Percent of years with precipitation None	Trace	.01 or more	.10 or more	.50 or more	Total snowfall Avg	High	Year	Percent with snowfall None	.1 or more	2.0 or more	ETo
1	0.03	0.39	1983	72.1	10.3	17.6	10.3	0.0	0.0	0.7	1971	98.2	1.8	0.0	0.10
2	0.03	0.47	1976	72.1	7.4	20.6	11.8	0.0	0.0	0.0†	1995	98.2	0.0	0.0	0.10
3	0.06	1.34	1951	64.2	14.9	20.9	13.4	3.0	0.0	0.0†	1995	98.1	0.0	0.0	0.10
4	0.03	0.44	1939	70.6	5.9	23.5	11.8	0.0	0.0	0.0†	1995	98.2	0.0	0.0	0.10
5	0.04	1.00	1941	75.0	10.3	14.7	8.8	2.9	0.0	0.0†	1995	98.2	0.0	0.0	0.10
6	0.03	0.64	1977	75.0	10.3	14.7	5.9	1.5	0.0	0.0†	1995	96.4	0.0	0.0	0.10
7	0.07	1.53	1993	67.6	7.4	25.0	11.8	5.9	0.0	0.0†	1995	92.7	0.0	0.0	0.10
8	0.03	0.50	1981	75.0	5.9	19.1	11.8	1.5	0.0	0.0†	1995	98.2	0.0	0.0	0.10
9	0.03	0.46	1960	67.6	8.8	23.5	13.2	0.0	0.0	0.0†	1995	96.4	0.0	0.0	0.09
10	0.05	1.05	1947	66.2	11.8	22.1	14.7	1.5	0.0	0.0†	1995	96.4	0.0	0.0	0.10
11	0.04	0.57	1984	72.1	16.2	11.8	10.3	1.5	0.0	0.0†	1995	100.0	0.0	0.0	0.10
12	0.04	0.59	1928	60.3	14.7	25.0	13.2	1.5	0.0	0.0†	1995	98.2	0.0	0.0	0.09
13	0.04	0.84	1966	66.2	5.9	27.9	10.3	2.9	0.1	3.6	1966	96.4	1.8	1.8	0.09
14	0.05	0.95	1968	67.6	11.8	20.6	11.8	4.4	0.0	0.1	1969	92.7	1.8	0.0	0.09
15	0.05	1.06	1937	70.6	4.4	25.0	14.7	1.5	0.0	0.2	1984	92.7	1.8	0.0	0.09
16	0.06	0.94	1938	69.1	5.9	25.0	10.3	5.9	0.0	0.0†	1995	94.5	0.0	0.0	0.09
17	0.04	0.64	1969	77.9	5.9	16.2	10.3	2.9	0.1	4.8	1984	94.5	1.8	1.8	0.09
18	0.05	1.23	1984	76.5	2.9	20.6	13.2	2.9	0.3	13.8	1984	94.5	1.8	1.8	0.09
19	0.03	0.65	1979	72.1	10.3	17.6	10.3	1.5	0.0	0.0†	1995	94.5	0.0	0.0	0.09
20	0.04	0.67	1949	73.5	8.8	17.6	7.4	1.5	0.0	1.0	1949	94.5	1.8	0.0	0.09
21	0.03	0.40	1943	67.6	16.2	16.2	10.3	0.0	0.0	2.0	1961	89.1	3.6	1.8	0.09
22	0.02	0.41	1985	70.6	13.2	16.2	5.9	0.0	0.0	0.5	1995	92.7	1.8	0.0	0.08
23	0.04	0.53	1991	69.1	13.2	17.6	10.3	2.9	0.0	0.0†	1995	96.4	0.0	0.0	0.08
24	0.03	0.64	1956	77.6	6.0	16.4	7.5	3.0	0.1	6.6	1956	92.7	5.5	1.8	0.08
25	0.03	0.52	1989	77.9	7.4	14.7	7.4	1.5	0.0	0.0†	1995	98.2	0.0	0.0	0.08
26	0.07	0.90	1982	72.1	11.8	16.2	13.2	5.9	0.0	1.6	1984	94.5	3.6	0.0	0.08
27	0.05	0.82	1991	67.6	8.8	23.5	14.7	2.9	0.2	5.8	1971	87.3	9.1	3.6	0.08
28	0.07	1.08	1946	60.3	10.3	29.4	17.6	2.9	0.2	6.3	1961	83.6	10.9	5.5	0.08
29	0.05	0.86	1981	55.9	20.6	23.5	14.7	4.4	0.1	3.5	1972	85.5	7.3	3.6	0.08
30	0.05	0.45	1968	63.2	13.2	23.5	16.2	0.0	0.1	2.2	1981	90.9	3.6	1.8	0.07
31	0.08	0.83	1933	61.8	10.3	27.9	17.6	4.4	0.2	8.5	1971	89.1	5.5	3.6	0.07

† Also occurred on earlier date(s).

SALT LAKE CITY NWSFO
Daily Data Summary

November

Day	Average temperature Max	Min	Mean	High	Extreme maximum Year	Low	Year	Extreme minimum High	Year	Low	Year	HDD	Degree Days CDD	GDD40	GDD50
1	55.6	32.9	44.3	72†	1988	37	1971	51	1987	16†	1971	20	0	8	3
2	54.6	32.4	43.5	73	1965	33	1936	50	1988	14†	1956	21	0	7	3
3	55.0	31.9	43.4	71	1965	30	1936	49	1988	6	1936	21	0	7	3
4	55.0	32.3	43.7	70†	1983	33†	1956	54	1977	15	1936	21	0	7	3
5	55.4	32.5	43.9	71	1945	37†	1957	47	1945	18†	1959	21	0	8	3
6	55.5	32.9	44.2	74	1931	32	1947	52	1966	16	1947	20	0	8	3
7	53.9	32.4	43.1	74†	1980	36	1945	47	1980	19	1961	21	0	7	2
8	54.5	31.7	43.1	70	1973	34	1945	43	1974	17	1948	21	0	7	3
9	54.0	31.1	42.6	74	1958	32	1950	43†	1973	17	1948	22	0	7	2
10	53.3	31.5	42.4	69	1973	34	1978	45	1944	13	1950	22	0	6	2
11	53.2	31.4	42.3	72	1954	35	1938	47	1954	17†	1935	22	0	6	2
12	53.2	31.5	42.4	75	1967	31	1938	48	1953	15	1929	22	0	6	2
13	52.5	31.0	41.8	70	1953	34	1964	50	1981	14	1959	23	0	6	2
14	51.4	30.2	40.8	71	1967	33	1964	51	1953	3	1955	24	0	6	2
15	49.8	28.1	38.9	70	1941	15	1955	46	1966	-10	1955	26	0	5	2
16	49.3	28.8	39.0	68	1981	16	1955	49	1941	-14	1955	25	0	5	1
17	48.1	29.5	38.8	68	1981	27	1958	46	1950	10	1958	26	0	4	1
18	46.8	28.1	37.4	66	1995	30†	1994	47	1942	6	1958	27	0	4	1
19	45.5	27.4	36.4	67	1943	27	1985	45	1946	3	1930	28	0	3	0
20	46.2	27.0	36.6	65	1966	26	1977	44†	1966	2	1930	28	0	3	1
21	45.4	25.8	35.6	65	1932	25	1931	45	1974	5	1931	29	0	3	0
22	44.3	25.2	34.8	63†	1962	27	1931	41†	1981	3	1930	30	0	2	0
23	45.4	25.6	35.5	61†	1988	25	1931	43	1965	5	1940	29	0	3	0
24	46.4	27.0	36.7	65	1995	22	1931	47	1960	0	1931	28	0	4	1
25	45.8	26.3	36.1	69†	1995	27†	1993	46	1960	1	1931	28	0	3	1
26	44.1	25.2	34.7	68	1949	27	1952	46	1960	2	1952	30	0	2	0
27	43.2	24.4	33.8	67	1949	25	1976	39	1955	6	1952	31	0	2	0
28	43.0	24.8	33.9	66	1932	27	1930	39	1970	7	1976	31	0	2	0
29	43.5	24.8	34.2	63	1932	28	1975	41	1945	5	1931	30	0	2	0
30	44.0	25.8	34.9	68	1995	26	1930	43	1995	6	1931	30	0	2	0

Day	Total precipitation Avg	High	Year	None	Percent of years with precipitation Trace	.01 or more	.10 or more	.50 or more	Total snowfall Avg	High	Year	Percent with snowfall None	.1 or more	2.0 or more	ETo
1	0.05	0.88	1936	58.8	16.2	25.0	14.7	2.9	0.1	2.9	1956	85.7	3.6	1.8	0.05
2	0.06	1.00	1992	66.2	8.8	25.0	17.6	1.5	0.2	5.5	1957	87.3	5.5	5.5	0.05
3	0.04	0.44	1940	64.7	10.3	25.0	14.7	0.0	0.1	3.1	1973	90.9	5.5	1.8	0.05
4	0.03	0.45	1940	63.2	14.7	22.1	10.3	0.0	0.1	1.1	1956	80.0	9.1	0.0	0.05
5	0.04	0.71	1972	72.1	8.8	19.1	8.8	2.9	0.0	0.0†	1995	92.7	0.0	0.0	0.05
6	0.04	0.55	1953	63.2	16.2	20.6	11.8	1.5	0.0	2.6	1986	90.9	1.8	1.8	0.05
7	0.06	0.63	1970	55.9	10.3	33.8	20.6	2.9	0.1	2.0	1948	89.1	3.6	1.8	0.05
8	0.03	0.47	1966	67.6	8.8	23.5	11.8	0.0	0.1	2.9	1966	87.3	9.1	3.6	0.05
9	0.03	0.78	1995	66.2	14.7	19.1	10.3	1.5	0.0	0.9	1985	89.1	3.6	0.0	0.05
10	0.04	0.82	1949	64.7	8.8	26.5	8.8	1.5	0.1	4.8	1978	83.6	5.5	1.8	0.05
11	0.04	0.66	1985	55.9	14.7	29.4	10.3	2.9	0.2	4.7	1985	80.0	9.1	5.5	0.05
12	0.08	0.96	1994	64.7	4.4	30.9	14.7	4.4	0.3	5.1	1985	83.6	9.1	5.5	0.05
13	0.03	0.43	1983	60.3	8.8	30.9	7.4	0.0	0.3	8.3	1994	83.6	12.7	1.8	0.05
14	0.05	0.71	1955	55.9	13.2	30.9	16.2	1.5	0.4	6.9	1955	70.9	18.2	5.5	0.04
15	0.07	0.93	1952	57.4	16.2	26.5	14.7	4.4	0.5	9.5	1958	70.9	16.4	10.9	0.04
16	0.06	1.13	1954	60.3	17.6	22.1	13.2	2.9	0.4	5.0	1994	70.9	12.7	7.3	0.04
17	0.08	1.01	1941	41.8	17.9	40.3	25.4	3.0	0.6	11.0	1930	67.3	27.3	9.1	0.04
18	0.07	0.82	1973	48.5	16.2	35.3	19.1	4.4	0.3	4.1	1985	63.6	18.2	3.6	0.04
19	0.05	0.50	1977	60.3	13.2	26.5	19.1	1.5	0.3	6.1	1977	76.4	18.2	5.5	0.04
20	0.05	0.52	1992	57.4	11.8	30.9	16.2	1.5	0.4	5.7	1992	70.9	25.5	7.3	0.04
21	0.05	0.50	1955	52.9	20.6	26.5	13.2	1.5	0.3	4.3	1961	61.8	18.2	3.6	0.04
22	0.03	0.78	1974	61.8	11.8	26.5	5.9	1.5	0.1	3.6	1992	74.5	12.7	1.8	0.04
23	0.03	0.57	1946	66.2	16.2	17.6	10.3	1.5	0.2	3.0	1931	74.5	12.7	3.6	0.04
24	0.04	0.44	1951	52.9	17.6	29.4	17.6	0.0	0.4	4.9	1951	67.3	16.4	9.1	0.04
25	0.04	0.52	1970	59.7	11.9	28.4	11.9	1.5	0.4	4.1	1984	67.3	20.0	12.7	0.04
26	0.03	0.49	1973	53.7	20.9	25.4	11.9	0.0	0.3	7.0	1973	61.8	23.6	5.5	0.04
27	0.04	0.84	1960	58.8	13.2	27.9	10.3	1.5	0.3	4.6	1960	60.0	29.1	7.3	0.03
28	0.02	0.31	1975	61.8	11.8	26.5	8.8	0.0	0.2	3.5	1975	65.5	20.0	1.8	0.03
29	0.02	0.31	1975	63.2	17.6	19.1	4.4	0.0	0.2	5.3	1991	70.9	10.9	3.6	0.03
30	0.03	0.56	1945	58.2	19.4	22.4	7.5	1.5	0.2	4.2	1967	69.1	16.4	1.8	0.04

† Also occurred on earlier date(s).

SALT LAKE CITY NWSFO
Daily Data Summary

December

Day	Max	Min	Mean	High	Year	Low	Year	High	Year	Low	Year	HDD	CDD	GDD40	GDD50
	Average temperature				Extreme maximum				Extreme minimum				Degree Days		
1	43.1	24.5	33.8	69	1995	24	1930	39	1947	6†	1991	31	0	2	0
2	44.2	25.4	34.8	61	1939	24	1930	40†	1977	6†	1934	30	0	2	0
3	44.1	25.7	34.8	59†	1987	27	1963	49	1980	5	1931	30	0	3	0
4	43.6	24.9	34.2	58†	1980	25	1992	47	1946	3	1992	30	0	2	0
5	43.0	24.1	33.5	60	1946	17	1972	42	1946	-3	1972	31	0	2	0
6	41.6	24.7	33.2	58	1987	23	1978	41	1946	4	1931	31	0	1	0
7	42.0	24.8	33.4	60	1939	19	1978	38	1983	1	1951	31	0	2	0
8	40.8	22.9	31.8	62	1939	18	1978	41	1950	-3†	1956	33	0	2	0
9	40.4	23.0	31.7	62	1939	13	1972	48	1939	-11	1972	33	0	2	0
10	40.4	22.8	31.6	66	1939	8	1972	51	1929	-13	1972	33	0	2	0
11	39.9	22.2	31.1	62	1993	12	1972	45†	1937	-12	1932	33	0	2	0
12	38.9	22.1	30.5	61	1995	8	1932	48	1929	-20	1932	34	0	1	0
13	37.7	21.6	29.6	60	1929	11	1932	45	1929	-21	1932	35	0	1	0
14	37.7	20.3	29.0	64	1929	15	1932	46	1977	-19	1932	35	0	1	0
15	38.5	20.6	29.6	59†	1977	11	1972	39	1946	-15	1972	35	0	1	0
16	37.7	20.8	29.2	58	1939	18	1932	41	1957	-14	1932	35	0	1	0
17	37.1	21.0	29.1	58	1939	19	1932	37	1939	-4	1931	35	0	0	0
18	36.7	20.9	28.8	53	1960	23	1964	36	1955	1	1932	36	0	0	0
19	37.9	21.2	29.5	54	1955	25	1992	46	1955	-1	1931	35	0	0	0
20	37.5	21.1	29.3	61	1981	22	1949	40	1941	-7	1990	35	0	1	0
21	37.8	22.2	30.0	67	1969	11	1990	44	1964	-9	1990	35	0	1	0
22	37.1	22.3	29.7	57	1964	2	1990	49	1955	-10	1990	35	0	1	0
23	37.8	21.5	29.7	58†	1955	9	1990	52	1955	-11	1990	35	0	1	0
24	36.8	20.8	28.8	57	1955	11	1990	41	1971	-7	1990	36	0	0	0
25	37.3	21.3	29.3	59	1955	18	1990	46	1955	-7	1930	35	0	1	0
26	36.2	19.9	28.1	60	1933	19	1970	43	1955	-6	1930	36	0	1	0
27	37.2	19.9	28.6	57	1933	18	1988	41	1934	-4	1930	36	0	0	0
28	36.9	20.2	28.6	57	1933	24	1939	40	1945	-9	1932	36	0	0	0
29	35.9	19.6	27.8	58	1933	20	1988	41†	1965	-8	1932	37	0	0	0
30	35.8	19.6	27.7	51	1933	13	1990	42	1933	-9	1990	37	0	0	0
31	34.8	18.5	26.6	58	1942	20†	1978	39	1942	-7	1990	38	0	0	0

Day	Avg	High	Year	None	Trace	.01 or more	.10 or more	.50 or more	Avg	High	Year	None	.1 or more	2.0 or more	ETo
	Total precipitation			Percent of years with precipitation					Total snowfall			Percent with snowfall			
1	0.06	0.74	1982	58.8	8.8	32.4	14.7	4.4	0.5	7.3	1982	67.3	21.8	10.9	0.03
2	0.04	0.73	1942	54.4	17.6	27.9	11.8	1.5	0.4	4.5	1952	63.6	21.8	5.5	0.03
3	0.03	0.63	1938	60.3	16.2	23.5	10.3	1.5	0.1	2.0	1971	70.9	16.4	1.8	0.03
4	0.06	0.63	1948	51.5	13.2	35.3	20.6	1.5	0.6	8.7	1948	63.6	29.1	12.7	0.03
5	0.04	0.72	1956	58.8	16.2	25.0	13.2	1.5	0.3	4.4	1956	67.3	27.3	3.6	0.03
6	0.03	0.40	1951	58.8	17.6	23.5	5.9	0.0	0.3	6.1	1956	63.6	21.8	5.5	0.03
7	0.05	0.74	1946	50.0	16.2	33.8	14.7	1.5	0.4	4.5	1994	54.5	23.6	9.1	0.03
8	0.03	0.91	1985	60.3	20.6	19.1	7.4	1.5	0.5	10.5	1985	70.9	16.4	7.3	0.03
9	0.05	0.98	1970	54.4	17.6	27.9	14.7	1.5	0.6	5.5	1931	70.9	23.6	14.5	0.03
10	0.03	0.35	1965	54.4	19.1	26.5	13.2	0.0	0.3	4.0	1949	60.0	20.0	3.6	0.03
11	0.04	0.79	1968	57.4	16.2	26.5	8.8	1.5	0.3	9.5	1968	63.6	20.0	3.6	0.03
12	0.04	0.89	1937	58.8	14.7	26.5	11.8	2.9	0.2	4.0	1993	63.6	23.6	3.6	0.02
13	0.05	0.73	1994	58.8	13.2	27.9	17.6	1.5	0.5	7.3	1994	63.6	23.6	9.1	0.02
14	0.02	0.48	1983	57.4	27.9	14.7	5.9	0.0	0.1	2.6	1948	61.8	16.4	1.8	0.02
15	0.03	0.51	1934	50.0	26.5	23.5	11.8	1.5	0.2	3.2	1992	52.7	21.8	5.5	0.02
16	0.04	0.75	1936	51.5	23.5	25.0	10.3	2.9	0.6	8.5	1967	54.5	29.1	12.7	0.02
17	0.05	0.77	1970	51.5	16.2	32.4	13.2	2.9	0.6	8.8	1970	50.9	30.9	12.7	0.02
18	0.03	0.52	1977	48.5	26.5	25.0	8.8	1.5	0.3	3.7	1977	45.5	30.9	5.5	0.02
19	0.04	0.37	1929	44.1	22.1	33.8	16.2	0.0	0.5	5.2	1951	47.3	32.7	7.3	0.02
20	0.03	0.45	1967	50.0	25.0	25.0	11.8	0.0	0.4	6.6	1967	50.9	21.8	5.5	0.02
21	0.03	0.34†	1979	44.1	22.1	33.8	13.2	0.0	0.4	4.0	1979	47.3	29.1	7.3	0.02
22	0.04	0.46	1951	36.8	30.9	32.4	13.2	0.0	0.6	4.7	1987	49.1	29.1	10.9	0.02
23	0.05	1.10	1964	41.2	25.0	33.8	8.8	2.9	0.4	3.8	1948	52.7	27.3	9.1	0.02
24	0.04	0.53	1964	48.5	26.5	25.0	11.8	1.5	0.5	7.6	1932	61.8	20.0	9.1	0.02
25	0.06	0.56	1959	44.1	22.1	33.8	16.2	2.9	0.4	3.9	1983	50.9	29.1	7.3	0.02
26	0.04	0.57	1946	41.2	29.4	29.4	13.2	1.5	0.3	3.2	1957	45.5	27.3	3.6	0.02
27	0.04	0.58	1948	50.0	22.1	27.9	13.2	1.5	0.3	8.1	1948	50.9	29.1	3.6	0.02
28	0.06	1.21	1972	36.8	23.5	39.7	20.6	1.5	0.7	12.6	1972	41.8	34.5	14.5	0.02
29	0.05	0.61	1972	33.8	23.5	42.6	19.1	1.5	0.4	5.5	1972	41.8	32.7	5.5	0.02
30	0.05	0.59	1995	36.8	27.9	35.3	19.1	1.5	0.7	5.8†	1992	43.6	38.2	12.7	0.02
31	0.03	0.41	1940	41.2	29.4	29.4	8.8	0.0	0.4	4.7†	1965	45.5	27.3	9.1	0.02

† Also occurred on earlier date(s).

Location: St. George Period of Record: 1862-1996

Utah Climate Center

ST GEORGE
Daily Data Summary

January

Day	Average temperature			Extreme maximum				Extreme minimum				HDD	Degree Days		
	Max	Min	Mean	High	Year	Low	Year	High	Year	Low	Year		CDD	GDD40	GDD50
1	50.8	23.6	37.2	66	1981	35†	1919	43	1934	2	1901	27	0	5	1
2	49.9	22.7	36.3	68†	1981	32	1974	38†	1938	-1	1901	28	0	5	1
3	50.8	22.6	36.7	68	1981	35†	1937	40	1938	5†	1912	28	0	5	1
4	50.7	23.0	36.8	69	1918	28	1950	43	1978	6	1912	28	0	5	1
5	51.5	24.1	37.8	68	1893	30	1910	44	1978	5†	1973	27	0	5	1
6	51.9	24.4	38.1	69	1893	28	1913	41†	1978	1	1973	26	0	6	2
7	51.6	24.3	38.0	67	1893	29†	1973	42	1965	3	1913	27	0	6	2
8	52.4	23.7	38.1	69	1948	27	1937	40†	1995	6†	1937	26	0	6	2
9	52.6	24.4	38.5	67†	1953	23	1937	42	1995	-1	1937	26	0	6	2
10	52.5	24.6	38.5	70	1996	32	1937	45	1980	4	1937	26	0	6	2
11	53.0	24.8	38.9	70	1996	35	1930	45	1940	6	1937	26	0	6	2
12	53.3	25.3	39.3	68†	1996	33†	1963	45	1940	6	1963	25	0	6	2
13	53.6	24.8	39.2	70	1986	29	1963	45	1957	2	1963	25	0	6	2
14	53.7	25.3	39.5	68†	1986	35†	1930	46	1957	8	1963	25	0	7	2
15	53.8	26.8	40.3	70	1908	35	1932	48	1988	10†	1904	24	0	7	2
16	54.1	27.0	40.6	68	1976	26	1917	45	1993	10	1904	24	0	7	2
17	53.6	26.4	40.0	69	1976	33	1917	45	1996	7	1968	24	0	7	2
18	53.2	26.0	39.6	68	1959	32	1937	44	1914	10†	1968	25	0	6	2
19	53.3	25.7	39.5	71	1986	26	1922	43†	1978	10	1992	25	0	6	2
20	53.1	25.6	39.3	71	1986	31	1937	46†	1969	8	1922	25	0	6	2
21	53.1	25.2	39.2	71	1986	21	1937	50	1969	-9	1937	25	0	6	2
22	52.6	25.0	38.8	66†	1981	17	1937	48	1969	-11	1937	26	0	6	2
23	53.5	25.3	39.4	70	1948	23	1937	42†	1956	-1	1937	25	0	6	2
24	54.3	25.8	40.1	72	1948	19	1937	44	1943	-2	1937	24	0	7	2
25	54.6	26.1	40.3	70	1948	24	1937	42†	1995	-1	1937	24	0	7	3
26	55.3	26.2	40.7	69†	1975	25	1937	46†	1969	-11	1937	24	0	7	3
27	55.2	26.7	40.9	70†	1906	25	1937	49	1956	-7	1937	24	0	7	3
28	55.7	26.9	41.3	70	1931	29	1937	46	1987	8	1902	23	0	8	3
29	56.1	26.6	41.3	72	1931	31	1979	44†	1983	5	1949	23	0	8	3
30	55.9	27.1	41.5	70†	1940	30	1979	45†	1911	2	1902	23	0	8	3
31	56.3	28.0	42.1	71	1893	31	1979	46	1911	6†	1949	22	0	8	3

Day	Total precipitation			Percent of years with precipitation					Total snowfall			Percent with snowfall			ETo
	Avg	High	Year	None	Trace	.01 or more	.10 or more	.50 or more	Avg	High	Year	None	.1 or more	2.0 or more	
1	0.04	0.78	1942	86.7	1.9	11.4	8.6	2.9	0.1	5.0†	1974	97.0	3.0	2.0	0.05
2	0.02	0.44	1922	86.7	1.9	11.4	5.7	0.0	0.0	1.5	1863	96.9	2.0	0.0	0.05
3	0.02	0.50	1920	88.6	3.8	7.6	4.8	1.0	0.0	0.0†	1995	99.0	0.0	0.0	0.05
4	0.03	0.65	1991	82.9	1.9	15.2	8.6	1.9	0.1	6.0	1973	97.0	2.0	1.0	0.05
5	0.04	1.00	1974	80.0	5.7	14.3	11.4	1.9	0.1	10.0	1974	98.0	1.0	1.0	0.05
6	0.02	0.62	1939	84.8	3.8	11.4	7.6	1.9	0.0	0.1	1937	98.0	1.0	0.0	0.05
7	0.03	0.68	1987	84.8	1.0	14.3	6.7	2.9	0.0	2.5	1987	97.0	3.0	1.0	0.05
8	0.02	0.51	1985	88.6	1.0	10.5	4.8	1.0	0.0	0.3	1974	99.0	1.0	0.0	0.05
9	0.02	0.39	1980	88.5	1.9	9.6	7.7	0.0	0.1	6.0	1898	97.0	3.0	1.0	0.05
10	0.03	0.93	1905	84.8	1.9	13.3	9.5	1.0	0.1	4.0	1949	97.0	2.0	1.0	0.05
11	0.04	0.56	1995	76.2	1.0	22.9	15.2	1.9	0.1	4.5	1921	97.0	3.0	1.0	0.05
12	0.03	1.18	1897	85.6	0.0	14.4	8.7	1.0	0.0	1.2	1949	98.0	2.0	0.0	0.05
13	0.03	0.67	1957	83.7	1.0	15.4	10.6	1.0	0.0	2.5	1909	98.0	2.0	1.0	0.05
14	0.03	0.55†	1909	82.9	1.0	16.2	11.4	1.9	0.0	1.5	1930	98.0	1.0	0.0	0.05
15	0.04	0.72	1980	80.0	1.0	20.0	11.4	3.8	0.0	2.8	1925	99.0	1.0	1.0	0.05
16	0.04	0.77	1945	74.3	0.0	25.7	11.4	1.0	0.0	3.0	1932	96.0	3.0	1.0	0.05
17	0.05	0.91	1973	80.0	0.0	20.0	12.4	1.9	0.0	0.3	1928	99.0	1.0	0.0	0.05
18	0.05	0.68	1952	82.9	1.9	15.2	11.4	4.8	0.1	5.5	1930	97.0	3.0	2.0	0.05
19	0.05	1.28	1895	77.9	1.9	20.2	13.5	2.9	0.1	5.5	1895	95.9	3.1	1.0	0.05
20	0.04	0.62	1938	82.9	0.0	17.1	10.5	1.0	0.1	4.0	1917	96.0	3.0	2.0	0.05
21	0.03	0.52	1982	80.0	1.0	19.0	10.5	1.0	0.0	0.0†	1995	99.0	1.0	0.0	0.05
22	0.04	1.14	1943	82.9	0.0	17.1	11.4	1.9	0.0	0.5	1929	98.0	1.0	0.0	0.05
23	0.04	1.10	1943	81.9	3.8	14.3	10.5	2.9	0.1	7.0	1898	96.0	3.0	3.0	0.05
24	0.03	0.53	1941	81.9	1.9	16.2	8.6	1.9	0.0	3.0	1902	97.0	3.0	1.0	0.05
25	0.05	1.04	1969	77.1	0.0	22.9	11.4	2.9	0.0	2.5	1902	95.9	2.1	1.0	0.05
26	0.05	1.50	1865	79.0	1.0	20.0	12.4	1.9	0.0	2.5	1949	96.9	3.1	1.0	0.06
27	0.03	0.60	1961	80.8	1.9	17.3	10.6	1.0	0.0	0.0†	1995	100.0	0.0	0.0	0.06
28	0.03	0.84	1916	80.8	1.0	18.3	7.7	1.0	0.0	2.5	1975	96.9	2.1	1.0	0.06
29	0.05	1.36	1915	80.8	0.0	19.2	12.5	1.9	0.0	4.0	1898	97.0	2.0	1.0	0.06
30	0.02	0.64	1907	84.5	3.9	11.7	6.8	1.9	0.1	7.0	1933	94.8	3.1	1.0	0.06
31	0.04	0.65	1931	81.4	1.0	17.6	12.7	2.0	0.0	1.0	1975	97.9	1.0	0.0	0.06

† Also occurred on earlier date(s).

February

Day	Average temperature				Extreme maximum				Extreme minimum				HDD	Degree Days		
	Max	Min	Mean	High	Year	Low	Year	High	Year	Low	Year		CDD	GDD40	GDD50
1	56.1	27.2	41.6	73	1935	33	1949	47	1945	3	1949	23	0	8	3
2	56.1	27.2	41.7	73	1995	35	1949	44	1909	5	1902	23	0	8	3
3	56.0	26.9	41.4	73†	1995	31	1939	44	1958	11†	1902	23	0	8	3
4	56.8	27.8	42.3	73	1995	31	1979	44	1905	9	1903	22	0	8	3
5	57.0	28.1	42.6	73	1963	34	1899	44	1931	6	1979	22	0	8	4
6	57.3	28.1	42.7	74†	1963	27	1989	45	1931	1	1899	22	0	8	4
7	57.5	28.7	43.1	74	1963	29	1989	42†	1935	1	1899	21	0	8	4
8	56.6	28.9	42.7	75	1970	32	1989	45	1959	6	1949	22	0	8	3
9	57.3	29.6	43.4	74†	1970	34	1929	47	1978	5	1949	21	0	8	4
10	58.6	29.6	44.1	75	1951	31	1933	51	1970	5	1933	20	0	9	4
11	58.9	29.6	44.2	76	1951	39	1948	50†	1970	11	1905	20	0	9	4
12	59.1	30.2	44.6	75†	1957	31	1905	47	1941	6	1905	20	0	9	4
13	58.8	29.3	44.0	78	1921	33	1903	49	1954	5	1903	20	0	9	4
14	59.1	30.5	44.8	79†	1957	32	1903	50	1957	9	1903	20	0	9	4
15	59.0	29.8	44.4	75	1907	34	1903	45†	1957	5	1903	20	0	9	4
16	60.2	30.4	45.3	75	1907	37†	1911	47	1991	8	1903	19	0	10	5
17	61.1	30.7	45.9	77	1930	41	1903	50	1957	10	1903	19	0	10	5
18	60.8	30.5	45.7	76†	1930	41†	1932	49	1980	13	1903	19	0	10	5
19	61.2	30.8	46.0	77†	1930	40	1955	51	1986	15	1903	18	0	10	5
20	61.5	31.5	46.5	77	1995	40	1897	47	1957	17	1903	18	0	10	5
21	61.3	31.5	46.4	79†	1995	40	1975	49	1914	11	1897	18	0	10	5
22	61.6	31.6	46.6	77†	1995	36	1913	46†	1995	10	1897	18	0	11	6
23	62.0	31.9	47.0	79	1995	40	1919	50	1957	11	1897	18	0	11	6
24	62.7	32.0	47.3	81†	1986	42	1987	45†	1941	16†	1897	17	0	11	6
25	63.9	31.9	47.9	84	1986	40	1987	49†	1995	16	1894	17	0	12	7
26	63.6	32.3	48.0	84	1986	43	1911	48	1940	14	1912	17	0	11	6
27	63.9	32.7	48.3	84	1986	43	1962	52†	1989	16	1903	16	0	12	7
28	64.3	32.4	48.3	83	1986	44	1919	49	1920	14	1962	16	0	12	7
29	68.1	33.4	50.7	78	1972	57	1960	47	1908	15	1912	14	0	14	9

Day	Total precipitation				Percent of years with precipitation				Total snowfall			Percent with snowfall			ETo
	Avg	High	Year	None	Trace	.01 or more	.10 or more	.50 or more	Avg	High	Year	None	.1 or more	2.0 or more	
1	0.04	0.63	1901	77.9	1.0	21.2	15.4	1.9	0.0	4.0	1901	96.9	3.1	1.0	0.07
2	0.03	0.62	1960	79.8	1.9	18.3	12.5	1.0	0.0	1.5	1932	99.0	1.0	0.0	0.07
3	0.03	0.37	1928	79.8	2.9	17.3	9.6	0.0	0.0	1.0	1939	97.9	2.1	0.0	0.07
4	0.05	0.98	1928	79.8	1.0	19.2	14.4	2.9	0.1	6.0	1939	98.0	2.0	2.0	0.08
5	0.03	0.80	1948	86.5	1.0	12.5	7.7	1.9	0.1	5.0	1948	98.0	2.0	1.0	0.08
6	0.04	0.81	1976	79.8	1.0	19.2	11.5	3.8	0.0	0.0†	1995	99.0	0.0	0.0	0.08
7	0.04	0.48	1973	75.0	1.0	24.0	14.4	0.0	0.1	5.0	1929	95.9	4.1	3.1	0.08
8	0.04	0.60†	1993	75.0	2.9	22.1	13.5	2.9	0.0	1.5	1920	94.9	2.0	0.0	0.07
9	0.06	0.98	1893	78.8	1.0	20.2	13.5	3.8	0.0	0.8	1989	98.0	1.0	0.0	0.08
10	0.04	0.67	1963	76.0	0.0	24.0	10.6	1.0	0.0	2.0	1894	95.9	3.1	1.0	0.08
11	0.03	0.58	1982	78.6	1.0	20.4	9.7	1.0	0.0	0.0†	1995	100.0	0.0	0.0	0.08
12	0.02	1.00	1959	86.5	1.0	12.5	6.7	1.0	0.0	0.0†	1995	100.0	0.0	0.0	0.08
13	0.04	0.70	1895	78.8	2.9	18.3	13.5	1.9	0.0	0.0†	1995	99.0	0.0	0.0	0.08
14	0.05	1.10	1980	73.8	1.0	25.2	15.5	2.9	0.1	4.5	1903	95.9	4.1	2.0	0.08
15	0.03	0.55	1954	80.6	0.0	19.4	6.8	1.9	0.0	0.6	1941	99.0	1.0	0.0	0.08
16	0.03	0.95	1927	80.6	1.9	17.5	10.7	1.0	0.0	0.0†	1995	100.0	0.0	0.0	0.08
17	0.04	0.98	1904	83.5	0.0	16.5	8.7	1.9	0.0	1.5	1919	99.0	1.0	0.0	0.08
18	0.03	0.66	1990	83.7	1.9	14.4	10.6	1.0	0.0	0.0†	1995	100.0	0.0	0.0	0.08
19	0.03	0.60	1920	79.4	1.0	19.6	9.8	1.0	0.0	1.0	1918	98.0	2.0	0.0	0.08
20	0.04	0.74	1993	77.9	2.9	19.2	11.5	1.0	0.0	1.0†	1932	98.0	2.0	0.0	0.08
21	0.04	0.45	1979	79.8	0.0	20.2	11.5	0.0	0.0	4.0	1897	99.0	1.0	1.0	0.08
22	0.05	0.85	1970	79.8	1.0	19.2	15.4	2.9	0.0	3.0	1913	99.0	1.0	1.0	0.08
23	0.04	0.64	1944	82.7	1.0	16.3	11.5	1.9	0.0	0.0†	1995	100.0	0.0	0.0	0.09
24	0.03	0.46	1941	83.7	1.9	14.4	8.7	0.0	0.0	1.0	1987	98.0	1.0	0.0	0.09
25	0.02	0.56	1902	82.7	1.9	15.4	8.7	1.0	0.1	3.0	1911	98.0	2.0	2.0	0.09
26	0.02	0.80	1969	83.7	1.9	14.4	8.7	1.0	0.0	0.0†	1995	99.0	0.0	0.0	0.09
27	0.02	0.43	1938	88.5	0.0	11.5	6.7	0.0	0.0	0.0†	1995	100.0	0.0	0.0	0.09
28	0.02	0.46	1991	81.7	1.0	17.3	5.8	0.0	0.0	0.0†	1995	100.0	0.0	0.0	0.09
29	0.01	0.13	1960	84.0	0.0	16.0	4.0	0.0	0.0	0.0†	1988	100.0	0.0	0.0	0.10

† Also occurred on earlier date(s).

March

Day	Average temperature				Extreme maximum				Extreme minimum					Degree Days		
	Max	Min	Mean	High	Year	Low	Year	High	Year	Low	Year	HDD	CDD	GDD40	GDD50
1	64.3	33.4	48.9	83	1986	42	1915	51	1920	12	1903	16	0	12	7
2	64.5	34.1	49.3	83†	1986	43	1951	58	1974	14	1903	15	0	12	7
3	63.6	34.5	49.1	85	1921	46	1896	54	1949	16	1966	15	0	12	6
4	63.2	33.7	48.4	82	1986	43	1896	47†	1978	14	1894	16	0	11	6
5	63.9	34.0	49.0	83†	1986	42	1948	55	1991	15	1896	16	0	12	7
6	64.9	33.4	49.1	83†	1986	46	1948	52	1925	17	1896	15	0	12	7
7	65.7	33.5	49.6	84†	1972	45	1964	51	1987	17	1903	15	0	13	7
8	67.0	33.6	50.3	86	1904	45	1964	52	1986	19	1897	14	0	13	8
9	67.1	34.8	51.0	87	1972	47	1935	53	1943	17	1964	14	0	13	8
10	66.3	35.6	51.0	87	1972	45	1964	53	1985	19	1897	14	0	13	8
11	65.6	35.7	50.6	85	1900	45	1954	52	1918	15	1899	14	0	13	7
12	65.2	34.8	50.0	86	1900	48†	1990	54	1944	16†	1899	15	0	12	7
13	66.2	34.5	50.3	86†	1946	48†	1990	50	1968	16	1897	14	0	13	8
14	66.0	35.0	50.5	85	1934	48	1964	59	1984	16	1899	14	0	13	8
15	66.9	34.7	50.8	87	1934	49	1917	48†	1992	18†	1902	14	0	13	8
16	67.8	35.4	51.6	85	1934	49	1987	48†	1994	22	1917	13	0	14	8
17	68.3	36.0	52.1	85	1972	45	1920	50	1994	20	1896	12	0	14	9
18	68.3	36.0	52.2	85†	1972	49	1983	51	1993	20	1898	12	0	14	9
19	69.0	36.6	52.8	89	1925	52†	1982	55	1946	18	1898	12	0	14	9
20	68.6	37.0	52.8	87	1946	42	1894	52	1939	17	1897	12	0	14	9
21	68.9	36.2	52.5	86	1960	43	1897	59	1995	15	1897	12	0	14	9
22	69.0	37.0	53.0	86	1960	47	1952	50†	1994	12†	1898	11	0	14	9
23	69.1	37.0	53.0	86	1896	49	1954	54	1930	13	1897	11	0	14	9
24	70.1	37.3	53.7	89	1956	49	1954	51	1993	21	1904	11	0	15	10
25	70.0	38.4	54.2	87	1895	45	1937	55†	1993	19	1901	10	0	15	10
26	69.2	37.8	53.5	85	1988	50	1920	55†	1993	19	1898	11	0	15	9
27	68.7	38.0	53.4	89	1986	45	1975	55	1967	18†	1901	11	0	15	9
28	69.3	37.5	53.4	88	1986	45	1975	57	1963	22	1898	11	0	15	9
29	70.0	37.5	53.8	87†	1934	43	1897	58	1986	20	1898	11	0	15	10
30	70.6	37.6	54.1	87	1934	48	1897	58	1960	12	1897	11	0	15	10
31	71.4	37.9	54.6	88	1966	50	1896	54	1971	15	1896	10	0	16	10

	Total precipitation			Percent of years with precipitation				Total snowfall			Percent with snowfall			
Day	Avg	High	Year	None	Trace	.01 or more	.10 or more	.50 or more	Avg	High	Year	None	.1 or more	2.0 or more	ETo
1	0.04	0.82	1995	81.0	2.9	16.2	12.4	1.9	0.0	0.0†	1995	99.0	0.0	0.0	0.12
2	0.06	1.27	1935	72.4	4.8	22.9	15.2	3.8	0.0	0.0†	1995	100.0	0.0	0.0	0.12
3	0.05	1.23	1938	73.3	1.9	24.8	14.3	1.9	0.0	0.0†	1995	98.0	0.0	0.0	0.12
4	0.04	0.58	1943	75.2	1.0	23.8	11.4	1.0	0.1	2.5	1897	97.0	3.0	2.0	0.12
5	0.03	0.51	1978	81.9	1.0	17.1	11.4	1.0	0.0	0.0†	1995	100.0	0.0	0.0	0.12
6	0.04	1.33	1995	84.8	1.0	14.3	10.5	3.8	0.0	0.0†	1995	100.0	0.0	0.0	0.12
7	0.02	0.46	1973	87.6	0.0	12.4	5.7	0.0	0.0	0.0†	1995	100.0	0.0	0.0	0.12
8	0.01	0.34	1968	87.6	2.9	9.5	5.7	0.0	0.0	0.0†	1995	100.0	0.0	0.0	0.13
9	0.02	0.51	1958	85.7	1.0	13.3	8.6	1.0	0.0	0.0†	1995	100.0	0.0	0.0	0.13
10	0.05	0.86	1912	77.1	1.9	21.0	14.3	2.9	0.0	2.5	1923	99.0	1.0	1.0	0.12
11	0.05	0.95	1906	74.0	2.9	23.1	11.5	1.9	0.0	0.0†	1995	100.0	0.0	0.0	0.12
12	0.04	0.57	1980	77.1	1.0	21.9	14.3	1.9	0.0	0.1	1917	98.0	1.0	0.0	0.12
13	0.04	0.71	1905	72.4	1.0	26.7	16.2	1.9	0.0	0.0†	1995	99.0	0.0	0.0	0.13
14	0.03	0.69	1944	81.9	1.9	16.2	11.4	1.0	0.0	2.5	1944	99.0	1.0	1.0	0.12
15	0.02	0.47	1948	83.8	1.9	14.3	3.8	0.0	0.0	0.0†	1995	100.0	0.0	0.0	0.13
16	0.03	0.36	1963	80.0	3.8	16.2	11.4	0.0	0.0	0.0†	1995	100.0	0.0	0.0	0.13
17	0.03	1.27	1958	81.9	1.9	16.2	10.5	1.0	0.0	0.0†	1995	100.0	0.0	0.0	0.13
18	0.03	0.98	1983	84.0	1.9	14.2	9.4	0.9	0.0	0.0†	1995	100.0	0.0	0.0	0.13
19	0.02	0.64	1985	87.7	0.9	11.3	7.5	1.9	0.0	0.0†	1995	100.0	0.0	0.0	0.13
20	0.02	0.36	1979	77.4	4.7	17.9	10.4	0.0	0.1	3.0	1894	97.0	2.0	2.0	0.13
21	0.04	0.60	1869	83.0	1.9	15.1	12.3	0.9	0.0	0.0†	1995	99.0	0.0	0.0	0.13
22	0.05	0.88	1978	77.4	0.9	21.7	11.3	2.8	0.0	0.0†	1995	100.0	0.0	0.0	0.13
23	0.02	0.45	1916	83.0	1.9	15.1	6.6	0.0	0.0	0.0†	1995	100.0	0.0	0.0	0.13
24	0.02	0.58	1983	83.0	0.9	16.0	7.5	0.9	0.0	0.3	1929	98.0	1.0	0.0	0.14
25	0.03	0.72	1910	78.3	3.8	17.9	12.3	0.9	0.0	0.1	1913	98.0	1.0	0.0	0.14
26	0.02	0.47	1975	84.9	0.0	15.1	6.6	0.0	0.0	0.0†	1995	100.0	0.0	0.0	0.14
27	0.03	0.61	1993	84.9	0.9	14.2	8.5	2.8	0.0	0.0†	1995	100.0	0.0	0.0	0.13
28	0.03	0.80	1979	82.1	1.9	16.0	11.3	1.9	0.0	0.0†	1995	100.0	0.0	0.0	0.13
29	0.02	0.35†	1912	76.4	4.7	18.9	6.6	0.0	0.0	0.0†	1995	99.0	0.0	0.0	0.14
30	0.03	0.72†	1984	84.9	2.8	12.3	5.7	2.8	0.0	0.0†	1995	100.0	0.0	0.0	0.14
31	0.02	0.95	1978	87.7	0.9	11.3	4.7	0.9	0.0	0.0†	1995	100.0	0.0	0.0	0.14

† Also occurred on earlier date(s).

April

Day	Average temperature Max	Min	Mean	High	Extreme maximum Year	Low	Year	High	Extreme minimum Year	Low	Year	HDD	Degree Days CDD	GDD40	GDD50
1	72.8	39.7	56.3	93	1945	51	1949	56†	1986	18	1896	8	0	16	11
2	72.0	39.4	55.7	90	1966	52	1975	52	1937	22	1896	9	0	16	10
3	72.0	39.4	55.7	89	1966	52	1945	53	1989	25	1897	9	0	16	10
4	73.1	39.2	56.2	89	1959	51	1921	55	1951	24	1945	8	0	16	11
5	74.1	39.7	56.9	91	1930	46	1921	52†	1990	23	1901	8	0	17	12
6	74.9	41.5	58.2	94	1930	48	1929	61	1972	24†	1901	7	0	18	12
7	74.5	40.4	57.5	95	1989	53	1901	57	1959	21	1897	7	0	17	12
8	74.8	40.7	57.7	93	1989	50	1922	56	1963	18	1901	7	0	17	12
9	74.9	40.6	57.7	91	1989	49	1922	54†	1989	26	1900	7	0	17	12
10	74.6	41.1	57.9	92	1934	45	1893	63	1972	25	1900	7	0	17	12
11	75.3	41.5	58.4	94	1934	50	1893	62	1982	28†	1933	7	0	18	12
12	76.5	41.6	59.0	95†	1934	49	1965	53	1992	30†	1901	6	0	18	13
13	77.4	42.3	59.8	94	1907	55	1922	69	1987	24	1903	5	0	18	13
14	77.4	42.3	59.9	94†	1962	52	1921	64	1971	30†	1933	5	0	18	13
15	77.6	42.8	60.2	96	1936	54	1924	66	1955	30	1913	5	0	19	13
16	77.9	42.9	60.4	95	1936	50	1894	61	1985	28†	1922	5	0	18	13
17	77.9	43.5	60.7	96	1936	54	1917	59†	1989	21	1896	5	1	19	14
18	77.8	43.6	60.7	95	1989	54	1933	65	1987	27†	1978	5	1	19	13
19	77.1	42.8	59.9	97	1994	54	1966	57	1994	24	1896	5	0	18	13
20	78.1	43.5	60.8	97	1994	58	1995	58	1895	28†	1912	5	1	19	13
21	78.4	43.7	61.1	96	1994	53	1925	59	1989	27	1904	5	1	19	13
22	78.7	44.8	61.8	94	1994	47	1900	60	1994	28	1904	4	1	19	14
23	78.7	44.4	61.6	95	1994	54	1900	61†	1994	32†	1912	4	1	19	14
24	78.6	44.9	61.7	96†	1946	57	1921	62	1956	23	1904	4	1	20	14
25	79.0	44.7	61.9	100	1946	62†	1994	63	1962	24	1899	4	1	20	14
26	78.0	44.9	61.5	98	1898	58†	1984	60†	1981	29	1899	4	1	19	14
27	78.1	45.0	61.6	95	1981	55	1900	61	1946	25	1896	4	1	20	14
28	78.6	45.8	62.2	94	1992	55	1970	61	1950	28	1904	4	1	20	14
29	78.9	45.7	62.3	95	1981	55	1899	62†	1987	27	1904	4	1	20	14
30	79.7	45.8	62.8	95	1981	50	1915	62	1995	25	1899	4	1	20	14

Day	Total precipitation Avg	High	Year	Percent of years with precipitation None	Trace	.01 or more	.10 or more	.50 or more	Total snowfall Avg	High	Year	Percent with snowfall None	.1 or more	2.0 or more	ETo
1	0.03	0.54	1975	84.0	0.0	16.0	9.4	0.9	0.0	0.0†	1995	100.0	0.0	0.0	0.18
2	0.02	0.40†	1974	80.2	1.9	17.9	8.5	0.0	0.0	0.0†	1995	100.0	0.0	0.0	0.17
3	0.01	0.40	1981	87.7	0.9	11.3	4.7	0.0	0.0	0.0†	1995	100.0	0.0	0.0	0.17
4	0.02	0.40	1929	86.8	0.9	12.3	5.7	0.0	0.0	0.0†	1995	100.0	0.0	0.0	0.18
5	0.01	0.49	1906	89.6	0.0	10.4	3.8	0.0	0.0	0.0†	1995	100.0	0.0	0.0	0.18
6	0.01	0.25	1964	87.7	2.8	9.4	3.8	0.0	0.0	0.0†	1995	100.0	0.0	0.0	0.18
7	0.03	0.53	1943	81.1	0.0	18.9	10.4	0.9	0.0	0.0†	1995	100.0	0.0	0.0	0.18
8	0.02	0.58	1944	83.0	2.8	14.2	6.6	0.9	0.0	0.0†	1995	100.0	0.0	0.0	0.18
9	0.01	0.20†	1943	87.7	0.9	11.3	5.7	0.0	0.0	0.0†	1995	100.0	0.0	0.0	0.18
10	0.02	0.73	1941	86.8	2.8	10.4	3.8	0.9	0.0	0.0†	1995	100.0	0.0	0.0	0.18
11	0.01	0.23	1948	84.0	1.9	14.2	6.6	0.0	0.0	0.2	1927	99.0	1.0	0.0	0.19
12	0.02	0.50	1865	84.0	3.8	12.3	7.5	0.9	0.0	0.0†	1995	100.0	0.0	0.0	0.19
13	0.00	0.18	1972	90.6	2.8	6.6	0.9	0.0	0.0	0.0†	1995	100.0	0.0	0.0	0.19
14	0.01	0.28	1976	89.6	0.9	9.4	2.8	0.0	0.0	0.0†	1995	100.0	0.0	0.0	0.19
15	0.01	0.43	1898	95.3	0.9	3.8	1.9	0.0	0.0	0.0†	1995	100.0	0.0	0.0	0.19
16	0.01	0.40	1988	88.7	2.8	8.5	5.7	0.0	0.0	0.0†	1995	100.0	0.0	0.0	0.20
17	0.02	0.70	1988	89.6	1.9	8.5	5.7	1.9	0.0	0.0†	1995	100.0	0.0	0.0	0.19
18	0.03	0.53	1995	81.1	1.9	17.0	9.4	0.9	0.0	0.0†	1995	100.0	0.0	0.0	0.19
19	0.02	0.40	1981	84.0	1.9	14.2	6.6	0.0	0.0	0.0†	1995	100.0	0.0	0.0	0.19
20	0.01	0.21	1951	92.5	0.9	6.6	2.8	0.0	0.0	0.0†	1995	100.0	0.0	0.0	0.20
21	0.02	0.76	1988	89.6	3.8	6.6	5.7	0.9	0.0	0.0†	1995	100.0	0.0	0.0	0.20
22	0.02	0.42	1900	82.1	2.8	15.1	6.6	0.0	0.0	0.0†	1995	100.0	0.0	0.0	0.20
23	0.02	0.70	1942	88.7	0.9	10.4	7.5	0.9	0.0	0.0†	1995	100.0	0.0	0.0	0.20
24	0.01	0.36	1990	89.5	3.8	6.7	1.9	0.0	0.0	0.0†	1995	100.0	0.0	0.0	0.20
25	0.01	0.62	1915	87.7	3.8	8.5	2.8	0.9	0.0	0.0†	1995	100.0	0.0	0.0	0.20
26	0.02	0.48	1994	86.8	0.9	12.3	8.5	0.0	0.0	0.0†	1995	100.0	0.0	0.0	0.19
27	0.01	0.19	1940	84.0	5.7	10.4	3.8	0.0	0.0	0.0†	1995	100.0	0.0	0.0	0.19
28	0.03	0.69	1994	81.1	2.8	16.0	9.4	1.9	0.0	0.0†	1995	100.0	0.0	0.0	0.19
29	0.04	1.10	1917	81.0	1.0	18.1	6.7	2.9	0.0	0.0†	1995	100.0	0.0	0.0	0.20
30	0.02	0.50	1954	90.6	0.9	8.5	5.7	0.9	0.0	0.0†	1995	100.0	0.0	0.0	0.20

† Also occurred on earlier date(s).

Utah's Weather and Climate

May

| Day | Average temperature | | | High | Extreme maximum | | Year | High | Extreme minimum | | Year | HDD | Degree Days | | |
---	Max	Min	Mean		Year	Low			Year	Low			CDD	GDD40	GDD50
1	80.2	45.8	63.0	97	1985	51	1915	59†	1987	25	1899	3	1	20	15
2	80.1	46.7	63.4	99	1947	53	1915	65	1928	26	1899	3	2	20	15
3	82.0	46.5	64.2	102	1947	60	1898	67	1985	20	1899	3	2	21	15
4	83.1	47.8	65.5	100	1947	52	1905	65	1992	27	1899	2	2	21	16
5	82.6	47.7	65.1	99	1947	56	1915	63	1984	31	1910	2	3	21	16
6	82.8	48.1	65.4	99	1989	57†	1964	63	1994	28	1896	2	3	21	16
7	82.8	48.2	65.5	99	1895	54	1964	62	1990	33	1938	2	3	21	16
8	83.5	48.4	65.9	99	1895	61	1930	65	1946	31	1897	2	3	22	16
9	83.5	48.1	65.8	97	1923	64†	1933	65	1989	32	1948	2	2	22	16
10	83.8	48.8	66.3	100	1934	60†	1922	62	1946	28	1896	2	3	22	16
11	84.6	49.0	66.8	101	1960	62	1933	67	1988	32	1948	1	3	22	17
12	84.7	49.6	67.1	100	1984	62	1907	67	1993	31	1896	1	3	22	17
13	85.7	49.4	67.5	101	1936	65	1907	67	1994	36	1933	1	4	22	17
14	86.2	50.4	68.3	100†	1938	64	1977	65	1984	34	1912	1	4	23	17
15	85.9	50.4	68.1	101	1927	63	1951	68	1994	32†	1896	1	4	23	17
16	86.4	50.7	68.5	100	1927	61	1898	67	1985	33	1899	1	4	23	18
17	86.5	50.7	68.6	100†	1956	64†	1977	63†	1988	37	1899	1	4	23	17
18	86.8	51.4	69.1	98†	1970	65	1949	68†	1982	35	1903	1	5	23	18
19	86.6	51.9	69.3	98†	1986	57	1902	65	1987	31	1903	1	5	24	18
20	86.6	51.8	69.2	99†	1946	69	1902	67	1992	30	1899	1	5	24	18
21	86.5	51.5	69.0	99†	1967	58	1975	69	1989	34	1902	1	5	24	18
22	87.4	51.4	69.4	103	1967	67	1903	67	1955	33	1899	0	5	24	18
23	88.1	52.0	70.1	102	1984	71†	1921	69	1953	37†	1927	0	5	24	18
24	88.5	52.9	70.7	101	1984	57	1965	75	1984	39	1902	0	6	24	19
25	89.1	53.5	71.3	103	1986	66	1977	70	1967	37	1903	0	6	25	19
26	89.2	53.4	71.3	102†	1983	69	1929	65	1985	36	1980	0	6	25	19
27	89.4	54.0	71.7	104	1896	68	1929	68	1947	40	1980	0	7	25	19
28	88.9	53.9	71.4	104†	1984	63	1895	68†	1994	37	1899	0	7	25	19
29	89.0	53.6	71.3	105	1984	67	1918	66†	1974	38	1895	0	7	25	19
30	88.8	54.1	71.4	107	1910	60	1906	69	1939	40	1906	0	6	25	19
31	89.0	53.8	71.4	108	1910	63	1991	72	1984	38	1895	0	7	25	19

| | Total precipitation | | | | | Percent of years with precipitation | | | Total snowfall | | | Percent with snowfall | | | |
Day	Avg	High	Year	None	Trace	.01 or more	.10 or more	.50 or more	Avg	High	Year	None	.1 or more	2.0 or more	ETo
1	0.02	0.45†	1954	85.3	2.8	11.9	7.3		0.0	0.0	0.0†	1995	100.0	0.0	0.0	0.23
2	0.02	0.27	1895	86.2	0.9	12.8	8.3		0.0	0.0	0.0†	1995	100.0	0.0	0.0	0.23
3	0.02	0.53	1905	89.0	0.9	10.1	5.5	1.8	0.0	0.0†	1995	100.0	0.0	0.0	0.24
4	0.01	0.45	1930	91.7	1.8	6.4	1.8		0.0	0.0	0.0†	1995	100.0	0.0	0.0	0.24
5	0.01	0.32	1900	88.1	4.6	7.3	2.8		0.0	0.0	0.0†	1995	100.0	0.0	0.0	0.24
6	0.02	0.75	1971	87.2	3.7	9.2	6.4	0.9	0.0	0.0	0.0†	1995	100.0	0.0	0.0	0.24
7	0.03	0.90	1869	85.3	0.9	13.8	7.3	1.8	0.0	0.0	0.0†	1995	100.0	0.0	0.0	0.24
8	0.01	0.41	1971	87.2	1.8	11.0	2.8		0.0	0.0	0.0†	1995	100.0	0.0	0.0	0.24
9	0.00	0.26	1977	92.7	2.8	4.6	0.9		0.0	0.0	0.0†	1995	100.0	0.0	0.0	0.24
10	0.02	0.60	1922	89.0	1.8	9.2	5.5	0.9	0.0	0.0	0.0†	1995	100.0	0.0	0.0	0.24
11	0.03	1.52	1958	89.9	0.9	9.2	5.5	1.8	0.0	0.0	0.0†	1995	100.0	0.0	0.0	0.25
12	0.02	0.49	1968	83.5	3.7	12.8	6.4		0.0	0.0	0.0†	1995	100.0	0.0	0.0	0.25
13	0.00	0.08†	1968	87.2	1.8	11.0	0.0		0.0	0.0	0.0†	1995	100.0	0.0	0.0	0.25
14	0.01	0.84	1977	89.8	3.7	6.5	2.8	0.9	0.0	0.0	0.0†	1995	100.0	0.0	0.0	0.25
15	0.01	0.81	1951	89.7	1.9	8.4	2.8	0.9	0.0	0.0	0.0†	1995	100.0	0.0	0.0	0.25
16	0.01	0.40	1987	88.0	1.9	10.2	2.8		0.0	0.0	0.0†	1995	100.0	0.0	0.0	0.25
17	0.00	0.10†	1987	89.9	0.9	9.2	1.8		0.0	0.0	0.0†	1995	100.0	0.0	0.0	0.25
18	0.03	1.02	1949	90.8	0.9	8.3	3.7	1.8	0.0	0.0	0.0†	1995	100.0	0.0	0.0	0.25
19	0.01	0.59	1916	91.7	1.8	6.4	3.7	0.9	0.0	0.0	0.0†	1995	100.0	0.0	0.0	0.25
20	0.01	0.32	1864	89.0	2.8	8.3	4.6		0.0	0.0	0.0†	1995	100.0	0.0	0.0	0.25
21	0.01	0.39	1956	86.2	1.8	11.9	3.7		0.0	0.0	0.0†	1995	100.0	0.0	0.0	0.25
22	0.00	0.10	1903	94.5	0.9	4.6	0.9		0.0	0.0	0.0†	1995	100.0	0.0	0.0	0.26
23	0.00	0.22	1957	94.5	0.0	5.5	0.9		0.0	0.0	0.0†	1995	100.0	0.0	0.0	0.26
24	0.02	0.61	1977	92.6	0.0	7.4	4.6	1.9	0.0	0.0	0.0†	1995	100.0	0.0	0.0	0.26
25	0.02	1.00	1869	91.7	0.9	7.4	3.7	1.9	0.0	0.0	0.0†	1995	100.0	0.0	0.0	0.26
26	0.01	0.21	1936	90.7	1.9	7.4	3.7		0.0	0.0	0.0†	1995	100.0	0.0	0.0	0.26
27	0.02	1.15	1975	89.0	1.8	9.2	5.5	0.9	0.0	0.0	0.0†	1995	100.0	0.0	0.0	0.26
28	0.01	0.35	1906	90.8	0.9	8.3	5.5		0.0	0.0	0.0†	1995	100.0	0.0	0.0	0.26
29	0.01	0.67	1896	94.4	0.9	4.6	1.9	0.9	0.0	0.0	0.0†	1995	100.0	0.0	0.0	0.26
30	0.01	0.35	1917	91.7	2.8	5.6	1.9		0.0	0.0	0.0†	1995	100.0	0.0	0.0	0.26
31	0.01	0.12	1870	89.9	1.8	8.3	3.7		0.0	0.0	0.0†	1995	100.0	0.0	0.0	0.26

† Also occurred on earlier date(s).

ST GEORGE
Daily Data Summary

June

Day	Average temperature Max	Min	Mean	High	Extreme maximum Year	Low	Year	Extreme minimum High	Year	Low	Year	HDD	Degree Days CDD	GDD40	GDD50
1	89.8	54.5	72.2	105	1910	68	1899	65†	1972	35†	1908	0	7	25	20
2	90.9	54.5	72.7	104	1968	67	1899	71	1986	36	1902	0	8	25	20
3	90.9	55.5	73.2	103†	1968	72	1908	69	1956	38	1902	0	8	26	20
4	92.0	56.0	74.0	105	1957	65	1925	72	1986	40†	1915	0	9	26	20
5	92.3	56.5	74.4	104	1957	71	1949	79	1987	40	1902	0	9	26	21
6	92.3	55.8	74.1	105	1893	65	1934	71†	1994	40	1902	0	9	26	20
7	92.8	56.4	74.6	108	1985	75	1932	75	1981	41†	1932	0	9	26	21
8	92.5	55.7	74.1	107†	1985	69	1995	69	1985	41	1894	0	9	26	20
9	93.2	56.2	74.7	109	1918	73	1968	70†	1992	43†	1914	0	9	26	21
10	94.0	56.9	75.5	110	1918	74	1913	74	1955	45	1954	0	10	26	21
11	94.8	57.0	75.9	114	1918	73	1928	75	1910	41	1894	0	10	26	21
12	95.8	57.7	76.8	115	1918	80	1907	73	1911	37	1894	0	11	27	21
13	95.7	58.4	77.0	110	1918	72	1901	76	1918	41†	1915	0	12	27	22
14	96.0	58.2	77.1	112	1940	77	1901	77	1959	43	1894	0	12	27	22
15	95.3	58.7	77.0	110	1896	75	1907	77	1994	37	1901	0	12	27	22
16	95.4	58.0	76.7	112	1896	73	1965	72†	1964	42	1901	0	11	27	21
17	96.4	58.7	77.6	109†	1985	75	1995	77	1949	41	1895	0	12	27	22
18	97.0	58.5	77.8	112	1940	77	1979	74	1994	41	1895	0	12	27	22
19	97.5	58.9	78.2	110†	1985	81	1975	73†	1983	45	1895	0	13	27	22
20	98.4	59.8	79.1	114	1902	80	1923	74	1959	45	1895	0	14	28	22
21	98.9	60.0	79.4	114	1902	84	1916	74	1959	46	1895	0	14	28	23
22	99.4	60.6	80.0	114	1902	85	1898	78	1916	46	1915	0	14	28	23
23	99.5	61.0	80.2	110†	1968	82	1898	72†	1970	47	1948	0	15	28	23
24	99.5	61.2	80.3	111	1994	86†	1952	75	1959	48†	1911	0	15	29	23
25	99.8	61.4	80.6	115	1970	84	1985	81	1988	48†	1904	0	15	29	23
26	99.7	61.1	80.4	115	1970	82	1906	75	1987	47	1899	0	15	29	23
27	99.9	61.7	80.8	114	1970	76	1991	82†	1981	46	1899	0	15	29	23
28	100.1	61.9	81.0	113	1994	84	1913	80	1988	44	1915	0	16	29	24
29	100.2	62.7	81.5	114	1994	81	1938	81	1956	40	1893	0	16	29	24
30	100.8	62.7	81.8	114	1994	88	1912	82	1976	41	1893	0	16	29	24

Day	Total precipitation Avg	High	Year	None	Trace	Percent of years with precipitation .01 or more	.10 or more	.50 or more	Total snowfall Avg	High	Year	Percent with snowfall None	.1 or more	2.0 or more	ETo
1	0.00	0.22	1899	94.4	0.9	4.6	0.9	0.0	0.0	0.0†	1995	100.0	0.0	0.0	0.28
2	0.01	0.24	1948	94.4	0.0	5.6	2.8	0.0	0.0	0.0†	1995	100.0	0.0	0.0	0.28
3	0.01	0.24	1952	91.7	0.9	7.4	2.8	0.0	0.0	0.0†	1995	100.0	0.0	0.0	0.28
4	0.03	1.16	1925	89.8	2.8	7.4	3.7	1.9	0.0	0.0†	1995	100.0	0.0	0.0	0.29
5	0.01	0.35	1932	90.7	1.9	7.4	2.8	0.0	0.0	0.0†	1995	100.0	0.0	0.0	0.29
6	0.01	0.25	1934	92.6	0.9	6.5	0.9	0.0	0.0	0.0†	1995	100.0	0.0	0.0	0.29
7	0.01	0.20†	1987	90.7	0.0	9.3	5.6	0.0	0.0	0.0†	1995	100.0	0.0	0.0	0.29
8	0.01	0.21	1964	89.7	1.9	8.4	3.7	0.0	0.0	0.0†	1995	100.0	0.0	0.0	0.29
9	0.00	0.15	1900	97.2	1.9	0.9	0.9	0.0	0.0	0.0†	1995	100.0	0.0	0.0	0.29
10	0.02	0.99	1957	90.7	4.6	4.6	2.8	1.9	0.0	0.0†	1995	100.0	0.0	0.0	0.30
11	0.00	0.16	1990	93.5	0.9	5.6	0.9	0.0	0.0	0.0†	1995	100.0	0.0	0.0	0.30
12	0.00	0.37	1947	96.3	0.9	2.8	0.9	0.0	0.0	0.0†	1995	100.0	0.0	0.0	0.31
13	0.00	0.12	1911	99.1	0.0	0.9	0.9	0.0	0.0	0.0†	1995	100.0	0.0	0.0	0.30
14	0.00	0.23	1927	98.1	0.0	1.9	1.9	0.0	0.0	0.0†	1995	100.0	0.0	0.0	0.31
15	0.00	0.12	1927	96.3	0.0	3.7	0.9	0.0	0.0	0.0†	1995	100.0	0.0	0.0	0.30
16	0.01	0.47	1995	95.4	0.0	4.6	2.8	0.0	0.0	0.0†	1995	100.0	0.0	0.0	0.30
17	0.00	0.15	1925	93.5	0.9	5.6	0.9	0.0	0.0	0.0†	1995	100.0	0.0	0.0	0.31
18	0.00	0.17	1930	94.4	0.9	4.6	2.8	0.0	0.0	0.0†	1995	100.0	0.0	0.0	0.31
19	0.00	0.20	1930	96.3	0.9	2.8	0.9	0.0	0.0	0.0†	1995	100.0	0.0	0.0	0.31
20	0.01	0.27	1988	96.3	0.9	2.8	2.8	0.0	0.0	0.0†	1995	100.0	0.0	0.0	0.32
21	0.01	0.41	1988	93.5	0.9	5.6	1.9	0.0	0.0	0.0†	1995	100.0	0.0	0.0	0.32
22	0.00	0.38	1972	95.4	2.8	1.9	0.9	0.0	0.0	0.0†	1995	100.0	0.0	0.0	0.32
23	0.00	0.35	1898	97.2	1.9	0.9	0.9	0.0	0.0	0.0†	1995	100.0	0.0	0.0	0.32
24	0.00	0.15	1934	95.4	0.0	4.6	0.9	0.0	0.0	0.0†	1995	100.0	0.0	0.0	0.32
25	0.00	0.06	1988	95.4	1.9	2.8	0.0	0.0	0.0	0.0†	1995	100.0	0.0	0.0	0.32
26	0.01	0.62	1954	98.1	0.0	1.9	1.9	0.9	0.0	0.0†	1995	100.0	0.0	0.0	0.32
27	0.00	0.04	1895	96.3	0.9	2.8	0.0	0.0	0.0	0.0†	1995	100.0	0.0	0.0	0.32
28	0.02	0.62	1912	92.6	1.9	5.6	3.7	1.9	0.0	0.0†	1995	100.0	0.0	0.0	0.32
29	0.01	0.20†	1925	94.4	0.9	4.6	3.7	0.0	0.0	0.0†	1995	100.0	0.0	0.0	0.32
30	0.01	0.50	1956	91.7	2.8	5.6	0.9	0.9	0.0	0.0†	1995	100.0	0.0	0.0	0.33

† Also occurred on earlier date(s).

July

Day	Average temperature			High	Extreme maximum			Extreme minimum				HDD	Degree Days		
	Max	Min	Mean		Year	Low	Year	High	Year	Low	Year		CDD	GDD40	GDD50
1	101.2	62.6	81.9	113	1994	88	1911	88	1909	44	1893	0	16	29	24
2	100.9	63.8	82.3	112†	1985	83	1912	83	1994	50†	1896	0	17	30	24
3	100.6	63.3	82.0	114	1985	79	1912	79	1986	41	1902	0	17	30	24
4	100.9	64.1	82.5	115	1985	81	1902	80	1986	44	1902	0	17	30	25
5	101.4	62.8	82.1	117	1985	84	1902	75†	1986	50†	1921	0	17	29	24
6	102.1	63.5	82.8	115	1985	89	1933	81	1957	43	1902	0	17	30	24
7	101.9	64.3	83.1	113	1985	85	1947	81	1981	44	1893	0	18	30	25
8	101.6	65.7	83.7	113	1985	84	1992	82	1975	49	1893	0	18	31	25
9	101.4	65.6	83.5	112	1985	80	1930	83	1985	50	1903	0	18	31	25
10	101.7	65.8	83.8	110†	1973	85†	1936	80	1985	50	1893	0	18	31	25
11	102.0	65.7	83.8	111†	1959	85	1936	80	1981	41	1893	0	18	31	25
12	102.5	65.6	84.1	111	1917	79	1918	79	1964	51†	1902	0	19	31	25
13	102.3	66.2	84.3	112†	1939	85	1918	80	1959	48	1902	0	19	31	26
14	102.3	66.8	84.5	112†	1972	86†	1914	80	1959	49	1932	0	19	31	26
15	102.5	66.9	84.7	112	1922	83	1896	89	1970	48	1893	0	19	31	26
16	101.9	67.5	84.7	115	1925	84	1896	80†	1985	50†	1904	0	19	32	26
17	101.6	67.1	84.4	111	1936	89†	1896	80	1970	49	1904	0	19	32	26
18	101.3	66.8	84.0	110†	1927	83	1912	80	1994	45	1903	0	19	31	26
19	101.6	66.6	84.1	110†	1966	84	1909	80	1970	49	1897	0	19	31	26
20	101.8	66.8	84.3	115	1989	87	1943	82	1989	50	1897	0	19	31	26
21	101.9	66.4	84.2	114	1989	82	1911	79	1990	50	1902	0	19	31	26
22	101.0	67.9	84.4	110†	1960	81	1986	81	1982	55†	1914	0	19	32	26
23	100.9	67.1	84.0	110	1931	87	1897	82	1955	50	1897	0	18	31	26
24	101.9	67.4	84.7	112	1931	90	1923	78†	1990	51	1897	0	19	32	26
25	101.5	67.3	84.4	110†	1995	79	1941	81	1981	48	1903	0	19	32	26
26	101.2	67.7	84.4	112	1931	85†	1941	78	1994	54	1913	0	19	32	26
27	101.1	67.4	84.3	113	1898	89	1929	80	1989	52	1909	0	19	32	26
28	101.5	67.1	84.3	114	1995	80	1919	81	1994	49	1903	0	19	32	26
29	101.3	67.1	84.2	115	1898	81	1912	84	1994	46	1903	0	19	32	26
30	101.1	66.9	84.0	113	1995	80	1912	80	1994	49	1896	0	18	31	26
31	101.2	66.7	84.0	109†	1982	81	1968	79	1989	51	1896	0	18	31	26

Day	Total precipitation			Percent of years with precipitation					Total snowfall			Percent with snowfall			ETo
	Avg	High	Year	None	Trace	.01 or more	.10 or more	.50 or more	Avg	High	Year	None	.1 or more	2.0 or more	
1	0.01	0.47	1980	96.3	0.9	2.8	1.8	0.0	0.0	0.0†	1995	100.0	0.0	0.0	0.32
2	0.01	0.39	1914	93.6	1.8	4.6	2.8	0.0	0.0	0.0†	1995	100.0	0.0	0.0	0.32
3	0.00	0.25	1909	94.5	2.8	2.8	1.8	0.0	0.0	0.0†	1995	100.0	0.0	0.0	0.31
4	0.02	0.75	1961	93.6	1.8	4.6	4.6	0.9	0.0	0.0†	1995	100.0	0.0	0.0	0.31
5	0.01	0.31	1952	96.3	0.0	3.7	3.7	0.0	0.0	0.0†	1995	100.0	0.0	0.0	0.32
6	0.02	0.45	1980	91.7	0.0	8.3	4.6	0.0	0.0	0.0†	1995	100.0	0.0	0.0	0.32
7	0.01	0.21	1967	85.3	4.6	10.1	3.7	0.0	0.0	0.0†	1995	100.0	0.0	0.0	0.32
8	0.01	0.40	1936	90.8	0.9	8.3	2.8	0.0	0.0	0.0†	1995	100.0	0.0	0.0	0.32
9	0.02	0.65	1927	86.2	3.7	10.1	4.6	0.9	0.0	0.0†	1995	100.0	0.0	0.0	0.31
10	0.01	0.40†	1936	89.8	0.9	9.3	3.7	0.0	0.0	0.0†	1995	100.0	0.0	0.0	0.32
11	0.02	0.70	1919	89.0	1.8	9.2	4.6	0.9	0.0	0.0†	1995	100.0	0.0	0.0	0.32
12	0.01	0.37	1984	90.8	0.9	8.3	3.7	0.0	0.0	0.0†	1995	100.0	0.0	0.0	0.32
13	0.02	0.40	1918	87.2	1.8	11.0	8.3	0.0	0.0	0.0†	1995	100.0	0.0	0.0	0.32
14	0.02	1.23	1905	88.1	2.8	9.2	3.7	1.8	0.0	0.0†	1995	100.0	0.0	0.0	0.32
15	0.03	1.18	1896	86.2	2.8	11.0	6.4	1.8	0.0	0.0†	1995	100.0	0.0	0.0	0.32
16	0.02	0.60	1910	84.4	1.8	13.8	6.4	0.9	0.0	0.0†	1995	100.0	0.0	0.0	0.31
17	0.03	0.87	1987	85.3	3.7	11.0	6.4	2.8	0.0	0.0†	1995	100.0	0.0	0.0	0.31
18	0.02	0.87	1912	85.3	1.8	12.8	7.3	0.9	0.0	0.0†	1995	100.0	0.0	0.0	0.31
19	0.03	0.62	1951	76.9	7.4	15.7	11.1	2.8	0.0	0.0†	1995	100.0	0.0	0.0	0.31
20	0.04	1.22	1911	82.6	2.8	14.7	9.2	0.9	0.0	0.0†	1995	100.0	0.0	0.0	0.31
21	0.03	0.75	1970	78.9	0.9	20.2	11.9	0.9	0.0	0.0†	1995	100.0	0.0	0.0	0.31
22	0.03	1.03	1913	84.4	3.7	11.9	6.4	1.8	0.0	0.0†	1995	100.0	0.0	0.0	0.31
23	0.03	1.48	1903	84.4	3.7	11.9	7.3	0.0	0.0	0.0†	1995	100.0	0.0	0.0	0.31
24	0.03	0.80	1908	81.5	1.9	16.7	9.3	1.9	0.0	0.0†	1995	100.0	0.0	0.0	0.31
25	0.06	1.82	1902	82.6	2.8	14.7	10.1	3.7	0.0	0.0†	1995	100.0	0.0	0.0	0.31
26	0.02	0.69	1964	82.6	2.8	14.7	5.5	1.8	0.0	0.0†	1995	100.0	0.0	0.0	0.31
27	0.02	0.36	1964	82.6	1.8	15.6	7.3	0.0	0.0	0.0†	1995	100.0	0.0	0.0	0.31
28	0.04	0.93	1916	82.4	0.9	16.7	10.2	2.8	0.0	0.0†	1995	100.0	0.0	0.0	0.31
29	0.03	0.65	1985	79.8	1.8	18.3	10.1	0.9	0.0	0.0†	1995	100.0	0.0	0.0	0.31
30	0.03	0.70	1917	82.6	1.8	15.6	8.3	0.9	0.0	0.0†	1995	100.0	0.0	0.0	0.31
31	0.02	0.48	1968	86.2	0.9	12.8	7.3	0.0	0.0	0.0†	1995	100.0	0.0	0.0	0.31

† Also occurred on earlier date(s).

ST GEORGE
Daily Data Summary

August

Day	Average temperature				Extreme maximum				Extreme minimum				HDD	Degree Days		
	Max	Min	Mean	High	Year	Low	Year	High	Year	Low	Year		CDD	GDD40	GDD50
1	101.3	67.1	84.2	112	1995	89†	1968	82	1951	43	1903	0	19	32	26
2	101.2	67.0	84.1	112	1995	78	1899	80	1987	54	1913	0	19	31	26
3	101.3	66.7	84.0	111	1995	82	1899	80	1993	54†	1944	0	19	31	26
4	100.9	66.4	83.7	112	1893	90	1951	80	1957	52	1944	0	18	31	26
5	100.3	66.7	83.5	113	1895	83	1929	78†	1992	52	1912	0	18	31	26
6	100.5	65.8	83.2	110†	1994	85	1925	78	1937	50	1912	0	18	31	25
7	101.1	65.8	83.5	110†	1978	90	1968	81	1975	52†	1912	0	18	31	25
8	100.8	66.1	83.4	110	1978	86	1930	79†	1995	50	1896	0	18	31	26
9	100.7	66.5	83.6	111†	1978	84	1941	80†	1981	50	1896	0	18	31	26
10	100.6	66.5	83.5	110†	1969	80	1989	82	1964	51†	1899	0	18	31	26
11	99.7	66.0	82.8	112	1940	81	1941	80†	1995	47	1894	0	17	31	25
12	99.8	65.5	82.6	111†	1937	86†	1945	79	1995	48	1900	0	17	31	25
13	99.9	65.3	82.6	110	1933	79	1931	80	1958	46	1899	0	17	31	25
14	99.6	65.7	82.7	109	1963	78	1979	80	1958	50	1899	0	17	31	25
15	99.0	65.1	82.1	110	1994	81	1941	79†	1994	48	1902	0	17	31	25
16	98.9	64.3	81.6	110	1994	80	1990	78†	1995	47†	1902	0	16	30	25
17	99.4	64.2	81.8	110	1994	87	1909	82	1994	44	1899	0	16	30	25
18	98.8	64.1	81.5	109	1897	79	1983	79	1986	48†	1902	0	16	30	25
19	98.5	64.7	81.6	110	1897	77	1922	77	1993	46	1899	0	16	30	25
20	98.2	64.3	81.3	107†	1937	83	1893	84	1992	47	1899	0	16	30	25
21	98.6	64.3	81.5	109†	1969	81	1975	78	1953	50	1899	0	16	30	25
22	98.9	63.6	81.3	110	1969	89†	1957	77	1994	44	1900	0	16	30	24
23	98.5	63.3	80.9	110	1969	84	1921	79	1955	45	1900	0	15	30	24
24	98.5	63.3	80.9	110†	1985	76	1921	76	1953	45†	1900	0	15	30	24
25	98.4	63.7	81.0	109†	1985	82†	1982	78	1991	47	1899	0	16	30	24
26	98.1	63.2	80.7	108	1985	85	1980	73	1956	47	1978	0	15	30	24
27	97.7	62.5	80.1	108	1924	82	1925	77	1991	49	1900	0	15	29	24
28	98.1	61.9	80.0	109	1918	73	1896	76	1991	48	1903	0	15	29	23
29	97.4	62.3	79.8	107	1954	74	1951	78	1981	48	1895	0	14	29	23
30	97.7	61.2	79.5	107†	1995	81	1912	76†	1976	43	1902	0	14	29	23
31	97.2	60.7	79.0	109	1995	82	1931	78	1958	45	1932	0	13	28	23

Day	Total precipitation			Percent of years with precipitation					Total snowfall			Percent with snowfall			
	Avg	High	Year	None	Trace	.01 or more	.10 or more	.50 or more	Avg	High	Year	None	.1 or more	2.0 or more	ETo
1	0.02	0.53	1974	85.2	0.9	13.9	5.6	0.9	0.0	0.0†	1995	100.0	0.0	0.0	0.28
2	0.05	1.89	1899	82.4	0.9	16.7	7.4	3.7	0.0	0.0†	1995	100.0	0.0	0.0	0.28
3	0.05	1.07	1951	79.6	0.9	19.4	10.2	4.6	0.0	0.0†	1995	100.0	0.0	0.0	0.28
4	0.02	0.33	1908	81.5	0.9	17.6	9.3	0.0	0.0	0.0†	1995	100.0	0.0	0.0	0.28
5	0.02	0.70	1929	86.1	3.7	10.2	3.7	0.9	0.0	0.0†	1995	100.0	0.0	0.0	0.28
6	0.01	0.37	1925	86.1	0.0	13.9	5.6	0.0	0.0	0.0†	1995	100.0	0.0	0.0	0.28
7	0.02	0.57	1939	87.0	1.9	11.1	3.7	0.9	0.0	0.0†	1995	100.0	0.0	0.0	0.28
8	0.02	0.53	1930	87.0	2.8	10.2	7.4	0.9	0.0	0.0†	1995	100.0	0.0	0.0	0.28
9	0.02	0.52	1930	87.0	0.9	12.0	5.6	1.9	0.0	0.0†	1995	100.0	0.0	0.0	0.28
10	0.02	0.50	1908	80.6	0.9	18.5	8.3	0.9	0.0	0.0†	1995	100.0	0.0	0.0	0.28
11	0.03	0.42†	1959	77.8	3.7	18.5	12.0	0.0	0.0	0.0†	1995	100.0	0.0	0.0	0.27
12	0.04	1.30	1945	85.2	0.0	14.8	10.2	1.9	0.0	0.0†	1995	100.0	0.0	0.0	0.28
13	0.02	0.45	1955	87.0	1.9	11.1	5.6	0.0	0.0	0.0†	1995	100.0	0.0	0.0	0.28
14	0.03	0.56	1964	85.2	1.9	13.0	9.3	0.9	0.0	0.0†	1995	100.0	0.0	0.0	0.27
15	0.03	1.25	1970	84.3	1.9	13.9	6.5	0.9	0.0	0.0†	1995	100.0	0.0	0.0	0.27
16	0.02	0.62	1990	86.1	1.9	12.0	6.5	0.9	0.0	0.0†	1995	100.0	0.0	0.0	0.27
17	0.03	1.02	1983	88.9	1.9	9.3	7.4	1.9	0.0	0.0†	1995	100.0	0.0	0.0	0.28
18	0.03	0.73	1983	83.3	2.8	13.9	9.3	1.9	0.0	0.0†	1995	100.0	0.0	0.0	0.27
19	0.02	0.71	1922	87.0	1.9	11.1	4.6	1.9	0.0	0.0†	1995	100.0	0.0	0.0	0.27
20	0.01	0.20	1975	84.3	1.9	13.9	5.6	0.0	0.0	0.0†	1995	100.0	0.0	0.0	0.27
21	0.03	0.75	1904	86.1	0.9	13.0	7.4	2.8	0.0	0.0†	1995	100.0	0.0	0.0	0.27
22	0.02	0.35	1935	82.4	0.9	16.7	7.4	0.0	0.0	0.0†	1995	100.0	0.0	0.0	0.27
23	0.01	0.67	1921	89.8	2.8	7.4	2.8	1.9	0.0	0.0†	1995	100.0	0.0	0.0	0.27
24	0.02	0.53	1921	86.1	2.8	11.1	8.3	1.9	0.0	0.0†	1995	100.0	0.0	0.0	0.27
25	0.02	0.82	1940	86.1	0.9	13.0	4.6	1.9	0.0	0.0†	1995	100.0	0.0	0.0	0.27
26	0.03	0.39	1953	77.8	2.8	19.4	10.2	0.0	0.0	0.0†	1995	100.0	0.0	0.0	0.27
27	0.02	0.88	1925	82.4	5.6	12.0	5.6	1.9	0.0	0.0†	1995	100.0	0.0	0.0	0.27
28	0.03	1.81	1896	84.3	0.9	14.8	2.8	0.9	0.0	0.0†	1995	100.0	0.0	0.0	0.27
29	0.02	0.80	1951	89.8	0.0	10.2	5.6	0.9	0.0	0.0†	1995	100.0	0.0	0.0	0.27
30	0.02	0.45	1961	88.0	1.9	10.2	7.4	0.0	0.0	0.0†	1995	100.0	0.0	0.0	0.27
31	0.03	2.40	1909	87.0	1.9	11.1	6.5	0.9	0.0	0.0†	1995	100.0	0.0	0.0	0.27

† Also occurred on earlier date(s).

ST GEORGE
Daily Data Summary

September

Day	Average temperature				Extreme maximum				Extreme minimum					Degree Days		
	Max	Min	Mean	High	Year	Low	Year	High	Year	Low	Year	HDD	CDD	GDD40	GDD50
1	97.0	60.4	78.7	109	1995	84	1913	74	1954	45	1901	0	13	28	23
2	96.4	60.7	78.6	107	1950	79	1900	78	1981	46	1902	0	13	28	23
3	96.5	59.5	78.0	109	1995	81	1918	73	1983	43	1898	0	12	28	22
4	96.5	59.9	78.2	108	1995	79	1912	76	1950	42	1898	0	13	28	23
5	96.4	59.9	78.2	105	1984	75	1939	75	1995	38	1912	0	13	28	22
6	96.2	58.7	77.5	105	1976	73	1939	71†	1952	39	1912	0	12	27	22
7	95.4	59.1	77.3	104	1994	82	1893	75	1947	39	1911	0	12	28	22
8	95.1	58.2	76.6	104†	1979	76	1929	74	1947	38	1911	0	11	27	22
9	95.3	58.0	76.6	104†	1979	78	1912	74	1983	41	1901	0	11	27	22
10	94.8	57.1	75.9	105†	1990	81†	1917	72	1994	38	1901	0	10	27	21
11	94.5	57.1	75.8	106	1990	79	1982	75	1968	43†	1900	0	10	27	21
12	93.6	56.3	74.9	105†	1990	73	1988	72	1959	36	1903	0	9	26	21
13	92.9	55.4	74.1	105	1971	78	1988	73	1910	33	1894	0	9	26	21
14	93.0	54.6	73.8	104	1971	74	1903	69	1960	34	1894	0	8	25	20
15	93.0	53.7	73.4	103	1971	73	1903	70	1992	36	1903	0	8	25	20
16	93.5	53.9	73.7	103	1928	76	1906	69†	1992	33	1903	0	8	25	20
17	93.0	54.2	73.6	104	1935	79	1940	72	1947	33	1903	0	8	25	20
18	92.5	54.1	73.3	104	1962	66	1965	73	1983	34	1903	0	8	25	20
19	91.7	52.6	72.1	102†	1987	67	1965	71	1983	33	1900	0	7	24	19
20	91.0	52.6	71.8	102	1949	72	1902	68	1984	33	1900	0	7	24	19
21	90.6	51.5	71.0	100†	1967	66	1895	68	1962	25	1895	0	6	24	19
22	90.2	51.3	70.7	102†	1966	68	1941	67	1966	31	1895	0	6	24	19
23	89.8	51.7	70.7	101	1966	71	1941	68	1958	29	1895	0	6	24	19
24	89.2	50.8	70.0	100†	1936	59	1900	71	1992	33	1901	0	5	23	18
25	89.1	51.0	70.1	103	1947	65	1986	67	1982	31	1901	0	5	23	18
26	88.8	50.7	69.8	100	1969	71	1986	66	1989	33	1912	0	5	23	18
27	88.8	50.8	69.8	102	1942	68†	1923	69	1989	32	1896	0	5	23	18
28	88.4	50.3	69.3	100	1942	62	1986	65	1995	31	1900	0	5	23	18
29	88.0	50.7	69.3	100†	1969	58	1905	74	1994	31	1900	1	5	23	18
30	87.2	49.7	68.5	99	1963	61	1905	65	1946	32	1900	1	4	23	18

	Total precipitation			Percent of years with precipitation					Total snowfall			Percent with snowfall			
						.01 or	.10 or	.50 or					.1 or	2.0 or	
Day	Avg	High	Year	None	Trace	more	more	more	Avg	High	Year	None	more	more	ETo
1	0.03	1.07	1960	88.5	1.0	10.6	4.8	2.9	0.0	0.0†	1995	100.0	0.0	0.0	0.23
2	0.03	0.67	1910	86.7	1.0	12.4	8.6	1.0	0.0	0.0†	1995	100.0	0.0	0.0	0.22
3	0.01	0.37	1918	91.4	0.0	8.6	3.8	0.0	0.0	0.0†	1995	100.0	0.0	0.0	0.22
4	0.03	0.93	1905	86.7	1.0	12.4	6.7	2.9	0.0	0.0†	1995	100.0	0.0	0.0	0.22
5	0.03	0.93	1978	85.7	1.0	13.3	6.7	1.9	0.0	0.0†	1995	100.0	0.0	0.0	0.22
6	0.02	0.90	1939	87.6	1.0	11.4	4.8	1.9	0.0	0.0†	1995	100.0	0.0	0.0	0.22
7	0.02	0.65	1929	84.8	1.0	14.3	5.7	1.0	0.0	0.0†	1995	100.0	0.0	0.0	0.22
8	0.03	0.69	1908	85.7	1.0	13.3	5.7	2.9	0.0	0.0†	1995	100.0	0.0	0.0	0.22
9	0.01	0.22	1924	92.4	1.0	6.7	3.8	0.0	0.0	0.0†	1995	100.0	0.0	0.0	0.22
10	0.01	0.44	1977	90.5	2.9	6.7	5.7	0.0	0.0	0.0†	1995	100.0	0.0	0.0	0.22
11	0.01	0.30	1939	91.4	1.0	7.6	4.8	0.0	0.0	0.0†	1995	100.0	0.0	0.0	0.22
12	0.03	1.44	1939	87.6	1.9	10.5	5.7	1.0	0.0	0.0†	1995	100.0	0.0	0.0	0.22
13	0.01	0.47	1910	91.4	1.9	6.7	3.8	0.0	0.0	0.0†	1995	100.0	0.0	0.0	0.21
14	0.01	0.70	1910	92.4	1.9	5.7	2.9	1.0	0.0	0.0†	1995	100.0	0.0	0.0	0.22
15	0.01	0.50	1906	94.3	0.0	5.7	4.8	1.0	0.0	0.0†	1995	100.0	0.0	0.0	0.22
16	0.01	0.61	1948	91.4	1.0	7.6	1.9	1.0	0.0	0.0†	1995	100.0	0.0	0.0	0.22
17	0.01	1.05	1940	91.4	1.9	6.7	1.9	1.0	0.0	0.0†	1995	100.0	0.0	0.0	0.22
18	0.02	0.62	1963	89.5	1.0	9.5	6.7	1.0	0.0	0.0†	1995	100.0	0.0	0.0	0.21
19	0.03	1.63	1972	89.5	1.0	9.5	4.8	1.9	0.0	0.0†	1995	100.0	0.0	0.0	0.21
20	0.01	0.25	1952	90.5	1.9	7.6	3.8	0.0	0.0	0.0†	1995	100.0	0.0	0.0	0.21
21	0.02	0.69	1967	92.4	2.9	4.8	2.9	1.9	0.0	0.0†	1995	100.0	0.0	0.0	0.21
22	0.01	0.60	1918	92.4	1.0	6.7	3.8	1.0	0.0	0.0†	1995	100.0	0.0	0.0	0.21
23	0.02	0.54	1937	91.4	0.0	8.6	6.7	1.0	0.0	0.0†	1995	100.0	0.0	0.0	0.21
24	0.02	0.63	1967	90.5	1.9	7.6	4.8	1.0	0.0	0.0†	1995	100.0	0.0	0.0	0.20
25	0.02	0.68	1909	89.5	1.0	9.5	7.6	1.0	0.0	0.0†	1995	100.0	0.0	0.0	0.20
26	0.03	1.26	1909	90.4	2.9	6.7	5.8	1.9	0.0	0.0†	1995	100.0	0.0	0.0	0.20
27	0.01	0.40	1982	89.5	2.9	7.6	5.7	0.0	0.0	0.0†	1995	100.0	0.0	0.0	0.20
28	0.03	1.08	1951	87.5	1.9	10.6	6.7	1.9	0.0	0.0†	1995	100.0	0.0	0.0	0.20
29	0.02	0.97	1905	87.5	2.9	9.6	5.8	1.9	0.0	0.0†	1995	100.0	0.0	0.0	0.20
30	0.03	1.01	1911	87.5	1.0	11.5	8.7	1.9	0.0	0.0†	1995	100.0	0.0	0.0	0.20

† Also occurred on earlier date(s).

October

Day	Average temperature				Extreme maximum				Extreme minimum					Degree Days		
	Max	Min	Mean	High	Year	Low	Year	High	Year	Low	Year	HDD	CDD	GDD40	GDD50
1	86.5	49.4	68.0	99	1980	65	1903	65	1976	32	1893	1	4	22	17
2	86.0	48.8	67.4	99	1963	63	1903	67	1967	28	1898	1	3	22	17
3	85.3	48.7	67.0	98	1892	65	1916	69	1967	34†	1908	1	3	22	17
4	84.8	47.4	66.1	99†	1917	69	1895	65	1967	32†	1899	2	3	22	17
5	84.7	47.4	66.0	97†	1917	56	1912	62†	1993	30	1898	1	2	22	17
6	85.1	46.4	65.8	97	1904	58	1946	70	1977	26	1913	1	2	21	17
7	84.9	46.5	65.7	98	1892	66	1946	64	1977	28	1913	1	2	21	17
8	84.5	45.6	65.1	96†	1979	60	1938	59†	1981	28	1913	2	2	21	16
9	83.8	45.1	64.5	96	1910	52	1912	57†	1945	30	1900	2	1	20	16
10	83.5	45.5	64.5	97	1950	61	1930	65	1981	30	1900	2	2	21	16
11	82.9	45.0	64.0	96	1950	64†	1973	61	1956	27	1913	2	1	20	16
12	81.4	44.8	63.1	96	1991	57	1947	66	1988	29	1893	3	1	20	15
13	81.5	43.8	62.6	94†	1950	56	1981	63	1994	31†	1915	3	1	20	15
14	82.0	43.9	62.9	95	1964	59	1899	60	1988	32†	1906	3	1	20	15
15	80.8	43.4	62.1	92†	1991	50	1908	63	1971	30†	1906	3	0	19	15
16	80.0	42.2	61.1	94	1927	50	1908	57	1907	25	1899	4	0	19	14
17	79.8	41.9	60.8	92†	1958	54	1908	59	1949	27†	1913	4	0	19	14
18	79.4	42.1	60.7	96	1947	55	1908	56	1957	26	1898	4	0	19	14
19	78.3	41.7	60.0	93†	1927	57	1920	55	1902	29	1971	5	0	18	13
20	78.4	41.4	59.9	92†	1927	52	1949	59	1955	27†	1911	5	0	18	14
21	77.3	41.0	59.2	92	1921	53	1941	61	1947	27	1898	6	0	18	13
22	77.6	40.0	58.8	89	1924	59†	1953	58	1921	25	1911	6	0	18	13
23	77.1	40.2	58.7	90	1959	58	1953	63	1991	26	1911	6	0	18	13
24	76.0	39.6	57.8	90†	1959	56†	1975	60	1992	27	1935	7	0	18	13
25	76.4	39.1	57.7	92	1915	57	1919	53	1907	23	1899	7	0	18	13
26	76.4	38.3	57.4	93	1926	52	1951	57	1927	21	1895	7	0	17	13
27	76.4	39.1	57.8	91	1964	58	1970	58	1912	23	1899	7	0	18	13
28	75.4	38.7	57.0	91	1915	50	1922	54†	1992	22	1970	8	0	17	12
29	74.1	38.3	56.2	92	1915	40	1971	56†	1987	23	1970	8	0	17	12
30	72.2	37.5	54.9	90	1915	46	1971	57	1968	20	1971	10	0	16	11
31	71.7	37.2	54.5	93	1915	53	1991	55	1945	20†	1900	10	0	16	10

	Total precipitation			Percent of years with precipitation					Total snowfall			Percent with snowfall			
Day	Avg	High	Year	None	Trace	.01 or more	.10 or more	.50 or more	Avg	High	Year	None	.1 or more	2.0 or more	ETo
1	0.03	0.94	1912	84.9	1.9	13.2	9.4	2.8	0.0	0.0†	1995	100.0	0.0	0.0	0.15
2	0.04	1.53	1903	85.8	2.8	11.3	6.6	1.9	0.0	0.0†	1995	100.0	0.0	0.0	0.15
3	0.01	0.51	1974	90.6	0.9	8.5	4.7	0.9	0.0	0.0†	1995	100.0	0.0	0.0	0.15
4	0.03	0.88	1912	89.6	0.9	9.4	5.7	2.8	0.0	0.0†	1995	100.0	0.0	0.0	0.15
5	0.03	0.84	1925	87.7	1.9	10.4	4.7	2.8	0.0	0.0†	1995	100.0	0.0	0.0	0.15
6	0.03	0.95	1916	90.6	1.9	7.5	6.6	1.9	0.0	0.0†	1995	100.0	0.0	0.0	0.15
7	0.01	0.52	1912	91.5	0.9	7.5	3.8	0.9	0.0	0.0†	1995	100.0	0.0	0.0	0.15
8	0.01	0.43	1985	90.6	0.9	8.5	2.8	0.0	0.0	0.0†	1995	100.0	0.0	0.0	0.15
9	0.01	0.71	1912	90.6	1.9	7.5	3.8	0.9	0.0	0.0†	1995	100.0	0.0	0.0	0.14
10	0.02	1.10	1930	89.6	1.9	8.5	4.7	1.9	0.0	0.0†	1995	100.0	0.0	0.0	0.14
11	0.03	0.65	1930	86.8	0.0	13.2	8.5	0.9	0.0	0.0†	1995	100.0	0.0	0.0	0.14
12	0.03	0.56	1980	85.8	1.9	12.3	9.4	0.9	0.0	0.0†	1995	100.0	0.0	0.0	0.14
13	0.02	0.61	1941	86.8	1.9	11.3	7.5	0.9	0.0	0.0†	1995	100.0	0.0	0.0	0.14
14	0.01	0.64	1910	91.6	1.9	6.5	3.7	0.9	0.0	0.0†	1995	100.0	0.0	0.0	0.14
15	0.02	0.52	1994	89.7	0.0	10.3	8.4	0.9	0.0	0.0†	1995	100.0	0.0	0.0	0.14
16	0.01	0.28	1908	91.6	1.9	6.5	3.7	0.0	0.0	0.0†	1995	100.0	0.0	0.0	0.14
17	0.00	0.16	1908	91.6	1.9	6.5	0.9	0.0	0.0	0.0†	1995	100.0	0.0	0.0	0.13
18	0.02	0.73	1936	84.1	1.9	14.0	5.6	0.9	0.0	0.0†	1995	100.0	0.0	0.0	0.13
19	0.02	0.38	1949	86.9	0.0	13.1	7.5	0.0	0.0	0.0†	1995	100.0	0.0	0.0	0.13
20	0.03	0.72	1957	82.2	2.8	15.0	9.3	1.9	0.0	0.0†	1995	100.0	0.0	0.0	0.13
21	0.02	0.49	1957	86.7	1.0	12.4	5.7	0.0	0.0	0.0†	1995	100.0	0.0	0.0	0.13
22	0.02	0.71	1957	90.5	1.9	7.6	3.8	1.9	0.0	0.0†	1995	100.0	0.0	0.0	0.13
23	0.03	0.90	1921	91.6	0.0	8.4	7.5	1.9	0.0	0.0†	1995	100.0	0.0	0.0	0.13
24	0.03	0.51	1971	88.8	0.0	11.2	8.4	1.9	0.0	0.0†	1995	100.0	0.0	0.0	0.13
25	0.02	0.62	1864	86.9	0.0	13.1	4.7	1.9	0.0	0.0†	1995	100.0	0.0	0.0	0.13
26	0.02	1.80	1912	94.3	0.9	4.7	2.8	0.9	0.0	0.0†	1995	100.0	0.0	0.0	0.13
27	0.02	0.53	1912	89.6	0.9	9.4	3.8	1.9	0.0	0.0†	1995	100.0	0.0	0.0	0.13
28	0.02	0.45	1974	92.5	0.9	6.5	6.5	0.0	0.0	0.0†	1995	100.0	0.0	0.0	0.12
29	0.02	0.50	1974	86.8	1.9	11.3	5.7	0.9	0.0	1.0	1971	99.0	1.0	0.0	0.12
30	0.04	1.48	1920	85.0	1.9	13.1	6.5	2.8	0.0	0.3	1971	99.0	1.0	0.0	0.12
31	0.04	1.05	1927	85.0	0.0	15.0	9.3	2.8	0.0	0.0†	1995	100.0	0.0	0.0	0.11

† Also occurred on earlier date(s).

ST GEORGE
Daily Data Summary

November

Day	Average temperature Max	Min	Mean	Extreme maximum High	Year	Low	Year	Extreme minimum High	Year	Low	Year	HDD	Degree Days CDD	GDD40	GDD50
1	71.4	35.7	53.6	87	1945	53	1935	53	1990	19†	1896	11	0	16	10
2	71.5	35.7	53.6	88	1945	51	1936	51	1959	19	1896	11	0	16	10
3	71.1	35.2	53.2	86	1924	52†	1994	49	1987	17	1896	11	0	15	10
4	70.5	34.7	52.6	83	1924	49	1895	51	1960	15	1896	12	0	15	10
5	70.7	34.7	52.7	83	1931	53	1957	53	1944	17	1896	12	0	15	10
6	70.3	34.2	52.3	85	1934	54†	1938	50	1927	11	1896	12	0	15	10
7	69.3	33.9	51.6	80	1898	54	1946	52	1907	15	1896	13	0	15	9
8	68.4	34.0	51.2	82	1894	51	1945	49	1982	18	1897	13	0	14	9
9	68.6	33.7	51.2	81	1934	51	1946	52	1987	20†	1898	13	0	14	9
10	68.1	34.2	51.1	82	1934	53	1940	50†	1995	14	1898	13	0	14	9
11	66.6	33.7	50.2	78†	1980	47	1911	53	1944	18†	1950	14	0	13	8
12	66.5	32.8	49.7	83	1934	45	1985	53	1983	17†	1950	15	0	13	8
13	65.8	32.2	49.0	81†	1953	46	1909	49†	1983	15	1898	15	0	13	7
14	64.8	32.2	48.5	82	1953	44	1916	47	1910	14	1898	16	0	12	7
15	64.6	31.9	48.2	82	1934	43	1964	54	1963	13	1898	16	0	12	7
16	63.0	31.8	47.4	78	1995	41	1930	48	1963	14	1955	17	0	11	6
17	63.0	31.5	47.2	76	1995	41	1964	47	1966	17	1894	17	0	11	6
18	62.8	30.9	46.9	77†	1943	46†	1930	51	1986	16	1964	18	0	11	6
19	62.4	30.3	46.4	79	1932	41	1906	49	1942	17	1893	18	0	11	6
20	61.2	29.7	45.5	76	1936	44†	1947	44†	1950	15	1956	19	0	10	5
21	62.0	30.0	46.0	76†	1899	36	1906	47†	1965	14	1898	19	0	11	6
22	61.0	29.3	45.2	75	1933	37	1906	52	1984	13	1914	19	0	10	5
23	60.6	28.7	44.6	78	1959	37	1931	43†	1984	11	1895	20	0	10	5
24	60.2	29.8	45.0	77	1959	32	1991	46	1965	12	1895	20	0	10	5
25	60.7	29.0	44.8	74	1933	41	1906	46	1935	14	1895	20	0	10	5
26	59.7	28.5	44.1	72†	1950	43†	1931	45	1985	9	1896	20	0	9	4
27	58.5	27.3	42.9	72	1932	39	1928	46	1926	9	1896	22	0	9	4
28	58.1	26.6	42.4	73	1901	40†	1919	43†	1985	5	1896	22	0	9	4
29	58.1	26.8	42.5	76	1929	33	1909	45	1985	4	1896	22	0	9	4
30	58.6	27.2	42.9	72†	1966	35	1909	45	1941	8	1911	22	0	9	4

Day	Total precipitation Avg	High	Year	None	Trace	.01 or more	.10 or more	.50 or more	Total snowfall Avg	High	Year	None	.1 or more	2.0 or more	ETo
1	0.02	0.70	1995	89.6	0.9	9.4	6.6	0.9	0.0	0.0†	1995	100.0	0.0	0.0	0.09
2	0.03	0.62	1906	84.0	1.9	14.2	5.7	1.9	0.0	0.0†	1995	100.0	0.0	0.0	0.09
3	0.02	0.48	1987	89.6	0.0	10.4	7.5	0.0	0.0	0.0†	1995	100.0	0.0	0.0	0.09
4	0.01	0.36	1895	93.4	1.9	4.7	2.8	0.0	0.0	0.0†	1995	100.0	0.0	0.0	0.09
5	0.01	0.60	1944	94.3	0.0	5.7	3.8	0.9	0.0	0.0†	1995	100.0	0.0	0.0	0.09
6	0.02	0.68	1960	94.3	0.0	5.7	4.7	0.9	0.0	0.0†	1995	100.0	0.0	0.0	0.09
7	0.02	0.56	1944	89.6	1.9	8.5	4.7	0.9	0.0	0.0†	1995	100.0	0.0	0.0	0.08
8	0.02	0.60	1966	92.5	0.9	6.6	3.8	0.9	0.0	0.0†	1995	100.0	0.0	0.0	0.08
9	0.01	0.50	1931	93.4	0.0	6.6	2.8	0.9	0.0	0.0†	1995	100.0	0.0	0.0	0.08
10	0.03	0.66	1923	87.7	0.9	11.3	7.5	2.8	0.0	0.0†	1995	100.0	0.0	0.0	0.08
11	0.03	0.42	1958	85.8	0.9	13.2	10.4	0.0	0.0	0.0†	1995	100.0	0.0	0.0	0.08
12	0.04	0.77	1913	85.8	0.0	14.2	9.4	2.8	0.0	0.5	1985	99.0	1.0	0.0	0.08
13	0.02	0.55	1910	85.6	1.9	12.5	3.8	1.0	0.0	0.0†	1995	100.0	0.0	0.0	0.08
14	0.03	0.55	1909	88.7	0.9	10.4	8.5	0.9	0.0	0.0†	1995	100.0	0.0	0.0	0.07
15	0.03	0.40	1931	82.1	0.0	17.9	11.3	0.0	0.0	0.0†	1995	100.0	0.0	0.0	0.07
16	0.02	0.56	1969	86.8	1.9	11.3	8.5	0.9	0.0	0.0†	1995	100.0	0.0	0.0	0.07
17	0.03	0.86	1972	84.0	4.7	11.3	7.5	2.8	0.0	0.0†	1995	100.0	0.0	0.0	0.07
18	0.02	0.40	1973	84.0	4.7	11.3	8.5	0.0	0.0	0.0†	1995	99.0	0.0	0.0	0.07
19	0.01	0.41	1902	88.7	0.9	10.4	6.6	0.0	0.0	0.0†	1995	100.0	0.0	0.0	0.07
20	0.01	0.20	1905	86.8	1.9	11.3	1.9	0.0	0.0	0.0†	1995	100.0	0.0	0.0	0.07
21	0.02	1.00	1967	91.5	0.0	8.5	4.7	1.9	0.0	4.0	1931	98.0	1.0	1.0	0.07
22	0.01	0.12	1967	88.7	0.0	11.3	0.9	0.0	0.0	2.0	1906	97.1	2.9	1.0	0.07
23	0.03	0.93	1965	87.7	0.9	11.3	7.5	0.9	0.0	1.0	1931	99.0	1.0	0.0	0.07
24	0.02	0.49	1978	86.8	0.0	13.2	6.6	0.0	0.0	0.0†	1995	100.0	0.0	0.0	0.07
25	0.03	0.65†	1983	87.7	0.0	12.3	7.5	2.8	0.0	0.0†	1995	100.0	0.0	0.0	0.07
26	0.02	0.81	1970	87.7	1.9	10.4	4.7	1.9	0.1	8.0	1919	97.1	2.0	1.0	0.07
27	0.02	0.60	1919	90.5	1.9	7.6	3.8	1.0	0.1	8.0	1919	96.1	2.0	1.0	0.06
28	0.02	0.86	1864	93.3	1.0	5.8	4.8	1.9	0.0	0.3	1981	99.0	1.0	0.0	0.06
29	0.03	0.88	1967	93.3	0.0	6.7	4.8	2.9	0.0	0.1	1981	99.0	1.0	0.0	0.06
30	0.03	0.98	1982	90.6	0.0	9.4	6.6	0.9	0.0	0.0†	1995	100.0	0.0	0.0	0.06

† Also occurred on earlier date(s).

ST GEORGE
Daily Data Summary

December

Day	Average temperature			High	Extreme maximum			High	Extreme minimum			HDD	Degree Days		
	Max	Min	Mean		Year	Low	Year		Year	Low	Year		CDD	GDD40	GDD50
1	58.6	27.9	43.2	70	1973	43	1913	46	1973	7	1911	21	0	9	4
2	58.2	27.8	43.0	69†	1995	45†	1991	43†	1973	10	1911	21	0	9	4
3	57.6	27.4	42.5	75	1941	41	1909	48	1966	13†	1911	22	0	8	3
4	57.9	27.8	42.8	70	1977	40	1909	47	1926	8	1898	22	0	9	4
5	57.5	28.1	42.8	73	1977	39	1909	48	1926	12	1896	22	0	8	3
6	56.9	27.5	42.2	71	1901	38†	1978	51	1956	9	1903	22	0	8	3
7	56.0	27.0	41.5	69†	1995	35	1978	47	1926	6	1903	23	0	8	3
8	55.3	26.4	40.8	67†	1981	34	1978	43	1984	5	1903	24	0	7	3
9	54.6	25.8	40.2	70	1893	37	1898	45	1965	10	1903	24	0	7	2
10	54.9	26.3	40.6	70	1950	35†	1972	45	1906	9	1899	24	0	7	2
11	54.1	26.4	40.3	69	1939	30	1972	46	1906	8	1898	24	0	7	2
12	53.5	25.4	39.5	70	1950	29	1932	46	1906	3	1898	25	0	6	2
13	53.2	25.0	39.1	69	1958	26	1932	53	1995	5	1898	25	0	6	2
14	52.8	25.0	38.9	66	1942	31	1967	45	1922	5†	1940	26	0	6	2
15	53.4	24.7	39.1	68†	1977	30	1940	40	1934	4	1940	25	0	6	2
16	53.3	24.3	38.8	68	1977	37	1940	43	1957	3	1940	26	0	6	2
17	53.2	24.9	39.0	68	1980	38	1909	47	1970	7	1892	25	0	6	2
18	52.8	25.4	39.1	67	1979	35†	1967	43	1952	5	1895	25	0	6	2
19	53.2	25.3	39.2	66†	1917	35	1924	41	1938	3	1897	25	0	6	2
20	52.8	24.8	38.8	66	1893	34	1897	50	1921	2	1897	26	0	6	2
21	52.6	25.1	38.9	65†	1981	33	1990	47	1921	4	1897	26	0	6	2
22	52.1	24.9	38.5	66	1941	30	1990	45	1921	5	1898	26	0	6	1
23	52.2	25.1	38.6	75	1955	27	1990	50	1959	3	1990	26	0	6	2
24	52.5	24.3	38.4	69	1955	32	1909	56	1955	4†	1990	26	0	6	2
25	52.1	23.3	37.7	67	1955	29	1924	51	1955	-4	1909	27	0	6	2
26	52.0	24.1	38.0	70	1980	30	1924	46†	1983	-4	1909	26	0	6	2
27	51.7	23.6	37.7	69	1955	30†	1924	49	1983	-4	1909	27	0	6	1
28	52.0	24.8	38.4	68	1917	26	1916	42	1921	0	1909	26	0	6	1
29	52.1	24.0	38.0	68	1980	34	1909	43	1951	0	1895	26	0	6	1
30	51.9	24.1	38.0	68	1917	34	1909	46	1977	1	1895	27	0	6	1
31	51.3	24.2	37.7	70	1995	33†	1924	43	1977	1	1898	27	0	5	1

	Total precipitation			Percent of years with precipitation					Total snowfall			Percent with snowfall			
Day	Avg	High	Year	None	Trace	.01 or more	.10 or more	.50 or more	Avg	High	Year	None	.1 or more	2.0 or more	ETo
1	0.03	0.85	1932	86.8	0.0	13.2	6.6	0.9	0.0	0.0†	1995	100.0	0.0	0.0	0.06
2	0.02	0.45	1955	87.7	0.0	12.3	8.5	0.0	0.0	0.0†	1995	100.0	0.0	0.0	0.06
3	0.02	0.39	1908	85.8	1.9	12.3	6.6	0.0	0.0	2.0	1865	99.0	1.0	1.0	0.05
4	0.03	0.55	1906	85.8	0.9	13.2	9.4	2.8	0.0	0.0†	1995	99.0	0.0	0.0	0.05
5	0.02	0.38	1951	83.0	0.9	16.0	9.4	0.0	0.0	2.0	1909	98.0	1.0	1.0	0.05
6	0.03	0.58	1966	90.6	0.0	9.4	6.6	0.9	0.0	0.0†	1995	100.0	0.0	0.0	0.05
7	0.02	0.37	1946	83.0	3.8	13.2	7.5	0.0	0.0	0.0†	1995	100.0	0.0	0.0	0.05
8	0.02	0.40	1947	85.8	3.8	10.4	5.7	0.0	0.0	1.5	1924	97.1	2.0	0.0	0.05
9	0.02	0.75	1931	86.8	0.9	12.3	6.6	0.9	0.0	0.0†	1995	100.0	0.0	0.0	0.05
10	0.03	0.79	1965	86.8	0.0	13.2	9.4	0.9	0.0	2.0	1898	98.0	2.0	1.0	0.05
11	0.02	0.44	1984	84.0	0.9	15.1	6.6	0.0	0.1	7.0	1945	94.1	3.9	1.0	0.05
12	0.04	0.71	1940	81.1	0.9	17.9	13.2	2.8	0.1	6.0	1940	97.0	2.0	2.0	0.05
13	0.03	0.95	1933	85.8	0.9	13.2	8.5	1.9	0.0	1.0	1971	99.0	1.0	0.0	0.05
14	0.02	0.65	1934	86.8	0.9	12.3	4.7	0.9	0.0	1.5	1932	98.0	2.0	0.0	0.05
15	0.01	0.35	1895	85.8	0.9	13.2	5.7	0.0	0.0	1.0	1967	99.0	1.0	0.0	0.05
16	0.02	0.57	1908	89.6	0.9	9.4	6.6	1.9	0.1	4.0	1968	98.0	2.0	2.0	0.05
17	0.04	0.74	1940	83.0	0.9	16.0	9.4	2.8	0.1	2.5†	1967	95.1	4.9	3.9	0.05
18	0.02	0.30	1949	76.2	2.9	21.0	10.5	0.0	0.1	5.5	1897	97.1	2.9	1.0	0.05
19	0.04	0.57	1949	79.2	1.9	18.9	12.3	0.9	0.0	0.0†	1995	99.0	0.0	0.0	0.05
20	0.03	0.60	1984	83.0	2.8	14.2	7.5	0.9	0.1	4.0	1968	97.1	2.9	2.0	0.05
21	0.03	0.91	1921	86.8	0.9	12.3	7.5	0.9	0.1	4.0	1909	98.0	2.0	2.0	0.05
22	0.03	0.50	1965	81.0	2.9	16.2	12.4	1.0	0.0	2.5	1926	98.0	2.0	1.0	0.05
23	0.03	0.44	1982	84.0	0.9	15.1	7.5	0.0	0.1	4.0	1941	95.1	2.9	2.0	0.05
24	0.02	0.51	1940	87.6	1.9	10.5	6.7	1.0	0.0	0.0†	1995	100.0	0.0	0.0	0.05
25	0.04	1.01	1942	83.8	0.0	16.2	9.5	2.9	0.1	6.0	1865	97.1	2.0	1.0	0.05
26	0.02	0.46	1921	80.0	3.8	16.2	5.7	0.0	0.0	0.0†	1995	100.0	0.0	0.0	0.05
27	0.04	0.90	1936	89.5	0.0	10.5	9.5	3.8	0.0	1.5	1932	98.0	1.0	0.0	0.05
28	0.04	0.85	1992	81.9	1.0	17.1	9.5	2.9	0.0	2.5	1905	98.0	2.0	1.0	0.05
29	0.02	0.56	1894	82.1	1.9	16.0	4.7	0.9	0.0	0.0†	1995	99.0	0.0	0.0	0.05
30	0.04	0.65	1951	78.3	4.7	17.0	13.2	0.9	0.0	2.3	1966	98.0	1.0	1.0	0.05
31	0.01	0.37	1909	84.9	1.9	13.2	7.5	0.0	0.0	1.3	1905	95.1	3.9	0.0	0.05

† Also occurred on earlier date(s).

Selected Bibliography

Alder, William J., ***Monthly Climatic Summary for Salt Lake City and Utah, January 1980 through December 1995.*** National Weather Service Forecast Office, Salt Lake City, Utah.

Alder, William J., R. Clayton Brough, David R. James and Sean T. Buchanan, ***Utah's Tornadoes and Waterspouts, 1869-1995.*** Salt Lake City, Utah. January 1996. 16 pages.

Ashcroft, Gaylen L., Donald T. Jensen and Jeffrey L. Brown. ***Utah Climate.*** Utah Climate Center, Utah State University, Logan, Utah. 1992. 127 pages.

Brough, R. Clayton, Dale L. Jones and Dale J. Stevens. ***Utah's Comprehensive Weather Almanac.*** Publishers Press, Salt Lake City, Utah. 1987. 517 pages.

Eubank, Mark E. and R. Clayton Brough. ***Utah Weather.*** WeatherBank Inc., Salt Lake City, Utah. 1979. 284 pages.

Greer, Deon C., Klaus D. Gurgel, Wayne L. Wahlquist, Howard A. Christy, and Gary B. Peterson. ***Atlas of Utah.*** Weber State College and Brigham Young University, Utah. 1981.

National Oceanic and Atmospheric Administration (NOAA) and the Environmental Protection Agency (EPA), ***The Experimental Ultraviolet Index Factsheet: Explaining the Index to the Public***, EPA: 430-F-94-017, June 1994; and ***Experimental UV Index***, EPA:L 430-F-94-021, June 1994.

Partners for Sun Protection Awareness, ***A National Ultraviolet Index: A Meteorologist's Guide to Educating Americans About Using a UV Index.*** (Includes various articles and factsheets.) 901 31st Street N.W., Washington, D.C., 20007-3838. June 1994.

Stevens, Dale J., R. Clayton Brough, Rodney D. Griffin and E. Arlo Richardson, ***Utah Weather Guide.*** Department of Geography, Brigham Young University, Provo, Utah. 1983. 46 pages.

Index

R

S